Developments in Tall Buildings 1983

In Dedication

Fazlur R. Khan
1929-1982

The Council on Tall Buildings and Urban Habitat dedicates this volume to our late chairman, Dr. Fazlur R. Khan. It was with deep sorrow that the Council learned of his death on March 27, 1982, while on a business trip in Jeddah, Saudi Arabia. Dr. Khan was a major moving force for the Council, and a friend to us all.

The engineering and architectural world knew Dr. Khan as the designer of the world's tallest building (The Sears Tower), as the designer of the world's tallest multiuse building (The John Hancock Center in Chicago), and as an innovator of structural form of tall buildings.

In addition, his colleagues knew him as a master at the art of blending the practical with the functional and esthetic.

Fazlur R. Khan was born in Dacca, Bangladesh, and came to the United States on a Fulbright Scholarship in 1952 to do graduate work at the University of Illinois from which he received his doctorate in 1955. He then joined the design firm of Skidmore, Owings & Merrill, advancing to the position of senior partner in 1970. Throughout his career he was accorded many honors, including election to the National Academy of Engineering in 1973.

We who were privileged to work with Dr. Khan in various professional activities quickly became aware not only of his keen intellect but also of the generosity with which he gave of his time and effort beyond all expectations. In a world of fast-paced technology, Dr. Khan always paused to remember whom it was all for—the people. His love for them, both as a whole and as individuals, was evident in everything he did.

The loss of Dr. Fazlur Khan to the engineering and architectural professions is irreplaceable. The Council on Tall Buildings and Urban Habitat therefore dedicates this volume, to which he contributed so greatly, to his memory. It was our good fortune to reap the benefits from his professional, personal and humanitarian generosity.

The five-volume Monograph on the Planning and Design of Tall Buildings was published by the American Society of Civil Engineers sequentially between 1978 and 1981. The Monograph is the major focus of the Council on Tall Buildings and Urban Habitat. For reference purposes, the broad outline of the Monograph and its Chapters is as follows:

PC PLANNING AND ENVIRONMENTAL CRITERIA FOR TALL BUILDINGS

1. Philosophy of Tall Buildings
2. History of Tall Buildings
3. Social Effects of the Environment
4. Sociopolitical Influences
5. Economics
6. Architecture
7. Interference and Environmental Effects
8. Urban Planning and Design
9. External Transportation
10. Parking
11. Operation, Maintenance, and Ownership
12. Energy Conservation
13. Motion Perception and Tolerance
14. Project Management
15. Application of Systems Methodology

SC TALL BUILDING SYSTEMS AND CONCEPTS

1. Structural Systems
2. Mechanical and Service Systems
3. Electrical Systems
4. Vertical and Horizontal Transportation
5. Cladding
6. Partitions, Walls, and Ceilings
7. Foundation Systems
8. Construction Systems

CL TALL BUILDING CRITERIA AND LOADING

1. Gravity Loads and Temperature Effects
2. Earthquake Loading and Response
3. Wind Loading and Wind Effects
4. Fire
5. Accidental Loading
6. Quality Criteria
7. Structural Safety and Probabilistic Methods

SB STRUCTURAL DESIGN OF TALL STEEL BUILDINGS

1. Commentary on Structural Steel Design
2. Elastic Analysis and Design
3. Plastic Analysis and Design
4. Stability
5. Stiffness
6. Fatigue and Fracture
7. Connections
8. Load and Resistance Factor Design (Limit States Design)
9. Mixed Construction

CB STRUCTURAL DESIGN OF TALL CONCRETE AND MASONRY BUILDINGS

1. Characteristics of Concrete and Masonry Tall Buildings
2. Design Criteria and Safety Provisions
3. Concrete Framing Systems for Tall Buildings
4. Optimization of Tall Concrete Buildings
5. Elastic Analysis
6. Nonlinear Behavior and Analysis
7. Model Analysis
8. Stability
9. Stiffness, Deflections, and Cracking
10. Creep, Shrinkage, and Temperature Effects
11. Design of Cast-in-place Concrete
12. Design of Structures with Precast Concrete Elements
13. Design of Masonry Structures

This volume is the first updating since the publication of the Monograph, documenting the most recent of the new developments and the state-of-the-art planning and design of tall buildings. The material contained in this volume is organized to correspond with the chapters listed above. This volume and future update volumes are based on the proceedings of the annual Council meetings, supplemented by contributions from professionals in the field. This volume and the entire Monograph set can be ordered by writing to the Council.

Council Headquarters
Fritz Engineering Laboratory
Building 13
Lehigh University
Bethlehem, Pennsylvania 18015
USA

Developments in
Tall Buildings
1983

Council on Tall Buildings
and Urban Habitat

Lynn S. Beedle, Editor-in-Chief

Hutchinson Ross Publishing Company

Stroudsburg, Pennsylvania

Copyright © 1983 by **Hutchinson Ross Publishing Company**
Library of Congress Catalog Card Number: 83–18556
ISBN: 0–87933–048–1

85 84 83   1 2 3 4 5
Manufactured in the United States of America.

Library of Congress Cataloging in Publication Data
Main entry under title:
Developments in tall buildings, 1983.
    Based in part on papers presented at a meeting of the Council on
Tall Buildings and Urban Habitat, New York City, May 1981.
    Bibliography: p.
    Includes indexes.
    1. Tall buildings—Design and construction.   I. Beedle,
Lynn S.   II. Council on Tall Buildings and Urban Habitat.
TH845.D48   1984   721′.042   83–18556
ISBN 0–87933–048–1

Distributed worldwide by Van Nostrand Reinhold Company Inc.,
135 W. 50th Street, New York, NY 10020.

Contents

Criteria and Loading

Structural Design of Tall Steel Buildings

Structural Design of Tall Concrete and Masonry Buildings

Sheraton Hotel in Lisbon, the tallest building in Portugal at 27 stories

Preface

This book is about new developments in tall buildings. Its purpose is to provide the reader with some of the newest information available to date. *Developments in Tall Buildings—1983* highlights recent research results in a form suitable for the designer, presenting new techniques not previously made available. The book also constitutes information compiled since the publication in 1978-1981 of the Monograph on the planning and design of tall buildings.

In this sense the book may be viewed as an update of that Monograph—a new perspective and an addition to the wealth of material contained therein. At the same time it stands on its own feet as a collection of new material from the fields of tall buildings research and of design practice.

This work had its origins at a new series of meetings of the Council on Tall Buildings and Urban Habitat, the first of which was held in New York City in May of 1981. Some of the articles included here were first presented at that meeting. Many other contributions came from those persons who had new information to contribute to this field.

The Council on Tall Buildings and Urban Habitat was organized in 1969. It is concerned with the role of the tall buildings in the urban environment and with their impact on that environment. This concern involves a systematic study of the whole problem of providing adequate space for life and work, considering not only technological factors, but both the social and the cultural aspects as well.

The need for a continuing comprehensive examination of the various aspects of tall buildings stems from the following:

- the exploding world population, generally urban, creating an increased demand for tall buildings in areas experiencing growth;
- the consequent requirement of economy in construction;
- the frequent neglect of human factors in urban design at the expense both of livability and of the quality of life;
- the new research required in the field and the necessity of establishing priorities for such research; and
- the new information becoming available on high-rise buildings and the need to make that information available to the professions.

The Council is not an advocate for tall buildings per se; but in those situations in which they are viable, it seeks to encourage the use of the latest knowledge for their implementation.

A major focus of the Council is on the publication of a comprehensive Monograph on tall buildings for use by those responsible for their planning, design, construction, and operation. While the Monograph contains a full treatment of relevant topics, this volume brings the Monograph up to date—at least to the extent possible as of date of manuscript submission.

The reader will find in this volume, in addition to new research results and design concepts, the following: case studies; field tests; new problems; descriptions of particular projects; new evidence of historical note with respect to a technology less than 100 years old; new areas that should be explored; descriptions of revisions to codes and specifications; information on the performance of tall buildings under natural hazards—earthquake, wind, fire. Thus one will find many aspects of tall buildings planning, design, construction, and operation for which there are new contributions.

Unlike the Monograph, which was edited heavily by committees, the papers in this volume are authored by individual specialists in that field. Each paper was reviewed by the appropriate topical committees. Those reviews revealed elements of controversy and shades of healthy disagreement among the specialists. Such controversy is encouraged by the Council as it deals in ideas. Anything that sharpens decision making—from whether to build tall or not, to the pros and cons of a particular design approach—was considered appropriate to be included.

The arrangement of the material is according to five main topical groups:

Planning and Environmental Criteria (PC)
Systems and Concepts (SC)
Criteria and Loading (CL)
Structural Design of Tall Steel Buildings (SB)
Structural Design of Tall Concrete and Masonry Buildings (CB)

An introductory statement by the group coordinators introduces the topic. Within each group the material is arranged according to the same pattern as the Monograph (see inside cover). According to the open nature of the opportunity for submission, some topical areas have many contributions, others none.

The citations at the end of each authored paper are presented in the same condensed form as that used in the Monograph. The bibliography at the end of the book contains all of the cited references in each contribution as well as the bibliography supplied in early 1982 by members of the Council.

The Council is indebted to Jerome S. B. Iffland who was general chairman of the 1981 Council Meeting. His organizational ability and the involvement of a large number of New York City professionals had much to do with the initiation of the volume.

We acknowledge the group leaders for both their editorial and coordinating roles. These are Rai Okamoto and Yona Friedman (PC), John Rankine and Walter P. Moore (SC), Leslie E. Robertson and Takeo Naka (CL),

William McGuire and Charles P. Gaylord (SB), and Ignacio Martín and Troels Brondum-Nielsen (CB).

The committee chairman, vice chairman, and editors not only reviewed the submissions but many prepared summaries in their own right.

The role of the National Science Foundation in its support of research and, in particular, its support of the collection of needed information and of the technical workshops and meetings is gratefully acknowledged.

The sponsors of the Council are:

American Institute of Steel Construction, Chicago
Cheung Kong (Hldgs.) Ltd., Hong Kong
Gammon Building Constr., Ltd., Hong Kong
GCE International, Inc.
Gerald D. Hines Interests, Houston
Hip Hing Const. Co., Hong Kong
Jaors, Baum & Bolles, New York
Ahmad Moharram, Cairo
Walter P. Moore & Associates, Inc., Houston
National Science Foundation, Washington, D.C.
Otis Elevator Co.
Ove Arup Partnership, London
Oxford Properties, Inc., Toronto
Robertson, Fowler & Assoc., P.C., New York
Skidmore, Owings & Merrill, Chicago
Westinghouse Elevator Co.

The contributors to the Council are:

Acme Metal Works Ltd., Hong Kong
Albertis-Dimopoulos Engineers, Athens
Allison, McCormac and Nickolaus, Rockville
Antony Tod & Partners Pty. Ltd., Brisbane
BMI Limited, Sydney
Bates, Smart & McCutcheon Pty. Ltd., Melbourne
Alfred Benesh & Co., Chicago
Boundary Layer Wind Tunnel Laboratory (U. Western Ontario), Ontario
Brandow & Johnston Associates, Los Angeles
CBM Engineers, Inc., Houston
Capacete-Martin & Associates, San Juan
Cement & Concrete Associations of Australia, North Sydney
Century Development Corp., Houston
Cermak/Peterka & Assoc., Inc., Fort Collins
H. K. Cheng & Associates, Hong Kong
Collyer Associates, New York
Consentini Associates, New York
DeSimone, Chaplin & Assoc., New York

Deutscher Beton-Verein E. V., Wiesbaden
B. M. Dornblatt and Associates, Inc., New Orleans
Gervais F. Favrot, New Orleans
Franki Contractors Ltd., Kowloon Tong
Fujikawa Conterato Lohan, Assoc., Chicago
George A. Fuller Co., New York
Gammon India Limited, Bombay
The Hammerson Group of Companies, Sydney
Harris & Sutherland, London
Hayakawa Associates, Los Angeles
Howard Needles Tammen & Bergendoff, New York
Hsin-Chong Const. Co., Ltd., Hong Kong
Iffland Kavanagh Waterbury, P. C., New York
International City Holdings, Ltd., Hong Kong
International Iron & Steel Institute, Brussels
Kadri Consultants, Pvt., Ltd., Bombay
Victor F. Leabu, Southfield
Lehr Associates, Cons. Engr., New York
LeMessurier Associates/SCI, Cambridge
Lev Zetlin Associates, Inc., New York
Lidell Construction Co., Ltd., Hong Kong
Stanley D. Lindsey & Assoc., Nashville
John Lok & Partners, Ltd., Hong Kong
Mahendra Raj Consultants Private Limited, New Delhi
Maunsell Consultants Asia, Hong Kong
McWilliam & Partners Pty. Ltd., Brisbane
W. L. Meinhardt & Partners Pty. Ltd., Melbourne
Meltzer Management, New Orleans
Nan Fung Development Ltd., Hong Kong
On Lee Gen. Contractors Ltd., Hong Kong
Paramatta Investment Co., Ltd., Hong Kong
PSM International, Chicago
Ranhill Bersekutu, Kuala Lumpur
Rankine & Hill Pty. Ltd., Sydney
Rhodes-Harrison, Fee & Bold, Architects, Saxonwold
Mr. and Mrs. Leslie Robertson, New York
The Office of James Ruderman, New York
Ryoden Electric Engr. Co., Ltd., Hong Kong
Schindler Management A. G., Luzerne
Sepakat Setia Perunding (Sdn.) Bhd., Kuala Lumpur
Duiliu Sfintesco, Lamorlaye
Shui On Const. Co. Ltd., Kwun Tong
Skilling Ward Rogers Barkshire, Inc., Seattle
Smith, Hinchman & Grylls Assoc., Inc., Detroit
South African Inst. of Steel Const., Johannesburg

Mr. and Mrs. M. J. Stacom, Greenwich
Syarikat Pembenaan Yeoh Tiong Lav Sdn. Bhd., Kuala Lumpur
Tishman Construction Corp. of N.Y., New York
Tishman Research Corp., New York
Tishman Speyer Properties, New York
Turner Construction Co., New York
Urban Invest. & Develop. Co., Chicago
Voss & Partners, West Germany
Weiskopf and Pickworth, New York
Wellform Const. Co. Ltd., Hong Kong
Wing Tai Const. & Engr. Co., Hong Kong
Wiss, Janney, Elstner and Associates, Northbrook
Wong & Ouyang & Associates, Hong Kong
M. S. Yolles & Partners Limited, Ontario
Zaldastani Assoc., Inc., Boston

Among the Hutchinson Ross publishing staff particular thanks is expressed
to Charles Hutchinson and Shirley End.

Many in the Lehigh University Staff have contributed in a significant way
to this effort, in particular Group Secretaries Roy Herrenkohl, Le-Wu Lu,
and Ti Huang. Especial thanks are due to Dolores Rice, Publications
Associate on the Fritz Lab Staff whose editing skill and attention to detail
made possible the orderly and timely production of this volume.

Our final debt is to Fazlur Khan, whose guiding genius strongly comple-
mented his matchless vision of structural form. His untimely and tragic
death is an irreplacable loss. We dedicate this volume to him as a tribute to
his skill, his service, and his love of humanity.

Lehigh University   Lynn S. Beedle
Bethlehem, Pennsylvania   *Editor-in-Chief*
1983

Contributors

The following list acknowledges those who have contributed materials for this volume. The names, affiliations, and countries of each contributor are given.

Some contributions were a direct result of the first annual Council meeting, and some were received from professionals in the field.

Akiyama, H., University of Tokyo, Tokyo, Japan
Arciszewski, T., Wayne State University, Ann Arbor, Michigan, USA

Baum, R. T., Jaros, Baum and Bolles, New York, New York, USA
Beedle, L. S., Lehigh University, Bethlehem, Pennsylvania, USA
Brainov, M., Committee of Culture, Sofia, Bulgaria
Brotchie, J. F., CSIRO, Victoria, Australia

Chen, W. F., Purdue University, West Lafayette, Indiana, USA
Cheong-Siat-Moy, F., California State University, Sacramento, California, USA
Christiansen, J. V., Skilling, Helle, Christiansen, Robertson, Seattle, Washington, USA
Clark, R. J., Skidmore, Owings and Merrill, Chicago, Illinois, USA
Codella, F. L., Tower Tech Ltd., Hazlet, New Jersey, USA
Conger, A., Skidmore, Owings and Merrill, Chicago, Illinois, USA
Coull, A., University of Glasgow, Glasgow, Scotland
Croft, D., Ove Arup and Partners, London, England

Davenport, A. G., University of Western Ontario, Ontario, Canada
DeBenedittis, C. A., Tishman Speyer Properties, New York, New York, USA
Degenkolb, J. G., Fire Protection Engineer, Glendale, California, USA

El Nimeiri, M. M., Skidmore, Owings and Merrill, Chicago, Illinois, USA
Emery, A. F., University of Washington, Seattle, Washington, USA

Fintel, M., Portland Cement Association, Skokie, Illinois, USA
Fitzgerald, J., Joseph F. Fitzgerald and Associates, Inc., Chicago, Illinois, USA
Foster, N., Foster Associates, London, England
Friedman, Y., Architect, Paris, France
Fuller, G. R., Housing and Urban Development, Washington, D. C., USA
Gaylord, C. W., Charlottesville, Virginia, USA
Gergely, P., Cornell University, Ithaca, New York, USA
Ghosh, S. K., Portland Cement Association, Skokie, Illinois, USA
Goodno, B. J., Georgia Institute of Technology, Atlanta, Georgia, USA
Gregorian, Z. B., Stone and Webster Engineering Corporation, Boston, Massachusetts, USA
Gujral, P. S., Skidmore, Owings and Merrill, Chicago, Illinois, USA
Gutman, A., Lev Zetlin Associates, New York, New York, USA

Halász, O., Technical University, Budapest, Budapest, Hungary
Heerwagen, D. R., University of Washington, Seattle, Washington, USA
Hendry, A. W., University of Edinburgh, Edinburgh, Scotland

Iffland J. S. B. Iffland Kavanagh Waterbury, P. C:, New York, New York, USA

Jha, C. K., PSM International Corporation, Chicago, Illinois, USA
Johnson, B. R., University of Washington, Seattle, Washington, USA

Kato, B., University of Tokyo, Tokyo, Japan
Khachaturian, N., University of Illinois, Urbana, Illinois, USA
Khan, F. R. (deceased), Skidmore, Owings and Merrill, Chicago, Illinois, USA
Kippenhan, C. J., University of Washington, Seattle, Washington, USA
Kowalczyk, R., Bialystok Technical University, Bialystok, Poland
Krell, W. C., Grosse Point Woods, Michigan, USA
Krupp, J., CTICM, Puteaux, France
Kwieciński, M., Warsaw Technical University, Warsaw, Poland
Kwok, S., Gordon Wu and Associates, Hong Kong

Law, M., Ove Arup & Partners, London, England
Lew, P., Lev Zetlin Associates, Inc., New York, New York, USA
Lewis, W. S., Jaros, Baum and Bolles, New York, New York, USA
Lorenz, R. F., American Institute of Steel Construction, Chicago, Illinois, USA
Łubiński, M., Warsaw Technical University, Warsaw, Poland

Manheim, D. N., University of California, Berkeley, California, USA
Marryatt, H. W., Harborough, Victoria, Australia
Martín, I., Capacete-Martín and Associates, San Juan, Puerto Rico
McGuire, W., Cornell University, Ithaca, New York, USA
Meckler, G., Haines Lundberg Waehler, New York, New York, USA
Moore, W. P., Jr., Walter P. Moore and Associates, Inc., Houston, Texas, USA
Moukalian, M., Richard C. Rich and Associates, Inc., Southfield, Michigan, USA
Munse, W. H., University of Illinois, Urbana, Illinois, USA
Muto, K., Muto Institute of Structural Mechanics, Inc., Tokyo, Japan

Nair, R. S., Alfred Benesch and Company, Chicago, Illinois, USA
Naka, T., University of Tokyo, Tokyo, Japan

Ojiako, G. U., University of Nigeria, Nsukka, Nigeria
Okamoto, R., Okamoto Murata AIA Architects and Planners, San Francisco, California, USA
Oudheusden, A. J., Bethlehem Steel Corporation (retired), Center Valley, Pennsylvania, USA

Pawlowski, A. Z., Warsaw Technical University, Warsaw, Poland
Picardi, E. A., Oxford Properties, Inc., Toronto, Ontario, Canada
Popov, E., University of California, Berkeley, California, USA

Ramati, R., Raquel Ramati Associates, New York, New York, USA
Rankine, J., Rankine and Hill Pty. Ltd., Sydney, Australia
Rhodes-Harrison, G. (deceased), Rhodes-Harrison, Fee and Bold, Saxonwold, South Africa
Robertson, L. E., Skilling, Helle, Christiansen, Robertson, P. C., New York, New York, USA
Ruchelman, L., Old Dominion University, Norfolk, Virginia, USA

Schaefer, W. D., Baltimore City, Baltimore, Maryland, USA
Schulz, G. W., Universitat Innsbruck, Innsbruck, Austria
Sfintesco, D., CTICM, Lamorlaye, France
Shiga T., Tohoku University, Sendai, Japan

Stockbridge, J. G., Wiss, Janney, Elstner and Associates, Northbrook, Illinois, USA
Stafford Smith, B., McGill University, Montreal, Canada
Swiger, W. F., Consulting Engineer, Buhl, Idaho, USA

Taylor, J. F., Gerald D. Hines Interests, Houston, Texas, USA
Thomas, P. H., Building Research Establishment, Watford, England
Troup, E. W. J., American Institute of Steel Construction, Dedham, Massachusetts, USA

Vernez-Moudon, A., University of Washington, Seattle, Washington, USA
Vesey, J. J., Kinney System Inc., New York, New York, USA

Williamson, R. C., Lehigh University, Bethlehem, Pennsylvania, USA
Winter, G. (deceased), Cornell University, Ithaca, New York, USA
Witteveen, J., Delft University of Technology, Delft, Netherlands

Young, R., Iffland Kavanaugh Waterbury, New York, New York, USA

Zhu, Y. X., Tong Ji University, Shanghai, China

The Developer and the Product Relative to High-Rise Buildings

E. Alfred Picardi

The developer's product, in its purest form, is net rentable square feet of office space. The lease rate the product commands will vary with the current demand for office space in a particular location and with the quality of the space offered compared to other space on the market. The developer's object is to be in the right place at the right time and to offer his product at the right price.

Having determined a future need for office space in a particular location, the developer approaches production by constructing an economic model or pro forma for his project. The model is constructed based on an anticipated income stream projected to the time the building is completed and available for leasing. The capitalization of this income stream determines the amount of money that can be spent on development.

Items that must be considered in estimating project costs are land acquisition, legal and planning costs, operation and maintenance costs, return on investment, and finally actual construction cost. Architects and engineers are primarily concerned with the last item in their involvement with developers.

This article is based on the theme paper presented at the First Council Meeting, May, 1981, New York.

Construction cost generally represents about 60% of the total development cost presented in a pro forma. To design the product within a specific cost budget and to control that cost, the developer can set up an economic model, which is shown, in its simplest form, in Table 1. For example, if an expected income stream of $25 per net rentable square foot is capitalized upon, and construction cost is assumed to be 60% of total development cost, and the building will have an efficiency of 85% (i.e., net rentable space will be 85% of gross area), it can be determined that the maximum allowable cost per gross square foot of construction will be $75.

The next step in the design process should be to construct a cost model for the building, such as the one shown in Table 2. This model shows the 16 systems making up the total building and the expected percentage of the total cost that each system will account for. The percentages are taken from past experience on similar buildings with adjustments for floor plate size, number of stories, differences in finishes, elevator system differences, time of construction and buy-out, geographical area, and so on.

It is also possible to introduce a risk-analysis approach in the construction of a cost model, which then would be used as a cost-control tool during the design and buy-out period. This approach is illustrated in Table 3, where past data from projects shows three figures for each system's percentage of total cost, i.e. the lowest-10 percentile, the mean, and the highest-10 percentile. When this type of data is put into a risk-analysis program using a Monte Carlo simulation technique, the probability of staying within a predetermined cost budget can be computed. As the project is bought out and individual systems' cost risks become zero, then the probable costs become more determinate and adjustments can be made in the design to keep within the budget.

Table 1 Economic model formula: High-rise office building

$$\frac{L}{R} \times A \times E = C$$

L = Rent per Net Rentable Square Foot ($/ft^2)
R = Amortization Rate
A = Ratio of Construction Cost to Total Development Cost
E = Efficiency (Ratio of Net Rentable ft^2 to Gross ft^2)
C = Allowable Cost of Construction per Goss ft^2

EXAMPLE

$$\frac{25}{0.17} \times 0.6 \times 0.85 = 75$$

In adjusting a design to remain within a predetermined budget, the developer must consider the three basic elements of a building—quantity, quality, and cost (see Fig. 1).

Quantity is the amount of space to be built, i.e., the amount of product the developer wishes to put on the market.

Quality is the desired level of sophistication of detail, materials, and performance characteristics of the building's systems.

Table 2 Construction-cost model: High-rise office building

Item	Percent of Total	Budget
Demolition	0.05	15,500
Sitework	0.59	175,000
Excavation	0.24	70,000
Structure	24.59	7,448,300
Exterior walls	19.79	5,981,178
Interior finishes	8.72	2,675,354
Miscellaneous metals	1.26	375,000
Roofing and waterproofing	0.59	183,473
Electrical	8.49	2,621,726
Mechanical	17.38	5,407,881
Elevators and escalators	8.18	2,423,970
Specialties	0.68	209,452
Cash allowances	0.13	58,000
Other	0	0
General expense	4.73	1,414,472
Fee	4.59	1,404,154
Total	100.00%	30,463,460

Table 3 Risk-analysis model: High-rise office building—systems as a percentage of total cost

	Low	Average	High
Demolition	0.00	0.26	0.61
Sitework	0.00	0.42	1.35
Excavation	0.21	1.25	2.05
Structure	19.57	24.53	28.20
Exterior Walls	12.93	16.30	19.64
Interior Finishes	5.75	7.56	9.45
Miscellaneous metals	0.36	0.92	2.04
Roofing and waterproofing	0.32	0.61	1.16
Mechanical and electrical	19.56	25.32	28.44
Elevators and escalators	7.46	8.40	9.57
Specialties	0.00	0.76	1.02
Cash allowances and other	0.18	2.55	7.13
General expense	4.30	6.15	8.15
Fee	4.13	4.61	5.16

Cost is the dollars per gross square foot that must be spent to achieve the desired quantity and quality.

It should be apparent that all of these elements are variables, but that fixing any two of them automatically determines the third. Thus, if the goal is to market a fixed amount of space without exceeding a certain maximum cost per gross square foot, and these variables become fixed, then the quality of the project has also been fixed automatically.

As noted, in the case of most developers, the cost item must be fixed; the project must stay within the budget. Quantity of gross square feet can only be adjusted by an increase of efficiency in the design. The remaining item—quality—offers the most opportunity for adjustment to maintain cost control.

In making the decisions necessary to establish a quality level consistent with a project's cost budget, the designers should understand not only the principals of the economic model and the construction-cost model, but also the developer's priorities for determining the best product he can offer.

Certain elements of a building's design are essential—those concerning the safety and health of its users. The major items in this category are structural safety and competence, fire safety, the HVAC sytem's ability to maintain proper temperatures and air quality, the lighting system, and the building's sanitary system. Little or no compromise can be made on these systems because they are either governed by codes or are of such a nature that their downgrading would quickly affect the marketability of the product.

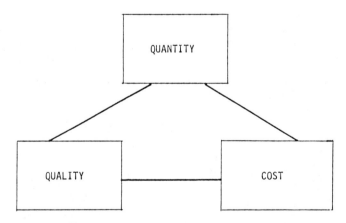

QUALITY - AMOUNT OF PRODUCT (NET RENTABLE SQUARE FEET)

QUALITY - LEVEL OF DESIGN SOPHISTICATION

COST   - ALLOWABLE DOLLAR AMOUNT WHICH CAN BE SPENT TO PRODUCE THE PRODUCT.

Fig. 1 Elements of design and construction process: High-rise buildings

The second level of design priorities relates to function. This category includes proper lease spans, which make for good and economical layout of offices; column-free areas; an adequate elevator system; natural lighting from windows; and a good ratio of exterior office space. Of equal importance is a well-designed main entrance and lobby.

Finally, the overall esthetics of the project makes up the third level of priority. Relevant items include lobbies on each floor of multitenant spaces; the general level of interior finishes, ceilings, floor coverings, etc.; and the basic form of the structure, its outside landscaping, and its relation and massing in its urban surrounding.

Thus, it is apparent that the developer's order of priorities, i.e., cost efficiency, health and safety, function, and overall aesthetics, may be the reverse of the order of priorities of some architects. Not all architects, therefore, are capable of understanding developers and designing their projects.

The future of commercial high-rise buildings is that most will continue to be built by developers. The profitable buildings will be those for which costs are controlled to relate to income streams and high quality is achieved within a predetermined budget. As profitable investments, those build-

Fig. 2 Aerial view of Denver, Colorado. The Anaconda Tower appears as the black high-rise on the left; the twin towers of the Great West Plaza are the black buildings on the right. The Republic Plaza, presently under construction, is superimposed right of center. *(Courtesy: Oxford Properties, Inc.)*

ings, simple in form, will outstrip the contrived, "trendy" architecture of the moment, which is different only for the sake of being different.

There is new emphasis on redevelopment of the downtown urban core. The negative economic, social, and cultural effects of suburban sprawl may soon be realized. A coming crisis in municipal services, transportation, and energy may make this apparent in the next decade. The high-rise building, now a prime target of critics, will soon be seen as the logical, and economical, structure for the urban environment.

Fig. 3 Great West Plaza, Denver—The Great West Life Tower (left); the Dome Tower (right)

Fig. 4 Denver Square—Fairmont Hotel (left back); the Anaconda Tower (right back); Fairmont Hotel Shopping Pavilion (center front)

Planning and Environmental Criteria

Introductory Review

Rai Y. Okamoto

Tall buildings today are increasingly dispersed beyond traditional regional centers to suburban centers and smaller cities. They are becoming more varied, and perhaps more interesting, in their architectural design; and yet they are growing as the all-encompassing bête-noire of late twentieth-century civilization. The high-rise office building, in particular, has come to symbolize not only the ultimate expression of gravity-based technology and the modus operandi of modern business, but also the loss of blue-collar employment, increased traffic and transit overload, the high cost of housing, and countless other undesired environmental impacts.

Despite the proliferation of tall commercial buildings in countries such as the United States, little housing of any sort is being created. One might expect more tall residential buildings to be built based on a mixed-use program that would respond to changing family sizes and life styles, the impact of conservation demands, and construction-cost considerations.

The Council therefore recognizes the need for research into appropriate models for multistory housing. The evidence to date is devastatingly negative and suggests that the high-rise form is inherently unworkable, or at least quite limited, in residential applications (St. Louis' Pruitt Igoe, and San Francisco's Pink Palace). For tall buildings to be successful for residential purposes, better balance among several key design factors is needed. The most fundamental of these factors is the needs and behavior patterns of users and their involvement in the process by which housing is designed and produced. Through this process a true community or neighborhood might evolve that would reflect the character of its inhabitants.

9

In response to both the impact of tall buildings on public transportation and services and the increased demand on housing, local governments have adopted policies calling for mixed-use developments. Thus, tall buildings in the United States are more and more frequently conceived as two-or three-layer sandwiches of uses. Commercial and pedestrian-oriented activities often occupy the lower levels, with offices above. Infrequently, but more so than in previous decades, residential space occupies the uppermost floors. In San Francisco, a housing "requirement" has been levied, as a condition of approval by the City Planning Commission. It is based on staff analyses and indicates the probable percentage of employees in a proposed high-rise who would live in the city. This housing obligation can be met off-site or by a contribution to a housing fund maintained by the city to produce affordable housing. There is presently no legislative basis for this requirement, but the market for high-rise space is such that developers make the commitments nonetheless.

However, the gradually accumulating imbalance between available housing and the employment opportunities resulting from high-rises has a secondary impact. The commuting load is what promises to finally overburden both public and private transportation in large cities. This problem, together with the lack of convenient and affordable housing, is also the probable cause of the dispersal of tall building office activity from primary urban centers to smaller cities. Of course, there are numerous other factors that affect the location of tall buildings. These include climate, labor force availability, ownership preference, quality of life, stability of political environment, etc. Still, housing and access remain fundamental requirements.

In general, the current generation of tall buildings includes some of the more interestingly designed structures. This fact results from several conditions. First, the buildings are often located in communities where the building type is a welcome new symbol of achievement in a mercantile society, or where there is as yet no firmly entrenched architectural tradition. Second, the architectural profession is in the throes of an attempt to either revise the tenets of modern architecture or reject them completely and establish a new "academy," i.e., the "Post-Modern Movement." Third, the emphasis on mixed-use buildings often results in visual variety. A substream of current architectural theory, contextualism, can also lead to buildings designed with forms reflecting their surroundings. Finally, there is much more responsible attention to energy conservation, which can give a building a more particular shape and form than was true in the "glass box" era. One could also attribute the more interesting architecture in recent tall buildings to technological advances or better analytical methods. It might even arise from the realization by developers that special designs can be more marketable and that developers can achieve greater return on their investments by creating more interesting environments.

If tall buildings are to remain a truly responsible solution to urban development problems, relevant design concepts that respond to a diverse range of needs must be the focus of all professionals concerned with this building form. The diversity of content expressed in the papers that follow hints at these new concerns. For example, Ramati directs us away from the buildings themselves to the street spaces and the life thereon that tall buildings both create and modify. Thus, designers are advised to consider not only the building and its program, but also its context. Another example of the broader view is presented by Ruchelman, who draws attention to the need for case studies of decision-making as it pertains to tall buildings. He argues that the complex nature, as structures, of such projects, their public service needs for transportation and access, and their social and economic impacts all mandate a process that views the tall building as part of an urban system and not simply as an isolated product.

In a thoughtful paper, Vernez-Moudon suggests several principles of esthetics based on the general premise that, increasingly, the issue is not simply the tall building, but the tall city. This emphasis on the whole as well as the part, on the process as well as the product, may well be the major issue ahead. The technical and esthetic skills required to produce individual buildings may be near their peak. Integrating them into a social and esthetic setting that meets the needs of its inhabitants is yet an unsolved task.

Philosophy of Tall Buildings (PC-1)

How To Save Your
Own Street

Raquel Ramati

The most successful tall buildings in history have been those that have clearly related the building to the street level through the use of human scale. Successful buildings have also provided environments that enhance the activities of strolling, sitting, and watching people go by in the context of city life. City officials have recognized the value of these activities and, through legislation and zoning ordinances, have used incentives to direct developers to design pedestrian amenities into the ground floors of their buildings.

THE REEVALUATION—THE '70s

The economic decline in the '60s, the rise in the cost of energy, the emerging power of the community, and the demand for more attention to human needs and values have all given rise to a fundamental reevaluation of our physical environment. The failure of the urban renewal approach, the separation of land uses that resulted in deserted downtown office areas, the tower-in-a-park concept that produced high-rise towers surrounded by vast concrete parking lots or wind-tunnel plazas—all contributed to the destruction of the street. Consequently, a greater focus fell on the reuse and renovation of older buildings, the development of infill sites, the provision of pedestrian amenities, and the revitalization of neighborhoods. New York City planners responded to these trends by creating innovative zoning techniques to reshape neighborhoods, as demonstrated in Little Italy. New York's planners concentrated on small-scale planning, as in the plaza and subway easement legislation, and reinforced landmark-preservation laws.

Both the street's importance as a pedestrian thoroughfare and a retail corridor linking buildings and its impact on architecture can be traced through the evolution of the skyscraper and its relationship to the street in New York City. As we proceed into the 80s, it is becoming clear that when new tall buildings relate to the street, it affects both the success of the buildings and the total street environment. In short, it is becoming evident that amenities and economics are interrelated.

Perhaps one of the most dramatic examples of why the articulation of a skyscraper's base is relevant to street continuity is demonstrated by comparing the Empire State Building and the World Trade Center, which clearly represent New York. In the case of the Empire State Building, a person at street level is hardly aware of the immense size of the building above. The stores at street level maintain street scale. In contrast, the towers of the World Trade Center could be placed anywhere. The ground level follows the basic tower frame. The towers appear as if they could continue endlessly underground or up to eternity; no relationship exists to any context.

As we study the evolution of the skyscraper in New York, it becomes clear that historically the buildings that have successfully related their bases to the street resulted from the ingenuity of individual architects, rather than from a trend or a movement. The concept of context at street level was missing in most historical architectural accounts. Montgomery Schuyler (1913) states in an article describing the Woolworth Building in the *Architectural Record*, "Only in the skyline, the upper termination, does the architect, as an artist, have a chance. It is here that the difference between architect and architect most clearly appears." Isn't it amazing that even the Rockefeller Center complex, known today as the best example of urban design in the city, had little or no influence on developments that followed?

In the design of the early skyscrapers, such as the Woolworth Building and the Chrysler Building, the street is expressed by means of decorative elevation treatment, articulation of entrances, and continuation of cornice lines.

Up until the construction of the Lever house in 1952, architects could not let go of the traditional way of expressing the beginning and end of a building. While they were using technology only as a means to an end, the second generation of skyscrapers uses technology as an end in itself. In an article called "What is America's Problem?" Le Corbusier (1936) says,

> "The skyscrapers have killed the street and made the city a crazy thing. The skyscraper in New York has now only a negative effect: It fills the street and the city, it destroys the possibility of circulation, worse still it is a cannibal; it draws the blood of life from whole quarters around it; it empties them and ruins them."

Yet his remedy is disastrous: "Make it larger, make it honest and useful, enormous ground area will be recovered, the city will have green open spaces and no traffic problems." His ideas are literally implemented by architects and are even reflected in a new zoning ordinance in New York that favors the tower-in-a-park concept.

In the process of celebrating technology, the base becomes merely an advertisement for the self-contained corporation displacing the stores that traditionally occupied the ground level. The building stands on a pedestal surrounded by "leftover" open space, thus emphasizing the tower's size and isolation from its environment.

By the end of the sixties some architects were trying to express the base of the tower differently from the typical floor above. Rather than succeeding in integrating the building into the street scale, these attempts accentuated the problem even more. Other efforts to rejuvenate the street by treating the base emphasized landscaping and art work on the plaza level. These efforts recognized the problem but failed to address the main issue of relating the skyscraper to the street. Although often attractive, these plazas appear to be afterthoughts—the "icing on the cake"—while the main image of the self-contained corporate structure remains predominant.

As the '70s emerged, amidst the major reevaluation of the values of the '60s, new realities confronted the developer in downtown. He was now competing with the amenities so easily available in the suburbs and was faced with an office worker who had more leisure time on his hands. Although the greenery and quiet of the suburb might not have been available, the employee sought the amenities more congenial to high-density areas. Mass transit, cultural facilities, and accessible shopping became the desired environment in downtown. Pedestrian experiences extended beyond just walking from Point A to Point B to sitting, strolling, and watching other people.

The government reacted not only by introducing new legislation mandating seating, landscaping, and lighting in all plazas, but also by introducing new definitions of pedestrian amenities, such as the covered pedestrian space and the throughblock arcade. In conjunction with introducing new definitions, government began looking at the total pedestrian network of downtown. Pedestrian maps show the variety of spaces, which alleviate congestion and provide both covered and open spaces, allowing a wide spectrum of activities. This may have been the first time that government planners engaged in preparing such maps.

Much of the government's work in New York was based on studying existing spaces. It became clear that people are searching not only for human scale, but also for a variety of ways to spend their leisure time. They desire active seating areas, quiet private corners, sun and shade. It is not suprising, therefore, that the most successful pedestrian space in the city turned out to be Bloomingdale's Department Store, which extends through the total block from Lexington to Third Avenue and offers a variety of shop designs. Rather than seeing all the merchandise at the same time, the pedestrian can discover shopping areas in the same way one would experience shopping on "Main Street."

THE EVOLUTION OF THE '70s SKYSCRAPER

To resolve the new complexity of architectural problems, the architect of the '70s and '80s translates the evolution of the skyscraper and its impact on street life until 1970 into new knowledge. The modern building of the '80s reflects the synthesis of architecture and urban design. The architect, charged with developing a public space that is continuous with the street's adjoining buildings and activities, places emphasis on the design of the base. The spaces invite the public in by introducing retail trade and providing alternative pedestrian experiences. Some of the spaces connect to the mass transit system; some are used as throughblock connections; others serve as outdoor rooms for use in inclement weather.

Some architects attempt to weave the street into their building by the extreme solution of completely separating the skyscraper from the street environment. This allows the street activity to continue below, thus maintaining two different scales.

In its early development, pedestrian space was forced into the tower of the skyscraper. The design of the space was mainly cosmetic. In the Olympic Tower building, residential, commercial and pedestrian space fit into the same box.

In some of the more recent buildings, such as the Fisher Bros. Building done by Skidmore, Owings, & Merrill on 52nd Street and Park Avenue, or the Philip Morris Headquarters on 42nd Street and Park, the pedestrian space dominates the ground level. Even so, it remains space cut out of the tower rather than space articulated as a separate element. Often, this results from the limitations of a small site.

Likewise, in the case of the AT & T Headquarters building, where the architect's individual statement is paramount, street activities are introduced into the building through the midblock arcade with a skylight and some retail activity (Fig. 1). Clearly the street environment is only one concern in the development of the AT & T Building's design.

Two examples, the Galleria on 57th Street and 100 William Street, articulate the public space as an integral part of the total architectural building

Fig. 1. Model of the AT & T Corporate Headquarters Building, New York

envelope. Yet the public spaces are expressed as separate and important entities and are of prime importance. The towers become secondary.

One way to articulate the public domain is to separate the covered pedestrian space completely from the skyscraper. This approach is demonstrated in the IBM Building designed by Ed Barnes (Figs. 2 and 3) and in the Trump Tower (Figs. 4 and 5).

In the Citicorp Building the design's major emphasis is on the base of the building, which contains the public spaces. The church and the plaza are articulated. The public areas extend beyond street level to the subway levels below. The tower above becomes incidental. Citicorp is maintained impeccably and offers a variety of 17 stores and restaurants and several levels of seating. The development of public spaces and their relationship to the street level was the designer's prime concern.

The Philip Morris Headquarters on 42nd Street and Park Avenue exemplifies design from the pedestrian space up, rather than from the tower down (Fig. 6). It demonstrates that it is possible to design a successful pedestrian space on a small site (such as 20,000 ft^2). Ingenious architectural efforts created a building that relates to the street environment, connects

Fig. 2. Model of the IBM Building *(Courtesy: Edward Larrabee Barnes, P.C., photo by Louis Checkman)*

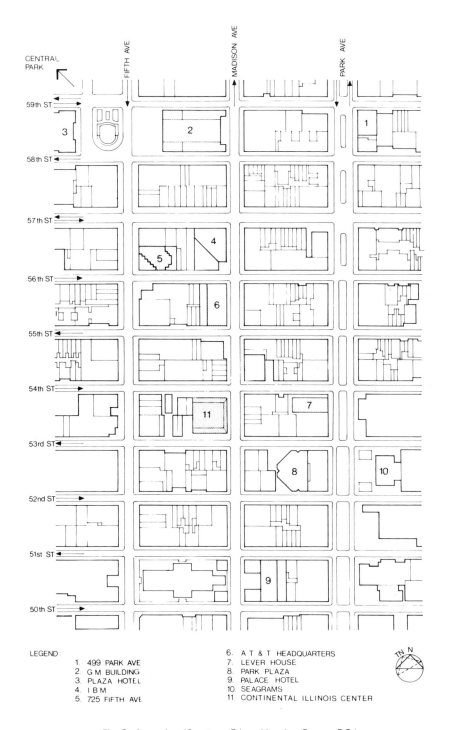

Fig. 3. Area plan *(Courtesy: Edward Larabee Barnes, P.C.)*

to subway levels, and also invites the public into its midst. The entrance to the Philip Morris Company is through public space, rather than through the major corporate lobby of the skyscraper of the '60s.

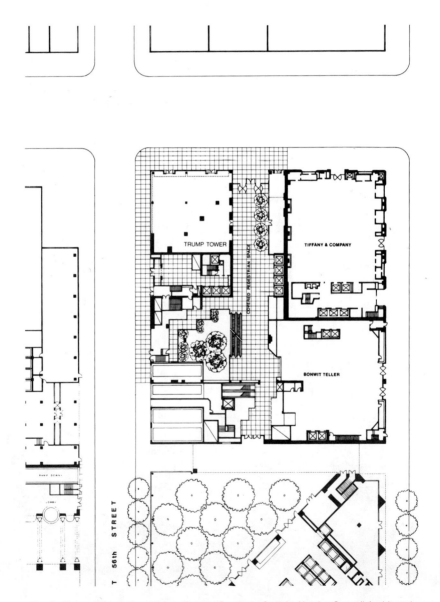

Fig. 4. Ground floor plan, Trump Tower *(Courtesy: Swanke Hayden Connell Architects)*

NEW QUESTIONS

The introduction of public spaces in the street's context raises major planning and architectural questions. Fundamental questions relating to the densities offered by bonuses of extra floor area in exchange for public amenities, and the impact of these densities on the city, have become

Fig. 5 Model of Trump Tower *(Courtesy: Swanke Hayden Connell Architects, photo by Louis Checkman)*

crucial. Other questions, more specifically relating to architecture, have definite impact on the design of the public spaces themselves. Here are some of them:

Relating to Pedestrian Spaces

How can the architect best express the transition from large public spaces to the smaller scale of the street environment, while still maintaining the architectural integrity of the building? (Contextual problems have always been the architect's dilemma, but they are now accentuated.)

Fig. 6 Model of the Philip Morris Building *(Courtesy: Ulrich Franzen Keith Kroger & Assocs., Architects, Photo by Lionel Freedman)*

Is there a relationship between inside space and outside forces around the space?

Is there a relationship between the scale of an amenity and the number of people living or working along its periphery?

How do we judge how appropriate an amenity will be in a specific location determined by real estate forces?

In view of the energy crisis, should a covered pedestrian space be air-conditioned? (Of the buildings mentioned, IBM has the only covered space that is not air-conditioned.)

How should an enclosed public space be announced from the street? Is a canopy or a sign the best way to address such a problem?

How can spaces be conceptually open to the public at all times and yet be closed at certain hours for security?

How can a space be lighted in a way that reduces the contrast between the street's natural light and the interior lighting?

What is the best way to delineate where the public right-of-way ends and the private domain begins?

What implications do matters of regulation and maintenance, such as safety, security, and hours of accessibility, have for the design of the space?

How can architects provide the amenities necessary for both residential tenants and office users within the structure of the vertical building?

How can the architect integrate a pedestrian space and several entrances and service areas, which are necessary for a multi-use building, within a small site?

Relating to Preservation Issues

What are the implications of developing a building on top of a landmark structure?

Should we preserve buildings on the basis of scale preservation, or should we limit preservation to buildings that are accessible to the public?

How are we to insure the future use and maintenance of our preserved buildings?

When would the sale of air rights over an adjoining site threaten to overwhelm a landmark with the increased density of its surrounding buildings?

In view of the need to develop on smaller sites and the pressure for demolition of institutional buildings, how can the architect be sure that the context within which he develops a sympathetic building will continue to exist?

For instance, at 800 Fifth Avenue, which occupies half a block fronting Fifth Avenue, a residential building was developed with a cornice line continuing that of the adjoining site. However, the older building was slated for demolition. Thus the new building's cornice would no longer relate to its context.

CONDENSED REFERENCES/BIBLIOGRAPHY

The following is a condensed bibliography for this article. It includes all articles referred to or cited in the text. The full citations will be found at the end of the volume, with additional citations for further reading. What is given here should be sufficient information to lead the reader to the correct article: the author, date, and title. In case of multiple authors, only the first name is listed.

Le Corbusier 1936, What is America's Problem?
Schuyler, 1913, Towers of Manhattan and Notes on the Woolworth Building

Tall Buildings in Australia

John Rankine

Australia has been settled by Europeans for just under 200 years. The first settlers arrived from England and established a colony at Sydney Cove in January, 1788 (Fig. 1). This first settlement was a penal colony, and the inhabitants were almost all convicts or their army guards. The buildings were mainly stone, hewn from quarries by the convicts and reflecting the solidarity of this small, isolated colony.

Australia has since developed and prospered as a primary producer of wool and grain. This agricultural development fostered the large towns and cities that grew up. By the outbreak of World War II, Australia had a population of some seven million people with a ground area nearly the size of the United States. The nation consisted of six States and a Territory (Fig. 2). Each state had its own state capital, and a federal capital city was located at Canberra.

The only city over one million people at the outbreak of the war was Sydney, which had a building-height restriction of 45.7 m (150 ft). Most of the city's buildings were load-bearing-wall structures of up to five or six floors, but intermingled with them were higher structures, up to ten floors, of simple concrete-encased steel frame.

The post-war years from the '50s to the '70s started a dramatic change. Population and industry exploded. The height limit on buildings was lifted, and the cities grew up and changed (Figs. 3, 4 and 5).

The first building in Australia to reach over 45.7 m (150 ft) was the 117-m (383-ft), curved-face A.M.P. Life Insurance Company's Head Office at Sydney

Fig. 1 Sydney Cove, 1794, from the oil painting by T. Watling in the Dixson Galleries *(Photo by Library Council of New South Wales, Australia)*

Fig. 2 Australia in the 1940s: The six states and their capitals

Cove (1961). Later this building was dwarfed by its own 203-m (666-ft) extension, built directly behind it (1976) (Fig. 6). This later building was the tallest structure in Australia when it was completed, but it has since been exceeded by the M.L.C. Centre and the Centrepoint Tower, which are both in Sydney.

THE MINING BOOM

The energy crunch of the late '70s brought a new boom to Australian industry—mining. Australia is abundant in coal, iron ore, and oil shale. These resources are being developed all over Australia but mainly in the northern half, where cyclones and hurricanes sweep the country.

With the vast output of these mining projects, the attendant crushing plants, washing plants, screening houses, bucket wheels, stackers, and retorts are becoming multimillion dollar structures up to 61 to 91 m (200 to 300 ft) high. They are *tall structures* (Figs. 7 and 8).

CONSTRUCTION

Australia's first major development beyond agricultural pursuits—the early industrial boom, as some say—occurred between 1914 and 1929. During this period the steel industry started and flourished. Australian steel was cheap, and with the advent of welding, many structural-steel fabricating

Fig. 3 Sydney, 1950 *(Photo by Max Dupain)*

Fig. 4 City of Sydney, 1981 *(Photo by Young & Richardson Pty., Ltd.)*

Fig. 5 City of Melbourne, 1981 *(Photo by Ian McKenzie Photography Pty. Ltd.)*

Fig. 6 A.M.P. Building and A.M.P. Centre, Sydney *(Courtesy: Rider Hunt & Partners; photo by Young and Richardson Pty. Ltd.)*

Fig. 7 Bauxite being carried by conveyor to grinding mills, Gove Peninsula, Northern Territory *(Courtesy: Nabalco Pty. Ltd.)*

shops were established. Consequently, all the early high-rise buildings were steel frame structures.

In the early and middle '60s shortages of materials and industrial unrest changed the economics of construction. At the same time, cement manufacturers produced a better product. Higher strengths, technological advances, and a more flexible and workable material changed the scene, so that today nearly all tall buildings are of reinforced or prestressed concrete construction.

CODES

Concrete and Steel Structures Codes—Standards Association of Australia AS1480-1974 and AS1250-1975

Previously each state had its own code and each capital city had its particular version of that code with specific requirements. However, there are now nationwide standard codes for structural steel and concrete: the

Fig. 8 Iron ore fines stacker under construction, Mt. Tom Price, Western Australia
(Courtesy: Minenco Pty. Ltd.)

Standards Association of Australia Concrete Structures Code AS1480-1974 and the Standards Association of Australia Steel Structures Code AS1250-1975, both with subsequent amendments.

Both structural codes stipulate a factor of safety against overturning to ensure overall stability of the structure (although some factors from the two codes seem to be inconsistent). Both codes also accept the use of experimental stress analysis as a design tool. It is interesting to note that in Australia experimentally based design has been used more extensively than in most other countries; for example Centrepoint Tower, M.L.C. Centre, and Qantas Centre, all in Sydney, employed structural scale models tested in the laboratory of the University of Sydney. Although it is permitted to use experimental analysis as the only design tool, this technique is frequently used as an aid to design when the base of assumptions made in structural calculations are doubtful.

Dead and Live Loads Code—Standards Association of Australia AS1170, Part 1-1971

This code stipulates the normal dead and live loadings to be used in buildings.

Wind Forces Code—Standards Association of Australia AS1170, Part 2-1975

Design wind speeds are given for different locations and are derived from annual maximum gust speeds recorded at a height of about 10 m and generally in open country. These values are adjusted for different heights and different terrain categories.

For the analysis of a tall building under direct wind loading, three approaches are permitted:

1. *Peak gust method:* This method makes use of the unaltered design wind speeds, which are based on maximum gust speed only.

2. *Gust Factor Method:* This is a more realistic approach that separates the mean and the fluctuating components of wind load and includes an allowance for size effects and dynamic effects. Information necessary for the computation is provided by a gust factor, which is an estimate of the ratio of the expected peak stress or deflection in a period of about one hour to the mean value of the same stress or deflection during that period.

3. *Wind Tunnel Tests:* This is, at the present time, the best a ailable method of evaluative wind loading on tall buildings.

For across-wind load, the code gives a semiempirical relationship between wind speed and across-wind response that is based on examinations of wind tunnel test results on a variety of model buildings.

However, the final choice of the actual design loading can also be a civic decision based on social values and priorities. For example, the Centrepoint Tower has been designed to withstand pressures of 1,000 year's return (frequency), and an additional safety factor provides a safety margin well above that normally required by the Australian code. These additional safety measures were considered commensurate with the importance of the Tower.

For cyclone-prone areas specified in the code, the basic design wind velocities must be multiplied by 1.15 to provide a risk of failure comparable with that for the rest of Australia.

Earthquake Code—Standards Association of Australia AS2121-1979

In 1979, an earthquake code was issued in Australia describing the equivalent static analysis and design process required in certain zones. In general, however, most areas in Australia are not susceptible to earthquakes.

FIRE SAFETY REQUIREMENTS

In New South Wales at least, fire safety and fire resistance provisions are based on local government ordinance. The general opinion about these provisions is that there are ambiguities in the interpretations and also that they are too severe toward many buildings.

As scientific progress in fire safety engineering is rapid, it will be desirable in the future to have a multitiered Standard Fire Code that will provide simple rules for different fire endurance levels. This code should also permit building structures to be designed using limit-state analysis and should allow dead, live, wind, earthquake, and fire loads to be probabilistically assessed in various combinations. For structural design will, in the forseeable future, be limit-state design.

HIGHLIGHTS OF AUSTRALIAN BUILDINGS

Sydney Opera House

Sydney has a very beautiful harbor, and with great vision and foresight, a former Premier of New South Wales called for a worldwide competition to build an opera house (Fig. 9). The site, probably the most prominent point overlooking the harbor, was occupied at the time by a large, ugly industrial-tram shed and repair shop. There was controversy over the winning design because it did not fall entirely within the conditions of the competition. Then later controversy arose with the architects and a change of architects occurred in midstream. However, from it all Sydney received and can be proud of a most beautiful and attractive building.

The sails, or roof structure, cover the two main halls and the restaurant. There are three main elements forming each roof structure: main shells (A), side shells (B) and infill or louvre shells (C) (Fig. 10).

The height to the top of the largest shell from its springing point is 54.6 m (179 ft). The overall length of the large hall is 121 m (397 ft), and the width is 57 m (187 ft).

Each main shell appears in elevation as a curvilinear triangle standing on one vertex. Each triangle, which forms the outer surface of the shell, is a portion of a sphere whose radius is 75 m (246 ft).

Each half main shell consists of a series of concrete ribs. The cross section of each rib varies in smooth transitions from a solid T to an open Y at its upper reaches. The ribs were poured in sections 4.6 m (15 ft) long, and were assembled by supporting the precast segments on a specially designed steel erection arch and stressing them together.

Fig. 9 Sydney Opera House *(Photo by Kurt Vollmer)*

The Centrepoint Tower, Sydney

The Centrepoint Tower is in the heart of the City of Sydney, built on top of the Centrepoint shopping center (Fig. 11). The design and erection was a great feat of engineering. Construction consisted of jacking a 7-story turret building some 244 to 274 m (800 to 900 ft) above street level up a shaft 6.7 m (22 ft) in diameter. Access to the turret is by means of three high-speed, double-decker elevators and two scissor stairs. The shaft itself grows out of a massive 16-level concrete building that offers an ideal base for the tower structure. An investigation of various methods of tying the shaft to the massive concrete base building suggested that an array of straight cables would provide the simplest solution. A study of problems associated with architecturally designed towers revealed the need for substantial torsional rigidity, and it was therefore suggested that the conventional array of radial guy cables should be replaced by two families of straight inclined cables extending from the base to the neck of the shaft and from there to the underside of the turret. Such an array generates a shape known as a one-sheet hyperboloid of revolution.

An extensive research program was undertaken that involved comprehensive testing with a static structural model. The results of the aero-elastic testing revealed that both the first and second modes of vibration were significant. However, maximum stress conditions were associated with drag loads rather than across-wind motion.

The mechanics of lifting the weights involved, the construction methods for putting the cables in position, and the methods of jacking and anchorage all had to be studied. Each stage of construction was then devised (Fig. 12).

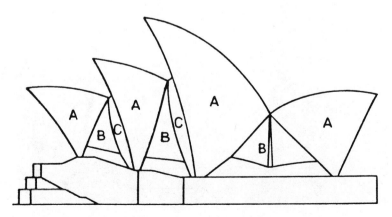

Fig. 10 Diagram of Sydney Opera House *(Courtesy: Ove Arup & Partners)*

Qantas Centre, Sydney

The tower rises through a podium that is more or less conventional. The lower floors are reinforced concrete, two-way-ribbed slabs, and the upper slabs are prestressed concrete coffered slabs.

The vertical elements of the tower are four major columns, approximately 15m by 1.7 m (50 ft by 5 ft 6 in), and a reinforced concrete core

Fig. 11 The Centrepoint Tower, Sydney *(Courtesy: Concrete Constructions Pty. Ltd.)*

containing the access and services. The four major columns are linked by trusses at three plant-room levels. The spans of these trusses are along the north and south faces and along the east and west faces. The trusses support steel rope hangers that support the floors. This is accomplished on the north and south faces by precast spandrel beams attached to the hangers, and on the eastern and western ends by precast beams that run from the hangers to the ends of the core. Precast floor units extended by the support beams span between the external periphery and the core.

Figure 13 is a photograph of the architectural model that shows the architectural development and expression of the structure. The photograph shows the north face. The steel trusses at the plant rooms are expressed, and the hangers, which are spaced at 4.8 m (16 ft) on center, can be seen terminating at the floor above the truss in each of the two upper sections. The hangers in the lower section stop at the floor above the podium.

The truss sits on the columns on PTFE-neoprene combination bearings that will permit lateral and rotational movement during the application of the dead loads. Each truss' vertical member supports a harness of individual wire rope hangers containing one rope for each floor supported. Figure 14 shows a typical floor plan.

Australia Square Tower and M.L.C. Centre, Sydney

These two unique buildings were designed by Harry Seidler & Associates, Architects. Civil & Civic Pty. Limited were the engineers and constructors.

Australia Square (Fig. 15) rises some 183 m (600 ft) above basement level and has 51 floors. The structure consists of an egg-crate-type concrete circular core with radial beams 521 mm (20½ in) deep spanning some 11 m

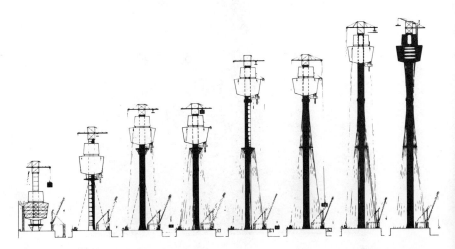

Fig. 12 Centrepoint Tower erection stages *(Courtesy: Concrete Constructions Pty. Ltd.)*

(36 ft) to outside columns. Of special interest is the use of precast formwork for columns and spandrel beams. The precast formwork, with its durable finish of integral white quartz, sand, and cement, becomes part of the stressed structure in the same way that reinforcing becomes stressed with the in-place concrete.

M.L.C. Centre (Fig. 16) is the largest building project undertaken in Australia. It consists of 68 floors and is 224 m (735 ft) high.

The system of construction of the building envelope's tower spandrel beams had each beam initially supported by a precambered steel erection truss spanning between columns. The truss' depth was limited by the height of the window space. The core was poured using a patented "Supershafter" system of formwork that makes fast construction possible for vertical box-type concrete elements. The floors consisted of primary steel trussed with secondary ribs and slabs. Their construction employed a patented "Progressive Strength System," which eliminated the need for propping.

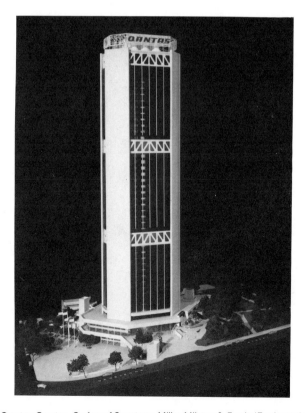

Fig. 13 Qantas Centre, Sydney [*Courtesy: Miller Milston & Ferris (Engineers) Pty. Ltd.*]

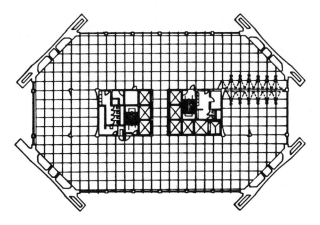

Fig. 14 Diagram of typical high-rise floor plan—floors 31-42, Qantas Centre, Sydney
[*Courtesy: Miller Milston & Ferris (Engineers) Pty. Ltd.*]

Fig. 15 Australia Square Tower, Sydney *(Photo by Max Dupain)*

Gold Fields House, Sydney

This is a very straight-forward commercial development building (Fig. 17). It is unique owing to the selection of its structural frame.

The builder/developer was at first adamant that the frame be concrete columns, beam and slab, as this method of construction was cheapest. The building was completely prelet before construction commenced. A structural report was prepared that investigated some ten completely different structural systems. The concrete frame was the cheapest and steel frame with steel deck the most expensive.

A critical-path building schedule was drawn up for the different schemes, firm prices were obtained from many subcontractors, including suppliers, fabricators, and erectors of steel and deck. The steel frame promised lighter construction, smaller column area and foundations, and a saving in electrical ducting. Overall, taking in all aspects of finance, costs and returns, the most expensive structure became the most economical.

Fig. 16 M.L.C. Centre, Sydney *(Photo by Max Dupain)*

CONCLUSION

In designing the structure for a tall building—in fact, for any building—all materials and methods of construction have to be considered. Each has to be examined in relation to cost, time of construction, method of financing, service and tenant requirements, etc. It requires the combined effort of financier, owner, developer, builder, agent, architect, quantity surveyor, and engineer to determine the relative pros and cons of each type of frame. This determination will make clear the most economical overall structural frame that will do the best job for a particular building.

Acknowledgement

This paper is an edited version of one that appeared as Preprint 81–149, presented at the ASCE Convention, New York, New York, May 11–15, 1981.

Fig. 17 Gold Fields House, Sydney *(Photo by Kurt Vollmer)*

Tall Buildings in Eastern Europe

Ryszard Kowalczyk
Marek Kwieciński
Mieczysław Łubiński
Adam Zbigniew Pawłowski

FUNDAMENTAL SPATIAL AND FUNCTIONAL CONDITIONS

The towns of Eastern Europe have gradually developed around existing buildings that are frequently of historical value. Over the last several years the following trends can be observed:

- growth in the average height of urban housing;

- a substantial share of buildings that are 11 to 15 stories high, accompanied by a number of taller ones (16 to 25 stories); and

- a small number of buildings that are above 25 stories high with 40 stories as an exception.

In our part of Europe it is considered very important to study the visual

effects of tall buildings from the architect's and the urban planner's standpoint. The studies focus on:

- tall buildings as a skyline-shaping factor;
- the interaction of tall buildings with their surroundings;
- the segregation of functional programs;
- the expansion of housing areas; and
- suitable facades.

The tall building, which adds much to the dynamics of spatial arrangement by suitably breaking its harmony, also plays a certain role as a kind of
beacon. Tall buildings' interactions with their vicinities are influenced
by such factors as their relative height, their building mass against the
background of other units or greenery, and their impact on transportation routes.

The so-called general city plans, as formed in most countries of Eastern
Europe, take into consideration the effect of tall buildings in their first 10
years, as well as in the not-so-near future. For instance, the general urban
planning of the city of Warsaw has been going on for 30 years and four
architectural competitions were held, each based on the assumptions worked
out by the city planners.

It usually happens that contemplating new tall buildings is severely
constrained by a town's living tissue. A possible high-rise development in
the Old Town's area or on the Vistula river bank has been under discussion
in Warsaw for many years.

The patterns and coloring of facades are also important. Natural stone
and ceramics are usually preferred to glass (which is appreciated mainly for
its various colors and reflections) and to metal cladding (which is often
perceived as interfering visually with older buildings).

An opinion has been formed that a tall building should be in harmony
with its surroundings, rather than in contrast. High-rise buildings are
mainly of residential, hotel and office character. Emphasis on their prestige
value is thought nowadays to be declining. Buildings not lower than 16
stories will now be discussed in more detail.

The most frequently erected buildings in Poland are those belonging to
the second category grouped by CIB. More specifically, they are 16 to 18
stories high. The structural requirements for these buildings are not very
stringent: shear-wall systems agree well with rather small areas of flats, on
average 56 to 60 m². The same applies to hotel buildings, where spacing of
walls amounts to 3.6 to 4.2 m.

Among the most impressive buildings in this category are the office edifices, whose functions should fulfill the following requirements:

- flexibility of set-up;
- diversity at different floors; and
- easy change of function, especially at lower floors, which entails larger spans.

A framed structure seems to be a fair proposition under the circumstances.

MATERIALS AND STRUCTURAL SYSTEMS

Choice of materials and a structural system is strongly influenced by the fact that, in this part of Europe, 16-to-25-story buildings prevail among high-rises. Therefore some 95% of the tall buildings are designed for concrete, mainly because of the following:

- the availability of cement;
- concrete's low cost compared with steel;
- concrete's adequate stiffness, good fire-resistance, and soundproof quality; and
- well-developed assemblage methods, particularly of large precast elements.

The remaining 5% of Eastern Europe's tall buildings are erected as steel skeletons. This type of structure becomes economical for buildings higher than 160 to 180 m.

The majority of the 16-to-25-story concrete buildings consist of lateral shear walls spaced at 6 m or less and tied together by segments of longitudinal walls acting as stiffeners. Large panels 0.16 to 0.2 m thick are usually used. In Eastern Europe, particularly in the Soviet Union, official opinion has maintained that large-panel structures are economically sound. Thus it is no wonder that in the Soviet Union and in Poland about 60% of all apartment blocks are erected in this way. In Czechslovakia and the German Democratic Republic fully 95% of all multistory residential buildings are assembled of large-dimension elements.

The consumption of basic structural materials in 16-story buildings is as follows:

concrete: 0.60 to 0.75 m^3/m^2

steel: 28 to 37 kg/m^2

These volumes are by no means satisfactory, and overall costs of such buildings are also rather excessive. Moreover, the visual effects are rather poor anyway.

Large panel buildings are usually more than stiff enough; apart from standard failure patterns, incremental collapse has come under study at the design stage recently as a result of the possible deterioration of some supports. Reinforced concrete or steel frames are used rather sporadically.

In contrast to 16-to-25-story buildings, office buildings of 25 stories or more are mainly reinforced concrete skeletons. Structural systems employed for buildings up to 70 stories are shown in Fig. 1. Frames, used often some 20 years ago, are now being avoided. Strip and hinged systems are also rare. Internal concrete-core systems are erected most frequently in Eastern Europe because they offer a number of advantages:

> fire-resistance, in particular of lift and piping shafts, is good;

> execution is efficient because of sliding and climbing shutterings; and

> lateral forces can be transmitted without employing the surrounding skeleton.

Columns are usually supported on subgrade footings (Fig. 1b, d) and spaced rather densely (2.4 to 4.8 m). Cantilevers, shown in Fig. 1a, c, should only be considered when justified by special requirements just above the ground level. Applying the hanging floor concept definitely adds to visual excitement; however, it requires excellent workmanship.

The tallness of a building can be expressed numerically by its slender-

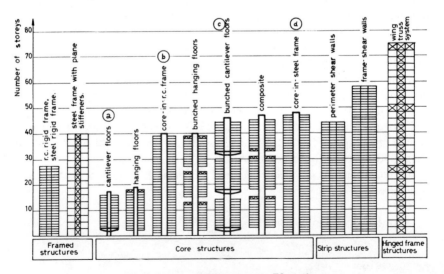

Fig. 1 Structural systems up to 70 stories

ness index ($w=H/B$), or in other words, by the height-to-minimum width ratio. Fig. 2 shows such ratios for some buildings erected in Poland compared against some Western European ones. This figure shows ratios for buildings having load bearing wall systems or steel skeleton or hybrid systems. The same ratios are depicted Fig. 3 for core systems alone. It follows that Polish buildings are more bulky, perhaps as a result of energy conservation considerations. From the architectural point of view, the more slender a building is, the more impressive it appears.

Various tall buildings erected in Poland and Czechoslovakia are shown in Fig. 4. Characteristically, most of the perimeters are complex to enhance the visual impact.

EXAMPLES

We will briefly describe some buildings that have been erected in Eastern Europe, mainly in Poland and Czechoslovakia, over the last several years.

Forum Hotel in Warsaw

This cast-in-place, 29-story building is 95 m high, with annexes. Its structural system consists of lateral shear walls linked by two longitudinal

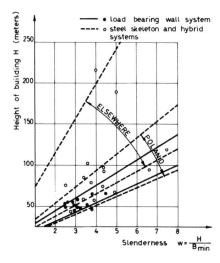

Fig. 2 Slenderness of tall buildings with regard to their structural system: Load-bearing wall, steel skeleton, and hybrid systems

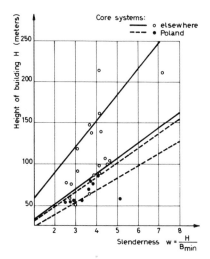

Fig. 3 Slenderness of tall buildings with regard to their structural system: Core systems

No	Purpose, site	Lay-out	Dimensions, height (no. of floors)	Type of frame material	System
1	Office, Warsaw-Poland	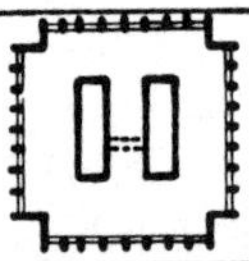	36,00 × 36,00 146,00 (45)	Cast-in-situ r.c. frame	Core-in-frame
2	Office, Warsaw-Poland	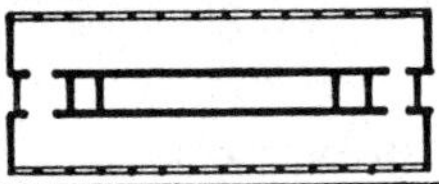	— 138,00 (38)	r.c. frame	Core-in-frame
3	Hotel, Warsaw-Poland (not erected)	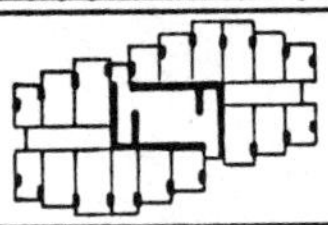	25,90 × 30,00 106,00 (27)	Cast-in-situ r.c. frame	Core-in-frame
4	Office, Warsaw-Poland	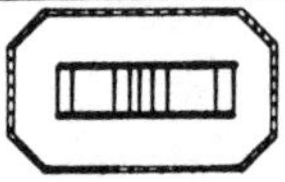	22,80 × 36,00 99,50 (29)	Core-in-frame, steel	Core-in-frame
5	Office, Wrocław-Poland	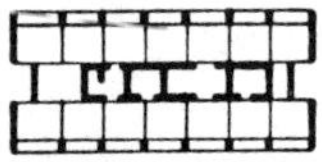	21,45 × 42,70 88,60 (26)	Cast-in-situ r.c. frame	Core-in-frame
6	Office, Moste-Czechoslovakia	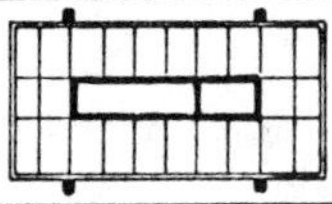	21,60 × 36,00 85,85 (20)	Steel-frame	
7	Residential, Łódź - Poland	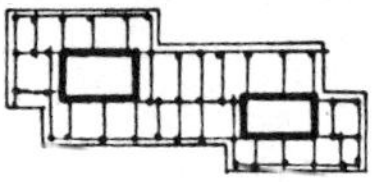	20,70 × 153,00 54,00 ÷ 78,00 (18) ÷ (24)	Prefab. r.c. frame	
8	Office, Gdańsk-Poland	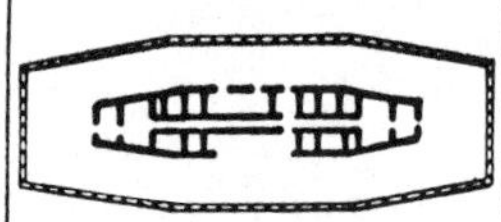	19,00 × 46,00 70,00 (20)		Cantilever-core
9	Office, Poważska Bystrica-Czechoslovakia	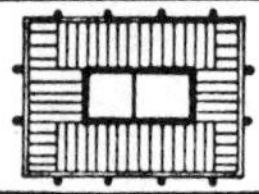	18,00 × 24,00 54,00 (16)	Steel hangers	Core-cable
10	Office, Katowice-Poland	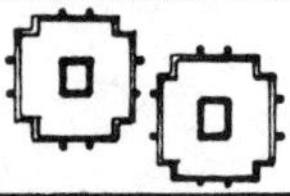	— 85,00 ; 96,00 (18) ; (20)	Steel hangers	Core-cable
11	Office, Warsaw-Poland		33,60(triangle side) 156,00 (42)		Composite

Fig. 4 Tall buildings erected in Poland and Czechoslovakia

ones and additionally stiffened by lift shafts. Flat-plate floors are mono-lithically connected with the bearing walls. Large-dimension shutterings were used.

West Region of the City of Warsaw

The first stage of the project consists of two high-rise buildings: the office of Bank Handlowy and the hotel of Polish Airlines LOT (Figs. 5 and 6). Each is 45 stories and 140 m high, both structural systems are similar. Central reinforced concrete core interacts with an external frame-type tube (Fig. 7); spacing of columns is 3.6 m. The corners are L-shaped to better resist lateral forces. The mat foundation is 2.2 to 3.3 m thick. Sliding shutterings were used. The bank was completed in 1979, the hotel is under construction.

Office building in Povazska Bystrica, Czechoslovakia

A visual accent on the new center of the town is created by an office building 56 m high (Fig. 8). The building has 13 suspended floors of 18 by 24 m. On the top of its central, 6 by 12 m core is a hat constructed of a double steel grid (longitudinal girders are of I-cross sections, the cross beams of box sections). The hat rests on the corners of the core, where there are neoprene bearings. The floors were preassembled on the ground level and then lifted into position.

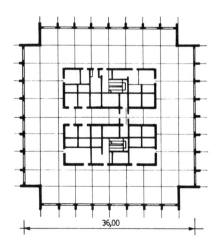
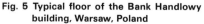
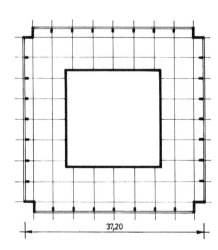

Fig. 5 Typical floor of the Bank Handlowy building, Warsaw, Poland

Fig. 6 Typical floor of the Polish Airlines LOT building, Warsaw, Poland

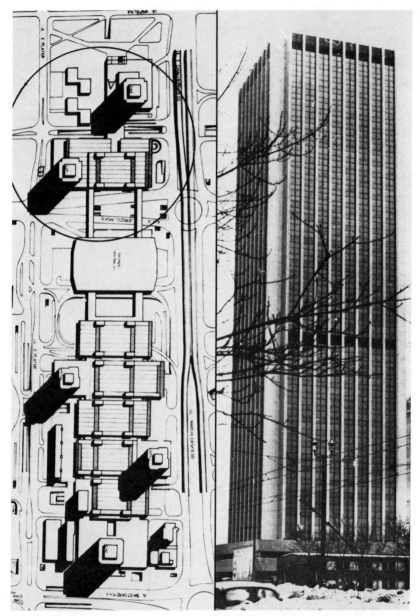

Fig. 7 Bird's eye view of the West Region and the general view of the Bank Handlowy building, Warsaw, Poland

TV Center in Bratislava, Czechoslovakia

This 29-story, 3-bay building is 107 m high (Fig. 9). All the floors and perimeter columns, transmitting gravity loads only, are made of steel. Two reinforced concrete cores resist wind forces. Inclined reinforced concrete walls at the corners transmit torque. The cores were cast in sliding shutterings.

Office building at Moste, Czechoslovakia

The structural system of this 23-story, 90-m-high building consists of a central reinforced concrete core of 21.6 by 36.0 m and four external, 0.84-by-2.24-m reinforced concrete columns. Reinforcement was first erected as a rigid weldment and then concrete was poured. A large unobstructed area 7.2 m deep has thus been obtained for functional flexibility. Steel wings at the top ensure interaction of the columns and the core against wind pressure. Floors are of composite steel and concrete.

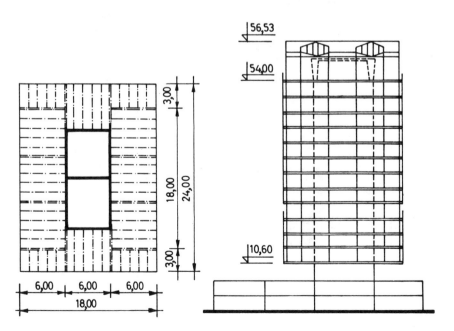

Fig. 8 Typical floor and cross-section of office building, Povazska Bystrica, Czechoslovakia

CONCLUDING REMARKS

The tall buildings of Eastern Europe are designed primarily as special accents on their cities and are treated as parts of the urban silhouette according to the urban planner's vision. So that they can coexist with other buildings, their height is usually confined to 150 m. Overall building technology is thought to profit from high-rise development, which necessarily raises standards of construction and design.

Concrete will probably be the favored construction material in the near future. Below a certain height, steel has been found to be noncompetitive. Structural systems such as skeleton, cast-in-place, or precast, will be strongly preferred. Large panels will be employed to a lesser extent.

A growing part in the decision-making process will be played by economic considerations concerning both direct and maintenance costs. Energy conservation has also become of primary importance.

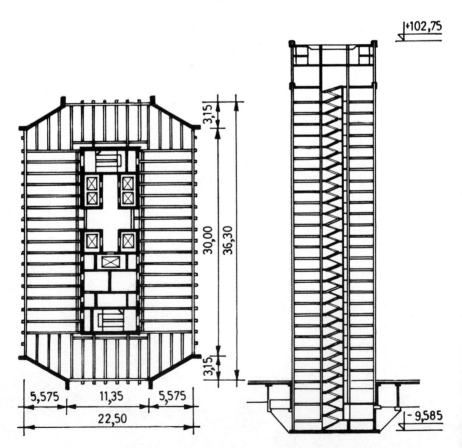

Fig. 9 Typical floor and cross-section of TV Center, Bratislava, Czechoslovakia

Acknowledgement

This paper is an edited version of one that appeared as Preprint 81-138, presented at the ACSE Convention, New York, New York, May 11-15, 1981.

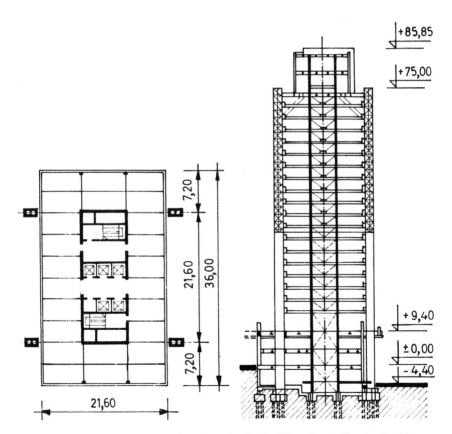

Fig. 10 Typical floor and cross-section of office building, Moste, Czechoslovakia

Tall Buildings in Japan

Takeo Naka

Roughly 120 buildings taller than about 60 m are under construction or have been erected in Japan from 1965 to 1983. They are used for offices, hotels, apartment houses, banks, and miscellaneous purposes. More than half of them are in Tokyo and its surrounding area. The others are in Osaka, Kobe, Kyoto, and other district cities throughout Japan. It is very interesting to note that the number of tall buildings between 55 and 85 m is equal to the number between 85 and 226 m. Buildings of the former group are uniformly distributed through their range in height, whereas the latter group has a peak concentration at around 100 to 150 m. The reason for this distribution has not yet been determined but may result from the particular building conditions in Japan and from the country's economic situtation.

The design of Japan's taller buildings should make use of new findings in the architectural and engineering sciences, especially in the prevention of disasters. Designing for resistance to great earthquakes is the most important consideration in structural analysis for tall buildings in Japan. Dr. K. Muto has a worldwide reputation in this field and has had success in the structural design of the Kasumigaseki-Mitsui Building and many other tall buildings.

Progress in seismic engineering is advancing at such a rapid rate that structural designers in Japan are always finding new developments. As part of a cooperative research project between Japan and the United States, experiments on full-scale multistory buildings are being conducted on a large seismic table that simulates real seismic conditions. The table is installed at the National Building Research Institute at Tsukuba.

Dr. H. Umemura devoted his efforts to the principles of assessing the earthquake-resisting capacity of individual buildings. The results are now contained in a building design code. It is very noticeable that earthquake damage to reinforced concrete buildings takes the form mainly of shear cracks that occur at the columns. Fortunately, in Japan there have been no major disasters caused by earthquakes, strong typhoons, or fires during the life of tall buildings. However, design for these disasters should always be kept in mind. Recent earthquakes that occurred in Sendai surprised designers by causing the collapse of steel buildings that were unsuitably designed and/or constructed. This event focused attention on steel buildings, which had for years seemed to be earthquake-safe structures. Dr. B. Kato and others have developed methods for evaulating the strength of steel buildings in resisting seismic actions; these methods have already been adopted in the Code of Practice in Japan.

The requirements for safety in tall buildings must allow for emergencies such as fires or earthquakes, even down to such details as whether enough automatic sprinklers are present on each floor of a building. In 1980, on Christmas Eve, an unusually heavy snowstorm hit the Sendai area. Many power transmission towers collapsed and all electric supplies were cut off until January 3rd in large housing areas of that city. This incident suggests that heavy snowfall is also a potential source of disaster for tall buildings in which all facilities depend completely on electrical supply.

Problems in the design of tall buildings for hotels, apartment houses, offices, or multi-use purposes arise when designers are required to increase rentable floor areas. Recent fires in hotels, such as the one in Las Vegas, and in multi-use offices, as in Sao Paulo, should be carefully evaluated for the problems encountered; and the overall safety of the buildings involved, not only for guests and occupants, but also for general visitors, should be assessed.

Japan had bitter experiences during and after the Great Kanto Earthquake in 1923, which directly struck Tokyo, Yokohama, and other surrounding cities. Almost all buildings were damaged or crushed or burned in fires that developed in many places just after the earthquake. Many people perished in this terrible disaster, and many lessons were learned. These lessons are still useful for the design and planning of ordinary buildings. Tall buildings in Japan, however, still have many unsolved problems.

Almost all tall buildings in Japan have steel skeletons, which have good ductility in even the most severe earthquakes. To increase the horizontal resistance, the rigid steel frames have earthquake-resistant walls that are specially designed to absorb horizonal displacement with adequate stiffness. Maximum story-drift is usually within 1/200. Frequently 25 mm is used for its ultimate limit value at the strongest design earthquake for ordinary tall buildings.

The cross-sectional shapes of columns used in tall buildings are important. The first tall building, the Kasumigaseki-Mitsui Building, has H-shaped columns because of the preference for joint welding techniques. However, box-shaped columns are more apt to be used today because of the savings in materials and cost. In the welding process the skill of the welders, with suitable procedures and sequences of welding, surveying, and inspecting, is required. Semiautomatic arc welding, shielded with carbon dioxide gas, and fully automatic welding processes are used for steel structures for both shop and site welding. Ultrasonic insection with 2 MHz and 5 MHz is used. Besides welding, high strength bolts are used equally at every connection.

An important feature in the erection of tall buildings' steel frames in Japan is that the top levels of each part of the columns should be kept on a horizontal plane at the erection site. This procedure is very valuable in obtaining good calibration of columns and beams in their proper positions (Fig. 1).

About 30 years ago such a procedure was used in the erection of all-welded steel frames for an office building in Tokyo to minimize unavoidable distortion due to welding, which caused the shrinkage of members and the slanting of columns toward the inside of the structure. At the above-mentioned horizontal plane the distortions can be measured to obtain better methods for succeeding projects. This procedure, even though it may be regarded as troublesome when carried out in the joint works of two or more steel fabricators on the same building site, is still of practical usefulness.

As to the structural design of tall buildings in Japan, simple types of frames are preferable when considering seismic activity. Tall buildings that have rectangular or square floor plans have less torsional stress.

However, for complex planning of tall buildings, special methods are available for structural analysis. Dr. Muto and Mr. M. Nagata have demonstrated one form of earthquake-resistant high-rise design in the Akasaka-Prince Hotel. It has 37 stories, with a notched, V-shaped framing plan, designed by Architect Dr. K. Tange using three-dimensional frame analysis and feed-back dynamic and static design systems.

SHINJUKU-NOMURA BUILDING

The Shinjuku-Nomura Building, located west of the old center of Tokyo, is an example of a building using earthquake-resistant design. It is near the circle line National Railway. Daily railway passengers at the Shinjuku Station number the highest in Tokyo. A description of the Shinjuku-Nomura Building appears in Table 1.

Table 1 Data of the Shinjuku-Nomura Building

Height from ground level to eaves	203.25 m
Maximum height	209.90 m
Number of floors	55
Substories	5
Total floor area	119,156.72 m²
Standard floor area	1,632.50 m²
Standard floor height	3.8 m
Depth of foundation	-28.00 m
Use	Office
Completion	1978

Fig. 1 The Mitsubishi Bank Ltd. Head Office under construction

The building uses steel construction, with box-shaped columns and H-shaped beam sections. Two types of box-shaped columns are used. One is the Universal Box, UB, which is composed of two rolled steel sections, each having a special U profile, that are similar to the channel section supplied by Nippon Steel Corporation. The maximum thickness of UB is 50 mm. The other type of column is a welded-plate box-shape.

Earthquake-resistant walls are steel plates that are connected to the columns and beams of the steel frames with a number of high-strength bolts. In this way the strength, toughness, and rigidity of the frames and the strength of members are dependent on the characteristics of the steel used.

The jointing method consists of the semiautomatic and automatic welding procedures described in connection with the Kasumigaseki-Mitsui Building; inspections on welded parts are mainly by ultrasonic 5 MHz.

The basic frame is 51 by 33 m with a rectangular plan maintained from the bottom to the top. In the subfloor four spans are added to the surroundings; however, the otherwise harmful effects on the towering structures are carefully eliminated.

Following the experience developed earlier, special attention is paid to the structural design in minimizing site welding. Columns, brackets, and parts of beams are welded in the shop. The main parts of the beams are field connected with high strength bolts. Therefore, the accuracy of tolerance at jointing parts is a very important factor in erection.

Special attention is given to preserving the toughness of steel structures and to considering the P-Δ effect. In addition careful consideration is given to the restriction of ratio of normal force N/Ny in columns, the spacing of lateral supports for beams, and the prevention of local buckling, through proper width to thickness ratio, shear panels at beam-to-column connections, and more. The greatest effort goes toward keeping the story-shear resistance and displacement within a permissible value.

As a result, the steel skeleton is rather heavy. Thicknesses of built-up columns are 60 mm or 55 mm, and UB columns are 50 mm. The steel used is weldable steel SM50 which has a carbon equivalent of less than 0.43 by the formula that follows:

$$C_{eq} = C + Mn/6 + Si/24 \% \qquad (1)$$

The building is carefully designed for evacuating smoke and toxic gases and for the prevention of fires.

SHINJUKU CENTER BUILDING

The Shinjuku Center Building, shown in Fig. 2, is also located at the Shinjuku New Center of Tokyo and is described in Table 2.

Table 2 Data of the Shinjuku New Center Building

Height from ground level to eaves	216 m
Maximum height	222.95 m
Number of stories	54
Substories	5
Total floor area	183,063 m^2
Standard floor area	2,629 m^2
Depth of foundation	-27.5 m
Use	offices, shops, clinics, and parking
Completion	1979

Fig. 2 The Shinjuku Center Building is shown as the second tall building from the right. This area is a part of Tokyo.

The building uses rigid steel frame construction, with earthquake-resistant, slitted precast concrete horizontal walls connected vertically with round steel bars. The walls resist seismic activity. Columns are box-shaped with a maximum thickness of 65 mm and beams are H-shaped sections having a depth of 700 mm.

The structural design is a basic rectangular frame of 63 by 42 m. There are four Warren-trussed floors, one of which is located at the top of the building. The others are at the 14th, 27th, and 40th floors. These four floors are used mainly for various mechanical installations.

The spans of perimeter columns are 3 m; those columns inside of the building are 15.40 m + 22.10 m + 15.40 m. The core is composed of earthquake-resistant walls in which 32 elevators for passengers and 3 for baggage are located.

This building was designed and constructed by Taisei Corporation. Construction took 22 months.

Tall Buildings in Nigeria

T. Arciszewski

G. U. Ojiako

HISTORY

Nigeria, a former British Colony that gained independence just over 20 years ago, is on the west coast of Africa. The country covers an area of 923,300 km². Thus it is about 3½ times the size of the United Kingdom.

Nigeria is the most populous country on the African continent, having a population estimated at over 80 million. The population is made up of many language groups, the largest three being the Muslim Hausa of the north, the partly Muslim, partly Christian Yoruba of the southwest, and the predominantly Catholic Ibo of the southeast. These three language groups make up more than 75% of the total population of the country. Within the language groups there are over 100 tribes with their dialects.

In 1970 the country emerged from three years of disastrous civil war during which at least 3 million people starved or were killed. The civil war resulted mainly from deep suspicions arising from differences in levels of political education, from religious beliefs, and from tribal self-interest, particularly among the largest language groups.

The end of the civil war marked the beginning of the nation's long process of reconstruction and reemergence. National unity became the main goal of successive military and civilian governments. The country also found itself with unprecedented wealth accruing from crude oil exports.

Internationally, with unity and peace assured at home, the country thrust its size, population, and wealth into African politics, in which it has been playing an important leading role.

CURRENT ECONOMIC DEVELOPMENT

Within the country itself, the oil boom (Fig. 1) has had one subtle but significant impact on the country's economic development. The huge sums of money it has generated have awakened the country to its industrial potentialities. Projects that would have been unthinkable in the past because of their huge cost can now be undertaken. Some projects—ambitious, prestigious, and costly—have been aimed mainly at inspiring confidence and a sense of belonging among the population. A new capital, Abuja, is to be built as a symbol of pride and unity.

The sudden upsurge in industrialization spurred rapid expansion of urban towns. This expansion resulted mainly from rural-urban income dif-

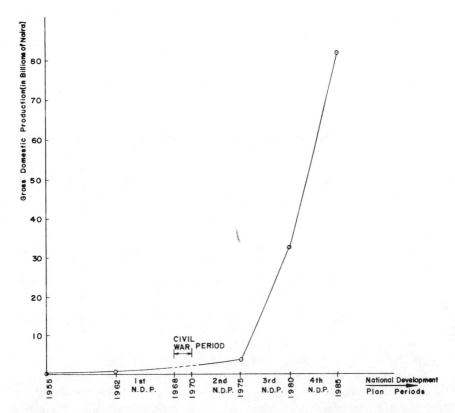

Fig. 1 Rising gross domestic production of Nigeria *(National Developments Plans, I, II, III, for Nigeria, Government Press)*

ferentials that reflect the greater number of white-collar jobs in urban areas, and from the provision of social amenities such as good water, medical facilities, and better education in urban areas. This growth saw the population of Lagos explode from 300,000 to 3 million in ten years, that of Ibadan from 700,000 to 1.06 million, of Port Harcourt from 128,000 to 328,000, and of Kano from 275,000 to 550,000. In many urban areas, particularly Lagos and Ibadan, which have approached their limits of horizontal expansion, the rapid growth has created acute shortages of housing and accommodation and problems of overcrowding. This situation is most serious in Lagos. For further growth, the only option now open is to undertake the challenges of massive vertical expansion.

TALL BUILDINGS—LANDMARKS IN NIGERIAN CITIES

In the very limited area of Lagos Island, which contains nearly all the federal government ministries, the legislative houses, and other government buildings, the shortage of land is particularly acute. In this area more than any other in Lagos and, indeed, in the Federation, the challenges of vertical expansion are being tackled rapidly. Old buildings are constantly being pulled down and high-rise buildings put in their places. Plans for the erection of over 30 new skyscrapers have been approved and more are on the way (Lagos Executive Development Board, 1980). These new high-rises, together with existing buildings and those under construction, would enable the Lagos Development Authority to achieve its ambitious aim of turning the island into the "New York" of Nigeria by the year 2000. The average height of tall buildings now in Lagos Island is 20 stories. By 1990, when most if not all of the approved tall buildings in the area will have been constructed, the average height may exceed 30 stories.

The first Nigerian high-rise was built in Lagos Island in 1960, not by a giant commercial enterprise as, for instance, the 1885 William Lebaron Jenney's Home Insurance Company Building of Chicago was, but by the federal government of Nigeria itself. This 23-story giant was to be a prestigious symbol of a great nation attaining independence from a colonial master—hence the name: Independence Building (Fig. 2). Today the importance of the building in the life of the nation can be judged from its role as the headquarters of the Ministry of Defence and site of the offices of all the nation's armed forces.

The Independence Building is now overshadowed by Necom House, a 37-story building less than half a kilometer away (Fig. 3). Necom House is Nigeria's tallest high-rise and, indeed, the tallest concrete building in West Africa. It was completed in January, 1979, and was designed by Nickson Borys and Partners (Architects) and constructed by Costain (W.A.) Ltd. to house the federal government's expanding external communications network and its administrative offices. A 12-story NET terminal sign with a lighthouse sits on the tower block. A 7-story ancillary building is attached to the main building. From the standpoint of design and structure, Necom House is the most complex building in Nigeria at the moment.

A happy trend in the development of tall buildings in the country is the federal government's increasing interest in building for residential purposes. Until recently, most if not all of the tall buildings in the country were used for official or commercial purposes only. The first high-rise residential buildings, the Eric Moore Towers, were constructed in 1976 in the thickly populated residential district of Lagos Mainland. They consist of six 12-story blocks that house the federal senior staff. There are several such residential high-rise developments, some still under construction, scattered over all of the residential districts in Lagos Mainland. Similar

Fig. 2 The Independence Building in Logos *(Courtesy: Leventis Stores Limited)*

but larger high-rise buildings were built to house members of the federal legislative houses.

Elsewhere in the country the development of high-rise buildings has been slow and isolated. All of the tall buildings are owned by the local state governments. In Lagos, shortage of land has been the primary driving force for the vertical expansion of buildings. However, the motive for constructing a few tall buildings in some of the state government capitals has been to gain prestige. An exception may be the construction of high-rise hotel buildings in the various state capitals all over the country. Because of many functional advantages (concentration of facilities, services, and the like), nearly all state-owned high-quality hotels are constructed in blocks 8 to 11 stories tall (Fig. 4).

Fig. 3 The Necom House in Lagos—tallest building in Nigeria *(Courtesy: Necom Journal)*

Ibadan, the second largest city in the Federation and the capital of Oyo State, is the main native town of the Yoruba people. The city's landscape of traditionally low native houses is broken by only three high-rise buildings. The most elegant and important of these buildings, the Cocoa House, stands out prominently against the landscape. It is a 24-story structure built in 1965 for the administration and promotion of cocoa production and trade, the predominating commercial activity in the region. The other two high-rise buildings are the 12-story AJE House (1960) and the 10-story Cooperative Building (1957). Both are used by the state government for official purposes.

In the oil-rich town of Port Harcourt, the most surprising aspect of high-rise development is the lack of interest shown by many giant companies involved in the oil industries in the area. All three tall buildings in this, the capital of Rivers State, are owned by the government. For nearly 20 years, the Hotel Presidential, an eleven story block hotel built in 1962, has dominated the entire urban landscape (Fig. 5). The hotel is now joined by the 10-story podium block secretariat opened in October, 1980, for offices of the state government ministries and agencies.

Soon the tallest building in the city will be the 17-story building called Point Block, now nearing completion (Fig. 6). The use to which this public building will be put has not yet been revealed, but the cost, estimated at 17 million naira (approximately 31 million U.S. dollars), represents a sizable part of the state government's annual budget expenditure.

Fig. 4 Hamdala Hotel in Kaduna *(Courtesy: John Hinde Ltd.)*

In the northern states of the country, where the population is predominantly muslim, the only state capitals having tall buildings are Kano and Kaduna. Each has an 8-story hotel similar to the Cocoa House and a high-rise secretariat building. Kano, the third largest city of Nigeria, also boasts a unique Mosque that is over a century old. This is an important example of a very long Nigerian tradition in constructing vertical landmarks.

The slow progress in the development of high-rise buildings in urban areas under state governments may be explained by the limited financial and technical resources available to those governments. The federal government has always been the big builder, and its efforts in this respect are concentrated in the capital territory under its direct developmental control. Abuja is to be the new Nigerian capital and thus a new Federal territory. Perhaps here the experience and benefits of tall buildings development gained in Lagos will inspire well-planned and coordinated construction of high-rise buildings that will give the new city a beautiful urban landscape.

ABUJA—THE NEW FEDERAL CAPITAL

Lagos, the current Nigerian Capital, is positioned more than 1000 km

Fig. 5 Hotel Presidential in Port Harcourt

from the center of the country. It is an overcrowded harbor town situated on islands and swamps with an unhealthy, malarial, hot, and very humid climate. The town has no chance for any further development because of existing constraints on geography, communications, and water resources (Aderibigbe, 1979). The capital is situated in the region of the Yorubas, one of the three most populous and rival tribes. Many Nigerians have assumed that this fact has always tipped the delicate state of political balance, tribal power, and prestige in favor of the Yorubas. It is an essential decision factor because, still ten years after the Nigerian civil war, the unity of the nation is the major objective of each Nigerian government. The present capital's position does not unite the nation as strongly as it should.

The new capital will be situated in the central part of the country in Abuja, on land belonging to a very small tribe, the Gwari. The proposed place satisfies the demands of all the Nigerian tribes, and the construction of the new capital will have an essential political meaning in the process of creating the new Nigerian society and a united nation.

In contrast to Lagos, the region of Abuja is an ideal location for the capital, with unlimited possibilities of development. This lcoation will activate the process of industrialization in a less developed central part of the country and will significantly reduce the region's present communication problems.

Fig. 6 Point Block in Port Harcourt

The creation of a new capital is perhaps the most significant and dynamic development being undertaken by the present federal government of Nigeria. A total of 1.6 million people are expected to live at Abuja by the year 2000. The city is ultimately planned for 3.2 million inhabitants. Because the new capital is located in the geographical center of the nation, it is easily accessible from all parts of the Federation by road, rail, and air (Fig. 7). The federal capital territory lies in open savannah with an excellent climate and beautiful scenery. Large hills of volcanic rock are typical on the landscape of this region. One such landmark, called Aso Hill, undisputably dominates the approaches to the capital.

The town was planned in the form of a large V, standing for the victory of national unity, pride, and progress (Federal Capital Development Authority, 1980). The point of the letter is directed toward Aso Hill. All Federal Institutions—the Presidential Complex, National Assembly, Supreme Court, and federal government offices and ministries—are located there, with a beautiful view of Aso Hill and the open savannah landscape. In the neighborhood of this governmental district is the "central business district," which will most likely be the largest concentration of tall buildings in Africa. Both arms of the town will consist of residential areas—large independent urban units for 230,000 inhabitants each that will be constructed gradually in the next 20 years. All residential areas will have their own local centers, with tall buildings for banks and other local institutions.

Development of the capital is, of course, in process. The central area consisting of the "government district" and an "accelerated residential district" will be developed first and completed by 1983.

Tall buildings will play an essential role in the development of the town. Their concentration in the central business district will create an impres-

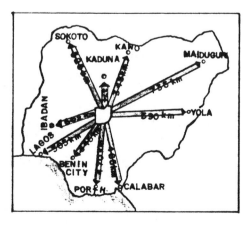

Fig. 7 Central position of the federal capital territory *(Federal Capital Development Authority, 1980)*

sive background for the federal complexes. Skyscrapers situated in local centers will diversify the monotonous, flat landscape of the presidential areas.

HIGH-RISE DECISION MAKING IN NIGERIA

The rapid development of tall buildings in Nigeria and their various, often accidental, character raised questions about the whole high-rise decision-making process here. The large sums of money spent on such buildings, their prestigious character, and their dominant role in some Nigerian urban centers sometimes arouse suspicions about whether these skyscrapers are constructed in their optimum urban, architectural, and technical form under Nigerian conditions. The problem is particularly urgent and important because present high-rise decisions will determine the shape of Nigerian cities for many years to come and will affect the lives of several future generations.

There are two main types of decision situations in Nigeria, both of which should be analyzed and improved. In the first type, a decision made on a local scale is necessary for single, isolated tall buildings. The second type, which is more complicated, involves the process of decision making for the whole urban center.

The first type is typical for existing towns, where buildings occupying a given area determine the shape of a tall building plot. Even the building's form and decision making about it have mainly technical and structural characteristics. The question is how to satisfy the customers' needs in the best possible way, fulfilling at the same time all given requirements and limitations. This situation is mostly the problem of new hotels or office buildings being located in old, overcrowded districts without sufficient water and power supplies.

The second type of situation occurs in new urban centers and is typical in the construction of the new capital. The number of limitations is less than for the first type, but the total complexity of the problem is much greater. The process of decision making must address not only the design of all individual buildings in a given area, but also the entire urban planning of building groups, services, and facilities. It is not a technical or architectural problem as in the first situation. A large number of added decision factors have to be included in the decision model. Social or climatic factors that are secondary in designing a hotel of assumed size in a given environment may be decisive in planning a new urban center.

Such a situation stands out in the planning of individual districts in Abuja, which are assumed to be independent urban units with their own local industry, local trade and banking facilities, and so on. Buildings will be of various heights: bungalows, blocks of flats, and tall buildings in local centers. The optimum proportion of each type of building must be determined.

In this two-sided situation, high-rise decision making may be improved by elaborating both a general, formal model of an urban center in a developing country (high-rise decision making on the urban scale), and a model of an isolated tall building in its complex environment (high-rise decision making on the local scale). The systems modeling approach seems to be most promising. Special attention should be given to a formal description of urban centers and tall buildings by design parameters to form a fully classified system.

It will be necessary to take into consideration all decision factors of local Nigerian importance, which may change the decision process from what it would be in a developed, highly industrialized country. There are, of course, many problems, which have to be formulated and solved. As an example, is it possible to include numerous cultural traditions of various tribes as special "tradition factors" in high-rise decision making and, if so, to what financial extent? As another example, how would one connect the problem of water supply with the selection of the optimum type of wind bracing? Would it be reasonable to assume that in countries where water supply might be interrupted, all tall buildings should be constructed with large water tanks on the top to provide sufficient fire protection and continuous water? How would one include this important factor in the model of high-rise decision making, and will it affect structural decisions? It seems probable that such an assumption would call for significant structural requirements, such as wind bracing in the form of belt-truss systems.

Another question might be how one can connect the conservation of energy and the outer form of a building under tropical conditions. Also, would the financial aspects of tall buildings be analyzed in Nigeria, where mixed private and governmental financial involvement is typical and the economic factor is often decisive?

The creation in Nigeria of an applicable theory of high-rise decision making that could improve the present unsatisfactory practices is a bold research challenge for scientists oriented toward the real needs of developing countries. The construction of the new Nigerian capital in Abuja only stresses the urgency and significance of the problem.

SUMMARY

During the last 20 years tall buildings have become important landmarks of Nigerian towns. Their growing number and various forms have changed the character of many traditionally flat Nigerian urban centers. Numerous new developments, particularly the federal capital in Abuja, require the advanced designer's approach to the problems of planning both urban centers and single tall buildings under Nigerian conditions. It would be challenging and significant to improve existing high-rise decision making, on both the urban scale and the scale of the single isolated building.

Acknowledgement

This paper has been prepared as an initial result of research on tall buildings initiated by the authors at the University of Nigeria. The financial support of that university is gratefully acknowledged, as well as the cooperation of many Nigerian experts, who provided detailed information and encouragement to publish this paper.

CONDENSED REFERENCES/BIBLIOGRAPHY

The following is a condensed bibliography for this article. It includes all articles referred to or cited in the text. The full citations will be found at the end of the volume, with additional citations for further reading. What is given here should be sufficient information to lead the reader to the correct article: the author, date, and title. In case of multiple authors, only the first name is listed.

Aderibigbe 1979, Lagos-The Development of an African City

Federal Capital Development Authority 1980, New Federal Capital . . . Abuja, Master Plan Phase 1
Federal Ministry of Planning, Lagos 1975, Federal Republic of Nigeria Third National Development
Federal Ministry of Planning, Lagos 1981, Federal Republic of Nigeria Outline of the Fourth National

Lagos Executive Development Board 1980, Annual Report

Ministry of Economic Development 1970, Federal Republic of Nigeria Second National

Tall Buildings in Southern Africa

George Rhodes-Harrison*

INTRODUCTION

It is important to understand the context within which tall buildings occur in Southern Africa and to recognize, in turn, their influence on the urban habitat and likely future trends therein. To do this it is essential, first of all, to describe briefly the economies of the countries of the subcontinent. These economies are as follows: primary (agricultural) in Mozambique; secondary (agricultural and mining) in Angola and Zambia; and tertiary (agricultural, mining, and industrial) in the Republic of South Africa (RSA) and Zimbabwe. We should also note that Angola, Zimbabwe, and the RSA have extensive country-wide transportation, municipal, and administrative infrastructures and networks.

Southern Africa has many innovative tall structures in the form of mining apparatus, TV or telephone transmission towers, and thermal electricity-generating stations. In addition, it has many tall buildings of 10 to 30 stories, that are used for flats (apartments), hotels, or offices. Tall buildings are common in the major cities of Southern Africa, such as Port Elizabeth, Cape Town, Johannesburg, Salisbury, and Luanda.

---

*George Rhodes-Harrison died shortly after the presentation of this manuscript at the Council Meeting in New York in May, 1981. His work is being continued.

The population and economic growth of these countries in the 30-year period after World War II markedly increased urbanization. In turn, the building of tall buildings in the urban habitat became widespread throughout the southern subcontinent of Africa. This increasing urbanization, together with the wider scope and complexity of local administration by government (at all levels) and by business, resulted in the formation of distinct city centers and central business districts (CBDs), both of which are becoming polynuclear and expanding.

THE FIRST POSTWAR GENERATION

The first generation of post-World War II tall buildings were naturally lit and ventilated, having simple reinforced concrete (RC) structures, brick wall panels, orthodox electro/mechanical elevators, and traditionally designed building services. Total gross floor areas varied from 4,500 to 9,000 m² (50,000 to 100,000 ft²), and the buildings were up to 20 stories high, with a 66 m (200 ft) maximum height.

In the immediate 20-year postwar period, the resident professionals and building industries in all of the countries of Southern Africa were both competent and accomplished in the design and construction of these buildings for flats, hotels, and offices. They were also well organized and financed and prompt in their service, and they constructed these buildings at comparatively low costs.

THE SECOND GENERATION OF TALL BUILDINGS

Since the mid-1960s increased economic growth and the complexity and concentration of the administrative function in government and business led to a demand for bigger office buildings in Zimbabwe, at Bulawayo and Salisbury, and in the RSA at Cape Town, Durban, Johannesburg, and Pretoria.

In the RSA a new and different class of office buildings began to appear in both public and private sectors after the mid-1960s. These buildings averaged 35 stories in height and had larger typical floor areas of approximately 900 to 2,000 m² (10,000 to 22,000 ft). They also had fully engineered HVAC, electrical, and plumbing systems, with electronic multirise elevator systems.

However, these buildings were not just taller than the then prevailing heights of 20 stories. They differed fundamentally from their predecessors in deep-space layout, building technology, capital outlay, and rentals. They had a most significant impact on the urban landscape, on building design, on consulting practices, on municipal administration and planning practices, and on the real estate and building industries (Rhodes-Harrison, 1975).

Among this second generation of tall buildings, the single most influential project was Carlton Centre—a complex comprising a 50-story office building, a 600-room, 28-story hotel and convention center, a major shopping center of 40,000 m² (450,000 ft²), and parking for 2,000 cars. Except for a similar project in North America, this was the largest project ever built in "one shot" (and not phased) anywhere in the world—and it still is!

The pioneering work done during this project included the following: closing intervening streets to create one super block out of four city blocks; improving high-rise technology, appropriate product innovation, technology transfer, and cross-pollination of American and South African practice; training for general contractors and subs; and applying South African engineering skills to geological investigation and excavation of deep basements and foundations. These great strides gave an injection of modernity to the building professions and industry, laying the foundation of know-how for creating this new breed of tall buildings in the very special environmental design conditions at 1,750 m (5,750 ft) above sea level. It was this super block that made the height of 50 stories possible.

Carlton Centre project, Johannesburg, South Africa *(Courtesy: S. Nigel Mandy)*

The surge of economic investment in the 1960s also led to the construction along the Natal coast and at Durban RSA, of a considerable number of 15-to-20 story beach-resort flats. In the main centers of Zimbabwe and the RSA it led to the construction of many multistory hotels for both the tourist and convention industries.

DESCRIPTION OF THE INDUSTRY IN THE 1970s

Since the early 1970s, Southern Africa has been severely afflicted by civil war, socioeconomic stagnation or regression, and political uncertainty. These problems have been compounded by inflation and rising oil prices. Throughout the subcontinent, except in the RSA, this situation has led to disruption and inadequate maintenance of both the industry's infrastructure and its logistical chain of supply, which are necessary to build or maintain tall buildings. Falling demand and substantial emigration of the persons with required skills and experience have contributed to the problems.

Political transition and social and economic rehabilitation have not yet stabilized conditions sufficiently in Angola, Zambia, or Mozambique to revive the investment and construction momentum of the 1950-1970 period; but momentum has revived in the RSA and may yet do so in Zimbabwe. When it does revive there, and even elsewhere in the subcontinent, it will benefit from ease of access to the RSA's tall building know-how, experienced personnel, special enginering systems, products, and general chain of supply. This access could well accelerate rehabilitation, and lessen its cost, in the war-ravaged portions of the subcontinent. The RSA's role is so pivotal not only because the second generation of tall buildings, with their immense CBD urban impact, occurred only in the RSA, but also because a third generation of such buildings, responding to the economic realities of the 1980s, is now underway there.

FACTORS REVIVING DEMAND FOR OFFICE
BUILDINGS, RSA 1980

Surplus Office Space

Approximately a 10% surplus of office accommodation persisted throughout the 1970s in the CBDs of Cape Town, Durban, Johannesburg, and Pretoria, severely constraining rental levels and inhibiting investment in new office projects, which virtually dried up. This surplus occurred through either incorrect project location, or the presence of older buildings or buildings that could not be upgraded to the level of quality then demanded.

Since mid-1979 this surplus of office accommodation has been absorbed rapidly. The construction of major new office buildings is now being resumed and is breeding a whole new set of criteria for rentals and procedures.

Economic Revival. In the RSA many international economic interfaces and national factors coalesced to revive economic demand in 1978. By mid-1980 this revival had grown into a full-scale boom. The effect of this growth has been to stimulate a radical revival of investment in transportation systems, socioeconomic infrastructure, educational buildings, industry, and now housing and office buildings.

The Special Nature and Influence of the Pretoria/ Witwatersrand Region

Pretoria, Johannesburg, the gold-mining Witwatersrand towns, Sasolburg/Vereeniging, and Vanderbijlpark together constitute the Pretoria/ Witwatersrand/Vereeniging (PWV) Region. This region is a complex interaction group of urban centers, containing the following segments of the Republic's population:

40% of the white population

18% of the brown population

16% of the black population

17% of the total population, RSA

Since 1910 the administration of the RSA has had a dual location. The central government is based in Pretoria and government business is based in Johannesburg. Together these two cities have become the primary urban and communications center of the RSA at both the national and international levels. This duo has unique leadership functions in the main sectors of the national economy, and its major economic activities include the following:

73% of the nation's banking activites

89% of its life insurance activities

54% of its building-society activities

95% of its property development

89% of its wholesale and retail trade

The prominence of Pretoria and Johannesburg started with political unification after the Boer War and the subsequent gold mining, and the system of mining-group administration, which soon attracted major service industries. The mining groups later extended their activities as major entrepreneurs, developing major industry and business in both South Africa and the international sphere.

Extraordinary Development Factors in the RSA

Since the resumption of economic activity in the late 1970s, there has been recognition of many other dominant influences on the cities of the RSA and on the socioeconomic nature of the entire Republic. These influences are gathering momentum and will have a substantial impact on the future course of both the country and its cities. A summary of these extraordinary influences follows:

1. A total population of 44 million people by A.D. 2000 has been projected for the RSA. Of these, 17 million will be economically active. (For relative scale, compare this figure with the 22 million people who are economically active in Great Britain.)

2. To maintain social stability, therefore, it is imperative to provide work opportunities at all social and economic levels for *all* black, brown, and white peoples in the RSA.

3. It will be necessary to provide the corresponding infrastructure, housing, education, and social and recreational facilities for this population growth. For example, electrical service and other improvements to Soweto. amounting in value to R400 million, are now under construction.

4. The need has arisen to decentralize government and to extend private-sector enterprizes. It will also be necessary to create mutually acceptable, constitutional/political forms of joint decision making for the Republic as a whole (at all government levels); black and brown people will have to participate with white people in this decision making. This need is being articulated currently as "A Constellation of States" or "A Consociational Democracy".

Note: This means achieving a sustained 20-year average growth for the economy of approximately 6% compound per annum, in real terms.

5. Finally, in combination these influences will require the conversion and application of the RSA's *immense* mineral wealth, its sophisticated industrial capability, its agricultural production, its very distinct entrepreneurial drive, and its personnel utilization.

The "Catalytic Function" of the Corporate Head Office

The driving-force for realizing these requirements will be the growth of the "head-office" function in both the public and private sectors. South Africa's major cities have advanced into the *quarternary economic stage,* where the processes of research, analysis, feasibility studies, decision making, transactions, government, and management (that is, "the knowledge industries") are paramount.

Doubling the RSA's Office Space

For example, the sustained average growth of office space in Johannesburg from the 1950 total of 1,200 m² (12,900 ft²) until 1970 was 80,000 m² (860,000 ft²) per annum. This is a trend, interrupted in the 1970s, to which Johannesburg's growth of office space must return. Only thus can the "catalytic function" of the RSA's corporate headquarters of mining and financial institutions be maintained to serve the required purposes. Fulfilling this need means doubling the office center of Johannesburg by A.D. 2000 to a total of 5 million m² (54 million ft²) of office space!

The influences identified here mean the revival of the surge in building activity that doubled the CBD office accommodation of the major South African cities between 1950 and 1970.

THE RSA's TREND TOWARD POLYNUCLEAR AND DECENTRALIZED CITIES

Pre-World War II South African CBDs were a conglomerate of retail shops, wholesalers, professional offices, and corporate offices. This combination is illustrated by the Mining House HQ clustered around the Stock Exchange. In the first generation of postwar office buildings, this configuration separated into distinct retail shop zones and office zones, the latter being a grouping like that of Mining House HQ (diversifying to Mining-Finance Corporate HQ) together with corporate headquarters of other South African industrial or finance companies. This office zone also incorporated the corporate headquarters decentralized from Europe and the growing satellite services that performed headquarters functions, for example, accountants, lawyers, engineers, agents, shippers, insurers, and the like. Although the CBD was formed into distinct zones, its periphery lay largely within the *ten-minute walking contour* of its epicenter, the Stock Exchange.

The major South African cities are now in the process of changing from mononuclear cities to polynuclear cities having *several nodes of activity* within the city center. Each node is surrounded by a zone of office buildings lying within the node's ten-minute walking contour. Further nodes have occurred when office and shopping activities (approximately 5% of the total that was formerly in city centers) decentralized to the suburbs and changed district convenience-shopping centers into full-scale regional centers. Each of these suburban nodes has an office block with a total area of approximately 27,000 m² (300,000 ft²).

It is projected that by 1984, some 55% of the total service workers in the office zones will be black. These workers' movement to and from the CBDs is being facilitated by the extension and looping of the electric suburban train routes, the availability of longer trains, and the scheduling of more frequent trains.

Decentralization does not mean the atrophy and decay of the city centers and a "flight to the suburbs", as many thought in the 1970s. There is now an increasing awareness of the very considerable importance of the existing transportation systems (rail, bus, car, and possibly future underground mass-transit) that serve the CBDs from the existing suburbs in all directions. They are being expanded to serve the CBD and are currently feeding in approximately 200,000 office and service-industry workers per day to Johannesburg's CBD. In contrast, none of the decentralized suburban centers have, or are likely to be served by, such transportation systems.

THE THIRD GENERATION OF CBD OFFICE BUILDINGS, RSA

The RSA today is very differently prepared for tall buildings than it was in the 1960s, when its first truly tall (33-story) downtown office buildings were contemplated; and it faces some very different problems now than it did then. These differences and preconditions together will effect the speed, ease, and scope of design realization, feasibility studies, decision making, procurement, construction, and real estate management. The essential, advantageously different, preconditions are described in the sections that follow.

Real Estate Developers or Owners

Before 1960 there were few property developers per se; most office buildings were initiated and managed by "In-House Premises Departments."

However, the 1970s have seen the advent of the professional developer, broker, and property manager. The level of client input, the criteria of yield, management performance, and project and property procurement is vastly better, more demanding, and more accomplished.

The RSA, too, had its share of opportunistic "whizz-kids" who fell by the wayside through insufficient homework, poor judgement, or lack of financial resilience.

The pressures of funding cash flow with inflation at around 14%, coupled with "lifetime costing" of energy and building-systems management, have brought new demand and scope to real estate management. The manager/developers who survived are the real "pros".

The Design/Consulting Professions and the Building Industry

The country's established firms in architecture, engineering, cost control, real estate management, and contracting come to this next generation of office buildings with talented, experienced, internationally travelled, and aware partners, managers, designers, job captains, foremen, and draftsmen. They do not, as in the 1960s come to their task *de novo*, and they have developed and together experienced their design and construction industry interface. Also, their orientation for new technology is no longer toward the United States alone, but also toward Japan, Singapore, and Hong Kong. Still, the design process, the methods of presentation, documentation, shop-drawing coordination, project procurement/management systems, and building management derive largely from U.S. practice and are now well established throughout the country.

Information, Research, and Standards Organizations

Equally important, the design professions and the investment and building industries have, as a source of basic information for guidance, testing, evaluation, and quality assurance, the very considerable resources, know-how, and experience of the National Building Research Institute, the universities, and the South African Bureau of Standards. All of these major institutions have changed vastly since the late 1950s. All have senior personnel who constantly travel internationally and attend conventions and are thus in contact with international thinking and the literature. They have studied or researched many of the problems inherent in tall building design, as well as observed the actual behavior in the RSA of such buildings. They also have access to testing facilities that did not exist in the mid-1960s.

Finally, the 35th Regional Conference of The Council on Tall Buildings and Urban Habitat, held in Johannesburg in 1975, marked a watershed by its interdisciplinary approach. It featured the uninhibited collaborative participation of public and private planners, the consolidation and intellectualization of research in learned papers, and the recording and consolidating of the second-generation experience. The conference was attended by a large number of national and international delegates.

The Municipal Authorities

For the first time in the history of the RSA, nearly all of the major municipal authorities have collected, interpreted, and structured their basic data for "long-range" or "forward" planning of their municipal areas and the interface of these areas with their metropolitan and regional frameworks. As a result, we are now much more able to identify trends and thrusts and to pinpoint transportation, infrastructure and municipal, financial, and user requirements than ever before.

Local authorities should be able to consider and approve plans much more easily and quickly, having now had some 15 years in which to innovate, observe, and consolidate the regulatory framework for tall buildings. This framework includes the waivers created to respond to the innovations of Carlton Centre, which set the countrywide precedents. Furthermore, the local authorities, being aware of the impact of construction logistics for tall buildings, are much more responsive to easing problems of delivery, building, and so on.

As incentives to developers to widen sidewalks and create plazas at street level, municipal authorities have relaxed their height restrictions and offer "bonus bulk," raising the floorspace indices.

CBD Associations

Throughout the last eight years major merchants, shopkeepers, and real estate developers or owners, together with the municipal authorities, have collaborated in a joint effort to form CBD associations. These associations offer a format for discussing common problems regarding parking, zoning, bus and traffic systems, and density of development. In both Cape Town and Johannesburg this has culminated in significant urban redesign and the creation of new bus routes and pedestrian malls. It has also resulted in the publication of major documents on the city centers or CBDs.

Probable Corrections—Third Generation of Tall (Engineered) Office Buildings

In the mid-1960s local authorities relaxed the previous height restrictions, which were equivalent to 20 stories. This relaxation gave a liberty that, coupled with the imperative to dominate attention with sheer height, meant that every office project strove for the maximum allowable height. Inexperience and insufficiently studied technology transfer, joined with the desire for increased height, led to the following defects or omissions common to nearly all second-generation buildings:

- typical floor areas of as little as 900 m² (9,700 ft²);

- absence of service elevators and mail transportation systems;

- poor toilet planning and restrooms that are too tight and small;

- inadequate or limited fire cut-off, fire jumps, and engineered fire protection;

- lack of awareness both of "down-draft" conditions, especially at plaza level, and of "boundary-layer" wind interruption, when exceeding 20-story heights;

- insufficient attention to noise insulation, especially seen in the use of false ceiling baffles; and

- poor window wall testing and design provisions.

PROBABLE BUILDING FORMS

Tall buildings are constrained by the common existing CBD grid-iron street framework and block size of 66 by 66 m (200 by 200 ft). Fifty-story heights, as at Carlton for example, are only permissible with super blocks of four consolidated city blocks. Floor space indicies of 6.5, as well, dictate that the overall building form or envelope will largely vary between slab blocks or point blocks of the following descriptions:

Form A

35 floors overall, 31 floors lettable, each *900 to 1,000 m² (9,700 to 10,800 ft²)* in area
3.75 m (12.3 ft) floor-to-floor height
low-, mid-, and high-level plant rooms
low- and mid-rise elevator systems, or

Form B

24 floors overall, 20 net lettable, *each 1,500 m² (16,000 ft²)* in area
3.75 m floor-to-floor heights
single-rise elevator systems only
bottom and top plant rooms only (double-volume)

Both examples have concentric cores, with square or rectangular forms.

However, the cost and time impact of increasing buildings from 20 to 30 stories is substantial in the areas of additional structure and foundations, elevatoring, HVAC, and facade costs. Whether the additional height increases lettability or rental rates sufficiently to balance and redeem such additional costs is arguable. Probably, with the exception of corporate, and therefore prestige, headquarters buildings, general speculative office buildings are likely to stay at the 20-net-floor maximum of 1,500 m² gross area per floor.

INNOVATIONS

Atriums: Atrium design has become a great attraction, especially in low-rise corporate headquarters buildings and for unifying new 1980 additions with existing buildings.

Energy conservation: The effects of energy requirements, not only on the "life-time costing" of a building but also on optimizing comfort control, have led to new approaches to facade design, such as limiting the glass area to between 20% and 30% of facade area or using a separate, detached outer solar-shading glass screen. Twenty-four hour continuous mechanical-fan air movement is also being incorporated to cool buildings overnight. The "cooled" structure has a "fly-wheel effect" on daytime use, thereby reducing the energy required for daytime cooling. The energy conservation industry's limited capacity has led in turn to design on a "plug-in" basis and contract award by negotiation rather than tender.

Access floors: An integrated floor sandwich incorporating all services *and providing a fully accessible HVAC distribution system* is a development of the "computer-type" floor system that responds to the need for full flexibility by providing the following:

- ease of changing partitions without having to alter the air-conditioning system;

- minimum costs of adaptation from cellular to landscaped offices and vice versa;

- positioning of HVAC, service, and communication outlet points with minimum functional and cost penalty; and

• ease of installation and maintenance for electrical, telephone, and other services and for anticipated future improvements in office equipment, that is, the intensification of electronic communication equipment and the addition of computer terminals.

Access-floor systems are emminently suitable for large, deep floor areas where high-density occupancy is accompanied by a lot of servicing and sophisticated equipment. Three such buildings currently are being erected in Johannesburg.

CONCLUSION

The most advanced developments in tall building technology in the southern subcontinent of Africa have occurred in the Republic of South Africa.

The art was given major momentum by what has been described as the second generation of tall buildings since the middle 1960s. During this development stage, the Carlton Centre project, costing R250 million in 1981 money value, was the vehicle of transfer of then current U.S. tall building technology and skills into the design professions, contracting industries, and real estate development and management field in the RSA. This transfer was rapid and took place on a large scale.

After a substantial lull in demand for office space caused by oversupply generated in the late 1960s and a general economic slowdown, South Africa is on the threshold of significant renewed activity in the field of office construction. Johannesburg's proportion of the space demand will be significant. The other major urban centers will require space to a lesser degree. Because of the shortage of suitable real estate in the CBD areas, development will inevitably be high-rise. The new breed of tall buildings will differ from their second-generation counterparts in response to the need for high levels of energy efficiency. This response will produce new attitudes toward structure, cladding, lighting, and air-distribution systems. Speed of erection has become a major consideration to counter the effects of cost escalation, which now has a substantially greater impact on capital cost than was the case in the late 1960s and early 1970s. This need indicates that steel frame structures, not viable before when compared to reinforced concrete, will be considered more seriously.

The South African design professions and construction industry are now completely capable of providing the skills to meet the demand for new tall buildings in an innovative, experienced, and efficient manner. The RSA's designers and builders will inevitably be responsible for transfering these skills and technology to the rest of the subcontinent, given the appropriate conditions of political and economic stability and growth.

CONDENSED REFERENCES/BIBLIOGRAPHY

The following is a condensed bibliography for this article. It includes all articles referred to or cited in the text. The full citations will be found at the end of the volume, with additional citations for further reading. What is given here should be sufficient information to lead the reader to the correct article: the author, date, and title. In case of multiple authors, only the first name is listed.

Rhodes-Harrison 1975, *Tall Buildings: The State of the Art in South Africa*

Social Effects of the Environment
(PC-3)

The High-Rise as a Habitat: A German and Italian Sample

Robert C. Williamson

The pros and cons of the high-rise as a living environment have been argued on several continents. The debate continues in the United States and Canada as documented in Herrenkohl (1976) and Michelson (1977). Any habitat must be considered according to the needs of the individuals who will live in it. For instance, data from Hong Kong and Singapore indicate the viability of the high-rise for a population that has known less appealing quarters. Yet people in other areas of the underdeveloped world may have other viewpoints. According to surveys of Puerto Rico and Venezuela, living in a housing complex of whatever height means bureaucratic rules and therefore invites negative reactions. European responses to the high-rise have generally been ambivalent, but again the previous housing of the individual is relevant. Those who have migrated from the countryside to Madrid are enthusiastic about their new quarters, even when they are on the tenth floor, but Swedish and French interviewees who have known a higher standard of living complain about the lack of play space for their children and isolation from their neighbors, along with problems as diverse as rubbish removal and wind velocity (Dahlström, 1957; LeCoq-Vallon, 1974). A less negative assessment of four German high-rise complexes is reported by Herlyn (1970), who found that residents generally adjusted to whatever problems they encountered in the environment.

It is in this context of controversy that the present inquiry is directed. To compare the level of satisfaction of high-rise dwellers, a sample of persons living in traditional housing was included. The total sample included 420 high-rise residents and 166 non-high-rise residents in the Cologne-Düsseldorf area, along with a Roman sample of 152 and 54 respectively. The interviews examined a number of areas of adjustment to habitat. Also, the study was concerned with differences in social background, such as nationality, age, sex, marital status, and social class. Detailed reports on the cross-national comparisons and on the subsamples of the German investigation are found elsewhere (Williamson, 1978, 1981). The present report brings together the analyses of these two samples with particular emphasis on selected intercorrelations in the German sample. The focus on the German respondents is because of the German sample's size and the diversity of high-rise structures involved.

METHODS AND THE SAMPLE

Underlying the study were a number of working hypotheses about the effect of social background variables (age, sex, presence of children, social class) on satisfaction with the high-rise. Even the age of the building, the type of financing, and the floor on which the resident lived were relevant. Many factors inevitably relate to adjustment to one's dwelling. Consequently

Fig. 1 **This structure in Madrid, Spain, is typical of the residential complexes of the 1950s and 1960s from Rome to Stockholm.**

the interviewing schedule, containing both standardized and open-ended items, was oriented toward the physical aspects of the dwelling, as well as toward the familial, social, and cultural life style of the interviewees.

The sample was chosen on a multistage-cluster basis in each of the two urban areas, with the aid both of the staff of the Social Science Research Institute of the Konrad Adenauer Foundation and of the University of Rome. The high-rise in Germany represented towers like Colonia and "minicities" like Churweiler or Kölnberg, along with more conventional high-rise structures. Whereas the German high-rise ranges up to 28 stories, the buildings in Rome have a maximum of 13 stories and most were built in the 1950s; the EUR complex is almost the only one that resembles the recent and innovative styles found in Germany. In both nations the non-high-rise sample was primarily in conventional three- and four-story buildings.

Both samples represented a mix of manual and white-collar occupations. The German sample was slightly younger, had a higher ratio of unmarried persons, and had fewer persons with children than did the Italian one.

FINDINGS

The data range, of course, over a wide spectrum of physical aspects, social networks, and family needs, especially the socialization of children. In both Germany and Italy, the majority of interviewees were satisfied with high-rise living. Especially in the German sample, tranquility, view, setting, architecture, convenience of room design, nearness of facilities, and presence of a balcony were perceived as positive. Most often mentioned among the disadvantages were the following: inconvenience of elevators and stairways; impersonality; lack of cleanliness (in Germany, notably, although in his casual inspections the author was impressed by the degree of cleanliness!); problems with building management (especially in Italy), and noise (obviously with considerable variation among the structures and apartments as the sound factor could be either positive or negative).

As in the Herlyn investigation, most respondents preferred to live on an upper floor: they had rejected the traditional multiple structure of three or four stories and knew that their ideal home (a single dwelling, preferably in the suburbs) was unobtainable for most Western Europeans. Reactions to the idea of height, say, living on or above the tenth floor, differed markedly. Some said that they would feel uneasy, others that an upper floor gave them a sense of exhilaration. In addition, an upper floor provides a greater feeling of security. Indeed, most subjects felt that they were somewhat more secure than they were where they had lived before.

The difference in social background variables is illustrated in the differential reaction by gender. Men tend to be more critical than women, and more general in their criticism; but because women spend more time in the home, they were more aware of specific problems. Men were more conscious of the quality of construction, women of the design and room arrangement. Men spoke of the quiet, whereas women praised the view. Women were more concerned with what floor they lived on.

Marital status, the presence or absence of children, and social class were additional predictive factors of the reaction to the high-rise. For instance, social class (whether measured by educational level, occupational income, or self-judgment) was positively related to satisfaction with the high-rise (or, for that matter, with traditional dwellings). The approval of one's residence can hardly fail to be related to one's social rank.

Other factors are also relevant. Modernism, that is, a nontraditional outlook, seems to be a marginal variable. At least, there was borderline statistical significance on certain items, for example, frequency of church attendance. In general, high-rise dwellers were younger, less religious, and more inclined to vote for the Social Democratic Party rather than the Christian Democratic Party. Moreover, high-rise inhabitants were more inclined to accept equality or shared decision making among family members. Age was an especially critical variable. To wit, older residents chose a lower high-rise and, whatever the complex, they preferred a lower floor.

Table 1 Correlation matrix of selected variables of satisfaction, socialization, and the physical structure (N = 420)

	Satisfaction with dwelling	Recommending high-rise for adults	Recommending high-rise for children	High-rise perceived as impersonal	Number of children	Neighbors different from self
Recommending high-rise for adults	.34					
Recommending high-rise for children	.23	.28				
High-rise perceived as impersonal	$-.17^a$	$-.19^a$	$-.28^a$			
Number of children	$-.13^b$	$.10^c$	$.11^c$	.03		
Neighbors different from self	$-.12^b$	$-.21^a$	$.09^c$	$.23^a$	.01	
Chatting with neighbors in elevator	$.15^a$	$.12^c$	$.19^a$	$-.32^a$	.04	$-.19^a$
Spaciousness of dwelling	$.35^a$	$.23^a$	$.09^c$	$-.09^c$	$.12^b$	$.13^b$
Satisfactory design of dwelling	$.42^a$	$.22^a$	$-.13^c$	$-.09^b$	$.10^c$	$.13^b$
Poor quality of construction	$-.41^a$	$-.23^a$	.12	$.13^b$	.08	.00
Complaints about management	$-.19^a$	$-.09^c$	$-.20^a$	$.09^c$	.04	.03
Lack of consideration by neighbors	$-.20^a$	$-.18^a$	$-.13^c$	$.15^a$	$-.02$	$.12^b$
User of utilities	$-.21^a$	$-.13^b$	$-.23^b$	$.16^a$	.08	$-.03$

[a]probability = <{.001
[b]probability = <{.01
[c]probability = <{.05

Social relationships were affected by high-rise living in several ways. High-rise interviewees knew more neighbors by name, but had less social contact, such as borrowing from or dropping in on their neighbors, among other items. They also described their neighbors as slightly less friendly than the ones where they had lived before, and would ideally like more friends among their neighbors. Yet well over half of both national samples were basically content with their social relationships. As with most questions, social class, marital status, and the presence or absence of children were conditioning factors.

Although the presence of children in the high-rise was the most controversial item, the majority of both high-rise samples felt that the high-rise children were either happier or about as happy as children living elsewhere. Significantly, individuals who were younger, were married, had children, or were of upper social status were more accepting of children living in the high-rise than were older or single persons. At the same time, most respondents felt that children, especially those on the upper floors, missed certain advantages, such as making friendships. Also, the inability to see children from outside the building caused difficulties, but most parents had developed ways of coping with the problem.

	Chatting with neighbors in elevator	Spaciousness of dwelling	Satisfactory design of dwelling	Poor quality of dwelling	Complaints about management	Lack of consideration by neighbors
Spaciousness of dwelling	$-.10^c$					
Satisfactory design of dwelling	$-.07$	$.47^a$				
Poor quality of construction	$.21^a$	$-.20^a$	$-.22^a$			
Complaints about management	$.02$	$-.09^c$	$.14^b$	$.24^a$		
Lack of consideration by neighbors	$.10^b$	$-.08^c$	$.05$	$.16^b$	$.37^a$	
User of utilities	$.16^a$	$-.12$	$.12^c$	$.15^b$	$.31^a$	$.43^a$

[a] probability = <{ .001
[b] probability = <{ .01
[c] probability = <{ .05

Table 1 points to the intercorrelations for physical, social, and family aspects of the high-rise. From this table, which lists the correlation coefficients of selected variables, and the other data, several generalizations are warranted:

1. Satisfaction is especially related to the physical features, the three most important attributes being spaciousness, room arrangement, and quality of construction. Hardly less important are the perceived presence or lack of congestion, the amount of light, and the attractiveness of entrances, stairways, and hallways.

2. Next to the physical aspects, the potential for social interaction is most important. Among the measures of interaction are the feeling that one's neighbors are like oneself and the frequency of conversing with neighbors while waiting for or riding in the elevator.

3. The adjustment of children produced fewer significant correlations than did the physical features, but a positive relation was found between the adjustment of the children and the physical features, particularly apartment size.

The attitude that the high-rise is impersonal relates to how one perceives one's neighbors and the degree of interaction one has with them. Also, there was considerable intercorrelation between physical and social aspects or, put another way, the more pleasing the high-rise structure, the more one makes social contacts within it.

In concluding, one is reminded of the statement that the tall office building may be visualized as a street in vertical form (Dufau, 1974). For most of the German respondents and a near majority of the Italian ones (who have a somewhat less satisfying high-rise setting than do the Germans), the tall apartment house is becoming a residential street. At least, the data

Fig. 2 A typical high-rise building complex in Milan, Italy

suggest that most high-rise residents learn to accommodate to this new life style. Although the interviewees viewed their habitat as less ideal than a single dwelling in the suburbs or countryside, they were aware of its newness, its convenience to their work, and the possibility of looking down on the world from a top floor. These and other advantages were a large part of the motivation that led them to choose this habitat.

Acknowledgment

The author wishes to acknowledge his debt and gratitude to the Social Science Research Institute of the Konrad Adenauer Foundation, to the Council on Tall Buildings and Urban Habitat, and to the Institute of Research at Lehigh University, as well as to the help of his colleagues in Bonn and Rome.

CONDENSED REFERENCES/BIBLIOGRAPHY

The following is a condensed bibliography for this article. It includes all articles referred to or cited in the text. The full citations will be found at the end of the volume, with additional citations for further reading. What is given here should be sufficient information to lead the reader to the correct article: the author, date, and title. In case of multiple authors, only the first name is listed.

Dahlstrom 1957, *Children in Highrises in 3 Story Residential Complex in Vallingby*
Dufau 1974, *Travels? Trips?*

Herlyn 1970, *Living in High-Rises*
Herrenkohl 1976, *Social Effects of the Environment*

LeCoq-Vallon 1974, *Some Aspects of Conditions of Living in Tall Buildings*

Michelson 1977, *Environmental Choice, Human Behavior, and Residential Satisfaction*

Williamson 1978, *Socialization in the Highrise: A Cross-National Comparison*
Williamson 1981, *Adjustment to the Highrise: Variables in a German Sample*

Urban Services in Support of High-Rise Development

Leonard Ruchelman

Tall building development and urbanization are related phenomena. Where land is relatively plentiful and population density is low, the high-rise structure is rarely seen. However, where land is scarce, and therefore expensive, and where there is a high concentration of people, the high-rise structure is fairly common. By using vertical space, the tall building allows the city to aggregate, a limited land area, a huge amount of space organized for work and/or habitation. Burgeoning urban populations, a product of industrial and technological development, require multistory structures that would otherwise be too costly.

Although the social and economic benefits of this form of development are understood and widely applied, the question of how best to fit the high-rise structure into its urban setting has not been adequately addressed. The higher the density and activity in an areas, the more problematic this question becomes. Only recently have we come to inquire into how such building forms fit into the social and political environment. Failure to plan for this fit effectively and to account for the full range of public services that are required has raised a range of issues.

In many cities today these issues are arising as questions of energy use, transportation, fire control, and environmental contamination. A second order of issues pertains to interference (for instance, with sunlight, views, topography, and television reception), feelings of congestion, crime, and safety. A third order of issues pertains to who must pay for necessary public services and who shares in the distribution of economic benefits; for example, it is not always clear how the general citizenry and effected neighborhoods are to benefit from tall building development.

TALL BUILDING DECISION MAKING

Underlying the aforementioned issues is the complexity of tall building decision making. Decision makers are drawn not only from the private sector, where the investor, developer, architect, and engineers come from; they are also drawn from the public sector, which employs the planners, city administrators, and heads of service agencies and utilities. Each participant has special views and interests that must be accommodated in the course of decision making. As the general citizenry has become more alert to the special effects of high-rise development, the public sector has become much more aggressive in establishing standards and mandating requirements. The full consequences of a more aggressive public posture in many cities are not clearly understood yet. Often, as in New York City or San Francisco, decision making leads to deadlock. This is particularly true of questions about who is to provide support services and public amenities: the city or the developer?

In this light, a range of case studies on how public and private decision makers plan for and decide questions of urban services can begin to provide some answers. Where services are taken for granted, as has often been the case in the past, service gaps become evident, leading to detrimental consequences. Which cities manage the provision of services, with a minimum of negative impacts, and how do they compare to cities that manage services poorly? The following are some other research questions: What institutional arrangements and special strategies best facilitate required services? Where are the special obstructions to accommodation between the public and private sectors and how can they be overcome? What are the unintended effects of public and private negotiations?

IMPLEMENTATION

The intended effects of tall building decision making are often not realized because of the failure to properly plan for implementation of support services. Concern about implementation stems from the recognition that plans cannot be understood in isolation from the means of their execution. There is ample evidence that shows grand design, faulty execution, and puny results. The reasons are many. In some instances the initial building design is based on poor understanding of the practical aspects of application; but more often than not, good ideas are poorly executed. How the design team can work effectively with public and private agencies in planning for the implementation of support services is a key question that needs to be explored more thoroughly.

Obstacles appear to arise from three basic sources: (1) from the operational demands implied by a particular design concept; (2) from the nature and availability of the resources required to carry out the initial design; and (3) from the need to share authority with, or retain support of, bureaucratic and political actors in the implementation process. Within these three broad categories, the following areas seem to deserve special attention: the kind of support services required; the likelihood of distortions or irregularities; the ability to control the building program through the coordination of personnel, funds, supplies, and technical equipment. These areas have been tentatively identified as requiring careful study to anticipate obstacles that the implementation of a tall building project will entail. Findings could be the basis of a framework for aiding decision makers in allocating managerial and financial resources.

THE CAPITAL PLANT OF CITIES

Because of their substantial bulk and height, tall buildings pose special demands on urban support systems such as transit, streets, roads, and water and sewage facilities. Relatively small-scale development usually requires incremental change in such systems; but high-rise buildings, some of which may accommodate as many as 60 or 70 thousand people a day, usually require substantial change, at least in the building's immediate environs, over a relatively short period of time. As tall buildings proliferate, particularly in the old downtown sections of cities, there is growing concern that the infrastructure is either too limited, obsolete, or worn out to sustain them.

Although key elements in the capital stock of cities have service lives of 50 years, 100 years, or even longer, many in the United States are reaching the end of their intended use and need to be replaced. A study by the Council of State Planning Agencies recently concluded that one-half to two-thirds of this nation's cities and other communities would be unable to support modernized development without large investments in their infrastructures. Since 1974–1975, however, when the financial problems of cities began to mount, capital investment requirements have been largely deferred.

How the public and private sectors can work together to deal with this condition is an important question. The construction of the World Trade Center in the 1970s provides a useful illustration. Recognizing the inadequacy of existing utilities, the World Trade Center developer (The Port Authority of New York and New Jersey) set a significant precedent when it decided to completely rebuild the entire underground utility system, which consisted of gas, steam, water and sewage, on its 16-acre site. The benefit of such reconstruction is that it assures sufficient capacity, as well as long-term protection against damage from pipe deterioration. The World Trade Center required this insurance because most of Manhattan's underground utility structure dates back to the nineteenth century and was designed primarily for five-story buildings. An underground subway transit station was also

Fig. 1 The World Trade Center in lower Manhattan

completely rebuilt, along with a special railroad terminal for commuters traveling the PATH railroad between New York and New Jersey.

It is believed that case studies of comparable situations in other localities would reveal useful strategies for combining high-rise development with infrastructure development. A related interest here is to identify the range of incentives and trade-offs that could solve both public and private development needs simultaneously.

CONCLUSION

A basic concern in this paper is the question of how far decision makers could move beyond the traditional view of a tall building as a final product in its own right. The purpose is to assure a better fit of such structures into their urban settings. Skyscrapers of great height and huge size have made the old assumptions passé, and efforts to define and expand the new rules have so far been tenuous at best. Research should help decision makers define them. Through more intensive research to find prototypical approaches, the tall building can be made more amenable and more functional which, in turn, will make the city a better place in which to live and work.

CONDENSED REFERENCES/BIBLIOGRAPHY

The following is a condensed bibliography for this article. It includes all articles referred to or cited in the text. The full citations will be found at the end of the volume, with additional citations for further reading. What is given here should be sufficient information to lead the reader to the correct article: the author, date, and title. In case of multiple authors, only the first name is listed.

Choate 1981, *America in Ruins: Beyond the Public Works Pork Barrel*
Grossman 1979, *The Future of New York City's Capital Plant*
Parrish 1981, *High Rise Fire!: A Realization of the Potential for Disaster*
Ruchelman 1977, *The World Trade Center: Politics and Policies of Skyscraper Development*
Whyte 1981, *How to Make Midtown Livable*

Architecture (PC-6)

Where Do We Go From Here—Architecturally

Frank L. Codella

Developments of the 1970s may presage the new developments of the '80s and '90s. Zoning effects on the density of tall buildings and solar design may raise ethical questions. Energy limitations will continue to be a unique design challenge. A combined project of old and new buildings may bring back human scale to our cities. Owners and conceptual designers will be challenged in the 1980s to produce economically sound, people-oriented buildings.

In 1980 the Lever House, designed by Skidmore, Owings and Merrill (SOM) received the 25-year award from the American Institute of Architects "in recognition of architectural design of enduring significance." This award is given once a year for a building between 25 and 35 years old. Lewis Mumford described the Lever House as "the first office building in which modern materials, modern construction, modern functions have been combined with a modern plan" (Abercrombie, 1980). At the time, this daring concept could only be achieved by visionary men like Gordon Bunshaft, the designer, and Charles Luckman, the owner and then-president of Lever Brothers. The project also included a few "firsts": (1) it was the first sealed glass tower ever built; (2) it was the first office building designed by SOM; and (3) it was the first office building on Park Avenue to omit retail space on the first floor. Today, after hundreds of look-alikes and variations on the grid design, we have reached what may be the epitome of tall building design: the nondescript building. Except for a few recently completed buildings that seem to be people-oriented in their lower floors, most tall buildings seem to be a repetition of the dull, graph-paper-like monoliths in many of our cities. Can this be the end of the design-line for tall buildings? Probably not. There are definite signs that are most encouraging. Architects and owners have recently begun to discuss the design problem publicly. Perhaps we are at the threshold of a new era. The 1980s may bring forth some new visionaries like Bunshaft and Luckman. If so, what kinds of restrictions or challenges do they face?

ZONING

Indications are strong that cities may restrict the density of tall buildings, that is, reduce the number of tall buildings per square mile. In 1980 the term *grid-lock* was used for the first time publicly in New York City. It caused a terror-like sensation in the pit of one's stomach. The term refers to a situation in which traffic comes to a standstill for many city blocks in all directions. The jam-up may even reach to the tunnels and bridges. Strangely enough, such an event happened in New York in a year of fuel shortages and high gasoline prices. If we are to avoid similar occurrences, it is obvious that the density of people, places, and vehicles must be drastically reduced. Zoning may be the only long-term solution.

Solar zoning may become more and more popular as city residents are blocked from the sun by tall buildings. Regardless of how effectively a tall building is designed to conserve energy, it may at the same time deprive a resident or neighbor of solar access. In the 1980s the right to see the sun may become a most interesting ethical question that may revolutionize the architectural fabric of the city. Mixed-use zoning, which became a financially viable alternative during the 1970s, may become commonplace during the 1980s, especially if it is combined with solar zoning to provide access to the sun for all occupants.

ENERGY

We may find that in critical areas of our country, energy allocation for buildings may become an increasingly limiting factor in design and economics. In the 1980s we may at last be ready to take Buckminster Fuller seriously when he says "build more with less"; that is, by decreasing the total weight of a building we can save the energy needed to produce those "heavy" materials. Perhaps, the idea of "creative cost control," first mentioned by Luckman many years ago, will be universally applied and will include life-cycle costing methods and energy-cost alternatives. Creative cost control may also usher in an era of disciplined designers who will refine the relationship between design and energy. They will most likely be the ones to implement the energy performance of buildings first, at the programming and design stage.

RENOVATION

Emery Roth and Sons designed the Palace Hotel in New York as an addition to a renovated historic Villard house on Madison Avenue. It is a striking example of what can be done with salvageable and beautifully detailed old buildings. Recycling both large and small buildings may become the way in which humanism and warmth will be returned to buildings during the '80s. If we must continue to design with glass and aluminum in stark grid patterns, for whatever reason, we may find that a combination of new and old will become the great humane design trend of the future. Up to the mid-1970s, our tax laws encouraged the demolition of older buildings and their replacement with newer ones, usually taller ones in the city. Now, recent changes in the law have caused our dollars-and-cents men to take another hard look: (1) the Public Building Cooperative Use Act of 1975 encourages federal agencies to occupy existing old buildings; (2) the Tax Reform Act of 1976 allows depreciation of rehabilitated buildings and penalizes the removal of historic ones; and (3) the Revenue Act of 1978 and the Tax Credit Bill of 1979 may provide still more incentives to recycle old buildings as we go on through the 1980s.

CONCEPTUAL DESIGN

It has been suggested in architectural magazines that the Bank of America office building in San Francisco is too large for the city's scale. It has also been suggested that the John Hancock Center in Boston is not only out of scale but also out of character with the city. Similar statements and opinions have been made about other significant tall buildings in cities throughout the world. These comments raise some basic questions about the design process and who really makes the design decisions on important structures—and about who will make these decisions in the 1980s.

Will the forthcoming visionaries—architects and owners—return to more humane designs? Will the sociologist or psychologist play a more important role in the years ahead to help convince these visionaries that a new, radically different, human-scaled architecture is long overdue? If these are valid questions, could it be that our "best" architectural designers of the '60s and '70s will become the worst designers of the '80s and '90s? Or will they learn and respond to a valuable lesson they should have learned in their "History of Architecture" course in college—that "architecture usually reflects the success or failure of a civilized society"? Only time will tell.

CONDENSED REFERENCES/BIBLIOGRAPHY

The following is a condensed bibliography for this article. It includes all articles referred to or cited in the text. The full citations will be found at the end of the volume, with additional citations for further reading. What is given here should be sufficient information to lead the reader to the correct article: the author, date, and title. In case of multiple authors, only the first name is listed.

Abercrombie 1980, *Twenty-Five Year Award Goes to Lever House*

The Renaissance of Our Cities—A Civil Engineering Challenge

William Donald Schaefer

THE NATURE OF THE RENAISSANCE

The renaissance of older American cities is underway, and Baltimore, Maryland, is one of its leaders. In Baltimore, as in other cities, the rebirth is composed of several different elements that might be grouped into two broad categories: the *physical* renaissance and the *human* renaissance.

The physical redevelopment in Baltimore, particularly the downton Inner Harbor development, is immediately obvious and impressive to the tourist or newcomer to the city. Harborplace, the Rouse Company development housing an assortment of shops and restaurants in two pavilions along the waterfront, is one of the focal points of the Inner Harbor (Fig. 1). The National Aquarium (Fig. 2), which opened in Baltimore in July, 1981, attracted 1.6 million visitors in its first year of operation. It has quickly become a great landmark of the Inner Harbor and Baltimore. The Maryland Science Center provides eduational exhibits and planetarium shows for harbor visitors. The Pier 6 Concert Pavilion for outdoor summer per-

---

This paper is based on a speech delivered by Mayor Schaefer at the American Society of Civil Engineers in St. Louis, Missouri, October 26, 1981.

Fig. 1 Harbor Place—Pratt Street Pavillion *(Courtesy: Interstate Division for Baltimore City)*

Fig. 2 Baltimore National Aquarium *(Courtesy: Interstate Division for Baltimore City)*

formances, the World Trade Center (Fig. 3), and the Baltimore Convention Center are additional attractions for Inner Harbor tourists. The convention business has led to the development of new hotel space, including a new Hyatt Regency, already completed (Fig. 4), and commitments for construction of a Howard Johnson's and a Days Inn. All of these developments are exceptional accomplishments that provide a mixture of commercial and recreational facilities at the Inner Harbor (Figs. 5, 6, and 7).

But the physical renaissance of the city extends far beyond the Inner Harbor. The Inner Harbor improvements are merely the most readily apparent ones. The thrust of the renaissance is the revival of individual neighborhoods. In fact, if it were not for the spirit and commitment of the city's neighborhoods, the dream of an Inner Harbor renewal would not have come true.

The neighborhood renaissance started with a few devoted people and neighborhood associations. These people and small groups committed themselves to improvements and turned to City Hall for assistance. The city's policy has always been to assist neighborhoods that are actively seeking to make improvements, because it recognizes that the neighborhoods and

Fig. 3 World Trade Center *(Courtesy: Interstate Division for Baltimore City)*

their ethnic and physical variety are the city's greatest assets. A city is, after all, only as strong as its neighborhoods and the people who live in them.

The rebuilding of Baltimore's neighborhoods has been a gradual and ongoing process. Housing is one of the key components. Old houses are being revived through innovative incentives such as homesteading. The city has sold abandoned buildings to urban pioneers for as little as $1.00. Homesteading has been broadened to shopsteading for the development of commercial facilities. Commercial buildings have been sold under some programs for $100 with a commitment for their rehabilitation. In addition to shops and homes, new parks and recreation centers and new social service centers have been added to strengthen communities. An efficient street and highway system, together with mass transit service, provides people with easy access to work and shopping.

Cities must be a place for people, where they can enjoy both their work and their leisure. The human rebirth of Baltimore is less visible than the

Fig. 4 Hyatt Regency, Baltimore *(Courtesy: Interstate Division for Baltimore City)*

Fig. 5 IBM Building *(Courtesy: Interstate Division for Baltimore City)*

Fig. 6 U.S.F. & G. Building (left center) and IBM Building *(Courtesy: Interstate Division for Baltimore City)*

physical rebirth, but it is equally important. Social services for the elderly and disabled, drug and alcohol treatment centers, and employment programs for the unemployed are all part of it. There has also been a tremendous cultural revival in Baltimore, celebrating a rich history and ethnic heritage. The history of Baltimore is documented and on display in a number of museums throughout the city. The arts are being promoted more than ever before. A new symphony hall and a new wing for the Baltimore Museum of Art have recently been opened.

THE CIVIL ENGINEER'S ROLE

The civil engineer is the unsung hero of urban redevelopment—the person who works behind the scenes, using load factors, soil conditions, and structural stability, to transform the planners' and architects' ideas into a buildable and workable product. In addition to bricks and mortar and nuts and bolts, however, the engineer of today and of the future must be concerned with the human side of development—this is the engineer's real challenge. All of the efforts to rebuild the Inner Harbor in Baltimore would have been useless if the physical structure had not been built to accommodate the needs of people. The harbor development is successful only because

Fig. 7 Equitable Trust Company *(Courtesy: Interstate Division for Baltimore City)*

it has become a place where people feel good mingling together and participating in activities made readily accessible to them. In the same vein, the successful neighborhood projects are the ones that have been designed to accommodate human needs.

Designers and engineers of the urban renaissance have a responsibility to assess human concerns. It is crucial to work with neighborhood groups and citizens to find creative resolutions to community problems because, as already stated, it is people who make neighborhoods, which are the backbone of any city. The balancing of human needs with design and construction criteria and with economic factors is not a simple process; but it can and must be done.

To address human concerns, there are several ways in which the civil engineer must approach a project. First, the engineer must listen to the public and the average citizen. The civil engineer must act as a public servant. He or she cannot operate in a vacuum or under the assumption that the community knows nothing. *No one* knows more about a neighborhood and what the results of a neighborhood project will be than its residents; and they have to live with the altered neighborhood once it is completed.

Second, the civil engineer must react to the ideas of the local neighborhood. The engineer must compromise to accommodate the neighborhood's needs, even if it means major modifications in design and utility relocation. People will respect the engineer's ideas if the engineer, in turn, respects and responds to their ideas.

Finally, starting and completing a project on time can go a long way in assuring support for the next project. Long delays create frustration, dissatisfaction, and a feeling that the project should never have been undertaken. There needs to be time to decide on the correct approach. Once it is determined, the project should be completed as rapidly as possible and within budget.

The challenge to the civil engineer is to question old assumptions about project formulation and implementation. New solutions integrating the human factor are necessary for successful urban redevelopment. Baltimore has made great strides. A lot of work remains, however, and provides continuing challenge to planners, architects, engineers, and all who serve people through public works.

City Form and Tall Buildings: Cathedrals, Palazzi, Tall Downtowns, and Tall Cities

Anne Vernez-Moudon

INTRODUCTION

Ever since members of the Council on Tall Buildings and Urban Habitat began to set the stage for critical analyses of the tall building as a new form of work place and habitat, concerns for the urban design and environmental dimensions of the phenomenon have been growing steadily. Now more than ever, the tall building is the trademark of new development in the center city (and it has been proliferating in the medium-size cities). Debates and confrontations are raging about the socioeconomic and esthetic impacts of the building type on existing cities. In this process, many of the issues raised by tall buildings are negotiated as they come up. The resulting decisions take the form of controls on development such as zoning ordinances and requirements for environmental impact assessments. It is interesting that in the meantime, theories of city form incorporating tall buildings trail far behind the pressure of these everyday decisions. Even the recent proposals by revisionist historians and designers who have revived such works as Camillo Sitte's have been conspicuously silent about the new role that tall buildings play in defining the form of our cities.

Ironically, Le Corbusier's Voisin Plan remains, despite sustained criticism of its harsh utopia, one of the few theoretical models of the tall city. It would be euphemistic to point to the vacuum between the Voisin Plan and the tall building developers' current determination and probable ultimate success in refurbishing our cities. For one thing, the French urbanist built his theory in exact opposition to what he saw as the basic structure of existing tall cities in 1935, specifically in New York City and Chicago. He said that the trouble with New York is that "its skyscrapers are too small, and there are too many of them...."

Today, tall buildings are increasingly larger indeed, but there are still more of them than in Le Corbusier's time. Cities have grown tall in many ways despite these modern dictates, and without any others who may have guided development.

There is no doubt that to proceed with the successful development of our cities we need to address the reality of the tall building filling our urban space, and to search for models that can help the planning and design process with (and some cynics will say despite) tall buildings.

This paper looks at the recent turn of events that has stimulated thoughts of the tall buildings in the city. Design professions have been advocating new forms of skyscrapers; also, a handful of urbanists have set forth a series of principles for revising the profile of cities. It appears that new forms now promoted as models for tall building design are not likely to substantially improve our urban environments. In fact, concern must be focused on the city as a whole, and the vision of the tall downtown expanded into the broader dimensions of the tall city. Within the tall city, the "palazzo" must replace the "cathedral" as the precedent leading the conceptual design of prevailing structures.

Finally, the paper proposes to initiate a debate on appropriate theories of tall city form. A list of desirable attributes of city form is compiled, partially based on the observation of existing tall environments. It also comprises elements of a consensus articulated by factions of professionals and the public, and which underlies many of new ordinances and codes controlling development (Choay, 1960).

DESIGN OF TALL BUILDINGS: AN ALLEGORY

The cover design of the May/June, 1981, issue of *Urban Design International* offers an interesting allegory for the current state of the art in the design and development of tall buildings (Fig. 1). It brandishes elevations of Antique Row in Reisterstown, Maryland, with homegrown suggestions for the restoration of the street, its furniture, planting, lighting, and so on. The intriguing revelation about this cover design is that the authors of this low-key project for an all-American town are no less than Skidmore, Owings and Merrill. For an instant, one wonders whether this fact means that tall glass structures will no longer be added to our cities' skylines, or whether

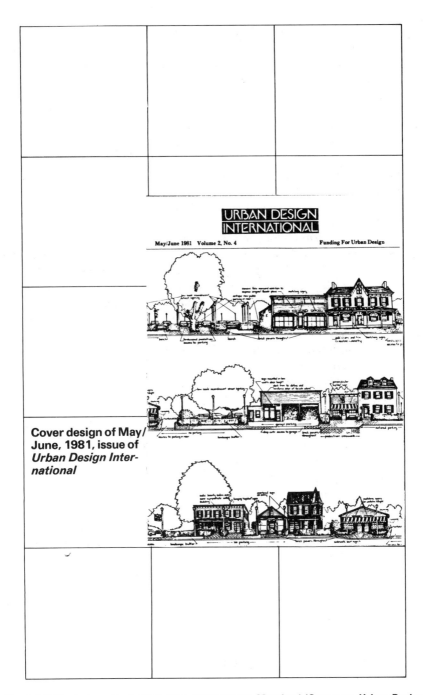

Cover design of May/
June, 1981, issue of
*Urban Design Inter-
national*

Fig. 1 S.O.M. designs for Antique Row, Reistertown, Maryland (Courtesy: *Urban Design
International*)

SOM is no longer involved in the making of U.S. downtowns. Of course, neither is true; still, the subject of the cover of the only urban design magazine in the country cannot be lightly attributed to a "fluke" or even to an oversight.

In fact, the symbolic significance of this cover must be viewed in the perspective of the great construction boom that downtowns across the country have recently been experiencing. The bulk of this new construction has taken the form of tall, steel or concrete and glass boxes. SOM remains heavily involved in this process; the firm has recently announced a project that is to surpass the tallest building in the world and will cover slightly less than 2 acres north of the Chicago Loop.

At the same time, this cover design showing Antique Row does suggest that SOM no longer needs to claim hegemony over the design of skyscrapers and that the firm no longer needs to stress the novel possibilities of the building, because tall structures are, by now, in good currency. In the United States and elsewhere, most skyscrapers have become mere tall buildings and, as such, rather ordinary (if not always accepted) elements of our urban vocabulary. Many variations on the theme of the tall glass box are already built and in use, and they continue to be produced at a decidedly fast pace. In fact, we are inescapably building our cities with them.

Finally, and importantly, the publication of the Antique Row project also suggests principles of design that are clearly in opposition to those used in tall building design. Aside from the mere difference in the height of the buildings, the approach argues for city design from the "inside out." As such, it represents a far cry from the "billboard design" that has been criticized as the plague of our urban environment. There is a definite renewed interest in this inward-looking approach to city design on the part of a number of design professionals. Not surprisingly, this interest is shared by a public that has strongly supported historic preservation, reuse of older environments, pedestrian amenities, and the like, and has also favored a generally fine-grain, conserving attitude in design.

We quickly come to feel the malaise that exists now and stems from the repeated use of the old steel-and-glass-box models by economically minded developers. This overuse is occurring just at a time when the creators of the steel and glass model are beginning to articulate their doubts about its redeeming features and viability. Fortunately, today there are two basic trends in response to this malaise: one focuses on the architecture of tall buildings, and the other on the urbanistic values of tall cities.

THE SHORTCOMINGS OF ARCHITECTURAL PROTOTYPES

Critics of urban form, including such prominent figures as Ada-Louise Huxtable, Peter Blake, and Philip Johnson, have been commenting profusely on the surge of tall buildings in cities. They have not directly addressed issues regarding city form or referred to the limitations of either the Voisin Plan or the characteristics of present-day development. However, they have strongly questioned the dictates of modern architecture, which they perceive as being at fault. They have pointed to the shortcomings of the early modern prototypes shaped by SOM and other pioneers of the modern skyscraper.

In response to these allegations, critics and designers such as Charles Jencks, Paul Goldberger, and Rem Koolhaas have stressed the need to revive aspects of the now historic skyscraper. Also, new prototypes are actually being built, including Philip Johnson's own AT & T Building and Michael Graves' Portland Building.

It seems unlikely, however, that this concentration on new prototypes will necessarily lead to a "better" city. First, experience has shown that prototypical building solutions that do make the annals of both the general and the architectural press will, in due time, be copied. The reality is that our speculative building practices constantly seek models to emulate and rapidly build. Second, and possibly much more detrimental to our urban environment than isolated poor copies of masterpieces can ever be, is the very predicament of what "normal" tall buildings currently are: the inevitable mass-repetition of copies of masterpieces (Fig. 2). Thus, for example, if one has been able to enjoy for a short time the marvels of a Seagram or a Lever House, one has, a few years later, had to confront various adaptations of these buildings sprinkled in cities throughout the country. Furthermore, a few years later, one has had to endure entire streets made of adulterations of these designs. This phenomenon is not restricted to the old symbols of modern architecture: recently, Philip Johnson's Penzoil Building in Houston has also become a reference for many developers around the country.

As a result, new architectural prototypes are not enough: experience indicates that the urban-design implications of extraordinary buildings must be anticipated. One must ask what poor copies would be like, and what entire streets lined with them would be like. The challenge can be seen as a need to realign the basic design concepts for tall buildings away from the cathedrals of the twentieth century and closer to the mere palazzi of our times.

CATHEDRALS VERSUS PALAZZI

When tall buildings first appeared in this country, they were few, and they stood as secular cathedrals; as time went by and tall buildings became more numerous, many U.S. downtowns served as parks for these cathedrals, and CBDs became nothing short of places for "higher business." Today, however, the sheer number of tall buildings, and their projected future production, warrant that we look for the elements of an urban cell that responds to the characteristics of the palazzo.

TALL CITY 1. Rio de Janeiro Copacabana: Avenida Atlantica 2. Manhattan: 58th Street looking west		
Salvador, Bahia		
TALL DOWNTOWN **Lower Manhattan: CBD rebuilt**		
1. Downtown Seattle: View from the north 2. Downtown Seattle: Fed, yet divided, by Interstate 5		
REPEATING COPIES OF MASTERPIECES 1. Manhattan: McGraw-Hill Plaza 2. Manhattan: Avenue of the Americas		

Fig. 2 The tall city, tall downtown, and tall masterpiece

Palazzi were basically functional buildings mixing residential and business purposes. Although they often celebrated their clients, these places were not ceremonial and, as such, were never designed to be more than a relatively minute piece of the city—a common cell repeated throughout in slightly different forms. Cathedrals, on the other hand, stood as symbols of the higher ideals of the collectivity. As essential public and special urban elements, they were designed as wholes, autonomous from the city fabric. One cannot very well say that palazzi were urban and cathedrals were not; they both belonged (and still do) to the city. One's imagination can tell that a city of palazzi lacks a monumental and ceremonial dimension, whereas a city of cathedrals becomes, in contrast, a place of "gods and priests."

If palazzi are the precedent that we are looking for, then we need to define what their attributes should be in contemporary terms. Two relatively minor pieces of writing by well-known urbanists shed light on the issue. One is Allan Jacobs' "They're Closing the Doors to Downtown", and the other is I. M. Pei's "Reflections on the Resurrection of Urban Design" (Jacobs, 1980; Pei, 1981). Both men argue for what can be termed collective principles of urban design that govern the form, organization, and use of the individual buildings. Indirectly, they suggest that we return to a comprehensive view of cities, one that rejects the concept of a downtown that is separate from the rest of the city.

TALL DOWNTOWNS VERSUS TALL CITIES

The tall downtown is to the tall city what the cathedral is to the palazzo: a special place within the city that stands within, yet segregated from, its surroundings (Fig. 2). Yet downtowns are taking on increasing importance both because of their size and because they have multiplied in many sections of our metropolises. They englobe an increasing number of urban uses, with recreation and entertainment becoming major focuses. As a result, it is no longer appropriate, in design terms at least, to dissociate the downtown from the city at large. Accordingly, the design principles of the tall building need to be realigned away from the tall downtown (where a tall building remains the trademark of the business district) and closer to the tall city (where it is one of many).

USEFUL PRECEDENTS

Explicit theories directed at the form of the tall city and its palazzi are not readily available. It is possible, however, and also necessary, to assemble a composite picture of what such cities may be like. An important source of information in this regard lies in selected existing cities, such as parts of Manhattan and a few cities of the developing world. They provide rich precedents against which newly formulated ideas of tall city design can be tested. They show, for instance, that building height is not an intrinsic handicap to creating exciting urban places. No doubt, these cities are congested, complex, and sometimes "rough" environments, but the opportunities for both work and recreation appear to counterbalance their inconveniences.

To begin putting together a composite picture of the tall city, design attributes that make cities desirable and livable must be discovered. An open-ended list of such attributes follows, based on the observation of a few selected precedents and on the compilation of concepts recently developed by planners and designers and ratified, by and large, by the public. The list is by its nature tentative, and is proposed for the purposes of discussion rather than for setting yet another dogma. Its items are not rank-ordered, but they address alternatively the architectural or building scale and the larger urban design scale.

DESIGN ATTRIBUTES OF THE TALL CITY: AN OPEN-ENDED LIST

(a) Edges and Hierarchies of Open Spaces

The spectacular "catastrophe" Le Corbusier projected when observing the relatively narrow, defined streets of the tall city turned out to be not only acceptable but desirable, provided traffic is selectively segregated. Hierarchies of streets exist in the tall city, from automobile- versus pedestrian-oriented ones to business- versus neighborhood-oriented ones (Fig. 3). There also are hierarchies of passive urban spaces (or spaces not reserved for through passage). Squares and plazas are private or public, monumental or ordinary, ceremonial or not, but whatever their character, they enhance the opportunity for the urban dweller and visitor alike to experience variety.

To create urban space and support such hierarchies the tall building must be subjugated to its lower counterpart—the urban space itself; when it is juxtaposed with its neighbors, it must participate in the weaving of the urban fabric. For example, in both New York City and Rio de Janeiro, buildings of different heights or even different bulks do meet at ground level and "make" streets; despite the otherwise cacophonous nature of their forms, they all tend to follow the same rules of set back, land use (at ground), and height of ground-related functions (Fig. 3).

In keeping with these principles, open space in the tall city is structured and modulated with different but coordinated elements. Autonomous, free-standing structures are, in that scheme of things, inconceivable unless the particular building either houses a special program or is significant to the community.

CATHEDRALS

1. San Francisco: TransAmerica building
2. Manhattan: World Trade Center looking at Liberty Plaza

PALAZZI

1. Copacabana: Buildings along Avenida Atlantica
2. Seattle: Housing in the Pike Place Market

EDGES AND HIERARCHIES OF OPEN SPACES
Business, retail, and some residential uses
1. Downtown Rio: Pedestrian mall
2. Manhattan: Fifth Avenue

Residential, business, and retail uses

1. Copacabana: Side street
2. Manhattan: 57th Street East

Mixing cars and pedestrians—as long as there are more problems for cars than for pedestrians.

Copacabana: Gustavo Sampaio Street

Fig. 3 The varied urban experience

(b) Special Places

The special status of a particular property may be transmitted by different shapes and forms at the ground level; it may also be perpetrated by heights that are different from the surroundings. Special places are not necessarily landmarks linked to ceremonial or historic significance; in Rio's Copacabana, there are two international hotels along the litoral that appear to have been given special status (Fig. 4). Both structures are substantially taller than the rest of the fabric, and their towers depart from a base that is itself wider than the neighboring buildings.

(c) Traces of History

The tall city strikingly accumulates a wide range of building types. First, tall buildings straddle many periods of history, albeit recent. Each one adds to the variety of heights, bulks, materials, and general architectural styles. History leaves indelible traces in building construction practices, designs, and detailing; it creates surprises and contrasts, providing relief from the sameness of today's constructions (Fig. 4).

In the tall city, buildings reflect not only land uses and the values that pertain to different locations within the city, but also individual owners' willingness or capability to take full advantage of their development rights. Thus, for instance, the East and West sides of Manhattan contrast sharply and provide vastly different settings. In Rio de Janeiro, the numerous prevailing building types can be attributed to the different stages of development of the distinct areas of the city, usually as a function of their distance from the center city. The area of Copacabana houses taller structures than the younger development in Ipanema, which is also located farther from the city center. In the yet younger parts of the city or in the city Salvador, Bahia (Fig. 4), which has only recently experienced pressures for development, tall building location is more erratic—the result of the impetuousness of a handful of land owners and of the recent spread of car ownership to the middle class.

(d) Fine-Grain Ownership

In the United States (there are exceptions in Manhattan) most tall buildings are also large buildings. The unusual heights involved, as well as the construction requirements associated with the building type, have made the tall building much more expensive than lower structures. As a result, the building type also corresponds with a special client type, namely, the few individuals, and more often the corporations, that are able to raise the necessary funds.

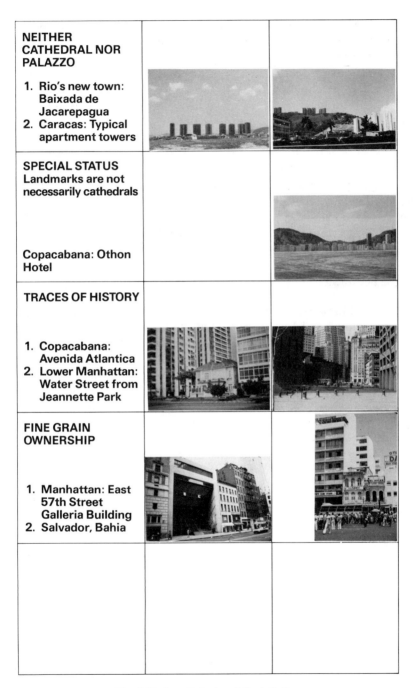

Fig. 4 Design attributes of the tall city

In cultures where either the banking establishment or the corporate structure have fewer and usually smaller resources in their hands, tall building owners are comparatively poorer; but they are also more numerous. Hence many smaller structures are built than in the United States. Furthermore, land prices in these cases are often, in relative terms, much higher than in the United States, making land aggregation even less feasible. Consequently, within a given area of the city, lot size, site coverage, building height, cladding material, and land use offer substantial variations, because unlike the tall downtown, the tall city houses a variety of land owners whose economic formulas for development are not identical.

Thus, despite zoning codes establishing maximum envelopes, tall buildings need not be uniformly calibrated or, for that matter, similarly wrapped; the sheer number and variety of land owners will create a variety of circumstances (incentives, problems, opportunities) that will govern decisions regarding development (Fig. 4).

(e) The Footprint

Tall buildings, because they are large, invariably precipitate a change in the grain of the host fabric. Because of their scale, they are often disruptive to the pedestrian environment. It is likely, however, that lot size bears more consequences on the perception of building scale and urban grain than height per se. For the pedestrian, the building footprint translates into either long or short street frontages that exhibit one kind of land use, or at least similar uses within the same envelope (Fig. 5); the impact will be negative if these uses occupy a long portion of the street and if they have little to do with the public. In general, it is the combination of sizable footprints and inordinate heights that generate disproportionate strains on both public facilities and services. This combination further exaggerates the differences between the old and the new; it facilitates the consolidation of land uses and encourages self-containment and segregation from the rest of the urban fabric.

In cultures where the tall building is an optional mode of development for a relatively large number of the land owners and where tall building owners represent a broader spectrum of the population, land aggregation techniques are less widely used than in the U.S. downtowns. Often only governments and a very few major industries can bear the costs of purchasing large tracts of urban land. In such cases, the majority of tall structures are erected on single pieces of property, which often even correspond to a colonial plot that survived centuries of urban development.

From an urban design point of view, it is important and appropriate to encourage variety and to maintain different sizes of new development in the same city. Although it used to be considered inequitable to regulate differ-

THE FOOTPRINT
Fine or Coarse Grain?
1. Manhattan:
   Coarse-grain, Park
   Avenue looking
   north
2. Manhattan:
   Coarse-grain, Third
   Avenue looking
   north-east

1. Rio de Janeiro:
   Fine-grain,
   Ipanema
2. Downtown Rio:
   Fine-grain

MIXING USES

Copacabana: Avenida
Atlantica, mixing
uses at ground level

1. Copacabana:
   Avenida Atlantica,
   Mixing uses at
   ground level and
   above
2. Manhattan: View
   from kitchen in
   Galleria apartment,
   Mixing uses at
   ground level and
   above

Fig. 5 Impact on the urban fabric

ent intensities of development rights within a given area, the currently common usage of Transfers of Development Rights (TDRs) has opened up new horizons for the fine tuning of urban form. Also, for example, the city of San Francisco has enforced a limit on building height based on views from the streets (an interesting version of the famous view corridors); the city is trying to respond specifically to changes in the direction of the street grid and catch the paramount visual amenity as much as possible.

In terms of controlling tall building footprints, regressive Floor Area Ratios (FARs), which are based on land size to discourage disproportionately large development in a given community, can also be used to discourage land aggregation.

The city of Portland, Oregon, has recently addressed the footprint issue: whereas "as-of-right" development packages are allocated for small plots, development schemes for large plots within the city must be submitted for design review prior to approval. The city has thereby recognized and reinforced the potential for variety among developments in the center city.

There are also interesting recent developments in fire code requirements for downtown locations that have opened up the possibility of using a variety of building approaches. They encourage smaller, framed structures and can be interpreted not only as a relaxation of the fire codes, but also as an encouragement to owners of small parcels to participate directly in the development process. This promises to add to the variety of environments in the tall downtown. (Cities that have revised their codes include Portland and San Francisco.)

These and other examples demonstrate that it is possible to plan today with the understanding that the distribution of building bulk is not necessarily only a matter of building economics and location, but also of design in the larger sense of the word. Desirable plans to apportion bulk may therefore be enacted.

(f) Mixing Uses

In the tall city, places of work and places of residence are not so much segregated by location as they are by type of physical environment. Thus, office buildings are structured and finished differently from residential buildings; the latter have different windows, balconies, entries, and so forth. U. S. downtowns have so far been primarily associated with the work place, containing mainly office and hotel facilities and to a lesser extent, luxury housing. Even in Manhattan, land uses are segregated — Lower Manhattan decidedly showing the attributes of a typical downtown and Midtown concentrating office development in a small area.

Mixing uses, of course, is yet another way to attenuate the impact of the tall building's size (Fig. 5); and even as the benefits of land use segregation are being widely questioned, such buildings as the Olympic Tower in New York and the John Hancock Center in Chicago have already pioneered mixed uses. Indeed, experience has shown that large monofunctional facilities seriously limit possibilities for exchanges between the building users and the city at large because they concentrate the interactions between the two at regular and predetermined intervals (that is, the rush in and the rush out). It is unfortunate, then, that most land use ordinances continue to perpetuate single-use zones, thereby restricting opportunities for direct communication between the various users of the city and limiting the range of experiences available. A few exceptional ordinances (in San Francisco, New York, and a handful of other cities) have favored housing and commercial uses over office development in specific downtown areas; these areas, contrary to the ones subject to urban renewal programs, remain relatively small and entail a variety of land owners.

(g) Interchanging Uses, Images, and Meanings

In all great cities, many structures and properties in general have been allowed to evolve and hold different programs interchangeably. The tall building in the tall city must also be able to project images and meanings beyond the achievements of its original owner.

The recent sale of the PANAM building in Manhattan begins to suggest that the tall building in the tall city can be used outside the limitations of its builders' charismatic image. In the case of the PANAM building, its shape and extraordinary location become less the symbol of its parent company than a landmark within the city. Similarly, the recent rehabilitation of the exterior cladding of the Woolworth building is an example of a tall building that is taking a prestigious place in history. Such evolution further reinforces the importance of an entire generation of tall buildings and emphasizes their meaning and significance to the public, rather than their individual economic value.

(h) Vertical Narrow Increments

Encouraging mixed and interchangeable uses is not novel in tall buildings; but the trend has not received widespread support so far. In the few well-documented landmark cases, the trend has been to stack the different uses in horizontal "slices" (Fig. 6). In fact, a vertical separation of uses may present certain advantages over the usual horizontal "piling up" of different functions. As we have seen, the latter distribution of uses has not helped the street environment, particularly in the case of large projects that occupy inordinate stretches of the street. The horizontally organized tall building

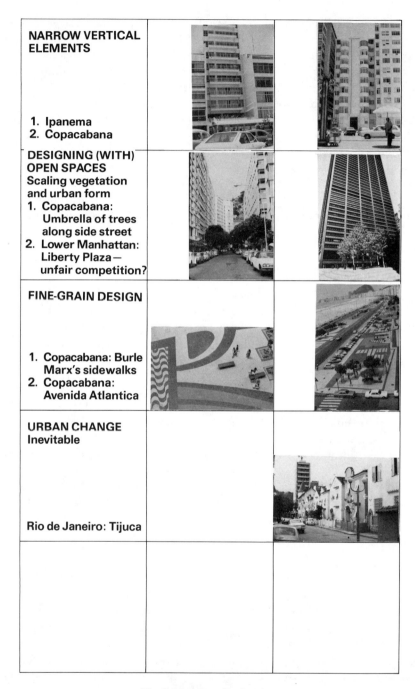

NARROW VERTICAL ELEMENTS

1. Ipanema
2. Copacabana

DESIGNING (WITH) OPEN SPACES
Scaling vegetation
and urban form
1. Copacabana:
   Umbrella of trees
   along side street
2. Lower Manhattan:
   Liberty Plaza —
   unfair competition?

FINE-GRAIN DESIGN

1. Copacabana: Burle
   Marx's sidewalks
2. Copacabana:
   Avenida Atlantica

URBAN CHANGE
Inevitable

Rio de Janeiro: Tijuca

Fig. 6 Interchanging images

depends on the "street-in-the-air" as a principal means of circulation; it has proved to be ineffective as a public or semipublic space because it cannot draw internally the large numbers of people who are necessary to ensure a lively environment.

Increments of tall buildings housing different and vertically spliced uses present an opportunity to reinforce the public environment at the ground; in such cases, the large program becomes an asset to the street because it brings to it the necessary numbers of people at regular and frequent intervals.

The concept of the vertical narrow increment of building is borrowed from the finer-grain environment of a city like Rio de Janeiro, where the comparatively smaller lots introduce an entirely different rhythm to the street environment; to each building that fronts the street for an average stretch of some 50 feet, there is a major entrance bringing people to and from the street. The design treatment, and possibly even the uses at the base of each building, may vary accordingly along the same street, again creating a varied stage for small-scale activity.

It is not unreasonable to suggest that street-level entries be mandated for tall buildings, to occur at regular and fine-grain intervals so as to increase intercommunication along the public way. Narrow increments of buildings will then facilitate vertical splices and animate the ground environment.

Underlying the above suggestions is the notion that tall and large buildings that are multifunctional run the risk of being too self-sufficient and hence of not participating with the public space at all. (Allan Jacobs recorded the problem well in his "They're Closing the Doors to Downtown," Jacobs, 1980). It is important to force a relatively high level of shared activities between the large building (and its program) and the city at large, between the private and the public sectors; restaurants, shops, and service facilities need to be directly related to the environment at ground level. Narrow increments will encourage such a sharing of activities.

(i) Variety of Materials and Types of Construction

Materials are another area where the tall city offers the opportunity for variety and the tall downtown, on the contrary, gives a contrived view of possible modern construction techniques and detailing skills. For instance, the entire structure of the Olympic Tower in New York is cladded uniformly with a dark polymeric and glass skin, when the opportunity for visual variety existed. The Olympic Tower has a steel structure supporting the bottom part of the building, which houses shops and offices, and the upper part, consisting of residences, is built out of concrete. It appears that in a technologically advanced society, only the glut of materials available stifles our current vision of what these structures could look like. It is now worth our attention to break down the monolythic shapes with different design and detailing treatments.

(j) Designing (with) Open Spaces

Recent criticism of the open spaces related to tall buildings has focused on the altogether redundant occurrence of plazas. However, another important element of the public open space is its own detailed design and supporting vegetation. The scale of tall buildings demands special concern for their corresponding open spaces: vegetation obviously cannot consist of meager young trees; rather it must be made to compete fairly by emphasizing the continuity of the open space. This is the case on Copacabana's side streets, where a green umbrella provides shade and protection from the rain (Fig. 6). This continuous umbrella also serves well to mitigate the differences in scale between the pedestrian environment and the height of the buildings themselves. Burle Marx's detailed attention to sidewalk paving further lessens the scale of the buildings and enlightens the contrasts between the relative harshness of the constructions and the brilliance of the natural setting.

CONDENSED REFERENCES/BIBLIOGRAPHY

The following is a condensed bibliography for this article. It includes all articles referred to or cited in the text. The full citations will be found at the end of the volume, with additional citations for further reading. What is given here should be sufficient information to lead the reader to the correct article: the author, date, and title. In case of multiple authors, only the first name is listed.

Blake 1977, *Form Follows Fiasco, Why Modern Architecture Hasn't Worked*

Choay 1960, *Le Corbusier*

Goldberger 1981, *A New American Skyscraper*

Huxtable 1981, *Is Modern Architecture Dead*

Jacobs 1980, *They're Closing the Doors to Downtown*
Jencks 1980, *Skyscrapers — Skycites*

Koolhaas 1978, *Delirious New York*

Pei 1981, *Reflections on the Resurrection of Urban Design*

Transportation Center

Ann Conger

The external transportation problems associated with tall buildings can best be alleviated by an effective integration of building design with the urban transportation network. A contemporary example of this design approach is Skidmore, Owings & Merrill's Transportation Center in Chicago. This structure was initially conceived as a downtown airline terminal to be directly linked to the O'Hare International Airport rapid transit extension now under construction. The multiuse facility's ambitious program has developed into one of unprecedented scope. With fully integrated connections to the city's downtown mass transit and pedestrian-circulation systems, the 26-story complex will also support thirteen levels of office space atop ten levels of parking, a two-story retail galleria, and two levels of below-grade rental car facilities (Fig. 1). As the first significant new project in the six-square-block North Loop renewal area, the Transportation Center is expected both to act as the catalyst in revitalizing the North Loop and to set the standards for future developments in the area.

The transit facility will be situated within the urban renewal area that was first identified in the Chicago 21 Plan (Skidmore, Owings & Merrill, 1973) as a part of the central business district where major redevelopment should be initiated. In 1979, the City of Chicago targeted the North Loop Redevelopment Area as critically in need of revitalization and published guidelines to coordinate a redevelopment effort.

The Transportation Center will be located in the northwest corner of the redevelopment area on the half-block parcel of land designated in the North Loop Guidelines (City of Chicago, 1981) as Parcel Block C. The 45,000-ft² site, currently occupied by seven commercial structures, lies immediately to the north of the State of Illinois building now under construction, and to the west of a proposed hotel development. The creation of a transportation interchange on this site will consolidate travel-related activities that historically have been dispersed throughout the city. It will also provide in the central business district a point of access via public transportation to virtually every corner of the city.

Of primary importance to the center's function will be its connection to the new rapid transit extension running to O'Hare International Airport, 18 miles to the northwest. For the first time, travelers will have access to a direct form of public transportation between Chicago's downtown and the airport. In addition to this convenience, the center's links to other forms of transit and its rental car facilities will allow the traveler easier transfer once in the central business district.

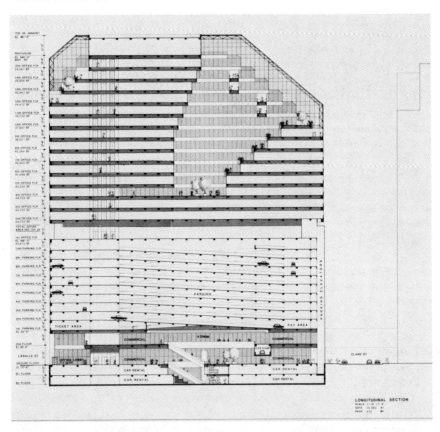

Fig. 1 SOM's Transportation Center—longitudinal section

A pedestrian bridge will link the elevated rapid transit system platform above Lake Street to the grade-level rail transit station serving the airport subway and located at the center's south entrance. Parallel to this station will be a passageway under Lake Street connecting the transportation interchange to the State of Illinois building and tying into the city's underground pedestrian-circulation system. This below-grade network runs from City Hall and the County Building on LaSalle Street east to the commercial district of State Street and south to offices on Monroe Street. It provides weather-protected movement through a 12-block area and indirect access to all downtown subway lines.

Complementing this connection to the underground precinct of the city, a second-level bridge over Clark Street to the proposed hotel development will coordinate the center with the recently initiated skywalk system. This link will enable hotel guests who require public transportation, rental cars, or travel services to enter the transit facility directly. The expanded skywalk network will also improve access throughout the downtown area and will tie into the existing mass transit system. Promoting grade-separated pedestrian movement will encourage commercial activity in the central business district, a key factor in the revitalization process.

The transit complex's multiple functions will generate activity in addition to that produced by the center's many links to circulation systems. Rising from ten levels of open-air parking facilities will be a 13-story office atrium space (Fig. 2). Corporations with heavy staff travel and companies currently located near O'Hare Airport that would like to become part of the downtown market are expected to become the tenants of the 400,000 ft² of rental office space. In addition to intensifying the population density of the North Loop, a fully leased office complex will increase the urban tax base; both results have been cited as redevelopment goals.

Car rental offices, travel agencies, and downtown airline terminal desks will line the two-story galleria of the center. Airline passengers will be able to buy their tickets, obtain their boarding passes, and check their baggage before boarding the train to O'Hare Airport later in the day. The galleria will also support restaurants, a foreign currency exchange, credit card offices, and visitor information desks. As a result, the center's interior promenade will serve as a focal point for pedestrian activity in the North Loop.

Ten levels of off-street parking for 1,260 automobiles will be provided beneath the office development of the transit facility. Commuters and visitors coming from the Dan Ryan and Kennedy expressways via Lake Street and from Lake Shore Drive via the Wacker Drive extension will be able to park in the Transportation Center's open-air garage and then make use of the convenient connections to the pedestrian and mass transit interurban networks. Providing parking and rental car facilities on the north edge of the downtown area will relieve traffic congestion in the central business district. Ease of transfer will attract visitors who would like to drive into the city for the day to shop and make use of the many cultural institutions located in the nearby area, as well as those who make frequent use of the airport but need the convenience of rental car facilities. The multifaceted nature of the Transportation Center as a transit interchange, office, and commercial development has the potential for attracting interest and regular activity in the North Loop, two essential ingredients to successful urban revitalization.

Fig. 2 North Loop Transportation Center *(Courtesy: Orlando Cabanban)*

CONDENSED REFERENCES/BILBIOGRAPHY

The following is a condensed bibliography for this article. It includes all articles referred to or cited in the text. The full citations will be found at the end of the volume, with additional citations for further reading. What is given here should be sufficient information to lead the reader to the correct article: the author, date, and title. In case of multiple authors, only the first name is listed.

City of Chicago 1981, *North Loop Guidelines for Conservation and Redevelopment*
Skidmore, Owings & Merrill 1973, *Chicago 21*

Introduction

Michael Moukalian

The design of parking projects today and in the future must be integrated with the various design considerations of the high-rise building development. From the initial concept through the final design, each phase of the project should be geared to mesh with the other.

Once the demand for parking has been established, each specific design item related to the parking is determined. The following design criteria represent the most proven methods by which the functional design can be accomplished. Some of the major items of interest are as follows:

1. Planning and application to the "Tall Building".

2. Zoning and building code requirements.

3. Size and conditions of site.

4. Traffic analysis around site.

5. Proximity to the generator.

6. Possibility of direct connection (bridge or tunnel).

7. Types of ramping systems (above or below grade).

8. Types of construction (structural types and methods).

9. Underground conditions (utilities and soil).

10. Flexibility of design for future modification.

The above items will serve as a practical and technical guide for planning a parking development related to the tall building.

NEW DEVELOPMENTS AND FUTURE OUTLOOK

In the United States, the last decade's energy crisis has left us acutely aware of the continuing depletion of our natural fuel resources. The anticipation of still higher fuel costs, along with growing foreign car imports, has been escalating the trend toward a larger proportion of small cars. The U. S. automobile industry has been concentrating primarily on smaller, fuel-efficient cars with reduced horsepower, body size, and weight. This is an indication that an even greater number of small cars will be on the road in the '80s.

Because of the downward trend in the size of the American automobile, the use of the small-car space in parking structures has continued to grow until, at this point, the number of small-car parking spaces is fast approaching that of so called full-size parking spaces. This increased volume has generated a number of parking-design systems accommodating the small-car parking stall.

The need for future conversion to small-car spaces is more or less restricted to the United States, as most other countries have a much higher percentage of small automobiles in operation. However, this consideration in the design of parking structures should be reviewed on an individual basis.

Parking studies of such conversion indicate a potential savings in the initial construction cost (depending on the size of the development) because of the design modification for the small-car parking space. Also, a net increase of approximately 25% of the total parking capacity could result if the structure is ever converted to all small-car parking in the future.

Parking

James J. Vesey

There are certain conditions that should be incorporated in the design of any structure that is intended to have an area set aside for parking. The premise is that the parking is necessary in this particular situation and is economically feasible to construct.

Parking facilities may be part of high-rise office towers, residential towers, or shopping complexes, or they may be stand-alone structures. Therefore, each facility will have a set of conditions and an environment that will be unique; and each will have to be analyzed from many aspects to determine if it is meeting the present need and if it is flexible enough to accommodate future change.

For example, office towers are generally a Monday-to-Friday, 9 A.M.-to-5 P.M. proposition. The tenancy of the tower will dictate the amount of space that will be required for parking; that is, multicorporate tenancy will mean many executives who will more than likely drive to work, whereas single-corporate tenants will likely have large clerical staffs who will normally use mass transit if available or even car-pool where possible. Moreover, office-tower tenants are usually all-day parkers with little in-and-out activity. However, adding shops, restaurants, and theaters—either in the tower itself or in the immediate surrounding area—creates a demand for short-term parking, with attendant turnover in space utilization.

The requirements for residential towers, on the other hand, will depend on the age and mix of the tenants. The parking facility will be either a constant in-and-out operation, having continuous space for transient parkers or be primarily for retired tenants with little in-and-out movement, having a lower availability of space for transients.

Shopping centers usually have short-term occupancy that runs two-and-a-half hours per stay for the average shopper. Turnover of space should be very high. However, depending on the proximity to mass transportation, turnover can be very low if the facility becomes a convenient place for commuters to park. In this case, safeguards would have to be built in to restrict such abuse; prevention can be easily achieved by matching the facility with shoppers' hours and not opening before 10 A.M., or by establishing a rate structure favorable to the shopper but unattractive to the commuter.

Stand-alone parking facilities are wholly dependent on their feeder sources. Therefore, it must be possible to predict the needs of the immediate area—the number of spaces required, the length of stay, the rates that are competitive, the method of operation, and the required hours of operation. It is equally important to consider actual design aspects for parking facilities, as described in the following sections.

SIGNAGE

Is the parking facility open to the public, and recognizable as such, or is it restricted to tenants of the supporting structure (Fig. 1)? Is the interior signage clear and limited in the length of message conveyed? Simply stated, can the driver find his way to a space, and then go from that space to the facility exit without becoming confused or lost (Fig. 2)?

COLUMNS

Are columns arranged to provide for the clear space required by today's vehicles? Can a vehicle drive through the facility with a minimum number of turns? Are clearances sufficient to permit two-way traffic? If one-way traffic is desirable—as it would be in a high turnover facility—are the columns arranged so that there is limited dead space?

In addition, we are now in a transition period with respect to vehicle size. It is estimated that by 1985 at least 70% of the vehicles on the road will be in the compact or small-car group. Consideration must be given to the redesign of the facility to accommodate the smaller car and the possible increase in the number of cars.

CONCRETE

As a minimum, 4,000 psi concrete should be specified. It should be air entrained, and the concrete cover over the top reinforcing steel should not be less than 1½ in. If possible, the reinforcing steel for the facility decks and driveways should be mill coated to reduce the possibility of rusting and the attendant deterioration of the slab.

Fig. 1 Signs make a facility easily recognizable as a parking structure open to the public

DRAINAGE

There should be positive drainage to the nearest floor drain. Moreover, climatic conditions impose special requirements. For example, in the snow belt, large amounts of snow and ice will be brought into the facility and, of necessity, equally large amounts of snow melting chemicals and salts will be deposited on its floor. In such a case, the faster the runoff flows to the drain, the less time the water has to penetrate the slab and start its destructive action.

LIGHTING

Good lighting is essential for the safe operation of the faciltiy. It is most important in driveways and in the entrance and exit areas where it should be equal to the exterior light conditions to minimize eye adjustment time.

INTERIOR LAYOUT

It is important to consider spaces for the handicapped. The federal government has established guidelines on the number of such spaces that must be included, especially in projects that receive federal funds. Where will they be located? Are there obstacles that prohibit the free movement of the handicapped? Handicapped parking areas should be located in the

Fig. 2 Clear signage marking the way for the driver in a parking facility

safest possible section of the facility, away from vehicular traffic lanes, if possible.

MAINTENANCE

Unbelieveable as it may seem, maintenance is probably the one aspect of parking that is most often overlooked; yet maintenance is the cheapest form of insurance for the long and trouble-free life of the facility. Floors must be cleaned; oil and hydraulic-fluid stains removed; light bulbs and fluorescent tubes replaced; fixtures repaired or replaced; draines cleaned; and, when they occur, spalled areas or potholes repaired. Floors should be sealed to prevent the penetration of salts and chemicals, and then resealed when the original surface wears away. This critical, though often ignored, step prevents the intrusion of salts into the concrete. It also prevents the concrete-destroying freeze-thaw cycle so prevalent in parking facilities, which tend not to be heated but usually have large openings to the outside that let in prevailing cold and winds. Maintenance can be the most important step in extending the life of the facility.

CONCLUSION

Yesterday's builders often ignored the savings that could have accrued from the suggestions of a parking consultant. Now, with space soaring in value, the owners are desperate; worse—and predictably so—they look for some sleight of hand to recycle wasted footage into productive parking space. But no magic can inexpensively transform columns, load bearing walls, or low-hung girders into free space. Accordingly, tomorrow's successful developer knows that every square foot of a structure must be professionally managed, beginning right from the conceptual stage, if valuable square footage is to be turned into even more valuable parking space—and profit.

Typical Lease Agreement

Jerry Taylor

INTRODUCTION

The aim of management systems in relation to the tall building, whether it is used for work, play, or residence, is both to provide efficient services so that human activity can function at its optimum level and to control that activity so that it operates within previously defined limits. Part of such management is a written agreement or lease that specifies mutually agreed upon areas of responsible operation, rules of tenancy, and general policy.

Owner, manager, and tenant alike must have a clear understanding of what their respective roles are in relation to the building. A typical lease agreement between the lessor and lessee of a building, such as the one that follows, outlines the major areas of responsibility, such as maintenance, energy use, payment of rent, legal obligations, and areas of overlap in the lessor-lessee relationship. Such a document is essential in today's complex society, especially in the case of the tall building owner. He has many tenants under one roof in a building that could be used for a wide variety of functions. The manager of a multi-use tall building therefore maintains several different kinds of leases with the lessors of office space, shop space, living space, or parking space.

The following is a lease agreement typical of the kind used in the State of Texas for the lease of office space in a building.

TYPICAL
LEASE AGREEMENT

THE STATE OF TEXAS
COUNTY OF

Lessor

THIS LEASE AGREEMENT made and entered into on this the
_____ day of _____, 19__, between _____
_____ whose address is _____
_____ ("Lessor"), and _____
_____ whose address is _____
_____ ("Lessee");

WITNESSETH:

I.

Leased
Premises

1.   Lessor does hereby lease, demise and let to Lessee and Lessee
does hereby lease and take from Lessor those certain premises
(called the "leased premises") in the building known as _____
_____ located at _____
(called the "Building") in the City of _____,
_____ County, Texas, such premises being more
particularly described as follows:

as reflected on the floor plan of such premises attached as Exhibit
_____ and initialed for identification by both parties.
The term "net rentable area", as used herein, shall refer to (i) in the
case of a single tenancy floor, all floor area measured from the inside
surface of the outer glass or finished column wall of the Building to
the inside surface of the opposite outer wall excluding only the areas
("service areas") within the outside walls used for building stairs, fire
towers, elevator shafts, flues, vents, stacks, pipe shafts and vertical
ducts, but including any such service areas which are for the specific
use of the particular tenant such as special stairs or elevators plus an
allocation of the square footage of the Building's elevators mechanical rooms and ground floor and basement (if applicable) lobbies, and
(ii) in the case of a floor to be occupied by more than one tenant, all
floor areas within the inside surface of the outer glass or finished
column walls enclosing the leased premises and measured to the
mid-point of the walls separating areas leased by or held for lease to
other tenants or from areas devoted to corridors, elevator foyers, rest
rooms, mechanical rooms, janitor closets, vending areas and other
similar facilities for the use of all tenants on the particular floor
(hereinafter sometimes called "common areas"), but including a
proportionate part of the common areas located on such floor based
upon the ratio which the tenant's net rentable area (excluding common
areas) on such floors bears to aggregate net rentable area (excluding
common areas) on such floor plus an allocation of the square footage
of the Building's elevator mechanical rooms and ground floor and

basement (if applicable) lobbies. No deductions from net rentable area shall be made for columns or projections necessary to the Building. The net rentable area in the leased premises has been calculated on the basis of the foregoing definition and is hereby stipulated for all purposes hereof to be _____ square feet, whether the same should be more or less as a result of minor variations resulting from actual construction and completion of the leased premises for occupancy so long as such work is done in accordance with the terms and provisions hereof.

II

1.   (a) Subject to and upon the Terms and Conditions set forth herein, or in any exhibit or addendum hereto, this lease shall continue in force for a term of _____ months beginning on the _____ day of _____, 19__, and ending on the _____ day of _____, 19__.

(b) If the leased premises are not ready for occupancy by the date stated above, Lessor is not liable or responsible for any claims, damages or liabilities, and the term of this Lease commences at the time that the leased premises are ready for occupancy.

Use

2.   The leased premises are to be used and occupied by Lessee solely for the purpose of office space.

Base Rental Adjustment Following Base Year

3.   (a) There is established under this lease a "Base Year", which for these purposes is the calendar year 19____. In the event that the Basic Costs (as hereinafter defined) of Lessor's operation of the Building during the first calendar year after the Base Year shall differ from the Basic Costs of Lessor therefor during the Base Year, Lessee shall pay its proportionate share of the year's increases in the Basic Costs for such year in the proportion its net rentable area bears to 95% of the total net rentable area of the Building ("Lessee's proportionate share"). Any increase payable by Lessee under this provision shall be deemed additional rent. Lessor shall, within the period of one hundred fifty days (or as soon thereafter as possible) after the close of the first calendar year after the Base Year, give Lessee a statement of such year's actual Base Costs and a comparison with the Base Year's Basic Costs. If such year's Basic Costs are greater than the Base Year's Basic Costs, Lessee shall pay Lessor, within thirty days of statement receipt, Lessee's proportionate share of such increase. If Basic Costs for the year covered by such statement are less than the Base Year's Basic Costs, Lessee shall not be obligated for rental in excess of Base Rental stated in Article II, Paragraph 3.

(b) For each year during the term of this lease following the first calendar year after the Base Year, Lessor shall provide Lessee a comparison of the Base Year's Basic Costs and the projected Basic Costs for such year prior to January 1 of such year, and Lessee shall thereafter pay an Adjusted Base Rental for such year which shall include Lessee's proportionate share of any projected increase in Lessor's Basic Costs of operating the Building over Base Year's Basic Costs. Lessor shall, within the period of one hundred fifty days (or as soon thereafter as possible), after the close of each calendar year after the Base Year, provide Lessee a statement of such year's actual

Basic Costs showing the actual increase in Lessor's Basic Costs of operating the Building from Base Year is greater than that projected, Lessee shall pay Lessor, within thirty days of statement receipt, Lessee's proportionate share of the difference. If such year's projected Basic Costs are greater than the actual Basic Costs, Lessor shall pay Lessee, within thirty days of said statement's issuance, Lessee's proportionate share of the difference; provided, however, the rental owed by Lessee shall never be less than the Base Rental stated in Article II, Paragraph 3.

(c) "Basic Costs" as said term is used herein shall consist of all operating expenses of the Building, which shall be computed on the accrual basis and shall consist of all expenditures by Lessor to maintain all facilities in operation during the Base Year and such additional facilities in subsequent years as may be determined by Lessor to be necessary. All operating expenses shall be determined in accordance with generally accepted accounting principles which shall be consistently applied. The term "operating expenses" as used herein shall mean all expenses, costs and disbursements (but not replacement of capital investment items nor specific costs especially billed to and paid by specific tenants) of every kind and nature which Lessor shall pay or become obligated to pay because of or in connection with the ownership and operation of the Building including but not limited to, the following:

1. Wages and salaries of all employees engaged in operating and maintenance, or security, of the Building. All taxes, insurance and benefits relating to employees providing these services shall be included.
2. All supplies and materials used in operation and maintenance of the Building.
3. Cost of all utilities for the Building including the cost of water and power, heating, lighting, air conditioning and ventilating for the Building.
4. Cost of all maintenance and service agreements for the Buildings and the equipment therein, including alarm service, window cleaning and elevator maintenance.
5. Cost of all insurance relating to the Building, including the cost of casualty and liability insurance applicable to the Building and Lessor's personal property used in connection therewith.
6. All taxes and assessments and governmental charges whether federal, state, county or municipal, and whether they be by taxing districts or authorities presently taxing the leased premises or by others, subsequently created or otherwise, and any other taxes and assessments attributed to the Building, or its operation. It is agreed that Lessee will be responsible for ad valorem taxes on its personal property and on the value of leasehold improvements to the extent that same exceed standard building allowances.
7. Cost of repairs and general maintenance (excluding repairs

and general maintenance paid by proceeds of insurance or by Lessee or other third parties, and alterations solely to tenants of the Building other than Lessee).

Notwithstanding any other provision to the contrary, it is agreed that in the event the Building is not fully occupied during the Base Year of any subsequent year, an adjustment shall be made in computing the Basis Costs for such year so that the Basic Costs shall be computed for such year as though the Building has been fully occupied during such year.

Lessee at its expense shall have the right at all reasonable times to audit Lessor's books and records relating to this lease for the Base Year and any year or years for which additional rental payments become due; or at Lessor's sole discretion Lessor will provide such audit prepared by a certified public account.

III

Lessor convenants and agrees with Lessee:

Services to be Furnished by Lessor

1. To use its best efforts to cause public utilities to furnish the electricity, gas and water utilized in operating any and all facilities serving the leased premises.

2. To furnish Lessee while occupying the premises:

    (a) Hot and cold water; central heat and air conditioning in season; (Saturday afternoons, Sundays and holidays to be furnished only upon the request and at the expense of Lessee); routine maintenance and electric lighting service for all public areas and special service areas of the Building.

    (b) Janitor service on a five (5) day week basis at no extra charge; (if Lessee's floor covering or other improvements is other than building standard, Lessee shall pay extra).

    (c) Electrical facilities to furnish sufficient power for business equipment of low electrical consumption (total consumption not to exceed one watt per square foot of net rentable area per month); but not for electrical equipment which (singly) consumes more than 0.5 kilowatts at rated capacity or requires a voltage other than 120 volts single phase.

    (d) All building standard fluorescent and incandescent bulb replacement in all areas.

    (e) Failure by Lessor to furnish these services, or any cessation thereof, beyond the control of Lessor shall not render Lessor liable for any damages, nor relieve Lessee from fulfillment of any agreement.

Keys and Locks

3. To furnish Lessee two(2) keys for each corridor door entering the leased premises. Additional keys will be furnished only by Lessor, at a charge. All keys remain property of Lessor. No additional locks are allowed without Lessor's permission.

Graphics

4. To install, at Lessee's costs, all letters or numerals on doors in the Building standards graphics. Lessor will install, at Lessee's expense, a listing on the Building Directory Board.

Improve-
ments to be
made by
Lessor

5.   All installations placed on the leased premises in excess of building standard items shall be for Lessee's account and at Lessee's cost, payable to Lessor as additional rent upon being invoiced. Failure to pay within 30 days constitutes default by Lessee, giving rise to all remedies available to Lessor for nonpayment of rent.

Peaceful
Enjoyment

6.   That Lessee may peacefully have, hold and enjoy the leased premises, subject to the other terms, provided that Lessee performs all of Lessee's covenants and agreements.

Limitation
of Lessor's
Personal
Liability

7.   Lessor is never personally liable for any judgement. This provision shall not limit any right of Lessee to obtain injunctive relief against Lessor and Lessor's successors in any action not involving the personal liability of Lessor.

Parking

8.   Parking shall be provided as defined in a separate document.

IV

Lessee convenants and agrees with Lessor:

Payments by
Lessee

1.   To pay all rent and sums to Lessor at the times and in the manner stated.

Repairs by
Lessor

2.   Unless otherwise stipulated, Lessor is not required to make any improvements or repairs during the term of this lease, except as may be necessary for normal maintenance operation.

Repairs by
Lessee

3.   As its own cost and expense, to repair, or replace any damage or injury done to the Building caused by Lessee's agents, employees, invitees or visitors. If Lessee fails to make such repairs promptly, Lessor may make repairs or replacements, and charge Lessee.

Care of the
Leased
Premises

4.   At the termination of this Lease, to deliver up leased premises to Lessor in as good condition as at date of possession by Lessee, ordinary wear and tear expected.

Assignment
or
Sub-lease

5.   Should Lessee desire to assign this Agreement or sublet the leased premises or any part, Lessee shall give Lessor written notice sixty(60) days in advance. Lessor then has a period of thirty(30) days following notice to notify Lessee in writing that Lessor elects either (1) to terminate Agreement for said space, or (2) to permit Lessee to assign or sublet such space, subject to written approval of the proposed assignee or sublessee by Lessor; or (3) to refuse to consent, and to continue this Lease in full effect. If Lessor should fail to notify Lessee in writing within thirty(30) day period, Lessor shall be deemed to have elected option (3) above.

Alterations,
Additions,
Improve-
ments

6.   Not to permit the leased premises to be used to any purpose other than stated in the use clause or make any alterations or place signs on the leased premises which are visible from outside without first obtaining the written consent of Lessor. This clause shall not apply to moveable equipment or furniture owned by Lessee.

Legal Use

7.   Not to occupy or use any portion of the leased premises for any business or purpose which is unlawful, disreputable or deemed to be extra-hazardous.

Laws &
Regulations

8.   To comply with all laws, ordinances, rules and regulations relating to the use, condition or occupancy of the leased premises.

Entry

9.   To permit Lessor or its representatives to enter at all reasonable hours to inspect the leased premises, clean or make repairs, alterations or additions.

Nuisance | 10. To conduct its business in such manner as not to create any nuisance, or interfere with, annoy or disturb any other tenant or Lessor.

Subordina-
tion to
Mortgage | 11. This lease is subject and subordinate to any first lien mortgage or deed of trust which may now or hereafter encumber the Building of which the leased premises form a part.

12. At Lessor's request, Lessee will execute either an estoppel

Estoppel
Certificate
or Three-
Party
Agreement | certificate addressed to Lessor's mortgage or a three-party agreement among Lessor, Lessee and said mortgagee certifying to such facts (if true) and agreeing to such notice provisions and other matters as such mortgage may reasonably require in connection with Lessor's financing.

V

Lessor and Lessee mutually agree as follows:

Condemna-
tion and
Loss | 1. If the leased premises shall for any reason be rendered untenantable, this lease shall, at the option of either party, cease and terminate. All proceeds from any taking or condemnation of the leased premises shall belong to Lessor.

Damages
from
Certain
Causes | 2. Lessor shall not be liable to Lessee for any loss or damage to any property or person by theft, fire, act of God, public enemy, injunction, riot, strike, insurrection, war, court order, requisition or order of governmental body or authority, or for any damage or inconvenience which may arise through repair or alteration of any part of the Building, or failure to make such repairs.

Lien for
Rent | 3. Lessee grants to Lessor a lien and security interest on all property of Lessee placed in or upon the leased premises, subject to such lien and security interest for payment or rent and other sums agreed to be paid by Lessee. The provisions of this paragraph shall constitute a security agreement under the Uniform Commercial Code.

Lessor's
Right to
Relet | 4. In the event of default by Lessee in any terms of this Lease or if the leased premises are abandoned by Lessee, Lessor shall have the right, but not the obligation, to relet same for the remainder of the term. Lessee shall pay the deficiency between the amount of the rent and that received through reletting, including, but not limited to, the cost of renovating and altering for a new occupant. But this does not deny Lessor the right, in abandonment or other breach of this Agreement by Lessee, to treat this as an entire breach and to terminate this Agreement and/or seek recovery for the entire breach of this Agreement and any damages which Lessor suffers.

Holding
Over | 5. In the event of holding over by Lessee after expiration or termination of this lease without written consent of Lessor, Lessee shall pay as liquidated damages double rent for the entire holdover period. (This does not extend the lease.) Lessee shall then indemnify Lessor against all claims for damages by any others to whom Lessor may have leased all or any part of the premises covered hereby effective upon the termination of this lease. Any holding over with the consent of Lessor in writing shall constitute a lease from month to month.

Fire
Clause

6.   In the event of a fire Lessee shall immediately notify the Lessor. If the leased premises, through no fault or neglect of Lessee, its agents, or visitors, is partially or totally destroyed by fire or other casualty rendering the premises untenantable, the rent shall abate until such time as the leased premises are made tenantable as determined by Lessor. If Lessor decides not to rebuild, all rent owed up to the time of such destruction or termination shall be paid by Lessee and this lease shall come to an end.

Attorney's
Fees

7.   If any matter regarding this lease lands in the hands of an attorney, Lessee agrees to pay Lessor reasonable attorney's fees of not less than 10% of the amount due to Lessor.

Alteration

8.   This Agreement may not be altered, changed or amended, except in writing signed by both parties.

Assignment
by Lessor

9.   Lessor has the right to transfer and assign, in whole or in part, all its rights and obligations, and upon transfer no further liability or obligation shall thereafter accrue against Lessor.

Default
by Lessee

10.   If Lessee defaults in payment, and default continues for ten (10) days, or if Lessee defaults in the performance of any of the other conditions of this contract, and default continues for twenty (20) days, then Lessor may treat the occurrence as a breach of this Lease (provided that no such levy, execution, legal process or petition filed against Lessee shall constitute a breach of this lease if Lessee shall vigorously contest the same by appropriate proceedings and shall remove or vacate the same within thirty(30) days from the date of its creation, service of filing), and may do any of the following, in addition to other rights provided at law or in equity.

(a) Lessor may terminate this lease and repossess the leased premises and be entitled to recover damages.

(b) Lessor may terminate Lessee's right of possession (but not the lease) and may repossess the leased premises without demand or notice of any kind to Lessee (Lessor may then relet for the account of Lessee). Lessor is then authorized to make any changes, to leased premises and (i) if Lessor shall fail or refuse to relet the leased premises, or (ii) if the same are relet and a sufficient sum is not realized from such reletting, then Lessee shall pay to Lessor specified damages. Lessee agrees that Lessor may file suit to recover any sums falling due under Article V, Paragraph 10 (b).

Non-Waiver

11.   Failure of Lessor to declare any default immediately upon occurrence or to delay in taking any action shall not waive such default.

Casualty
Occurrence

12.   Lessor shall maintain fire and extended coverage insurance on the portion of the Building constructed by Lessor, including additions and improvements by Lessee which will become the property of Lessor upon vacation of the premises by Lessee. Lessee shall maintain at its expense fire and extended coverage insurance on all of its personal property.

Lessor's
Liability
Insurance

13.   Lessor shall at its expense, maintain a policy of comprehensive general liability insurance with the premiums fully paid on or before due date, affording minimum protection of not less than $300,000.00 personal injury or death in any one occurrence and not less than $100,000.00 for property damage in any one occurrence.

Hold
Harmless

14. Lessor shall not be liable to Lessee or to Lessee's agents, or invitees for any damage to person or property caused by any act, omission or neglect of Lessee, its agents, servants or employees—and vice versa for the Lessor as regards to the Lessor and its agents, servants and employees.

Waive of
Subrogation
Rights

15. Anything in this lease to the contrary notwithstanding, Lessor and Lessee each hereby waive any and all rights of recovery, claim, action or cause of action, against the other, its agents, officers, or employees, for any loss of damage that may occur to the leased premises, or said Buildings or any personal property, by reason of fire, the elements, or any other cause which could be insured against under the terms of standard insurance policies referred to in Article V, Paragraph 12, regardless of cause or origin, including negligence of the other party, its agents, officers or employees, and convenants that no insurer shall hold any right of subrogation against such party.

This lease is binding upon the successor and assigns of Lessor, and upon Lessee, its successors, and Lessee's assigns.

All rights and remedies of Lessor under this lease shall be cumulative and none shall exclude any other rights or remedies allowed by law; and this lease is declared to be a Texas contract, and all of the terms thereof shall be construed according to the laws of the State of Texas.

IN TESTIMONY WHEREOF, the parties hereto have executed this lease as the date aforesaid.

_____

_____   _____
            Lessor   Lessee

THE STATE OF TEXAS
COUNTY OF
BEFORE ME, the undersigned, a Notary Public in and for said County and State, on this day personally appeared, _____
_____ a Texas Corporation, and acknowledged to me that he executed the same for the purpose and consideration therein stated, and as the act of said Corporation.
GIVEN UNDER MY HAND AND SEAL OF OFFICE, this _____ day of _____, 19__.

                              _____
                              Notary Public in and for
                              _____ County, Texas

New Developments in Energy Conservation in Tall Buildings

Gershon Meckler

New developments in energy-conscious design of tall buildings reflect a growing appreciation of the complex interrelationships among the energy characteristics of all building systems—architectural, structural, mechanical, electrical, and interior and landscape design. The increasing use of computer modeling as a design aid is one clear result. Another is a new interpretation of the proper—or most productive—role for the building envelope.

Today a new relationship is evolving between the building envelope and its surroundings. The envelope's static-barrier role is giving way to that of a more complex and dynamic intermediary between internal needs and external natural energy sources. Designers are increasingly sensitive to techniques and opportunities for manipulating energy flows between inside and out to reduce purchased energy.

The latest wave of tall buildings clearly points to the next level in state-of-the-art progress—the integration of passive solar design and alternative energy sources with advanced engineering technology. Increasingly sophisticated "hybrids" are emerging and proving themselves in terms of annual operating-cost savings and acceptable return on investment. As the "easy" solutions disappear, this level of integrated design is a major focus of current interest and action among energy-conscious designers.

New techniques are being combined with older concepts that are newly popular and practical, such as thermal storage and cogeneration. Cogeneration is increasingly competitive, in part because some utilities are no longer discounting electric rates to large users. Utilities are reevaluating the advantages of the capacity relief for their grids that results from private development of separate selective and total energy systems. The difficulty of siting new utility power plants supports the cogeneration trend.

The HVAC subsystem shown in Fig. 1, which interfaces solar, desiccant-dehumidification, and cogeneration systems, illustrates the kind of thermodynamically efficient integration that can save significant amounts of purchased energy. The key to savings in this system is the separation of the

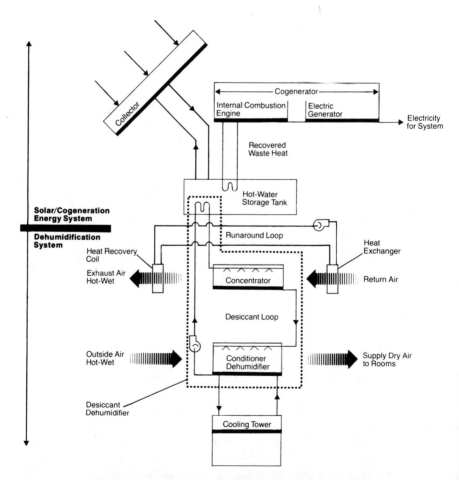

Fig. 1 Solar/cogeneration desiccant-dehumidification system

dehumidification task from the sensible cooling task. Conventional refrigeration air-conditioning systems dehumidify and cool simultaneously. Dehumidification is a substantial portion of the cooling load in these systems, since refrigeration dehumidification requires a temperature drop to the dew point level—lower than necessary for sensible cooling alone—and subsequent reheating to the comfort level.

In the system shown in Fig. 1, dehumidification is accomplished without refrigeration by using a liquid desiccant spray to absorb moisture. It is then feasible to use low-grade solar energy, which is available during most of the cooling season by way of an inexpensive flat-plate collector, to regenerate (dry) the desiccant. The dry air is then cooled by a conventional electric chiller. The reduced cooling load means that equipment and ductwork can be smaller, saving space as well as energy; and with this two-stage process, solar cooling becomes practical as well as thermodynamically efficient (that is, it matches a low-grade source to a low-grade task).

The system's energy savings can be increased by incorporating a cogenerator as a back-up for cloudy days, rather than relying on purchased energy for the incremental need. The cogenerator simultaneously generates heat to dry the desiccant and electricity to operate the chiller; and it provides emergency electricity during power outages. Referring again to Fig. 1, this system, which interfaces low-grade solar energy, heat storage, heat recovery, desiccant dehumidification, and cogeneration, provides an example of the current trend in the technology of energy efficiency. It combines thermodynamic awareness and systems integration with energy-conscious passive design to reduce the amount of purchased energy.

A major challenge facing tall building designers is the growing heat and space problem resulting from the rapidly expanding use of automation and large office equipment. New solutions are being explored in the effort to break away from the traditional tendency to handle increased thermal loads by expanding energy- and space-intensive refrigerated air systems. Figure 2 is one example of the new air-distribution systems and techniques that are being developed to respond effectively to increasing heat gains and diminishing space availability in tall buildings, while still meeting requirements for flexibility of control and zoning. The double-induction fan-terminal unit permits a reduction in ductwork and, thus, in the size of the floor-ceiling sandwich, as well as a reduction in central fan power. It achieves this by supplying from the central refrigeration plant a *smaller volume* of *colder air* than in conventional all-air, variable-volume systems. Colder air—with a greater temperature difference between the cold air and the room air—can handle a larger cooling load without an increase in the cold air quantity, primary ductwork, and fan power. The desired space temperature is maintained by mixing the primary air with return air from the room, in varying proportions depending upon space loads. The proportions are controlled by a space thermostat that regulates a damper in the primary (cold-air) supply duct. Although proportions vary, a constant volume is delivered to the room by the double-induction fan-terminal unit to assure uniform distribution and comfort. This system exemplifies the kinds of new systems and techniques being developed to handle current problems in tall buildings, such as the increasing automation and resulting heat already mentioned.

Future progress in energy use in tall buildings requires a better understanding of the operation and simulation of building systems and their complex interactions. Simulation techniques have progressed from various types of hand calculations, including the ASHRAE calculation and the use of the degree-day approach, to modern automated computer simulations. Hand calculations are adequate for a first approximation; but for large complex structures the computerized approach appears to be the best, and perhaps the only complete tool for comprehending energy use.

In summary, a substantial body of techniques is available now to save large amounts of energy in tall buildings with incremental costs. There is a general consensus that these techniques could be implemented in short order; but it would require a concerted educational program to inform and convince building owner/operators that advanced conservation techniques represent the right way—the economic way—to proceed. Certain barriers hamper this effort to conserve energy, including a lack of understanding of what the energy use in particular buildings actually is. Energy audits can help to surmount this barrier, followed by an analysis of how much energy

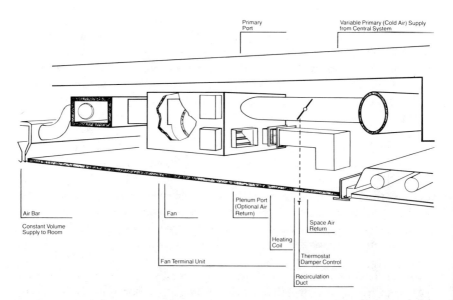

Fig. 2 Double-induction fan-terminal unit in the ceiling-floor sandwich

can be saved and at what cost. Utility regulations are loosening to allow cogeneration to be considered as a reasonable option; this would allow savings of fossil fuels. Increases in the use of peak load, demand, and ratchet-scale electricity pricing will reinforce the economic incentives for load management and conservation techniques. The large-scale nature of applying alternative energy sources in tall buildings also permits the first appearance of economies-of-scale, which reflect positively on the pressure to use such sources.

Assessing the Benefits of Employing Alternative Shading Devices to Reduce Cooling Loads for Three Climates

Ashley F. Emery
Dean R. Heerwagen
Brian R. Johnson
Charles J. Kippenhan

ABSTRACT

A continuing study of the thermal performance of a prototypical urban high-rise office building is reported. A series of alternative shading devices for reducing heat gain are evaluated for use on identical buildings located in New York, Phoenix, and Seattle. The thermal behavior of a single-occupant office with these shading devices employed as part of the glazing assembly is simulated with the computer program UWENSOL. Annual energy consumptions are derived and, applying the electricity rate structures for the three cities, energy costs are determined. Envelope and HVAC-system cost and energy savings are compared with a reference case and differentials noted. The economic desirabilities for the various compositions are then established using a "new-benefits" comparison.

INTRODUCTION

For buildings whose thermal behavior can be characterized as internal-load-dominant the magnitude of additional heat gains posed by incident solar radiation transmission through fenestration can be significant. These buildings will experience cooling loads whenever they are occupied and, depending on a number of variables (for example, building design, densities of occupancy, and usage rates of lighting systems and building machines), the rate of solar gain can easily contribute 50% of the total cooling load. This additional load can thereby cause appreciable increases in HVAC-systems capacities and the energy consumed for cooling, and they can engender concomitantly greater costs for systems installation and operation. Thus, the use of shading devices to inhibit heat gain by solar radiation appears well founded.

In two earlier papers (Heerwagen, et al., 1980; Emery, et al., 1981) continuing work examining the thermal performance of high-rise urban office buildings was discussed. Both papers described studies of the effects of the building envelope on occupant thermal comfort, and the latter report also included a cost-benefit analysis of alternative envelope compositions. These papers employed climatic conditions for Seattle. Hence, the findings were area-specific. The first paper showed that the room enclosure's surface temperature profoundly influenced occupant comfort and that nonuniformities in thermal conditions in a room adversely affected comfort. Necessarily, the degree of nonuniformity found in a room depended directly on the character of the envelope (that is, the greater the heat-transfer rate through the envelope, the larger the nonuniformity and the greater the deviation from thermally-neutral conditions). The second paper confirmed these findings and indicated that the most favorable comfort and cost results could be obtained with envelopes whose glazing assemblies (1) had areas reduced to the lowest practicable limits or (2) used high-resistance, low-solar-radiation-transmittance materials (for instance, gray tinted glass or heat-reflecting metallic films in double-pane assemblies).

STUDY ISSUES

In this paper we will describe a further study of the thermal behavior of the office building, here noting specifically the use of alternative shading devices to reduce heat-transfer rates at the building envelope. Our study will focus on a cost-benefit analysis examining the economic desirability of making the additional investments required to include these devices. In addition to results for Seattle, we will present those for New York City and Phoenix, Arizona.

Characteristics of the Prototypical Office

Consistent with our earlier papers we have used as our case study a private office located at the perimeter of an office tower. The office occurs on an intermediate floor and is essentially one of many placed along the building envelope. This office would have a single occupant, present from 8 A.M. until 6 P.M. Mechanical (HVAC) and lighting systems will operate during this time interval only. The mechanical system will function on a temperature dead-band control providing either heating when the interior air temperature falls below 72°F or cooling when it rises above 78°F. The basis for selecting these operating conditions is the ASHRAE Standard 90-75 (ASHRAE, 1975). The HVAC system will also include an economizer cycle for use whenever the outside air temperature is 55°F or less. The heat input from the lighting system is rated at 1.5 w/ft^2.

The office has a usable floor area of 150 ft^2 (10 ft wide by 15 ft deep). Its floor-to-floor height is 12 ft and the floor-to-ceiling height is 9 ft. One office wall is a part of the tower perimeter. All other enclosure surfaces are internal and shared (see Fig. 1). Glazing will constitute 25% of the envelope (or, 30 ft^2 per office) and will be placed as a nonoperable continuous strip in the middle third of the floor-to-ceiling dimension. The opaque curtain-wall assembly will be a Glasweld panel with an air-to-air resistance of 12.5 hr-ft^2 °F/Btu and a surface weight of 5.2 lb$_m$/ft^2. The specific envelope organiza-

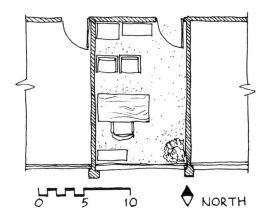

Fig. 1 Prototypical office floor plan

tions (including the various shading devices) will be catalogued in the section on results. The internal walls consist of two double layers of plaster drywall supported by steel stud framing. The floor and ceiling assemblies are composed of suspended acoustical tile beneath a horizontal air space (of sufficient depth for the environmental control services) and concrete on steel decking.

Analysis by Computer Simulation

This study has been performed using the thermal simulation computer program UWENSOL (Emery, et al., 1979), which was developed at the University of Washington specifically to analyze hybrid and passively controlled buildings. UWENSOL has been tested against Los Alamos Test Cell data, and very good correlations have been established (Arens, et al., 1980; Emery, et al., to be published). The thermal responses of the office for the several envelope organizations will be determined using annual climatic data taken from TMY weather records (National Climatic Center) for Seattle, New York, and Phoenix. These data have been treated with the ADJUST program to permit record compression (Arens, et al., 1980). The bases for selecting these three cities for study include the following:

1. All three are available in the TMY record format and have data adequate for hour-by-hour simulation.

2. Seattle and New York have somewhat similar winter weather conditions (when viewed on an averaged basis), but differ in summertime conditions (New York is generally warmer with greater solar fractions); Phoenix has mild winters and hot summers.

3. The costs of construction and energy consumption show variation. Specifically, building costs for Seattle and New York are similar overall (about 7.5% higher than the national mean) and Phoenix is 1.3% above the mean (Godfrey, 1981).

The unit energy costs for electricity for the three cities demonstrate a considerable variation. The utility company for each city (that is, Consolidated Edison of New York, Arizona Public Service of Phoenix, and Seattle City Light) employs a commercial rate structure based on (1) short-term peak-demand costs and monthly consumption costs jointly and (2) a cascading unit price that, essentially, means the more electricity one uses, the lower the unit price. Thus, unit costs for the three utilities (for office buildings of a scale similar to the one we are studying) are approximately $0.155/kwh for New York; $0.049/kwh for Phoenix; and $0.012/kwh for Seattle (including the effects of both demand and consumption charges).

Rating Alternatives by Net-Benefit Comparisons

The primary question in this study has been, "Is it cost-beneficial to improve the office building envelope beyond the commonly-employed combination of the double-pane, clear-plate glazing assembly and the medium-resistance opaque curtain wall?" To answer this question, this combination will be used as a reference case in examining the differential costs between using it and other envelopes. The analysis will use a net-benefits comparison (Marshall and Ruegg, 1980). The net-benefits calculation establishes the monetary value of energy savings (over some period of time) less the differential costs (of construction, salvage, maintenance, and replacement) for achieving these energy savings.

RESULTS

The ten envelope combinations employed in this study are catalogued in Table 1. Case 1 was chosen as the reference envelope (that is, the basis on which to make the several cost comparisons). This envelope combination easily satisfies the area-weighted U-values (U_o) and the Overall Thermal Transfer Value (OTTV) set for New York and Seattle in the ASHRAE Standard 90-75 (ASHRAE, 1975). For Phoenix this combination also complies easily with the U_o value and is borderline for the OTTV factor. Thereby, while examining the other nine envelope combinations, we have sought to determine whether it is economically desirable to construct buildings whose envelopes are better than those set forth by the authors of the ASHRAE Standard as being minimally acceptable.

How the Cost Savings Were Established

Envelope costs.   Envelope costs were prepared by itemizing the quantities of materials and estimating the labor times required for construction. Using the *1981 Means Building Construction Cost Data Book* (Godfrey, 1981), the average unit prices for the materials and labor were established. Multiplying these unit prices by the materials and labor quantities produced the national average construction costs for the several components of the envelope combinations. These component costs were then multiplied by regional cost factors supplied by the *Means* guide for the three cities. We summed the results, including percentages for contractor overhead and profit. The costs for the ten envelope assemblies for each of the three cities are shown in column 2 of Table 2.

HVAC Systems Costs.   HVAC systems costs were established in a similar manner. First, the design loads were computed for an HVAC system serving the study office. The use of a heat pump to condition a single zone of south-facing perimeter offices (including the study office) was presumed. The capacities (and thus the sizes) for the heat pump and the ducting network were calculated. With the sizes of these components set, we prepared cost estimates based on materials and labor requirements. Related components that would be essentially the same for all the study assemblies (for example diffusers, controls, dampers, and the like) were excluded because, again, we wished to establish cost differentials between the several

Table 1 Envelope compositions and annual energy consumption rates

Envelope	Alteration from Case 1	Shading coefficient	Annual energy consumed (in kwh) for New York	Phoenix	Seattle
Case 1	See Note 1	0.83	939	2825	339
2	Gray-tinted glazing lites	0.50	653	1939	273
3	Heat-reflecting gold film on interior surface of exterior lite	0.25	514	1471	198
4	Aluminum louvered blind external to glazing	Note 3	438	1534	208
5	Light-colored operable Venetian blind set between the lites	0.33	505	1502	220
6	Light-colored operable Venetian blinds used as interior shading	0.51	558	1922	256
7	Fixed overhang (projecting 18″ out from plane of external glazing lite)	Note 3	927	2835	388
8	Fixed vertical fins on either side of glazing (projecting 18″ from external lite)	Note 3	872	2689	363
9	Combination of overhang & fins (all projecting 18″ from external lite)	Note 3	863	2644	362
10	Interior drapery of light color, closed weave (cloth reflectance = about 0.50)	0.46	543	1866	268

Notes: (1)   The reference envelope (Case 1) consists of 90 ft² of a Glasweld assembly with an air-to-air resistance of 12.5 hr-ft²-°F/Btu and a surface weight of 5.2 lb$_m$/ft² and 30 ft² of a double-pane glazed assembly with clear plate lites and a ½″ air space.

      (2)   Source of the shading coefficients: *1977 ASHRAE Handbook of Fundamentals*, Ch. 26.

      (3)   These shading coefficients differ depending on the solar time and building latitude.

alternatives. Once the national mean costs were calculated, they were multiplied by the *Means* regional cost factors. We then divided these costs by the number of offices in the zone to create prorated HVAC systems costs on a per-office basis. These costs for the alternative envelopes and cities are listed in column 3 of Table 2. The sums of envelope and HVAC systems costs for the 30 cases appear in column 4. The building-cost differentials between Cases 2 through 10 and Case 1 are catalogued for each city in column 5. A positive value means that the alternative's construction would cost less than Case 1's would. A negative amount indicates that that combination would exceed the Case 1 cost by that much.

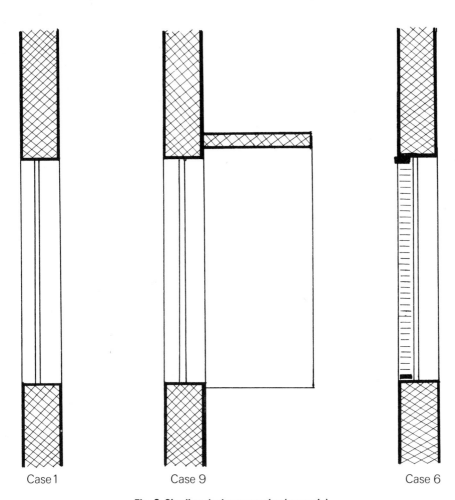

Case 1   Case 9   Case 6

Fig. 2 Shading device examples (no scale)

Table 2 Evaluation of the alternative envelopes using the net-benefit comparison

	Envelope	Envelope costs	HVAC costs	Envelope + HVAC costs	Equipment savings vs. Case 1	One-year energy cost sav.	20-year energy cost sav.	Net benefit vs. Case 1
	Case 1	1172	1067	2239	—	—	—	—
	2	1200	773	1973	+266	$ 47.16	$575	$ 841
	3	1297	732	2029	+210	74.07	903	1113
NEW YORK	4	1349	785	2134	+105	52.56	641	746
	5	1705	749	2454	−215	49.60	605	390
	6	1286	773	2059	+180	39.57	482	662
	7	1330	732	2062	+177	1.20	15	102
	8	1219	1067	2286	− 47	5.57	68	21
	9	1377	732	2109	+130	6.48	79	208
	10	1431	773	2204	+ 35	41.65	508	543
	Case 1	1113	758	1871	—	—	—	—
	2	1140	732	1872	− 1	40.91	499	498
	3	1229	694	1923	− 52	61.22	746	694
PHOENIX	4	1291	756	2047	−176	59.69	728	552
	5	1605	709	2314	−443	61.48	749	306
	6	1227	732	1959	− 88	41.52	506	418
	7	1274	709	1983	−112	1.25	15	− 97
	8	1162	758	1920	− 49	6.22	76	27
	9	1322	709	2031	−160	8.30	101	− 59
	10	1372	732	2104	−233	43.70	533	300
	Case 1	1181	1099	2280	—	—	—	—
	2	1209	796	2005	275	1.48	18	293
	3	1304	754	2058	222	2.37	29	251
SEATTLE	4	1367	807	2174	106	1.80	22	128
	5	1706	770	2476	−196	1.77	22	−174
	6	1300	796	2096	184	1.45	18	202
	7	1347	779	2126	154	− 0.25	− 3	151
	8	1231	1099	2330	− 50	0.28	3	− 47
	9	1397	779	2176	104	0.29	4	108
	10	1352	796	2148	132	1.53	19	151

Notes: (1)   All costs are expressed in 1981 U.S. Dollars.

(2)   The envelope and HVAC-systems costs are presented on a per-office basis and are each area-specific for the particular city and envelope assembly.

(3)   Maintenance- and repair-cost differentials (i.e., for each case versus Case 1) have been set equal to zero.

(4)   Salvage values for the heat pumps (at the end of 20 years) have been set at zero.

(5)   For each of the three cities the electricity unit prices ($/kwh) have been established recognizing local demand and consumption cost structures.

(6)   Where a "savings" is negative, that result should be interpreted that it would cost more to provide that building assembly or energy quantity than for the Case 1 reference.

Energy Cost Savings. The first step in this part of the analysis was to simulate the thermal performance of the study office using the computer program UWENSOL. From these simulations the peak hourly demands and monthly energy consumption quantities for the 30 cases were found. Second, a series of programs were written based on the electricity rate structures for the three cities. A mathematical model was employed within each program to enable us to determine prorated unit electricity charges recognizing the probable overall demand and consumption costs for the building as a whole. From these programs we established annual costs for providing thermal control for the study office in each case. Third, comparing the annual energy costs for Cases 2 through 10 with Case 1 for each of the three cities, we generated the annual energy-cost savings that would be realized. These savings are listed in column 6 of Table 2. Energy-cost savings for 20 years were calculated by multiplying the annual cost by the uniform-present-worth factor (for whose calculation we used an energy-cost escalation rate of 8.3% and a discount rate of 14.0%). These 20-year cost savings are listed in column 7 of Table 2. We chose a study period of 20 years primarily because it is a sometimes-quoted estimate of the useful life for heat pumps and it is a long enough period to indicate economic trends.

Net Benefits. Finally, net benefits were established by adding columns 5 and 7 of Table 2. The net benefits are essentially 20-year-life savings: they are derived recognizing differentials of both construction and operating costs. A resulting positive quantity indicates that the envelope alternative is economically desirable. A negative value shows that if that assembly is to be employed, such an application cannot be justified on economic bases.

Discussion of the Net-Benefit Results

New York. For New York, all nine alternatives (versus Case 1) provided net benefits over the 20-year study life. The primary explanation for these results was that the high unit cost of electricity rendered any energy conservation effort an important task. All but Cases 7, 8, and 9 produced substantial annual energy-cost savings compared with Case 1 (which had an annual energy cost of $140.93 for the study office at $0.152/kwh). Also, some combinations of envelope and HVAC system costs were less than that for Case 1. These equipment-cost reductions were due to reduced system capacities resulting from the various shading devices. The best alternatives in terms of highest net benefits were Case 3 (the gold-film-coated assembly), Case 2 (the gray-tinted glazing), and Case 4 (the glazing with the external louvered blinds).

Phoenix. Six of the nine alternatives produced substantial net benefits (that is, Cases 2, 3, 4, 5, 6, and 10). None of the nine alternatives showed positive building-cost savings versus Case 1 for the envelope and HVAC system, but the six alternatives noted generated large energy savings compared with the Case 1 annual energy cost (which was $137.08 at $0.0484/kwh.) The electricity unit costs for Phoenix were significantly lower than for New York but the annual consumption rates were appreciably higher. The most attractive alternatives were, in order, Cases 3, 4, and 2.

Seattle. Seven of the nine alternatives afforded net benefits, but none were as great as those for the other two cities. Most of the savings that created net benefits were in HVAC system costs. The energy-cost savings for the nine alternatives were all marginal and had little effect on the various net benefits. The explanation for these results is twofold: first, the electricity unit costs for Seattle are very low; and second the climate is quite mild. The best alternatives were Cases 2, 3, and 6 (that is, the three cases with the lowest building costs).

ACKNOWLEDGEMENTS

This paper was presented at the 1981 International Passive and Hybrid Cooling Conference, Miami Beach, Florida, November 1981, and appears in the Conference Proceedings published by the American Section of the International Solar Energy Society, Newark, Delaware.

ADDENDUM

The following discussion consists of a series of observations and criticisms of the preceding paper as offered by Committee Editor John Halldane. Where appropriate we have responded with some additional thoughts.

Comm. Ed.: The economic comparison of ten envelopes for one orientation in three locations is important in high-rise decisions. However, the simulation has too many variables of materials, climate control, and costing to be applied. Rather it is a demonstration of an approach to illustrate trends in decision-making.

There should be a discussion of the three forms of thermal transfer: air-to-air conduction, solar-to-air conduction, and solar-to-air transmission. This would help the reader to see the influence of outside air-temperature conduction for New York and Phoenix and summer solar for Seattle. Furthermore, the climatic data for the three cities shown in Table 3 should be noted.

Authors: It should be emphasized that the high-rise office building is, generically, internal load dominated. Alternately stated, the heat gained from occupants, lighting systems, and office and process-related equipment exceeds the heat lost through the building envelope. Thus, when solar heat gain through fenestration is also present, appreciable cooling loads are experienced.

The primary climatic influences that differentiate weather conditions for the three cities are (1) the rate of incidence of solar radiation on the envelope and (2) the external air temperature. The frequency of clear sky incidence (as documented by the Committee Editor above) is significantly greater in Phoenix, in both summer and winter, than in New York or Seattle. In terms of air temperatures, Seattle and New York have relatively similar annual heating loads. Each has a yearly heating requirement of about 5000 degree-days (65°F base) (ASHRAE, 1981), although the distributions of the degree-days are somewhat different: New York has the greater demand in the winter months, whereas Seattle experiences at least some demand throughout all 12 months. The most significant issue concerning the external air temperatures for the three cities is the ability to use an economizer cycle for cooling the office building interior. In Seattle where the monthly average air temperature for July is approximately 65°F (Phillips, 1973), an economizer cycle can be used beneficially virtually all year long. Alternately, in New York, the monthly average external air temperatures are above 65°F from June through

Table 3 Climatic data for New York, Phoenix, and Seattle

	New York Central Park	Phoenix Airport	Seattle Lake Union
Latitude	40 °N	33 °N	48 °N
Winter design temperature (97.5%)	15°F (−9°C)	34°F (1°C)	27°F (−3°C)
Summer design temperature (2.5%)	89°F (32°C)	107°F (42°C)	80°F (27°C)
Summer mean daily temperature range	17°F (9°C)	27°F (15°C)	19°F (11°C)
Sunshine Winter	60%	100%	40%
Summer	75%	90%	75%

             September (Trewartha and Horn, 1980), thereby reducing the availability of the economizer cycle as a cooling strategy (although some night-ventilation can, no doubt, be employed).

Comm. Ed.:   Life-cycle costing studies invariably take an "investor's" point of view rather than an "accountant's" or "manager's." As an energy consultant working with managers, I find nominal, undiscounted costing more realistic for them, as it relates to their budgeting in hard dollars. Economists are more interested in discounted present worth because they are concerned with return on an investment or profit making, instead of with saving operating costs per se. The two are not the same, and projected budgeting errors can be made with discounted costs.

             Also, a 20-year life cycle is not realistic in the commercial world. It warps the value of annual costs and reduces the problem of capital. With the high errors common in escalation rates I find 8 to 10 years to be a good balance (see Halldane, et al., 1977).

Authors: We generally agree with the Committee Editor on these interesting points. However, we would remind the reader that our basic question in the preceding paper concerned whether it made good economic sense to achieve greater degrees of energy conservation by exceeding energy code requirements. We are essentially asking if more money should be spent during construction to foster better building operation and later savings. Thus, our work focuses in the larger sense on the opportunity costs associated with using money. To recognize both the effects of inflation and the time-dependence of alternative investment opportunities, the related benefits and costs should be discounted to provide a fairer picture of the different ways to spend money.

      Finally, we would like to conclude this addendum with a qualifying statement based on some work in which we are presently engaged. In the preceding paper, recognizing that most traditionally designed office buildings are operated with their lighting systems constantly "on" when the building is occupied, we conducted our analysis setting our lighting-system loads to generate a continuous cooling-load requirement of 1.5 w/ft^2 (160 w/m^2). No provision was made for daylighting to illuminate, at least partially, the office spaces. Fenestration designed to admit daylight can reduce internal heat loads in electrically lighted buildings *if* solar heat-gain rates can be controlled. At the time we completed the preceding paper we had not yet determined to what extent such fenestration can affect solar heat-gain. However, in a recent paper, we have described a study method for investigating the trade-offs between controlling solar heat gain and fostering natural illumination through fenestration for internal-load-dominant buildings (Emery et al., 1982). We are presently refining this study method and applying it to qualify further our previous benefit-cost assessments.

CONDENSED REFERENCES/BIBLIOGRAPHY

The following is a condensed bibliography for this article. It includes all articles referred to or cited in the text. The full citations will be found at the end of the volume, with additional citations for further reading. What is given here should be sufficient information to lead the reader to the correct article: the author, date, and title. In case of multiple authors, only the first name is listed.

Arens, 1980, *Geographic Extrapolation of Typical Hourly Weather Data for Energy Calculations in*
ASHRAE 1975, *Energy Conservation in New Building Design*
ASHRAE 1981, *The ASHRAE Handbook: 1981 Fundamentals*

Emery 1979, *The UWENSOL User's Manual*
Emery 1981, *The Use of Cost-Effectiveness and Comfort Bases . . .*
Emery 1982, *A Study Method for Evaluating Fenestration Assemblies Considering the Control of*
Emery (to be published), *Energy and Buildings*

Godfrey 1981, *Building Construction Cost Data*

Halldane 1977, *Recommendations for Energy Conservation Actions: Social Security Administration,*

Heerwagen 1980, *Developing Office Design and Operation Strategies Using UWENSOL and the*

Marshall 1980, *Simplified Energy Design Economics*

Phillips 1973, *Washington Climate for King, Kitsap, Mason, and Pierce Counties*

Trewartha 1980, *An Introduction to Climate*

A Comparison of the Energy Efficiency of a High-Rise versus a Low-Rise/Atrium Building for Varying External Envelope Efficiencies

Parambir S. Gujral
Raymond J. Clark

INTRODUCTION

The emphasis of energy efficient building design becomes more and more evident with the depletion of natural resources and the rapidly increasing cost of energy. In developed countries, such as the United States, buildings have been found to consume 33% of the total energy being used (Standard Research Institute, 1972; NBS, 1973). With this large portion being consumed by a single sector, it is truly the responsibility of the architect/engineer to design energy efficient buildings. As building designers endeavor to achieve energy efficiency, they realize that initiating an architectural design that utilizes an energy efficient building base results in the most successful design, from an energy standpoint as well as from an esthetic one.

The National Bureau of Standards (1973) states that 62% of the energy being consumed by existing buildings goes toward the heating and cooling systems. To reduce this major contributor to energy use, early consideration must be given to such factors as building size, shape, and orientation. The shape of a building plays an important role in determining its energy consumption pattern, since a major portion of building heat loss or gain, and thereby building energy, is transferred through the external surfaces of the building. The amount of external surface area divided by the building floor area defines the building surface-to-area ratio. The term represents the external envelope area per usable floor area, and is very dependent on the building shape.

The relationship between the surface-to-area ratio and the energy consumed depends on the efficiency of the envelope elements, the operation of the building, and the climate in which the building is located. It is often of advantage to the building designer to maximize or minimize the surface-to-area ratio, depending on the circumstances. Minimizing the external surface area tends to make buildings more compact as they approach a cube-type shape. This poses esthetic problems, because for very large buildings the cube-type shape results in inner areas of the building being far removed from windows, which causes difficulty in marketing the space. A solution has been found through the use of external or internal building atria. The atria are designed and located to give visual relief from the large internal areas, thus offering both a marketable design and an efficient building shape.

This paper is to report on an investigation, during the design process, of the energy efficiency dependence of building shape of an actual office building located in Chicago. It compares a high-rise building shape with a low-rise/atrium design for varying efficiency levels of the exterior envelope. These considerations were taken into account very early in the design process to evolve an effective and energy efficient building design.

PHYSICAL MODELS

In the early stages of the design two building forms were studied in relation to their inherent energy efficiency. Each exhibited a different surface-to-area ratio and, therefore, each was anticipated to consume different amounts of energy. Table 1 lists all the assumptions and parameters used in the study, and the following two sections highlight the differences between the high-rise and low-rise/atrium building shapes (Fig. 1).

Table 1 Assumptions used in the analysis

A. Common assumptions:
  1. Floor areas
    a. Gross floor area   1,015,000 ft^2 (93,800 m^2)
    b. Net floor area   843,000 ft^2 (77,900 m^2)
  2. Design conditions
    a. Summer outdoor design temperature   91°F (32.8°C) db,
                                        73°F (22.8°C) wb
      Summer indoor design temperature   78°F (25.6°C) db, 50% RH
    b. Winter outdoor design temperature   0°F (−17.8°C) db
      Winter indoor design temperature   72°F (22.2°C) db
  3. Envelope parameters
    a. Wall U-value   0.10 Btu/(hr·ft$^{2·}$°F),
                                        (0.6 w/(m$^{2·}$ °K))
    b. Roof U-value   0.10 Btu/(hr·ft$^{2·}$°F),
                                        (0.6 w/(m$^{2·}$°K))
    c. High efficiency:
      i. Glazing percentage   32%
      ii. Glazing U-value   0.31 Btu/(hr·ft$^{2·}$°F),
                                          (1.8 w/(m$^{2·}$°K))
      iii. Glazing shade coefficient   0.57
    d. Mean efficiency:
      i. Glazing percentage   60%
      ii. Glazing U-value   0.53 Btu/(hr·ft$^{2·}$°F),
                                          (3.0 w/(m$^{2·}$°K))
      iii. Glazing shade coefficient   0.57
    e. Low efficiency:
      i. Glazing percentage   80%
      ii. Glazing U-value   1.10 Btu/(hr·ft$^{2·}$°F),
                                          (6.3 w/(m$^{2·}$°K))
      iii. Glazing shade coefficient   0.95
  4. Lighting   1.7 w/ft^2 (18.4 w/m^2)
  5. Miscellaneous   0.5 w/ft^2 (5.4 w/m^2)
  6. Occupancy   100 ft^2/person (9.2 m^2/person)
  7. Ventilation air quality   5 cfm/person (8.5 cmh/person)
  8. Mechanical systems:
    a. Primary systems:
      i. Cooling   Centrifugal chillers
      ii. Heating   Electric baseboard
    b. Secondary systems:
      i. Cooling   Variable air volume
  9. Utility cost:
    a. Average consumption $0.036/kwh
    b. Average demand $5.368/kw
B. High-rise configurations:
  1. Gross external wall area   365,000 ft^2 (33,700 m^2)
  2. Supply fan static pressure   5.5 in$_w$ (1370 Pa)
  3. Return fan static pressure   2.5 in$_w$ (620 Pa)
  4. Elevator load   1130 kw
C. Low-rise/atrium configurations:
  1. Gross external wall area   278,900 ft^2 (25,800 m^2)
  2. Supply fan static pressure   4.0 in$_w$ (995 Pa)
  3. Return fan static Pressure   1.5 in$_w$ (373 Pa)
  4. Elevator load   831 kw

High-Rise Configuration

A 45-story building enclosing a net area of 77,900 m² (843,000 ft²) was modeled. The external dimensions of the rectangular-shaped building are 55 m (180 ft) long by 36 m (120 ft) wide by 185 m (609 ft) high. The surface-to-area ratio for the high-rise configuration is 0.433. Due to the relatively small area available on each floor, the air-distribution fans are centrally located in the building. The elevators for the high-rise scheme require 1,130 kw of peak power.

Low-Rise/Atrium Configuration

The low-rise configuration consists of a 28-story structure enclosing the same floor area with two interior and one exterior atria (Figs. 1, 2, and 3). The building is 64 m (210 ft) long by 55 m (180 ft) wide at its base and 115 m (379 ft) high. The surface-to-area ratio is 0.331, and the large floor areas allow the distribution fans to be centrally located on each floor. The atrium floor to core ratio is 0.95. The elevators for the low-rise scheme require 831 kw of peak power.

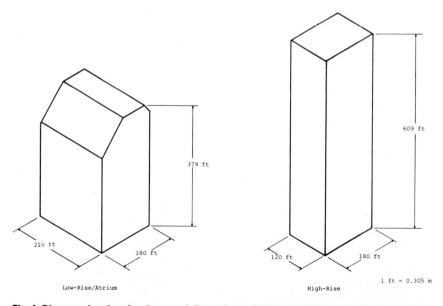

609 ft

379 ft

210 ft

180 ft

120 ft

180 ft

1 ft = 0.305 m

Low-Rise/Atrium

High-Rise

Fig. 1 Diagram showing the shape and dimensions of the two buildings used in the analysis

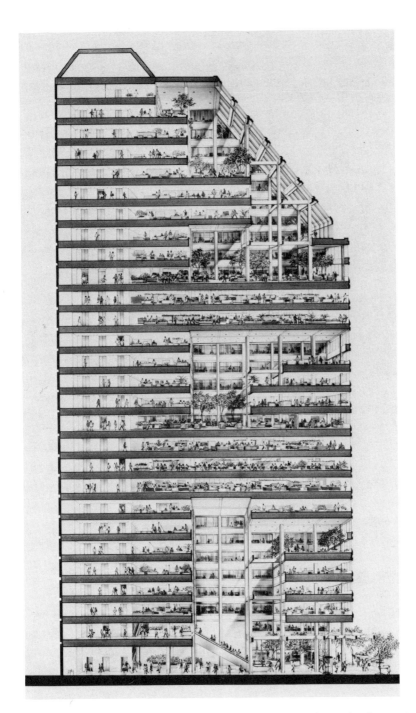

Fig. 2 A section through the low-rise/atrium building showing two internal and one external atria

Envelope Efficiency

An analysis of annual energy consumption, based on varying building shapes, would be incomplete without exploring the effect of the building envelope's efficiency. The more efficient the envelope, the less the impact that would be observed for varying building shapes. In this analysis, the efficiency of the envelope was varied by changing the glazing type and percentage as indicated in Table 1. Three envelope efficiencies are reported:

1. *High efficiency envelope:* Insulating reflecting glass comprising 32% of the gross wall area.

2. *Mean efficiency envelope:* Insulating tinted glass comprising 60% of the gross wall area.

3. *Low efficiency envelope:* Single clear glass comprising 80% of the gross wall area.

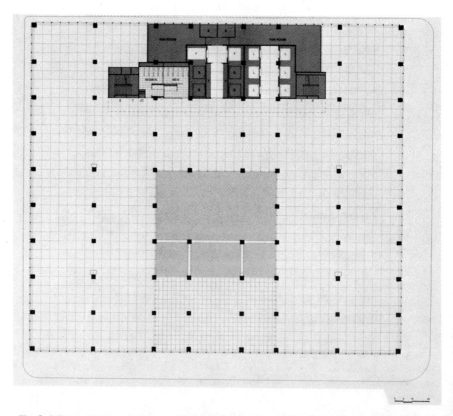

Fig. 3 A floor plan showing the extent of the lower atrium for the low-rise/atrium building

For each case the walls and roof are assumed to be well insulated. This is usually the case for a multistory building, because the opaque building elements readily lend themselves to insulation. The two variables in a building design that affect the envelope efficiency are typically the percentage and type of glazing. Therefore, these two values were chosen to be varied to represent the three levels of efficiency for the envelope.

ANALYTICAL TECHNIQUE

The theoretical responses of the two building shapes were investigated utilizing the TRACE computer program. The program simulates the performance of the building and its electrical and mechanical systems for a full year of weather data in the planned building location. The capability of this program to predict building loads and energy consumption has been reported elsewhere (Sales News, 1977; Kusuda, 1981).

The annual energy consumption of a building is very dependent on the hourly scheduling of internal loads, such as lights, occupancy, elevators, and mechanical systems. For this analysis the standard profiles for an office building compiled and published by the United States Department of Energy (1979) were used.

The computer simulations were performed for the weather conditions of Chicago. These conditions represent a harsh winter with a mild summer. The design conditions are listed in Table 1.

RESULTS

Responses were simulated for the two building shapes and the three envelope efficiencies. The performance of each was compared by studying the required refrigeration and heating capacity. Many of the building's architectural features depend on these two parameters. As the required installed capacity of mechanical equipment increases, the physical space needed for the equipment's location and its distribution systems also increases. The mechanical/electrical rooms must be larger, taking up usable space and resulting in decreased rentable floor area and decreased space-utilization efficiency. Higher capacity also necessitates an increase in floor-to-floor height to accommodate the larger air-distribution ducts, adding a substantial cost to the building. The mechanical system's first cost would also increase proportionally with an increase in mechanical load requirements.

The performance of the two building schemes was also compared by studying the effect on annual energy consumption and, therefore, annual utility cost. Since a major portion of energy is used to cool and heat a building, a major portion of utility cost is required for these functions. This cost is an annual expenditure; and because the cost of fuel is predicted to escalate between 5% and 7% above the rate of general inflation (U.S. Department of Energy, 1980), the energy cost becomes a most dominant factor in economic performance through the life of the building.

The results reported below reflect the dependence of the building-shape efficiency and the envelope efficiency on both the refrigeration and heating capacities and the energy usage and energy cost of the building.

Installed Refrigeration Capacity

The building shape, as well as the envelope efficiency, was observed to greatly influence the required capacity of the cooling systems. Figure 4 shows the required refrigeration capacity for each of the two schemes. The refrigeration load has been plotted as a function of the envelope efficiency. A term has been used for the absissa that represents the potential of solar heat gain to penetrate through the gross exterior wall area, solar heat being the dominant contribution to envelope heat gain. The term is the shading coefficient multiplied by the percentage of glass and divided by 100. The high-rise building shape required 9%, 17%, and 25% more cooling capacity

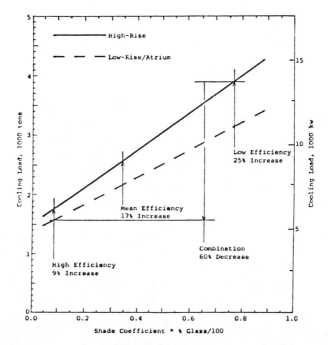

Fig. 4 Comparison of the required cooling load for the high-rise and the low-rise/atrium schemes depending on the envelope efficiency

than the low-rise/atrium scheme for the high, mean and low efficiency envelopes, respectively. It is evident that as the envelope becomes less efficient, its contribution to the overall cooling load becomes more pronounced. For the inefficient envelope the low-rise/atrium building shape saves 750 tons (2,637 kw) of refrigeration over its high-rise counterpart. It is interesting to note that the combination of efficient envelope and low-rise/atrium building shape results in a decrease of 60% in the installed refrigeration capacity.

Installed Heating Capacity

Figure 5 shows a similar decrease in the required heating capacity for the low-rise/atrium building. The heating load has been plotted dependent on the overall wall U-value (ASHRAE, 1980.) This term represents the combined thermal-transmittance factor for the opaque and transparent wall areas. The high-rise building shape requires 16%, 18%, and 26% more heating capacity for the high, mean and low efficiency envelopes, respectively. Again, the detriment of the inefficient building shape becomes more pronounced as the efficiency of the envelope is increased.

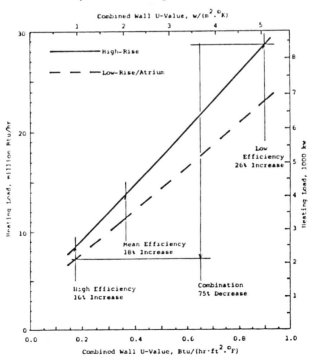

Fig. 5 Comparison of the required heating load for the high-rise and low-rise/atrium schemes depending on the envelope efficiency

Annual Energy Consumption

The effect of the building shape and the envelope efficiency on the annual energy consumption is shown in Fig. 6. Figure 6 does not report the values for the mean efficiency envelope. The annual energy consumed by lights and miscellaneous loads is 16,483 Btu/(ft²·yr) (52.3 kwh)/(m²·yr) and is common to all schemes.Vertical transportation in a high-rise building consumes 6,111 Btu/(ft²·yr) (19.4 kwh/(m²·yr)), which is 36% greater than the energy consumed in a low-rise atrium scheme.

The high-rise building shape consumes 20% and 37% more total annual energy than the low-rise/atrium scheme, for the high and low efficiency envelopes, respectively. The combination of the high efficiency envelope with the efficient building shape results in a decrease of 72% for the total building energy consumption. In other words, the combination of the efficient envelope with the efficient shape results in a reduction of heating/cooling energy by a factor of 3.6.

Figure 6 also shows the components of energy consumption of the high and low efficiency envelopes for the high- and low-rise schemes. With the high efficiency envelope, there is a balance between the major energy contributors: cooling, heating, and lighting. The low efficiency envelope

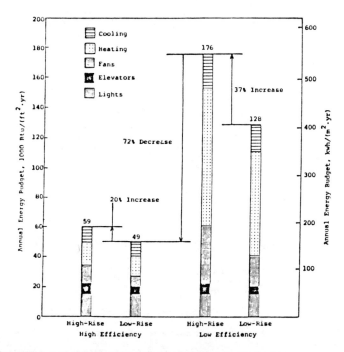

Fig. 6 Comparison of the annual energy budget for the high-rise and low-rise/atrium schemes for the high and low efficiency envelopes

shows drastic imbalance, with heating energy comprising more than half of the total energy consumed.

The energy savings exhibited by the efficient envelope and shape results in an economic savings based on the cost of utilities in the area. Table 2 shows the annual utility cost for each scheme, based on Commonwealth Edison's electric rates for Chicago as of June 1, 1981. For the high efficiency envelope, the low-rise/atrium building shape saves $82,153 for the first-year utility cost. The low rise/atrium building would save $401,155 per year if the low efficiency envelope was utilized. Combining the low-rise/atrium building with the high efficiency envelope results in an annual savings of $1,089,224 per year.

CONCLUSIONS

The largest reduction in mechanical equipment capacity and annual energy savings is attained by designing an efficient envelope. The reduction and savings may be further enhanced by providing an efficient building shape. The more efficient building shape of a low-rise/atrium building results in reductions of refrigeration and heating requirements, annual energy usage, and annual utility costs for both a high and low efficiency envelope. A substantial savings is incurred by designing for an efficient building shape combined with an efficient building envelope.

The low-rise/atrium building design with the reported high efficiency envelope was chosen for an office building located at 33 West Monroe in Chicago. The low-rise design with the high efficiency envelope is anticipated to 72% of the energy for heating and cooling, amounting to an annual utility cost savings of $1,089,224 per year, when compared with a high-rise building with a low efficiency envelope. The marketability of the efficient building shape is enhanced through the use of two internal and one external atria (Figs. 7, 8, and 9).

Table 2 Annual utility costs for the high-rise and low-rise/atrium schemes based on utility rates for an all electric building in Chicago

	Annual from base	Difference from base
A. Low-rise/atrium:		
1. High efficiency envelope	$416,465	base
2. Low efficiency envelope	$1,104,534	+$688,069
B. High-rise:		
1. High efficiency envelope	$498,618	+$82,153
2. Low efficiency envelope	$1,505,689	+$1,089,224

Fig. 7 The low-rise/atrium design was chosen for an office building at 33 West Monroe
(Photo by: Nick Merrick, Hedrich-Blessing)

Fig. 8 Two internal atria enhance the architectural design. The one pictured above rises from the ground floor through the eighth level and is completely enclosed by office space *(Photo by: Nick Merrick, Hedrich-Blessing)*

Fig. 9 A skydeck atrium at the top of the building offers a panoramic view of Chicago's skyline *(Photo by: Nick Merrick, Hedrich-Blessing)*

CONDENSED REFERENCES/BIBLIOGRAPHY

The following is a condensed bibliography for this article. It includes all articles referred to or cited in the text. The full citations will be found at the end of the volume, with additional citations for further reading. What is given here should be sufficient information to lead the reader to the correct article: the author, date, and title. In case of multiple authors, only the first name is listed.

ASHRAE 1980, *Energy Conservation in New Building Design*

Kusuda 1981, *A Comparison of Energy Calculation Procedures, ASHRAE*

NBS 1973, *Technical Options for Energy Conservation in Buildings*

Sales News 1977, *The Standard Oil Building: A Report from the Consulting Engineer*
Standard Research Institute 1972, *Patterns of Energy Consumption in the United States*

United States Department of Energy 1979, *Standard Building Operating Conditions*
United States Department of Energy 1980, *DOE-2 Reference Manual, Part 1, Version 2.1*

Current Trend in Project Management of Tall Buildings

Chandra K. Jha
Charles A. DeBenedittis

Project management is defined as the role of managing the overall activities of the owning, designing, and construction entities through all the various stages from initial conception of the tall building project to, and including, its occupancy. Since the publication of Vol. PC of the monograph several years ago, the methods and variation of project-management disciplines have not changed significantly. What have undergone dramatic change in this very dynamic industry are the product itself—the tall building—and the techniques used to finance, design, and build the product.

One of the most dramatic influences has been the cost of energy. This has had immediate bearing on the design and production of the environmental systems, including HVAC and lighting, as well as on the building enclosure. Another major influence has been the increased consideration of safety and fire control systems. This concern has been felt not only in those systems themselves, but also in the tradeoffs that they have generated in other building systems. New technology, in itself, has also been an important influence. It generally comes from the interaction with other industries, such as aerospace. It also comes from increased international exchange resulting from the mix of technology in the booming development of Third World countries, as well as from the many international forums such as the

Council on Tall Buildings and Urban Habitat. These influences create a dynamic, ever-changing, more complex set of systems that form the framework for producing a tall building.

In short, the function of project management has not materially changed, but the project itself has and continues to do so. The end result is that the role of the project manager has taken on increasing importance and complexity. To each of the many tasks of project management must be added a new dimension — change: What is different today? What can be different tomorrow when the project is to be delivered?

To continue the discussion, a narrower area of project management relates to the overlap of design and construction. Starting in the mid-1960s and during the 1970s, the construction-manager approach to large-project management took hold in the United States. The construction manager provided managerial and supervisory services during construction. His presence replaced the general contractor with a construction consultant to the architect-engineer during the design phase, bridging a vital gap between design and construction. This consultation was supposed to have provided the best of both worlds to bring about the most practical design packages, so as to complete the project within budget and on time.

The final verdict is still not in. But it can be said that the result has been less than ideal. Perhaps the prime culprit is the highly inflationary market in which it is difficult to get a real handle on continuously changing cost. However, there have been a few recent identifiable trends that if continued, may bring about some fundamental changes in the project management of tall buildings.

FINANCING

The developer/owner of a tall building is either an institution or an investor. Investment building is a very risky venture. The developer/owner must bring together all facets of the project — financing, design, construction, and leasing — so as to make his risk worthwhile. Because of the highly inflationary market and dynamic money market conditions, more and more lenders now insist on a lump-sum construction contract with a performance bond. This requirement is contrary to the construction-management philosophy of the 1960s and 1970s and puts the construction manager into an adversary relationship with the owner, defeating the very purpose of replacing the general contractor. This trend has limited the participation of the professional construction manager and blurred the distinction between the general contractor and the construction manager. A handful of large companies call themselves construction managers, but in reality many have become general contractors.

ENERGY MANAGEMENT

The buildings of the 1960s and early 1970s, wastefully designed from the energy standpoint, would not be viable projects now. Not only will the first cost be higher but operating costs of those buildings in today's market would be prohibitive. Today the energy efficient building is the norm, and the energy implications of mechanical and electrical systems and their related envelope for the structure are a major consideration in project management.

More than ever, designers must work closely with the construction consultant to bring about the most energy efficient building within budget and on time. It requires greater participation by qualified contractors during the design stage. For example, in a multi-use building, the structural frame and its configuration are very much affected by the type of HVAC system designed for apartments and offices. The cost of the concrete frame on tall buildings is extremely sensitive to formwork. The concrete frame may be optimally designed between concrete and rebar but if the contractor cannot gang form and/or fly form, the cost could be prohibitive. Similarly, the design of the HVAC system affects the cost not only of HVAC, but also of the electrical system and the structure. No construction manager has the ability to provide all answers in a dynamic market. It is essential that some methods be found by which qualified contractors of major trades can participate during design. The question is how.

INDEPENDENT CONSTRUCTION MANAGER

There are recent indications that some construction managers have modified their services in response to the market constraints described above. During the design stage, the construction manager coordinates and provides to the architect-engineer all construction consulting from in-house experts, outside consultants, structural frame contractors (concrete or steel), mechanical and electrical contractors, and other specialty contractors. Depending on his evaluation of the building's complexity, he selects at least two contractors from major trades with whom he will frequently consult and augment his in-house expertise. Of course, through his intimate knowledge of outside contractors, he is able to get up-to-date useful information that ordinarily would not be available to either the architect-engineer or the owner. The construction manager is able to maintain checks and balances through his own in-house expertise and thereby maintain an objective view of design, construction, and budget. Once the structural envelope is sufficiently developed and designed, he would negotiate with a general contractor (ideally with the frame contractor) who would be able to provide a bond and a lump-sum contract and still provide for flexibility and involvement of the construction manager in the award of other major trades. During construction the construction manager may only monitor scheduling and cost activities and coordinate services between the architect-engineer and general contractor, whereas the general contractor provides day-to-day field supervision. The construction manager receives a fixed fee, and his sole interest is to provide professional service to the owner. This arrangement allows lenders to be satisfied and the owner to be in control.

We have therefore seen over the last two decades a trend from general contracting to construction management and back again to variations of general contracting with the construction manager participating as a consultant to the owner. This trend, if it continues, may bring about a truly and universally accepted professional service that can expand itself to a complete project-management role. Such a role would deal with all stages of a project, from the initial conception of a building to its occupancy, while keeping abreast of the ever-changing aspects of the dynamic field of tall buildings.

Notes on Systems
Methodology

John F. Brotchie

Despite its relatively recent arrival on the scene, systems methodology requires little updating except by addition. Because of its wide generality of application, the basic concepts are transferable over geographic space and building type—and over time. New methods will continue to be developed from and to contribute to these concepts; and new applications will result from changes in technology, architectural style, organizational needs, and the socioeconomic environment.

Within this methodology the building is considered as a system. Its articulation into activities, and spaces and support systems for these activities, allows its abstraction for modeling purposes. These models may encompass planning, design, construction, operation, or the management of building use, or the coordination of these activities. The objective is to develop a building that provides the best overall performance for the resources expended. Systems methodology is the means of achievement, allowing interactions among the components of the building and its activities, and between phases in the life of the building, to be taken into account.

Mathematical modeling defines these components and relationships. Mathematical programming and design-sensitivity studies manipulate the model to seek the performance objective above. This may be technical and economic. Economic performance may be expressed in terms of benefits and costs, such as site purchase, planning, design, construction, letting up, operation, taxes, rental revenue or costs in use, and, finally, termination costs or costs of conversion for reuse. Discounting over time allows these costs and benefits to be considered together. Technical performance may be handled by serviceability constraints; or else costs incurred in failures of the system services, finishes, or structure, factored by the probabilities of these failures, can be included in economic performance as part of expected costs in use.

Since Vol. PC of the monograph was prepared, some unit costs, such as those of energy, have increased in importance. Others relating to information transfer and processing have decreased substantially, but the demands have correspondingly increased and will continue to increase with information technology development. The rental costs of capital for construction have also increased, with potential implications for the extended life of the building and later changes of use. The increasing rate of technological change in building services means more frequent obsolescence and replacement and requires provision for these factors in the design.

The continued development and application of the microprocessor and attendant reductions in cost are providing many design groups with access to computing. As a consequence, computers and computer graphics will play an increasing role in building decisions and activities (Crawford and Sharpe, 1979; Eastman, 1981; Gero, 1981), including location; siting; environmental impact studies; design, including studies of spatial form; determining air-conditioning loads, including solar heating and shading effects; documentation for construction; and monitoring, operation, and management of the building in use. Data bases will facilitate this process by storing, retrieving, and manipulating existing information about buildings, their construction, and their environments (Eastman, 1981). Expert systems, which are an outgrowth of artificial-intelligence studies (Webster and Miner, 1982), might also contribute by providing and manipulating corresponding knowledge of the procedures of problem solving in building management or design decisions and means for their improvement.

Further systems models are being developed at a hierarchy of levels from a building element to a building as a whole. At the architectural level, languages or grammars are being constructed to define patterns of building spaces and, hence, the details of building form (Mitchell, 1979; Stiny, 1979). Other models have been developed to locate these spaces among sites or within a site, to take inventory of them, to project demands for them, or to organize activities within them (Brotchie, et al., 1979).

Models of heating and cooling loads and actual building energy use have been given special emphasis to match the increased importance of energy costs. Monitoring and operation of building services, including air-conditioning, elevators, and fire protection, are also being handled increasingly by computer-based systems. Additional emphasis has been placed similarly on the life-cycle performance of the building and the factors that contribute to it (Blanchard, 1979; Bromilow, 1982). The tradeoffs between capital and operational expenditures and their impacts on design and performance objectives are being explored.

At an overall level, attention has been given recently to multiple objectives pertaining to different parties, such as owner and tenant, or to different performance criteria, such as the efficiency and robustness of the system. Efficiency is a measure of performance under design conditions. Robustness, on the other hand, is a measure of the adaptability of the building to variations in these conditions (for example in useful life, occupancy, and socioeconomic environment) and should be selected to match the degree of uncertainty involved (Brotchie, 1981). The sum of these two criteria provides a measure of overall effectiveness of the building. Uncertainty appears to be increasing with the rate of technological, social, and economic change; hence robustness is increasing in importance as a factor in design. Systems methodology is proving to be an effective framework for the consideration of problems of this kind and for planning, design, construction, operation, and use of the building as a whole.

CONDENSED REFERENCES/BIBLIOGRAPHY

The following is a condensed bibliography for this article. It includes all articles referred to or cited in the text. The full citations will be found at the end of the volume, with additional citations for further reading. What is given here should be sufficient information to lead the reader to the correct article: the author, date, and title. In case of multiple authors, only the first name is listed.

Blanchard 1979, *Life Cycle Costing—a Review*
Bromilow 1982, *Terotechnology Research in Australia—an Overview*
Brotchie 1979, *Physics, Economics and Planning—A New Generation of Urban and Building Models*
Brotchie 1981, *Unification of Social and Physical Science Models*

Crawford 1979, *Computer Graphics for a Planning Model*

Eastman 1981, *Recent Developments in Representation in the Science of Design*

Gero 1981, *The Design in Computer Aided Design*

Mitchell 1979, *Synthesis with Style*

Stiny 1979, *A Generative Approach to Composition and Style in Architecture*

Webster 1982, *Expert Systems, Programming Problem Solving*

High Density Housing in Shanghai

Ya-xin Zhu

Shanghai is the most densely populated city in China. Within its urban area, the population density reaches as high as 41,000 persons per square kilometer. The total urban population has doubled since 1949. Although the shortage of available land for large-scale housing construction is a common phenomenon in most metropolitan cities, this problem appears to be particularly acute here. China is a developing country; the volume of housing accommodations is enormous, and the young building industry has many limitations that must be resolved in the face of growing demands placed upon it. Therefore China's architects and engineers are confronted with certain problems not quite common with those of developed countries. This paper attempts to introduce some concepts in the development of the residential planning and design that are of great concern to the public of Shanghai today.

Early in the 1950s, mass housing construction began in Shanghai with a view toward improving the housing shortages left over from the old society. Residential developments started around the urban border and then stretched into the suburbs (Fig. 1). New dwellings were erected on unbuilt fields. Meanwhile housing expansion was making full use of most of the old urban houses, worn as they might be, instead of demolishing and rebuilding them. This approach was considered to be an effective way to obtain more floor area with a limited amount of investment. Therefore not many of the numerous old urban domestic quarters were redeveloped. But after over three decades, rebuilding these deteriorating old houses can no longer be delayed.

Moreover, with the relentless expansion of the city, the land available for housing development stretches far into the suburbs, farther and farther away from the city center. As city traffic does not extend so far and public service facilities could not be provided adequately, the urban inhabitants are reluctant to move away from their original sites. So there is no conflict today regarding the necessity of urban redevelopment. But the urban population density of Shanghai far surpasses what the current housing design can accommodate. The typical approach of current housing planning is strip block houses arranged in required spacing for sun exposure (Fig. 2). In some of the urban redevelopment projects, even the space between rows of houses had to be minimized for the sake of arranging sufficient dwelling units to rehouse the original households. In such cases, even the sun exposure, which is regarded as one of the essential requirements for housing, had to be compromised. This compromise seriously hampers the possibility of providing ample land to create a decent environment for a modern urban life.

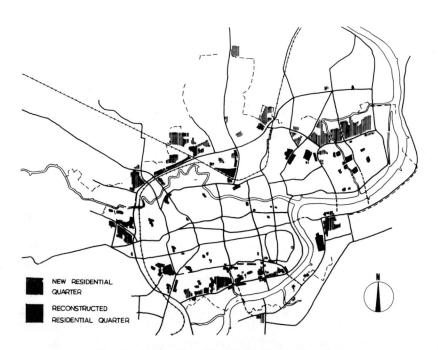

Fig. 1 Location of housing development in Shanghai

Thus, many planners, architects, and bureaucrats reached the conclusion that the tall building is the only way to create high-density housing. But in recent years the development of 12- to 16-story reinforced concrete structures has not proved satisfactory for mass construction, at least for the present. In comparison with the traditional wall-bearing 5- to 6-story walk-up apartments, taller buildings have quite a few discouraging shortcomings, which can be summarized as follows: firstly, the investment for each housing unit is doubled; secondly, construction requires a longer period— double or triple the time; thirdly, maintenance expenses increase, as under the current low rent policy (the rent of housing takes approximately, 5% of the average income of a family), it is impossible to maintain the estates with the rental; fourthly, larger amounts of essential building materials, such as cement and steel, are required and so are facilities of better quality; and fifthly, the consumption of energy increases both in construction and in maintenance. Besides all these drawbacks, the tenants complain of increasing domestic expenses, while living conditions are in no way improved.

Figure 3 compares 12-story middle-rises and 6-story houses with regard to the effectiveness of land-saving. Obviously, the space required for sun exposure remains constant in both schemes, and only the extra land for another building is required in the 6-story scheme. The figure also shows that, for instance, a 2-story building is doubled with 2 stories only, whereas a 6-story has to be doubled with 6 stories to save the same amount of land. This indicates that effectiveness of land-saving of the row house scheme declines with an increase in the height of the building.

Moreover, the average floor area required for each dwelling unit in the current strip block middle-rises (12 to 16 stories) is 20 to 30% more than that of the 5 to 6 story walk-up apartments, as additional floor space is required to accommodate elevators and corridors. This implies that unless a middle-rise scheme could increase floor-area ratio 20 to 30% over that of a walk-up apartment scheme, it could not even afford to provide the same number of dwellings as the walk-ups do.

Although low-rise high-density housing is a broadly studied topic in many countries, there is seldom existing low-rise development with average population density reaching as high as the 1,500 persons per hectare of some urban residential quarters in Shanghai. Therefore, it is inadequate to

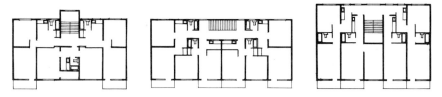

Fig. 2 Typical plan of present housing design in Shanghai

adopt experience from abroad. Developers are bound to search for a new type of low-rise housing with exceedingly high density. The objective is not merely to rehouse the inhabitants on the original site, but to make further improvement in the environmental condition. The initial aim is to strive for raising the "net density", that is the density of the housing group. Insofar as the essential housing requirements, such as adequate sun exposure, space for tree-shaded passages, and courtyards for ground floor occupants, can be fulfilled, high net density is acceptable to save land for urban residential accommodations.

As to how the solution was obtained, it is necessary to review the development of housing construction during the past three decades. In the residential quarters of the early 1950s, the green area was the dominating feature with free curved roads leading to the 2- to 3-story row houses. The space between the row houses was, in dimension, over 1.7 times the height of the buildings, so as to ensure more than two hours' sun exposure for the rooms facing south in the winter. A few years after construction, well-grown trees half hide the 2- to 3-story buildings and thus present an enchanting domestic landscape. But with the rapid growth of the population, it was necessary to put up buildings of more floors and the distance between the buildings has decreased to 1.1 to 1 times the height of the building to cope with the shortage of land. As a result, 5- to 6-story buildings actually dominate neighborhood design and the desired domestic atmosphere no longer exists. The relatively narrow spaces in between the tall 6-story houses were mostly cast with abominable shadows where plants could scarcely survive;

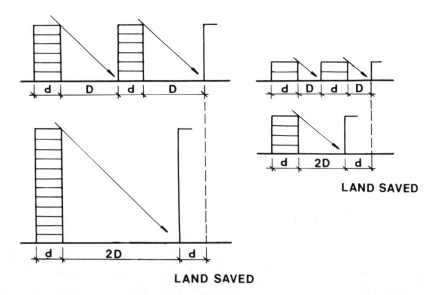

Fig. 3 Comparison between 12-story and 6-story houses with regard to land-savings

so dust blew from the unpaved ground, especially on windy days; even puddles were formed during rainy seasons. All these circumstances demanded a renovation of residential-quarter planning and housing design.

Through vast investigation of the old and new residences in Shanghai, researchers have not only learned the defects of the new housing developments, but have also been assured that the old-style high-density alley-type residences still appeal to their occupants. This fact suggests that it is advantageous to have the building as the dominating feature for a neat and clean environment, as long as it is well designed, because there is less ground surface that needs to be treated.

Figure 4 shows the plot plan of one of our housing projects. The general layout basically assimilates the technical merits of the alley-type residences; for example, the step-type apartment houses are arranged in parallel rows with the best orientation. Since the dwellings in Shanghai are usually not

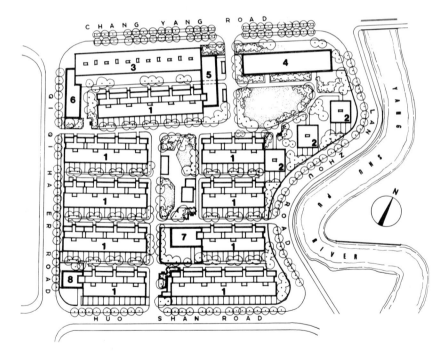

Fig. 4 Plot plan of an experimental residential quarter—Mo-lan Villa, Shanghai
  (1) 3-, 4-, and 5-story step-type apartments
  (2) 6-story apartments
  (3) 6-story apartments with department stores on the ground floor
  (4) 13-story apartments
  (5) Neighborhood committee building
  (6) Canteen
  (7) Kindergarten
  (8) Housing maintenance and repair office

air-conditioned or heated, the sun exposure in cold weather and the south-east prevailing wind in the summer are most precious to the inhabitants. In the project mentioned above, the buildings are arranged with their side walls built directly along the street border and connected by screen walls, thus creating a quiet living environment and making the utmost use of land. The simple composition of main alleys and side alleys in the traditional alley-type residences (Fig. 5) inevitably presents a rather monotonous sight; and only a small shop for cigarettes and daily necessities could possibly be found in these alleys. In the project mentioned above, improvements have been made to promote better living conditions and form a more lively and spacious environment. Two pieces of recreational ground are provided, one at the central area and one at the entry of the site. Community facilities, such as a neighborhood committee building, a kindergarten, a canteen, department stores, bicycle sheds, and a housing maintenance and repair office, are provided on the site. There should be 852 households rehoused on the total area of 2.44 hectares. The number of project housing units varies from 1216 to 1370 due to the introduction of the "adequate housing units" described later.

The main measure taken to raise density while improving living conditions is to adopt the step-type apartment house design (Fig. 6), which inherits many of the merits of the traditional houses (Fig. 7).

There are two related but different measures for land-saving in these houses. Firstly, they increase the "depth" of the floor plan while providing natural lighting and ventilation for the inner rooms by means of small wells. There will be relatively less exterior wall area exposed to nature, and small wells have a peculiar effect of causing constant draft whenever air is

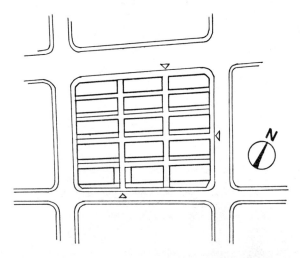

Fig. 5 An example of the traditional alley-type residential quarter

admitted by opening the windows or doors of the exterior walls. That is why the traditional houses are usually much cooler in the summer than the shallow new houses, and not so chilly in the winter. Figure 8 indicates the effectiveness in land-saving by increasing the depth of the floor plan. Secondly, the step-type construction, set back in the north side of the building, permits the space between houses required for sun exposure to be decreased, as shown in Fig 9. The step-type apartments adopt both measures and thus the net density of floor area per hectare can be increased up to 57.7% in comparison with the typical current housing designs. Under housing allotment norms, step-type housing can provide 525 to 565 households per hectare, whereas the average density of the existing old urban

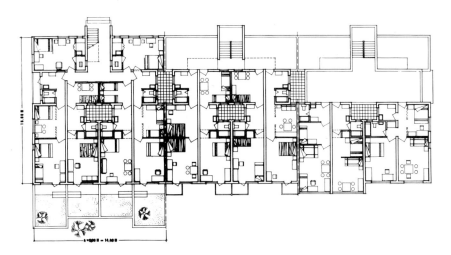

Fig. 6 Plan of the step-type apartments

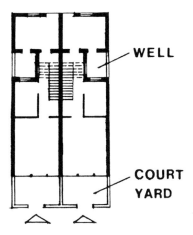

Fig. 7 Plan of a typical alley-type house

dwellings ranges from 400 to 500 households per hectare. The current housing design can only provide 300 to 350 households per hectare. Thus step-type high-density houses can rehouse the inhabitants on the original site, while providing land for recreation, green areas, community facilities, and the like. And the roof terraces supplement outdoor activity areas. These terraces, shared by two to four households, are ideal playgrounds for small children within the immediate care of their parents. They are also good for communication among occupants, for planting, and for the popu-

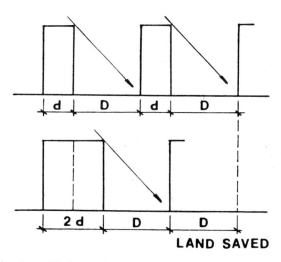

Fig. 8 Land saved by increasing the dimension of the depth of floor plan

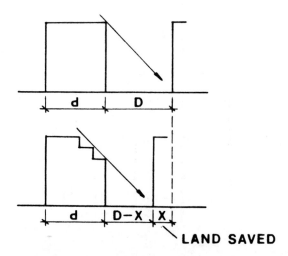

Fig. 9 Land saved by step-type construction

lar traditional Chinese physical exercises that are now usually done on the pedestrian walks in Shanghai.

As for esthetic presentation, step-type houses give a rather renovated silhouette in comparison with the monotonous strip block buildings. As one side of the building is lowered down to three stories, the neighborhood becomes more intimate and domestic in appearance. Figure 10 is a photo of a model of another step-type housing project.

Another vital problem in housing design is how to handle the single-room flat for small families, such as newly married couples or aged singles. The average norm for the floor area per housing unit, set by the government, is only valid for a certain period of time, and it is to be modified to foster better living conditions; so it can be anticipated that the numerous single-room flats will not be very much welcome in the near future. The simplest solution to the problem in the current housing design has been to let two families share a two-room flat, although most of the occupants complained about it. Then "adaptable housing units" were introduced in the above-mentioned projects. A two-room flat can be transformed into a three-room flat by opening up a door or a niche to a single-room flat when necessary.

When the step-type residential-quarter planning and housing design was first submitted to the Congress of the Architectural Society of China in 1978, it attracted the unanimous interest of architects from all over the country. A thesis was published in the Chinese *Architectural Journal,* (1979, vol. 3). Honored prizes were awarded for the design in the Shanghai Housing

Fig. 10 Model of a step-type housing project

Design Competition in 1979 and for the thesis by Tong-Ji University in 1980. This concept is obviously of great significance to the housing design of 1981 in Shanghai, as its main characteristic is great depth of floor plan. Many new designs have adopted the "steps" in vertical composition.

Planning and Environmental Criteria

CONDENSED REFERENCES/BIBLIOGRAPHY

The following is a condensed bibliography for this part. It contains bibliographic citations that are in addition to those cited with the articles in this part. The full citations can be found at the end of the volume. What is given here should be sufficient information to lead the reader to the correct article: author, date, and title. In the case of multiple authors, only the first name is listed.

Batten 1974, *Environmental Impact of Buildings*

Comision de Normas para Estructuras de Edificaciones 1980, *Steel Building Structures. Design,*

Halpin 1976, *Design of Process and Construction Operations*
Halpin 1980, *Construction Management*
Hayfield 1979, *Basic Factors for a Successful Project*

Rohner 1980, *The Management of the Zurich Fruit and Vegetable Market Project*
Roy 1977, *Introduction to Tall Building Structures*
Rutenberg 1981, *Dynamic Torsional Effects in Building: A Bibliograph·*

Universidad Central de Venezuela, Caracas 1978, *Bibliography on Earthquake Engineering*
Universidad Central de Venezuela, Caracas 1979, *Bibliography on Earthquake Engineering*
Universidad Central de Venezuela, Caracas 1980, *Bibliography on Earthquake Engineering*

209

Systems and Concepts

Introductory Review

John Rankine

The world's cities are building at a rapid rate; tall buildings are appearing in every corner of the globe. The number of geniuses who can think up new ideas, new concepts, and so forth, are few; but once given an idea, a method of construction, an innovation, or a view of what someone else has done, many people can take that idea, build on it, mold it, change it, work it into other thinking, and so come up with more innovation and better methods—so progresses the art of building.

Maintaining progress requires that every architect, designer, engineer, builder, and manufacturer be at all times up-to-date with the state of the art as it exists and as it changes. The dissemination of new ideas and information, however, is not an easy matter. As a rule it does not just happen—one has to go out and seek new ideas. It means looking at every building one sees, reading all the trade journals, questioning trade salesmen, attending seminars, mixing and talking with one's contemporaries, especially from other cities and other parts of the world, traveling, and looking.

The Monograph, when it came out, collated and disseminated to the world the knowledge at that time. In this update volume, some of the leaders and innovators of our profession have collected the newly formulated methods, ideas, and concepts, thus giving information not only to bring others up-to-date, but also to give everyone material to build and innovate upon.

This part deals with ideas and concepts relating to the physical systems of tall buildings.

Structural systems (SC-1) deals with the methods of combining vertical, horizontal, and dynamic forces through the skin, structure, frames, or core, or a combination of these elements. The first very tall buildings in a city are sometimes built around the structural systems, but architectural creation requires variation. Hence, the structural engineer has to use his ingenuity to combine one or all elements of the structure with the overall building design in an integrated way.

Today, comfort and services (SC-2, SC-3, SC-4) in a high-rise building are important and expensive. Tenants are becoming more sophisticated and demanding. Security, surveillance, and alarms are requirements of our turbulent world. Access, egress, vertical transportation, and evacuation have become major problems. In former days, in low-rise construction, these were not real problems; however today, although it is structure that puts and keeps the building up, services represent 40 to 55% of the total cost of the building proper. They are also the area where the most problems arise, where the most cost savings can be made, and where least is known by the general practitioner. These sections of the update are most innovative and show the need for complete integration into the total design.

The first structures ever built by man consisted merely of cladding (SC-5, SC-6) to keep off the elements. Today with the integration of high-rise buildings with structure and services, the cost of the cladding has been reduced from 100% for lean-to structures to maybe as low as 10 to 15% for tall buildings; nevertheless cladding has not lost its importance. On the contrary, it is subjected to greater stresses, greater changes in climatic conditions, more intricate building procedures, stricter building and fire codes, and a greater need to maintain its lustre and finish.

Foundations (SC-7) transmit and are influenced by the vertical, horizontal, and overturning moments of the tall building. They are also dependent on the soil and site conditions. They are more a problem in mathematics and soil mechanics than in esthetics, because they are usually covered over, out of sight, and not influenced by artistic and commercial concerns. However, new methods of construction and innovative ways of overcoming problems and cutting costs are always wanted.

Introduction

Walter P. Moore, Jr.

This chapter of the Monograph update includes three interesting articles dealing with new trends that are developing in tall building design. Christiansen emphasizes the current change in architecture that is influencing the tall building. The days of the "glass box" are gone, and the current designers of tall buildings are turning to many different shapes, as well as to "notches" in the building skin and "setbacks" up and down the building. These changes are causing structural engineers to rethink the systems necessary to resist the horizontal loads involved.

It is well known that the most efficient way to resist horizontal loads is by using the outside skin of the building. In the recent past the framed tube, the bundled tube, and the braced tube have allowed buildings to reach the 100-story range with reasonable efficiency. However the latest shapes, cut-outs, setbacks, and the like, have tended to force the structural engineer to move back into the core of the building or to consider "partial tube" solutions.

One system growing in popularity is the concrete core. Concrete does provide sufficient stiffness to build tall serviceable buildings. In many cases the core is "slip-formed" or "jump-formed" so that it proceeds very quickly. The rest of the building is a conventional steel frame that also can be constructed very quickly. It is important that the individual concrete walls within the core be coupled together so that the entire core acts as a unit rather than as individual pieces. This achievement is usually difficult since there is generally little depth available for structure across the elevator lobbies and around mechanical rooms. This "box-type" core, consisting of coupled shear walls, is also very stiff torsionally. Torsion is becoming significantly more important with the new building shapes.

Another variation of this concrete-core system is to build the frame with light steel members, come along behind and encase the outside steel columns in concrete, and encase the core columns within the concrete shear walls. Usually the concreting operation lags behind the steel erection by approximately ten floors. In this case the concrete walls are coupled together with steel girders. The same clearance problems associated with the first concrete system are also problems with the steel system. Nevertheless the composite building system is gaining in popularity as a means of combining the speed and light weight of steel construction with the inherent stiffness and low cost of reinforced concrete.

The only real disadvantage of this reinforced, concrete-core-braced building is the thickness of the walls themselves. Clearly as walls become thicker they occupy usable space within a given outside perimeter, which results in a lower floor efficiency, but the savings in building cost may well offset this drawback.

Another horizontal-load-resisting system that offers promise with the new building shapes is one that uses outrigger trusses connecting the core to belt trusses in the outside skin. Still another system would be a "cross-braced" or "k-braced" system on the interior of the building. All of these schemes have been resisted in the past unless they could be contained within floors devoted entirely to mechanical or electrical equipment. There is a general feeling that on usable floors, the space between the outside wall and the core should be column free and certainly should not contain sloping structural members. However, the practicalities of current building design suggest that space planners can and will learn to deal effectively with the problem when the cost savings reach a certain level.

Khan and El Nimeiri deal with yet another current problem, namely the multi-use facility. The authors clearly state the problems associated with enclosing office buildings, garages, hotels and apartments, and finally retail operations within the same space. Each of these building types, when considered separately, has an optimum column spacing and often an optimum structural system. Unfortunately none of these optimums are identical. When one stacks such different uses within a tall building and then begins to use unusual shapes, notches, and setbacks, the problems are compounded.

The authors go into considerable detail with regard to the optimum bay sizes and systems associated with each type of use. Unfortunately parking goes at the bottom of the stack—usually underground. The next use is the commercial retail space, which seldom occupies more than four or five levels above ground. If both of these activities can be held outside of the main tower, as suggested by the authors, the engineer can have many more options on the structural system used to resist the horizontal loads. Usually this outside positioning cannot be done due to the high land costs in the central business districts where tall mixed-use facilities tend to be located. The solution, then, has to be the use of transfer beams or trusses.

One trend that is beginning to surface is to locate hotel rooms lower in the building. This is very desirable, since the column spacing can be much closer for a hotel or apartment. The unfortunate recent incidence of fires in high-rise hotels in the United States has made hotel space on lower floors more attractive. Apartment or condominium space, which is usually structurally compatible with hotel space, still seems to be located high in the building, competing with office space for the "top view."

There have been several successful projects recently that have separated the functions into individual freestanding towers with an atrium roof bridging the towers and tying the mixed-used facility into a single building. Merchant's Plaza in Indianapolis, Indiana, and the Plaza of the Americas in Dallas, Texas, are very good and successful mixed-used projects. Examples of vertically stacked multi-use facilities are the John Hancock Center and The Water Tower Place in Chicago, Illinois, and The Energy Center Project in Denver, Colorado.

The multi-use facility and "post-modern architecture" are the structural engineer's challenges in the 1980s and beyond. Buildings will become taller and much more complex in the next decade. More research will be required as more sophisticated materials and systems are developed.

The third paper in this section, by Brainov, presents the concept that structural design is a very creative process that encompasses many different individual fields of science, economics, and esthetics. Hence, in order to prepare people to participate in the contemporary creation of structures, it will be necessary to organize a qualitatively new "multidisciplinary, fundamentally complex science and a systematic theory of structures." Tall buildings would only be a part of this new multidisciplinary science.

Professor Brainov then divides the general systematic theory of structures into six scientific directions. Of the six, he considers structural form-making and structural detailing to be the most creative but the least developed theoretically. The other four directions are loads, materials, structural mechanics, and measurement and reliability. He develops his ideas only briefly but lists references where he has presented his concepts in much greater detail.

Structural Systems (SC-1)

New Developments

J. V. Christiansen

New developments in tall building structural systems over the past five to six years are briefly discussed with respect to horizontal framing systems/floors, vertical framing systems, framing systems to resist horizontal loads, and energy-dissipation systems. A number of subjects are suggested for additional research.

INTRODUCTION

A recent, December 1980, issue of *Progressive Architecture* magazine devotes most of the issue to high-rise buildings under the general title of "Thinking Tall" (Murphy, 1980). To quote in part from the editorial comment in that issue,

> "It is rare nowadays to see a straightforward orthogonal tower on the boards of even the most established and conservative firms. The crop of high-rise design in the late 1970s and beginning 1980s are instead polygonal, sinuous, pleated, terraced, inflected, and eroded. There have been breaks from the box before—but nothing like the slice-and-dice manipulations currently surfacing."

The development of these new architectural shapes has required the development of complex structural systems of great variety. Nevertheless, these systems still consist of the primary elements discussed in the original Monograph—framed floors, moment-resisting frames, braced frames, and shear walls, combined to produce an endless variety of tube and interaction structures and mixtures of structural materials. The glass and aluminum window wall, while still the dominant cladding system, is increasingly being replaced by other materials, such as stone, steel plate, precast concrete, fiberglass-reinforced concrete, and even prefabricated brick.

FRAMING SYSTEMS TO RESIST GRAVITY LOADS

Horizontal Framing Systems/Floors

Thinner concrete slabs placed over shallower composite metal decks are being used for floor construction. The 2-in-thick (50.80 mm) slab is now in use, and it can be shown that considerable cost savings may be realized, resulting principally from the savings in the weight of supporting steel work and the competitive cost of sprayed-on fireproofing. The thinner slabs and shallower decks do create problems that must be considered: sound and vibration caused by footfalls and the reduced strength and stiffness of the floor diaphragm.

Deeper, heavier, wide-flange shapes suitable for longer-span floor construction are being rolled in Europe. Wide-flange shapes up to 44 in deep and weighing up to 677 lbs. per lineal ft are now available.

Concrete technology has advanced. Concrete is now being pumped up over 1,000 vertical feet in high-rise buildings. New concrete admixtures called "superplasticizers" are being used to produce high-slump, high-strength concrete. Concrete strengths of 7,000 psi are now commonplace in the columns and walls of high-rise buildings, and 9,000-psi concrete has been used extensively.

Vertical Framing Systems

Very high-strength concrete of up to 9,000 and 10,000 psi has been used to reduce the overall size of concrete columns. Composite steel and concrete construction has been used extensively in recent years. Very light steel frames have been erected, with concrete placed around columns and bracing to provide low-cost but efficient lateral stiffening and strengthening, and additional gravity-load-carrying capacity. Sophisticated formwork systems supported by, and rolling or skipping up, the steel work have been used to facilitate the placement of the concrete.

FRAMING SYSTEMS TO RESIST HORIZONTAL LOADS

As previously mentioned, very complex structural systems have been developed to laterally brace the more complex building shapes. Several uniquely different structural bracing systems have been planned, designed, and executed in recent years, including:

1. *Eccentric bracing:* For design in seismically active areas, the concept of eccentric bracing has been introduced, researched, tested, and used in several projects. This concept offsets the connection point for diagonal bracing from the column-beam joint and thus forces the beam to bend and develop plastic hinges and ductility.

2. *Steel plate cladding:* Steel plate cladding panels are being used as exterior cladding and also as a structural stiffening element to reduce the lateral response of the building to wind. Since these panels are not fireproofed, it is necessary to provide a frame with sufficient strength independent of the panels. We recognize, of course, that although this seems like a new concept, most high-rise buildings built before World War II had moment-resisting steel frames with masonry infill panels that, in fact, stiffened those frames and ensured that they would perform satisfactorily in the wind.

ENERGY-DISSIPATION SYSTEMS

Tuned mass dampers have been used in several high-rise buildings in recent years. Apparently, however, viscoelastic dampers, or other devices intended to artificially increase damping throughout a structural system, have not been used recently.

NEEDED RESEARCH

It is suggested that the following research efforts receive high priority:

1. *Load and resistance factor design:* Design of high-rise building structures involves the consideration of many critical "load effect" combinations and the interaction of several different material types. Until a properly calibrated load and resistance factor design method is developed, the design of our high-rise buildings will not have consistent levels of safety and performance.

2. *Design criteria for moment-resisting frames:* Criteria for the design

of moment-resisting frames with respect to the lateral support of the compression flange is needed.

3. *Analytical methods for the analysis of the dynamic effects of wind:* The present wind tunnel work is costly and time consuming, and the ultimate data, although extraordinarily useful, is usually not available soon enough in the design process to substantially influence the design.

4. *Inelastic analysis:* The inelastic analysis method for dynamic seismic analysis should be further developed and refined.

5. *Lateral support requirements:* More research could be done with respect to the lateral support requirements for high-rise building columns.

Structural Systems for Multi-Use High-Rise Buildings

Fazlur R. Khan*

Mahjoub M. El Nimeiri

Industrial urbanization created high-density living in urban spaces in city centers. These spaces were most often intermixed with each other in such a way that neighborhood stores, offices, and apartments were all in the same building at different levels. The ground level was mostly stores and commercial functions and the upper levels were mixed-use with offices and residential functions. The automobile was not a part of urban life, and therefore parking was never a requirement for these buildings. The nineteenth century urban centers in Europe, such as London, Paris, Prague, and Vienna, were very much of this kind of development. Industrial development during the late nineteenth and early twentieth centuries, combined with land speculation, forced a new kind of urban settlement pattern in which the living and working spaces became more and more separated in urban areas. The rise of downtowns and city centers consisting of office buildings and other commercial facilities created separate residential areas outside these urban centers. And even when some special residential centers

---

*Deceased

were built near the urban centers, they were distinctly separate buildings in no way connected with the commercial or office building complexes. The architectural/engineering solutions for such specialized buildings were therefore quite different from each other. The office and commercial buildings used larger-span structural systems consistent with the space requirements for offices and other commercial functions; whereas the housing and apartment buildings used relatively smaller-span structural systems consistent with residential room sizes. Although both reinforced concrete and structural steel were used for office buildings as well as residential buildings, the structural systems were quite different. The office building, requiring longer spans as well as much more complicated mechanical and electrical systems, almost invariably used false ceilings; whereas the residential buildings, with less complicated mechanical and electrical systems, did not require the use of false ceilings except for special cases. Flat-plate, reinforced-concrete-slab construction therefore became the most accepted floor system for residential buildings; whereas beams, joists, or grid beam (waffle) systems were used more frequently for office and commercial floors. Masonry bearing-wall construction almost always was used only for residential buildings of medium height.

In the 1960s, concerns about urban quality of life and better utilization of national energy resources raised questions about the earlier trend of total separation of office, commercial, and living spaces in the urban areas. Sociologists, economists, and citizens in general began to rediscover the great advantages of working and living within the same urban environment. As a result, multi-use projects became increasingly attractive to developers from an economic and marketing point of view. The 100-story John Hancock Center in Chicago is an excellent example.

One of the largest such projects built in the middle 1960s, it combines commercial, office, parking, residential, and recreational spaces into one large structure. Such a combination of spaces in one building created a 24-hour use of the land, rather than the 9-to-5 downtown environment of major cities. The John Hancock Center not only became a successful development; its success also encouraged a large number of similar projects that were developed around the same area of the city. The multi-use projects, often incorporated into a megastructure, raised new challenges and required new disciplines in formulating the overall building mass and a complimentary structural system. The earlier efficient structural systems that were developed only for the office building or the residential building could not be used in their pure forms to satisfy the multi-use requirements of such a project. New structural modifications and variations had to be developed to satisfy, within the same structure, the space requirements for both office buildings and apartment and parking.

Innovations leading to more economical and efficient buildings are only possible through a comprehensive understanding of the nature and behavior of various structural systems, an awareness of the relationship of the structure with other disciplines such as the mechanical system, and a practical sense of construction problems. A multi-use building is much more complex architecturally because of the different requirements for each use. For example, the maximum building width required for apartment space is generally much less than that required for an efficient office space; and the optimum column spacings for a residential building, as well as its plan flexibility, are distinctly different from those for commercial or office buildings.

For multi-use buildings it is therefore necessary to develop structural systems that respond effectively to the needs of the different functions. In developing such systems, the first step is to select an appropriate structural material. The selection process must start with the most commonly used structural materials (steel or reinforced concrete, both normal and lightweight; composite systems; and so forth). Although local relative economies must be considered, the selection process is much more difficult than it is for a single-use building. The different requirements of the different functions and their relative importance in the overall project will be the most important considerations.

FACTORS AFFECTING THE OPTIMUM
STRUCTURAL DESIGN

In searching for appropriate structural systems one must first recognize a number of important factors affecting the multi-use high-rise structure:

- Interior column spacing—each use has a different optimum spacing.

- Exterior column spacing—as a function of the planning module.

- Spandrel beam shape and size—office and apartment buildings have different requirements.

- Floor-to-floor height—generally different for different functions.

- Type of ceiling—traditionally the most economical and practical apartment ceiling is the exposed underside of concrete slab, while a hung ceiling is used in office and commercial buildings to provide access to HVAC and electrical system.

- Transfer levels and transfer systems.

- Floor plans—stepbacks, nonsymmetrical conditions, and site considerations.

VERTICAL LOCATIONS OF FUNCTIONS
IN A BUILDING

The structural flexibility in column spacings for different uses dictates that the closest column spacing should be at the ground level, which will allow some intermediate columns to be dropped off along the height of the building. This type of arrangement of columns will avoid the use of complicated and heavy transfer girders. Such girders would be required if smaller structural bays were used on the upper portion of the building and larger structural bays in the lower portion. Therefore, from the structural point of view, the below-grade function outside the tower should be for parking and should use longer spans; but from the ground level up, the first segment should be for a hotel, requiring closer column spacing. The next segment up should be for residential floors requiring somewhat greater column spacing. The topmost segment of the building should be used for commercial and office space, which requires the maximum column spacing. An ideal spacing arrangement is shown in Fig. 1. Another reason for such an arrangement is that lower-floor columns support much higher loads than the columns above. Therefore, if the upper-floor columns are transferred onto more numbers of closely spaced lower-floor columns, their loads and their cross

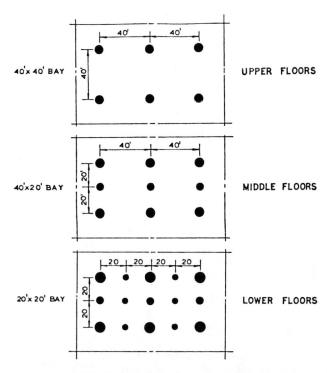

Fig. 1 Ideal interior column spacing

sections can be considerably reduced. This often results in simpler foundation systems. However, in the real world of a multi-use building, the office, commercial, and parking floors, with their larger spans, are generally placed below apartment floors, primarily to promote easier access to the heavily used floors and better views from the apartments (Fig. 2). In general, the parking floors require an efficient bay size of 60 ft by 20 ft or 60 ft by 30 ft, whereas the efficient bay size for an apartment floor may be 20 ft by 20 ft. In between these two typical bay sizes, the bay size for office floors is generally in the range of 30 ft by 30 ft. The question of optimum column spacing is in essence one of economics and can only be answered once the development's priorities are established. For example, for a structure that is primarily an apartment building, the apartment layout plan will govern column spacing. Where concrete construction is competitive, a flat-plate system would be optimum, because it minimizes the height of the structure without reducing usable space. If structural steel framing is more economical, the optimum floor framing in the apartment portion of a multi-use building can often be achieved by arranging the floor beams in such a way as to eliminate the need for a ceiling.

On examining optimum vertical location of function from the rentability and user preference points of view, it appears that although levels below grade should remain as parking, the first levels above grade should be for commercial uses, the next levels for office space, the next for hotel space, and the topmost levels for apartments. There is obviously, then, a conflict between desirable structural considerations and desirable rentability and user considerations. Developing an optimum structure is therefore a tantalizing challenge in the design of a multi-use urban building.

The discrepancy between desirable structure and functional need can often be resolved by one of two methods. The first method is to find a way to slope the exterior walls of the building towards the central core so that the effective clear span of the building's perimeter ("lease span")

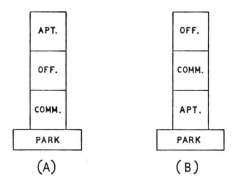

Fig. 2 (a) Preferred for use and rentability
(b) Ideal for structure

reduces with the height of the building. This gradual reduction of the lease span with height makes the overall structural system compatible with the most desirable location of functions along the height of the building, as shown in Fig. 3.

An excellent example of this first method is the John Hancock Center in Chicago (Fig. 4). The ground-floor plan of the building measures approximately 160 ft by 260 ft, and the clear span from the central core is approximately 60 ft. This is ideal for parking as well as for commercial and office uses (Fig. 5). However, the building is tapered to the top to a dimension of 100 ft by 160 ft, and the exterior clear span reduces to about 30 ft, which is very suitable for apartment layouts (Fig. 6). In addition, in the upper, apartment stories the floor beams were arranged in such a way that they would normally fall in line with partitions and walls. Therefore the concrete slab spanning between these steel beams can be used directly as ceiling. Such preplanning of beam locations in structural steel floor framing for apartment floors can make steel structures more economical for residential use.

The second method for resolving the discrepancy is to evaluate the importance of each of the functions in the building in terms of its relative floor area and its contribution to the total cost of the project. It is then possible to arrive at an optimum single span that can be used for all functions and will provide maximum satisfaction for the dominant function and lesser satisfaction for for other functions in the building. Table 1 gives an optimum interior column spacing for concrete buildings and illustrates the optimality criteria for the different functions. In a building where some portion is allotted for office space, commercial, and parking, but the dominant space is residential, close coordination between the different functions is required to obtain an optimum column spacing.

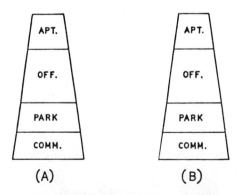

Fig. 3 (a) Preferred for use and rentability
(b) Ideal for structure

Table 1 Optimum interior column spacing

Floor	Bay size		Concrete slab thickness	Ideal spacing
	Regular	Large		
Apt.	20' x 20'	20' x 20'	7''	Dictated by layout
		20' x 30'	8''	
Office	20' x 20'	20' x 30'	7'' 8'' w/drop	28' x 28' fits core better 30' x 30' especially where considering atriums typ. office module: 5', 6' − generous
Comm.	20' x 20'	30' x 30'	8½'' 10'' w/drop	30' x 30' live load high
Park	20' x 20'	30' x 30' 20' x 30' 20' x 60'	8'' 8'' w/drop	

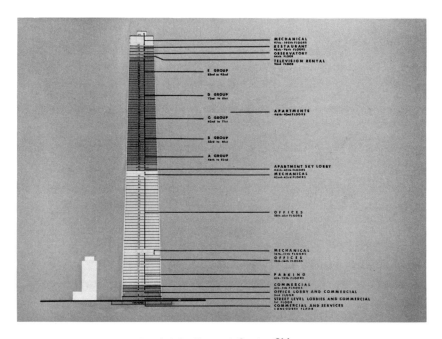

Fig. 4 John Hancock Center, Chicago

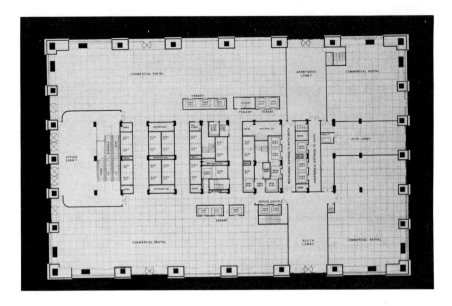

Fig. 5 John Hancock Center: Ground-floor plan

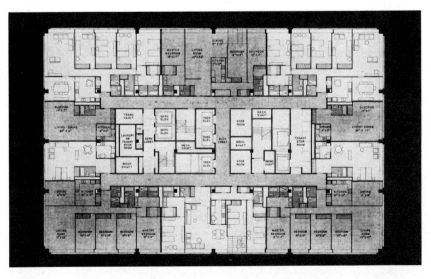

Fig. 6 John Hancock Center: High-rise apartment-floor plan

APPLICATION OF FRAMED TUBE STRUCTURES

A closely spaced exterior frame system, referred to as the framed tube system, is being used increasingly for high-rise structures because of its inherent advantages in resisting lateral loads. In the case of multi-use buildings, where parking spaces within the building are a frequent requirement, shear walls at the core create unacceptable interference and inefficiency. Framed tubes do not depend on shear walls or other trusses, and they can be used as a single tube form or arranged in a bundled form to respond to a special site configuration or larger floor-area requirements. Framed tubes should be looked at as thin-walled hollow tubes with punched out holes (windows). Therefore the spacing and size of window openings is arbitrary and should indeed respond directly to the most desirable floor layouts. For apartment buildings this means that the exterior window openings can be irregularly sized and spaced as long as the basic behavior of the tube effect can be maintained. This normally leads to opening sizes on the order of 50% of the wall surface.

For office buildings the exterior column spacing follows the office planning module. A typical office module is 5 ft. At commercial and parking floors, there is usually no specific requirement for the opening sizes for the exterior walls. However, at the ground floor, buildings require special entrances for pedestrians and access for trucks and cars. These special openings may require wider spacing of columns by use of transfer girders or other load redistribution methods.

APPLICATION OF BUNDLED FRAMED TUBE

When a number of framed tubes are bundled together to form a bundled tube structure, the common walls of any two joined tubes become an interior frame. The spacing of these interior tube columns has to be similar to that of the exterior, so that the spandrel beam at any one level is continuous and has the same shear and flexural stiffness as for the perimeter elements. However, the exact dimensions and locations of these interior tube columns need to be coordinated with the planning layout of the type of occupancy. In the apartment floors it is necessary that these columns not disrupt the room layouts; preferably they would be located along the partition walls. In the office floors such columns have to satisfy the office module, and in some cases they have to provide enough clearance for corridors and passageways. In commercial and parking levels some of these columns are usually transferred to create more open space.

An example of the second method of resolving the conflict between functional need and desirable structure is the One Magnificent Mile project, a 57-story concrete structure now under construction in Chicago (Figs. 7 and 8). The free-form structure is composed of three hexagonal reinforced concrete framed tubes bundled in a north-southwest orientation (Fig. 9). The north tube is 57 stories, the south tube is 49 stories, and the west

Fig. 7 One Magnificent Mile, Chicago *(Photo by: Hedrich-Blessing)*

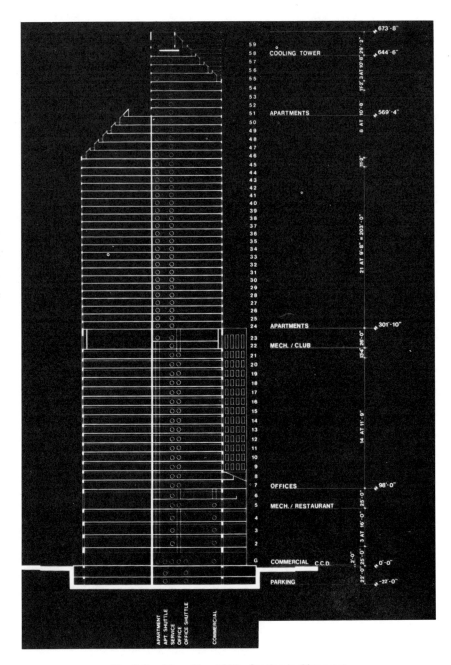

Fig. 8 One Magnificent Mile: Section looking west

tube is 22 stories. The structural system has been developed to provide for parking at lower levels and condominiums in the north and south tubes above the 22nd level. The west tube is used primarily for office space, and a 7-story bustle on the northeast corner is added for the commercial floors. A typical commercial-floor plan is shown in Fig. 10. An optimum interior column spacing of 30 ft by 30 ft was selected for the west tube. It is obvious that this spacing could have been much smaller for an apartment flat-plate floor. In the north tube where all the elevator cores are located, the location of the interior columns was determined exclusively by the most desirable apartment layout plan. In the south tube, a staggered column arrangement, 20 ft by 30 ft, was found to be optimum because, while it satisfied the apartment layout plan for the upper floors (Fig. 11), it also worked very well for the office space and also for the two parking levels. As for the exterior framed tube, architecturally the requirement was such that the column spacing would be different for different functions. At the apartments it varies from 2½ ft to 9 ft. At the office floors the spacing was 10 ft, and at the commercial and parking levels it was typically 20 ft. The interior-tube column spacing at both the apartment and office levels was typically kept to 10 ft. The three framed tubes bundled together in a

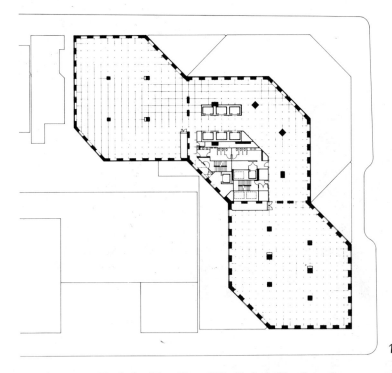

↑ NORTH

Fig. 9 One Magnificent Mile: Typical office-floor plan

free-form arrangement made it possible to satisfy both interior and exterior column-spacing requirements for each of the multiple-use functions in this complex building. Further, the structural efficiency of the bundled tube system made the design and selection of the form a natural choice.

In bundling tubes together, a number of special design considerations had to be taken into account.

The exterior spandrel beams at the apartment levels had to be up-turned, which required particular care in detailing to avoid an increase in their construction cost. However, along the interior column line

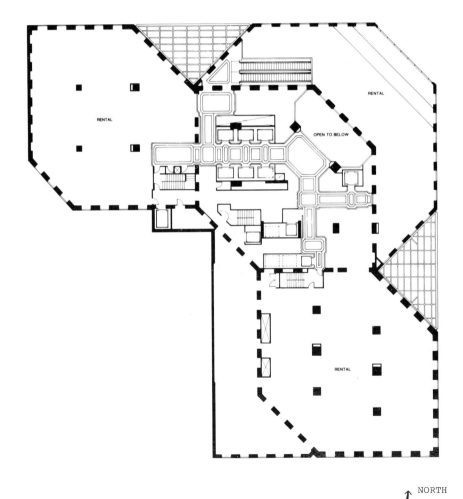

↑ NORTH

Fig. 10 One Magnificent Mile: Typical commercial-floor plan

between the north and south tubes, some of the beam segments had to be downturned to allow for a corridor to pass through. The changing of the spandrel beams from an upturned position to a downturned position, presented a special detailing and design problem.

One of the advantages of a concrete tube system is that wall openings can be rearranged according to the spacing of the exterior frame at each use. However, special large openings at certain levels may require specific transfer girders. Two such transfer girders were required. One transfer girder (8 ft deep) was located at the mechanical level

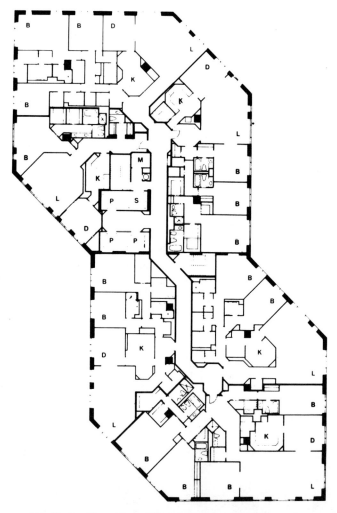

Fig. 11 One Magnificent Mile: Typical apartment-floor plan

separating the apartment levels from the office levels. The other transfer girder (7½ ft deep) was located at the second level above grade, where columns were transferred from 10-ft spacing to 20-ft spacing.

The One Magnificent Mile project is indeed a synthesis of recent concrete structural developments for tall buildings and recent trends in multi-use urban projects throughout the world.

CONCLUSION

Successful development of multi-use buildings in congested urban sites calls for development of optimum structural systems that can effectively fulfill the various functions of such buildings. The normal requirements of various types of use are discussed in this paper and methods of combining them for multi-use projects are explored. The specific factors affecting the structural-architectural design of such projects are illustrated in two projects, namely, the 100-story John Hancock Center in Chicago (steel structure) and the 57-story One Magnificent Mile in Chicago (concrete structure). The factors discussed in this paper and the examples used for elaborating these factors will hopefully be a future guide to structural engineers and architects responding to the increasing demand of multi-use urban buildings.

Structural Engineering Design — Creativity and Functional Considerations

Milcho Neshev Brainov

SUMMARY

This paper contains some thoughts on and concepts of structural engineering design as a creative process based on science and on a systematic application of structural theory. Structural design is considered as a function of economics and esthetics. Extensive use is made of the bibliography, in which the details are worked out in their entirety.

Structural design is a basic and indispensable component of all material things that have a definite form in space: buildings and bridges; instruments and mechanical equipment and installations; machines and manufactured goods; all modes of transportation; and many others. All of these things perform some necessary function, which tends to dictate the form of their structure. This form is supplied by a load-carrying structure, which is designed according to the appropriate method of structural analysis (Brainov, 1980b). Structure makes possible the material forms and spaces for all necessary functions and purposes. Structures support all applied loads and influences, whether these come from functional use or from

237

external conditions. They unite function and form as a *necessity* and structure and technology as a *possibility*. The various possible structural forms and the available methods of structural analysis have been, throughout time, the main determining factor in the nature of structures (Brainov, 1980b; Brainov, 1979).

It is through structural engineering design that present-day structures are created. Before their material manifestation is accomplished, a non-material project (an abstraction) is worked out. It is through this project that the abstract searching and creation of the final structure is accomplished. The project must consider all appropriate conditions and requirements if a rational fulfillment of the function is to be realized.

In this sense, structural design is a manifestation of functional modeling and creative imagination, both of which are based on abstract thinking and scientific prognosis. It has lasting technological and sociological consequences. Therefore, structural design is a creative process based on science and scientific theory. But at the present stage of development, it is divided into many separate fundamental theories and applied sciences. The spontaneous and haphazard development of theory, as well as the unsystematic accumulation of knowledge, are apparent here. The question of what would be a complete synthesis of the science and theory of structures still has no completely definite and satisfying answer (Brainov, 1980b; Brainov, 1972).

A new multidisciplinary science and general systematic theory is needed to express and classify complex and systematic laws. (A suggested approach is given in Brainov, 1980b.)

SYSTEMATIC THEORY

The proposed general systematic theory of structures has six basic components: (1) the development of a structural system, (2) structural loads and influences, (3) structural materials, (4) structural mechanics, (5) structural measurement and reliability, and (6) structural detailing.

The development of a structural system (1) and structural detailing (6) are the most creative components, but at the same time they are currently the most undeveloped theoretically. These two components (each with the help of the other) finally result in the most important creative process: the modeling of real structures.

The development of a structural system provides a theoretical basis for creation of the final structural form. It starts with a functional consideration that according to the available structural shapes and configurations, eventually leads to the final structural form.

Structural detailing provides a theoretical basis for *microcreative structuring*—the "dressing" of the structural form (or scheme or system) with material. It is accomplished through direct choice or form-making of structural cross sections and structural detailing of all elements and parts of the final structure.

Both the selection of a structural system and structural detailing, of course, take part in determining the final structure, together with the other four design components mentioned earlier. They all represent the scientific-theoretical and practically applied, multicyclic basis for the creation and design of a structure.

It is important to keep in mind that the creative modeling of the optimal structure must take into consideration many related factors, which include the following: function–form–structure; architecture–structure–industrialization; human settlements–buildings and equipment–structural systems; economics–sociology–psychology; actual structure–computing scheme–structural analysis; function–economics–esthetics; and so on (Brainov, 1980b; Brainov, 1972; Brainov, 1979; Brainov, 1980a). All of these factors come into play in the development of a fully systematic theory and approach (Brainov, 1980b).

SYSTEMATIC COMPOSITION

The general systematic composition of structures has four logical directions or components: (1) structural cross sections, (2) structural elements, (3) structural types, and (4) structural systems. Cataloging it into these four parts enables structural design to become a compositionally creative process, and thus a structural reality, thereby completing a technological, but nonetheless creative, activity (Brainov, 1979).

Both the general systematic theory and the systematic composition of structures were developed with the aim of computerization, the advantages of which are as follows: (1) it saves time and effort when highly labor-consuming and routine processes are involved and (2) it facilitates and intensifies the creative structural activity until it has been brought to a degree of systematic creative synthesis.

Up to now the creation (modeling) of structures has traditionally been regarded as a special (definite) function, realized through structural design. But here each function is considered with respect to the economics and esthetics involved.

In regard to economics, the final structure is always strongly controlled by two mutually contradictory requirements. The first one is for minimal material. Under all conditions, this criteria applies to established structural forms and details, usually as a characteristic in satisfying the functional form and internal stressed stage requirements.

The second requirement is for minimal labor and energy. Fulfilling this requirement is a dynamic process that depends on the particular conditions. In every case, it leads to different structural forms and details, usually corresponding to the technological possibilities and conditions of the time and the case. To take into consideration the economics in this sense means satisfying function with the optimal minimum of material, labor, and energy (Brainov, 1980b; Brainov, 1972).

With regard to esthetics, the structural design (modeling) of real material forms is always related to esthetics because each material form is in a position to be judged by its appearance. Structural creativity, in its fullest sense, creates material forms not only with an eye toward their functions, but also with an eye toward the role they play in the total form of the structure. In the case of buildings, this is realized with the architecture both of the building itself and of the surrounding structures.

These material forms, as basic components of human surroundings, always evidence the characteristics of an esthetic influence. Structural design creates new material forms by optimizing a complex series of factors and criteria and always presupposes the selection of only one structural form among many possibilities. First, the optimization can never become a routing process with an unconditionally unique solution. Second, the choice of one material form from among many is not only a techno-economic activity; it is also an artistic-esthetic one. The structures will always be a result of structural creativity based on science and theory.

There is a similarity with musical creativity, which is also based on science and theory—of form, harmony, rhythm, counterpoint, and so on. Both structural and musical creativity create new works: musical compositions, with an audio-esthetic effect, and material forms, with a visual-esthetic effect. However, the works of structural creativity have more lasting and popular esthetic effects, and form many new visual esthetic values and criteria. It is not by chance that structures remain more and more open to changes via direct visual effects and the resulting adoption of new resolutions. Structures are objective, form-making factors of man's visual material surroundings. They satisfy their utilitarian functions according to the techno-economic possibilities, and they have their own effect on esthetics.

With all of these considerations, the need arises to establish a multidisciplinary, fundamentally complex science and a systematic theory of structures, both of which need a higher scientific-organizational basis than presently exists. In this way, the possibility exists for scientists and engineers working in the field of structural design to realize "all material things that have a definite form in space." The author proposes the creation of appropriate national and international associations on structures, the scope of which would be to unify their ideas and thoughts, their efforts and achievements.

CONDENSED REFERENCES/BIBLIOGRAPHY

The following is a condensed bibliography for this article. It includes all articles referred to or cited in the text. The full citations will be found at the end of the volume, with additional citations for further reading. What is given here should be sufficient information to lead the reader to the correct article: the author, date, and title. In case of multiple authors, only the first name is listed.

Brainov 1972, *Differential Structural Analysis, Optimal Structural Composition, Automatic*
Brainov 1979, *Human Settlements-Tall Buildings-Architecture, Constructions,*
Brainov 1980a, *Aesthetics in Structural Engineering*
Brainov 1980b, *Structures-Complex Science-Systematic Theory-*

Recent Developments in Mechanical, Electrical, and Service Systems

Richard T. Baum

The primary advances in mechanical and electrical engineering have been in a reorientation of thinking to achieve the required building environment with a minimum of energy use. This altered thinking has resulted, in part, from the very considerable escalation of energy costs in the last several years. It also has resulted from the evolution of energy conservation codes by many authorities. These energy codes, without exception, derive from the American Society of Heating, Refrigerating and Air-Conditioning Engineers (ASHRAE) Standard 90-75, "Energy Conservation in New Building Design" (ASHRAE, 1975). The reorientation of thinking has involved not so much advances in hardware as changes in the architectural, mechanical, and electrical systems design approaches to permit hardware to be applied in a more energy-conserving manner. The major considerations are as follows.

There is greater cooperation between the engineer and the architect in determining a building-skin structure that is as thermally opaque as possible to minimize both heating and cooling loads. This cooperation is encouraged by the energy codes, which require building envelopes with high thermal resistance and low air leakage. The codes, although addressing heat transfer or U-values that are attainable with present-day construction methods and materials, are also influenced by the weather conditions that

243

exist for the geographic location of the building. Thus, buildings with cold harsh winters are required to be more thermally opaque than buildings in milder climates.

The effort to control the envelope of the building also addresses the amount of glass used, as well as its thermal characteristics (that is, both its shading coefficient or reflectivity and its thermal transmittance). Overall, consideration of the envelope and glazing results in drastically reduced energy flow through the building and, in many ways, is the beginning of the systemic changes outlined below. It clearly has a major impact on building design and construction.

Greater emphasis is also placed on efficient lighting techniques. These break down into two major subcategories: (a) the use of highly efficient lighting fixtures and the arrangement of such fixtures to achieve the minimum amount of energy use, and (b) the circuiting of such fixtures to permit turning off lighting, regardless of the time of day or night, in spaces that are not occupied. In office structures, typical installed wattages range from 1.2 w/ft^2 to 2 w/ft^2 for general office illumination. Moreover, depending on whether or not fixtures are installed uniformly in a space or locally only with respect to the task location, installed wattages below these values can be obtained. With individual room circuiting, lights can be turned off during normal occupancy periods when rooms are vacated or during the hours of building cleaning except when the room in question is being cleaned. Hardware is now available (infrared devices, motion detectors, and the like) that will automatically carry out this function. Proper training and discipline of building occupants can achieve the same result, however, without the addition of mechanical and electrical hardware that adds cost and needs continuous maintenance and repair.

With regard to the lighting of exterior spaces, the engineer is now, more than ever, cooperating and coordinating with the architect to achieve what is known in the profession as "daylighting". This effect, achieved through careful design of the building facade, permits the turning off of artificial lighting in exterior rooms (and even in interior rooms, under certain circumstances) when the natural light outside the building can provide proper internal illumination through suitably sized window areas. It is essential, however, that excess glass areas not be installed, or the energy saved by turning off electric lights will be exceeded by the additional energy expended to counteract the heating and cooling loads imposed by unnecessarily large glass areas. Similarly, careful study should determine the efficacy of reflective glass coatings (as opposed to internal shading devices or even more effective external shading devices) for optimizing cooling loads, since reflective coatings generally limit light transmission and may prohibit effective daylighting.

Greater emphasis is now placed on the minimum use of the outside air component (as opposed to the recirculated air component) in air-conditioning systems. Obviously outside air constitutes a cooling load in hot weather and a heating load in cold weather, and therefore increases energy use. In brief, the profession is gradually decreasing the use of outside air to the minimum consistent with proper health standards. There is some disagreement as to these standards; but depending on which authorities have jurisdiction, they now range down to a low of approximately 5 cfm per person for general occupancy in office buildings and general assembly-type occupancy. The American Society of Heating, Refrigerating and Air-Conditioning Engineers, in its recently revised Standard, ASHRAE 62-1981 (ASHRAE, 1981) addresses the issue of ventilation and acceptable indoor quality in considerable detail.

With regard to the design of air-handling systems, there is greater emphasis on increasing the temperature differentials of supply air (for both heating and cooling) to circulate the minimum amount of air consistent with occupant comfort. This results in a reduction in the fan energy needed to deliver the air. There is also greater emphasis on proper selection of filters, cooling coils, heating coils, air-terminal units, and air-duct sizes to minimize air-pressure drops, thus also minimizing fan horsepower.

Similarly, chilled-water and hot-water systems are now designed to higher temperature-spread standards and lower pressure-drop standards (consistent with resultant investment costs) to reduce pump horsepower.

Air-reheat systems are no longer used unless, psychrometrically, they are absolutely necessary. The favored method of control is volume control of the circulated air—variable air volume (VAV). Imposed interior comfort conditions have been relaxed to permit a greater variation of the internal relative humidity maintained with the required dry bulb temperature.

In the design of air-handling systems, greater attention is now given to the ability to have local air-handling systems. Alternatively, central systems may be fitted with dampers in the ductwork system working in conjunction with variable-speed fans, variable-inlet vane-controlled fans, or fans with variable-pitch blades. The aim is to permit the turning off of air-handling systems in spaces not occupied.

Heat-recovery systems are now installed whenever economically feasible. Examples of such systems are refrigeration heat-pump systems, used when cooling is required, and hot-gas reclaim systems (in either boiler flue exhausts or engine generator exhausts) when heating is required (for either building heating or as an energy source for absorption-type refrigeration). Such systems, of course, require considerably more initial investment. Their justification is now more frequent only because the saving in operating costs, as a result of higher energy costs, is so much greater today than it was some years ago. A computer center that years ago may have thrown away its internal heat load today would undoubtedly recover that heat load in the wintertime through the use of a heat pump. This recovered heat would be used for heating building spaces and tempering hot water.

Attention is now being given to the use of solar energy for the heating of both domestic hot water and space. The efficacy of such systems depends, of course, on the geographical location of the building. Generally, the use of such systems is more easily justified for domestic hot-water heating than for space heating. While their use is not extensive presently, it should be noted that if energy costs continue to escalate (in contrast to the present hiatus caused by the so-called oil glut), this picture may change.

Finally, greater attention is now being given to the installation of so-called energy management systems. These systems are becoming more and more sophisticated electronically. They use various degrees of computerized monitoring (obviously with the necessary hardware and software) to control building environment and to start and stop mechanical apparatus. Such systems can reasonably extend beyond energy reductions and be justified, in part, by increased efficiency of operating labor to the point of quantifiable staff reductions.

CONDENSED REFERENCES/BIBLIOGRAPHY

The following is a condensed bibliography for this article. It includes all articles referred to or cited in the text. The full citations will be found at the end of the volume, with additional citations for further reading. What is given here should be sufficient information to lead the reader to the correct article: the author, date, and title. In case of multiple authors, only the first name is listed.

ASHRAE 1975, *Standard 90-75 Energy Conservation in New Building Design*
ASHRAE 1981, *Standard 62-1981*

Recent Developments in Vertical and Horizontal Transportation

William S. Lewis

The vertical transportation sector is a mature industry with constant changes in the techniques of installation and the technology of its equipment, as compared to the horizontal transportation industry, which is embryonic and still emerging with multiple technologies for suspension and propulsion. The basic configurations and pedestrian and structural interfaces of the vertical transportation sector essentially have not changed since the original chapter in the Monograph. However, the vertical transportation industry has continued to work to improve its product through improving techniques of installation, as well as through the application of proven technology developments. Along with this progress, there has been a concerted effort among the industry participants in major countries for standardization with respect to architectural and structural interfaces. As a result, the following material will concentrate on developments in vertical transportation as they affect or interact with the building interfaces.

CODE STANDARDIZATION

A major development in the standardization of codes for the benefit of production and design considerations has taken place within the European

Economic Community, under the sponsorship of ISO, as a CEN Elevator (Lift) Code. This code ties together the manufacturing and design concepts among the members of the EEC. A major accomplishment had been the writing of the first parts of the code in a way that permits translation of the code, without ambiguities, into three languages. The first efforts in this area have emerged in English, French, and German, to the benefit of the participating manufacturers.

It should be emphasized that these standards relate to elevators as they are currently standardized in the "European" concept, as opposed to the "North American" concept. This difference is not very significant with respect to smaller installations that involve fewer elevators in a group, such as in residential applications. It can result, however, in conflicting philosophies about the larger groups of elevators that serve intensely occupied offices with a substantial amount of interfloor traffic.

It seems apparent that a number of standards have been generated based more on historical reference than on an evaluation of human-engineering factors. Essentially these standards relate to the width of elevator entrances (car and landing doors) with respect to simultaneous multiple pedestrian transfer. The current standard for geared elevators restricts this opening to only 1100 mm (3 ft 6 in) when, in fact, pedestrian study has indicated that a single pedestrian touch zone "body" ellipse is approximately 610 mm by 460 mm (24 in by 18 in). Observations currently being conducted confirm this fact and continue to verify the data acquired by Fruin (1970). This fact also presents an enigma in standardization of escalators, since observations have revealed that only one person normally occupies the standard step width of 1000 mm (33 in), when the industry has been stating that two passengers will occupy this step.

It is urged that future standardization be based on human-engineering factors, rather than on historical manufacturing or mechanical engineering practices, which may be a convenience for existing production facilities. As the cost of construction increases and the development of open space planning permits greater density of occupancy, it appears that the "fine tuning" of elevator installations will need to be based on these occupancy considerations, rather than strictly on mechanical engineering or architectural considerations.

Although metrication is proceeding slowly in the North American construction industry, the vertical transportation industry, with one multinational corporation, has begun to standardize on the location of manufacturing facilities and product lines. It is intended that essentially all escalator equipment may be manufactured for worldwide consumption in one country that has a metric standard. All gearless equipment may be manufactured in a country with imperial unit standards, but the equipment itself is designed to a metric standard. It is anticipated that such practices will continue until the construction industry in North America is forced to metricate by the adoption of metric units by the structural engineering discipline and the structural steel industry.

ELEVATOR ENTRANCE—WALL INTERFACE

Currently, the industry in North America has completed elevator entrance testing to interface appropriately with the emerging drywall shaft-wall construction. The standard shaft-wall construction is rated at two hours with a 1½ hour elevator entrance test procedure. The North American test procedures are currently the most stringent, requiring not only a furnace test for the test period, but also a hose-stream test which is not universally required. The industry is currently encountering problems with changing shaftway-wall construction requirements reducing the wall rating from 2 hours to 1 hour and reducing the elevator entrance rating from 1½ hours to ¾ hour. This change results in a serious consideration of the entrance design, since the elevator entrance requires support from the wall construction if it is to receive a valid label. It also results in a serious interface problem, since the integrity of the test and labeling procedures requires an appropriate marriage between the elevator entrance frame and the wall construction which, without a test, may not comply with the code requirements.

STANDBY POWER OPERATION

Most current codes in North America require the installation of standby power facilities to support a life-safety system in the event of a normal power failure. Such facilities are particularly required in high-rise buildings, which may simultaneously be involved in a fire condition. It is essential under these circumstances, whether involved with a power failure or a combined power failure and fire condition, that the elevators be arranged for immediate automatic self-evacuation upon indication of such a condition. The indication may come from smoke detectors going off in the elevator lobbies or from the water flow in the sprinkler system, if provided, on any floor involving the group of elevators. It has been found that manual selection of elevators is impractical in the event of power failure, and the elevators should be evacuated as quickly as possible without manual interference.

In major buildings, it is appropriate to have multiple elevator capability from the generating unit so that passenger elevators may be automatically evacuated, while the building personnel can freely use designated service elevators to reach critical mechanical or electrical areas. It has become increasingly important that the elevator system respond to the building life-safety systems early in the design stage so that it can be integrated appropriately with the specific electrical-signal and control requirements.

FIRE MODE OPERATION

The disparate requirements of various codes regarding fire emergencies vary widely with respect to the location and capability of firefighting personnel and their equipment. For high-rise buildings to be successful in all locations, it is essential that the international experience of firefighting be a part of the design process and involve local personnel and their capabilities. The practice in the United Kingdom requiring multiple firemen's elevators to be "dedicated" in addition to the main passenger elevators will not, for practical purposes, make high-rise buildings cost-effective and may impede the development of the next generation of high-rise buildings. At the opposite end of the philosophy spectrum, the New York City Fire Department will not use a dedicated service elevator (goods lift) as a "first wave" determination of the severity of a fire, since their experience indicates that over 75% of all fires in high-rise buildings occur in or near, and usually involve, a service elevator or elevators. Their first wave responsibility is to visually inspect all passenger elevators and service elevators to determine that civilians have been evacuated and, once having confirmed this, to proceed to a floor below the fire-involved floor by multiple passenger elevators. Subsequent events may indicate the use of one or more service elevators that have been determined to be uninvolved in any smoke- or fire-involved area. Conversely, the new Chicago High Rise Building Code dictates that there be one elevator for use of the Fire Department that serves every floor in a high-rise building.

All elevators are automatically recalled whenever a fire floor involves a group of elevators. The recall is to the main lobby unless that lobby itself is involved. Then an alternate floor recall is designated. Whether or not the doors of a recalled elevator remain open or closed after an initial door-open period continues to be a point of discussion among firefighting personnel. It has recently been resolved that, for practical purposes, after recall the doors will remain open, since the contribution to shaftway updraft is minimal and the ability to visually inspect the elevators for occupants is enhanced.

LOBBY AND SHAFTWAY PRESSURIZATION

Current code statements are being adapted to involve the pressurization of an elevator lobby to create an area of refuge, which includes a commensurate reduction in the immediately involved hoistway shaft-wall construction. Along with that is the consideration for the pressurization of elevator hoistways to deter their smoke contamination during the early stages of evacuation and firefighting. This consideration has been punctuated by considerations for the handicapped, since it is impossible for the handicapped to negotiate stairways as the only means of egress after elevators have been recalled. It is anticipated that the lobby "area of refuge," perhaps with an elevator "hoistway of refuge," will eventually prevail to accommodate the handicapped. At that point, it may be established that elevators will continue in operation until a second-phase emergency exists, so that the affected population of the building is evacuated in elevators, rather than by stairway, in very high-rise buildings. However, this has not yet been formulated and perhaps is many years away.

HOISTWAY VENTING

The recent elevator code changes in North America delete from the elevator codes the requirement and specification for venting. This change results from the conflicting concepts of the effect of smoke contamination during a fire and the contributing factor of a stack effect. The venting requirements are now relegated to the various building codes (as opposed to elevator codes) wherever possible. The aim is to establish the proper design responsibility for creating a "building system" that will inhibit smoke contamination as a result of the height of the building and take stack effect into consideration. In the future design of high-rise buildings it is essential that the contributing factors of the elevator hoistways to stack effect be studied further so that the hoistways do not become a major contributor to building operation problems, either under normal operating conditions or under emergency operating conditions.

SOLID-STATE LOGIC OPERATION

Reliable and programmable microprocessors have now emerged as a viable technology in the elevator industry. They permit major cost savings in elevator equipment as well as a reduction in elevator machine room cubature. The ability to use software to relate directly engineering design into the building permits essentially "zero-defect" production and shortens the debugging time taken when the elevators are ready for beneficial occupancy. The programmable features also permit reprogramming during the life of the building to accommodate specific occupancies as they change, rather than rigidly requiring compliance to the original concept in the design of the building. The ability to change or add operation subroutines is also valuable, as it allows the operation to be optimized with respect to the changing needs and changing occupancies of the building.

The substantial technological leap from relay logic to the solid-state logic of the programmable microprocessor has been successfully negotiated in North American installations and currently is undergoing acceptance in most other parts of the world as a function of the small ubiquitous computer applications in industrial and communication sectors.

SOLID-STATE MOTOR DRIVES

Emerging simultaneously with solid-state logic for the operation portion of the elevator has been the application of SCR (silcon controlled rectifier) "solid-state" drives, which replace the motor generator set by thyristor firing of the alternating current input resulting in an irregularly shaped waveform of direct current for the main drive motor. While this concept saves from 30 to 35% of the energy consumed by a motor-generator set drive, it introduces mechanical and electrical vibrations that can be serious if not anticipated in the design of the equipment or the associated structure. The drive introduces into the electrical feeder system supplying the elevators a notching on the alternating current wave form which, as a function of impedance in the supply system, may or may not be significant in disturbing other solid-state logic equipment that is installed by owners or tenants in the building. This notching, as it is transformed into the direct current supplying the drive motor, can create a mechanical vibration as a function of the supply hertz that is structureborne to other occupied areas. It is essential in designing a building to recognize that shortly most manufacturers will be standardizing this kind of equipment and that appropriate measures should be taken to understand the requirements of the electrical and structural interfaces so that the resulting human environment, along with sensitive electronic support equipment, is not disturbed.

TRAVELING CABLE COMPENSATION

Current practice in many applications is to substitute chain compensation for the traditional tensioned rope compensation involving tensioning weights and sheaves for speeds up to 4.0 m per second (800 fpm). Current developments have indicated that for speeds of 3.5 m per second (700 fpm) and below, chain compensation, with its attendant problems of noise and sway, can be eliminated by the installation of circular cross-section traveling cable with a steel core. The sole purpose of such cable is to provide mechanical compensation, as it does not interact electrically. It is provided with standard hitch arrangements on the underside of the car and on the underside of the counterweight frames, with circular restraints mounted horizontally in the pit below the buffers so as to prevent sway. This procedure has been prototyped successfully and indications from major manufacturers are that the concept will replace tensioned-rope compensation, free-rope compensation, or free-chain compensation at all speeds that do not require tied-down compensation.

Traveling cable compensation will allow the installation of elevators, without excessive pit equipment, at speeds below 4 m per second (800 fpm), even under conditions of building sway dynamics. It also will result in less deep-pit construction, which will conserve the space below the elevator hoistways. It cannot degrade into a noise-producing contact with the car enclosure or elevator platform.

MAIL CART LIFTS

The cart lifts that automatically inject-eject carts in hospitals and health care facilities, described in Chapter SC-4 of the original Monograph, have been extended successfully now to encompass mail cart delivery in high-rise buildings for distribution of on-floor manual carts to deliver mail, office supplies, computer printouts, and the products of reproduction facilities, such as bulk or engineering drawings. In New York City such an automated inject-eject cart lift is currently under construction that will travel over 40 stories at a speed 5.0 m per second (1000 fpm). The equipment is a gearless drive with a capacity of 400 kg (880 lbs) in each cart with its associated live load. This equipment has been successfully prototyped in lower-rise buildings at lower speeds. Where the horizontal delivery of mail, office supplies, and reproduced documents is manually conducted on the floor of a building, it seems that this concept will emerge as a highly cost-effective product addition to the vertical transportation industry.

ELEVATOR RIDE CHARACTERISTICS

The elevator ride characteristics suggested in Chapter SC-4 of the original Monograph have now been universally accepted as a performance specification among all the major manufacturers on an international basis, to respond to the concept of performance standards and specifications. It is essential to a major project that the elevators be designed to provide the most comfortable human environment during the transportation cycle that is commercially available. The advent of horizontal acceleration specifications should eventually be supplemented with vertical acceleration specifications to completely define the comfort of quality elevator installations.

FUTURE AREAS OF EMPHASIS

Building Sway

It is essential that all future high-rise buildings identify, prior to the development of bid documents, the static and dynamic deflections of a building so that the elevator manufacturers can appropriately respond to these conditions in the design of the equipment, since each manufacturer's equipment will respond differently to a given set of building conditions. As a minimum the specifications should identify the north-south axis period and anticipated displacement, along with the east-west axis period and displacement. If torsional data are available, they too should be included to fully acquaint the prospective elevator contractor with the environment in which the equipment must operate.

Human Engineering

During the development of elevators, escalators, moving walks, and all other vertical or horizontal transportation apparatus that involve pedestrian dynamics, it is important that the design engineers be concerned with the human-engineering factors of pedestrians, rather than accepting what has been postulated in the past without adequate testing or observation. It is further emphasized that any standardization programs should take into consideration human-engineering factors prior to standardization, so that the standards developed will be meaningful.

WAITING-PASSENGER EVALUATION

The next major step in the development of vertical transportation is expected to be, in conjunction with microprocessor logic, the determination of the number of passengers waiting for elevator service at each landing. At the moment, the elevator system in a busy high-rise office building can only acknowledge a single *up* and a single *down* landing call. It cannot evaluate the number of passengers waiting for elevator service behind that call. The advent of equipment that can determine the number of passengers waiting at a floor will assist the microprocessor logic in concentrating elevator service at floors with a large number of waiting passengers.

CODE-INDUSTRY INTERACTION

It is essential in the future to provide for meaningful interaction among building code officials and the elevator industry. Both must understand that all of the previously independent building systems now, when combined into the energy management and life-safety systems, become subsystems, and that independent code writing in some disciplines may seriously affect others.

As an example, in the United States a position that was taken by the NFPA in their Code 80 required immediate compliance in labeling an elevator entrance assembly, whereas previously only the door panels had to be labeled. This position resulted in a two-year debate as to the location of a fire since, if the fire was located in the elevator hoistway, there was no existing elevator hardware that would support the door panels and entrance frames in such a test. Subsequently, the code officials agreed that the fire would probably be on the landing side for practical purposes, and the test procedure was rewritten. Immediately following this development, with the technological introduction of drywall, eight years were required to accomplish an industry-wide standard of appropriately labeled construction to accommodate the drywall construction as opposed to the traditional construction using masonry, which supported the elevator entrance frames.

CONDENSED REFERENCES/BIBLIOGRAPHY

The following is a condensed bibliography for this article. It includes all articles referred to or cited in the text. The full citations will be found at the end of the volume, with additional citations for further reading. What is given here should be sufficient information to lead the reader to the correct article: the author, date, and title. In case of multiple authors, only the first name is listed.

Fruin 1970, *Pedestrian Planning and Design*

The Interaction Between Exterior Walls and Building Frames in Historic Tall Buildings

Jerry G. Stockbridge

In recent years, a large number of significant historic high-rise structures have been repaired and renovated. The Woolworth Building in New York, which was designed by Cass Gilbert in about 1910, the Wrigley Building in Chicago, which was designed by Graham, Anderson, Probst and White in about 1921, and the Atlanta City Hall, which was designed in about 1930 by Lloyd Preacher, had experienced significant deterioration (Figs. 1 and 2). The only two types of repairs that were being done were replacing damaged stones and tuckpointing. In no case had in-depth investigations been performed to actually determine what was causing the stones to crack or the mortar joints to deteriorate. In this paper some of the results of the in-depth investigations that now have been performed will be discussed.

During the course of these investigations and renovations, nothing new or revolutionary was discovered, but the importance of designing for realistic

Presented at SSRC Annual Technical Session, Chicago, IL, April 7, 1981. Appears in the 1981 SSRC Annual Proceedings.

interaction between exterior walls and building frames is something the early high-rise designers failed to do. A great deal of time and energy was spent by the original designers on the detailing of the ornamentation of the exterior walls, but there was little or no attention given to the interaction between the exterior masonry walls and the building frame.

The exterior walls of these older high-rise structures were normally about 2½ to 3 ft thick (.76 to .91 m). The exterior walls were usually constructed of 4 in (101 mm) of terra-cotta on the outside, backed up with brick, and finished on the interior with 4 in of clay tile and plaster. The frames in most early high-rise structures were of steel with riveted connections. Outriggers were normally provided at each floor line to support the outer masonry, and a shelf angle was usually provided on the face of the outrigger to specifically

Fig. 1 Woolworth Building, New York

carry the outer 4 in of terra-cotta. The outriggers at each floor line were normally sized to carry one story height of exterior wall. As shown in Fig. 3, the exterior walls were constructed rigidly and solidly around the steel frame members. No horizontal or vertical expansion joints were provided anywhere in the exterior walls to attempt to accommodate differential movements between the exterior walls and the building frame.

Needless to say, with no provisions to accommodate differential movement, significant cracking is developing in most of the historic high-rise structures. Some of the cracking is random and caused by rusting of the steel, freeze-thaw action, and the like. But by far the most cracking is being caused by compressive forces that have developed in the exterior walls

Fig. 2 Wrigley Building, Chicago

because of the failure to accommodate interaction between the frame and the exterior walls.

The unaccommodated vertical compressive forces that have developed in the piers have occurred because of a number of factors. First, terra-cotta, like all clay materials, is as small after firing as it is ever going to be in its entire life. While in service, it will have a tendency to grow. If this growth is restrained it will, of course, induce compressive stresses. Second, terra-cotta, like all other materials, has a tendency to expand when it gets hot and contract when it gets cold. Therefore, on hot summer days when the exterior walls try to expand and are restrained by the steel frame, which is in a controlled environment, compressive forces again will develop. Third, because no space was provided below the shelf angles at each floor line, the angles could not deflect slightly to carry the loads intended. Stacking has taken place in the exterior walls of the building, with the lower floors carrying loads that were intended for shelf angles higher up in the building. Fourth, because the steel frame is rigidly built into the exterior walls, many of the floor loadings that were intended to be carried by the columns in the exterior walls are actually being carried by the masonry in the walls. Fifth and finally, when wind forces hit the side of the building, the masonry walls tend to take a lot of the forces that were intended for the steel frame, because the steel frame is rigidly built into the exterior walls.

Fig. 3 Masonry removed during repair clearly shows how the exterior walls were constructed rigidly and solidly around the steel frame, with no provisions to accommodate differential movements.

To develop repairs that properly addressed the existing conditions, a number of strain-relief testing programs were undertaken on these old high-rise structures to determine the actual buildup of pressure that has taken place over the years. Strain-relief tests are performed by attaching strain gages to the face of the exterior walls, taking an initial set of readings, cutting around the piece of terra-cotta containing the gages to relieve any pressure in the face of the wall, and then taking a final set of readings. Figures 4 and 5 show strain-relief tests being performed. A comparison of the first set of readings with a follow-up set of readings indicates the amount

Fig. 4 Saw cuts being made to relieve stress in a pier after gages have been installed and initial readings taken

of strain that was released when the piece of terra-cotta was cut free from the wall. Samples of the terra-cotta are then removed from the wall, taken back to the laboratory, and tested to develop the modulus of elasticity of the material, and the recorded strains in the field are converted to stresses.

If the walls in the historic structures were performing as the designers had intended, the levels of the stress at each floor line would normally be on the order of 15 psi, assuming a 15-ft story height. The actual level of stress measured in many of the structures runs as high as 2,000 to 3,000 psi. The actual stresses that exist in the walls may even be greater than the levels actually measured, because it is highly unlikely that terra-cotta is completely elastic. It is much more likely that some plastic deformation has taken place

Fig. 5 Strain gages on a piece of terra-cotta that has been stress-relieved

over the years and complete recovery of the material is not taking place when it is cut free.

As part of the renovation of many of these high-rise structures, horizontal expansion joints have been installed into the existing building to relieve the buildup of high compressive forces before beginning the repair of the damaged pieces. To determine the spacing required for the horizontal expansion joints, it has been our normal practice to instrument a representative pier, cut in a horizontal joint at one floor level, and measure how much the forces are relieved horizontally, both up and down from the cut.

In the case of the Atlanta City Hall, it appears that the expansion joints can be spaced at more than one-floor intervals. On the Wrigley Building in Chicago, the joints were installed at every floor line; and at the Woolworth Building in New York, where the terra-cotta was very rigidly anchored to the back-up material, it was necessary to cut in at every other joint to relieve the buildup of pressure.

In the case of the Atlanta City Hall and the Wrigley Building, it is possible to install the joint at existing shelf angles and therefore the joints can be left open after cutting and then caulked to accommodate future movements.

On the Woolworth Building, however, where there are no shelf angles at floor lines and it was necessary to cut into the wall at every other course, it was impossible to install expansion joints to accommodate future movements. Instead, it was necessary to refill the joints with mortar again after they had been cut out. The mortar in the joints did not create a condition that could accommodate future movements without the development of some stress, but the cutting out of the joints did relieve some stresses that are unlikely ever to develop again. These were the stresses induced by the moisture expansion of the brick, those associated with stacking, and those resulting from the loads that were transferred in from the floor system. It is true that some compressive forces, related to thermal effects and wind forces, will continue to occur in the future, but these forces should be significantly lower than the ones the building had to tolerate in the past, and it is anticipated that the performance of the building will be substantially improved.

New Developments in Tall Buildings—Foundations

W. F. Swiger

This discussion reviews recent developments in foundation construction and design, especially slurry walls, large capacity piles, and increasing concerns about noise during pile driving.

Changes in the design and construction of foundations for tall buildings have been and continue to be developmental. Only rarely are there major changes or breakthroughs that suddenly alter methods or design. The general state of practice lags behind the state of the art, if we define the state of the art as the practices followed by a relatively few leading firms either in engineering or construction. Developments come when one of these bellwether firms adapts a new technique or new equipment to construction or undertakes a more advanced analysis permitting a modification in a foundation concept that results in savings. As they prove successful these new procedures are then adopted by other organizations.

SUPPORT OF EXCAVATIONS

Typical of the lag in the adoption of new techniques is the use of slurry walls for supporting the walls of deep excavations. A technique first used in Europe, it has been available in this country for more than 15 years, but initially usage was limited to a few projects. Today slurry walls are commonly used. Frequently they are designed to serve also as the exterior wall of inhabited spaces without requiring additional concrete walls. Decorative treatment, such as tile, may be used. A modification of slurry wall technique, which is being used to a limited extent, is post-tensioning the walls to develop greater rigidity, that is, to have less deflection or the ability to resist higher lateral loads for a given thickness of material.

About 20 years ago, cross-lot bracing was used almost routinely for the support of deep excavations. Today support by post-tensioned tiebacks anchored into soil or rock is far more common. Cross-lot bracing tends to be used only where tiebacks are impracticable because, for example, of interference with existing structures or soil conditions that are not suitable. There have been improvements in the equipment and methods for installing tiebacks. These procedures provide better anchor systems, more economical installation, and adaptability to more difficult conditions, such as bouldery soils and weathered rock.

DEEP FOUNDATIONS

Deep foundations employ either piles or caissons that basically are installed with techniques that have been available for some time. However, the availability of very large pile hammers that can deliver 200,000 ft-lb of energy or more per blow has resulted in some use of large, very high-capacity piles. These large hammers were originally developed for use on offshore structures, and the large piles may have loading capacity approaching that of the caissons of a few years ago. An example is socketed piles, which are constructed by driving a heavy steel pipe to refusal in the rock, then drilling a socket into the rock, and filling the pipe and socket with concrete. These are capable of loads on the order of 1,000 tons each. In some cases, large-capacity, very long piles are being driven to great depths in areas where rock cannot be reached.

NOISE

A factor affecting the design of structures and the construction of foundations is the concern today with noise and vibration. OSHA is concerned about the effect of noise and vibration on the health of operators. They presently require that the noise level should not exceed 90 db average over an 8-hour working day. EPA, however, is much more concerned with the impact of noise on the adjacent environment. Although EPA requirements have not yet been formalized, it appears probable at that their requirements will be more restrictive than those of OSHA and more difficult to meet. Some cities have adopted noise codes and are enforcing them now. Such codes frequently limit hours of operations as well as noise levels.

There have been some experimental programs in which attempts were made to reduce the noise levels of pile drivers. Steam-air hammers presently have peak noise levels of about 85 to 90 db. Reduction in noise levels has been achieved in such experimental programs but at a significant increase in the cost of driving piles. Vibratory hammers in themselves are usually less noisy than impact hammers, at about 70 to 75 db. However, power sources may be quite noisy. Several electrically powered vibratory hammers are available and could be used where there is a power supply. Further, available vibratory hammers generally operate in the 10 to 25 Hz range. Vibration of this frequency can be transmitted significant distances through the soil and thus could be a source of annoyance or could damage equipment sensitive to vibrations. High-frequency vibratory hammers have been used in the past, principally on a semiexperimental basis by C. L. Guild. These operate at frequencies well in excess of 100 Hz. High-frequency vibration attenuates quickly in the soil. However, these hammers are no longer available commercially.

THEORY AND DESIGN

Considerable theoretical interest is directed today towards better definition of constituitive relations for soil. The basic problem is expressing general stress-strain relations in mathematical terms, especially in terms adaptable to machine calculation. Such approaches have been used for certain problems, such as both heave of the bottom of deep excavations and soil structure interaction for static and dynamic loadings. However, at this time they are not generally adaptable to most problems and analysis is generally made using procedures that are well established in the literature. Still, continuing research may be expected in this field.

Research is also continuing in the investigation of gross instabilities in soils, such as liquefaction; group behavior of piles, a subject that has received attention on and off for more than 50 years; and soil dynamics. The use of probabilistic approaches to analysis and design is receiving some attention but is currently restricted to occasional special problems.

CONDENSED REFERENCES/BIBLIOGRAPHY

The following is a condensed bibliography for this article. It includes all articles referred to or cited in the text. The full citations will be found at the end of the volume, with additional citations for further reading. What is given here should be sufficient information to lead the reader to the correct article: the author, date, and title. In case of multiple authors, only the first name is listed.

Desai 1977, *Numerical Methods in Geotechnical Engineering*
Institution of Civil Engineering 1980, *Design Parameters in Geotechnical Engineering*
Kessler 1980, *Pile Driver Noise Control*
Weltman 1980, *Noise and Vibration from Piling Operations*

Systems and Concepts

CONDENSED REFERENCES/BIBLIOGRAPHY

The following is a condensed bibliography for this part. It contains bibliographic citations that are in addition to those cited with the articles in this part. The full citations can be found at the end of the volume. What is given here should be sufficient information to lead the reader to the correct article: author, date, and title. In the case of multiple authors, only the first named is listed.

Chen 1981, *Limit Analysis in Soil Mechanics and its Applications to Lateral Earth Pressure Problems*
Chen 1982, *Constitutive Equations for Engineering Materials*
Rosman 1981, *Classification of Floor Structures*
Roy 1977, *Introduction to Tall Building Structures*
Sarrazin 1979, *Isolation and Absorption of Seismic Actions in Buildings*

Criteria and Loading

Introductory Review

Leslie E. Robertson

In 1980, as the Monograph volume *Criteria and Loading* went to press, many of the more than 200 persons who contributed text to that volume were concerned that the material might not stand the tests of professional scrutiny and of time. Now, with this first Monograph update volume, it is clear that the original volume has provided well for the area of "Loading" but that some additions are needed in the area of "Criteria."

In the Foreword to the Monograph volume Dr. Beedle, responding to the available text, notes, "This volume deals with the loads to which tall buildings are subjected, and with the precise definition of the related structural requirements that are necessary before a client's basic needs can be translated into a safe design." In the Preface, Messrs. Naka, Gaylord, Mainstone, Lu, and Robertson reversed the emphasis in stating, "Structural safety and serviceability become increasingly important considerations in the choice of overall form of a building as its height increases. The design criteria by which they are assured should therefore be of interest not only to structural designers but also to all others connected with overall planning." The emphasis on "Loading," then, is likely to diminish in favor of the larger, more complex, and more difficult topic of "Criteria."

In May of 1981, the Council on Tall Buildings and Urban Habitat held a meeting in New York to discuss the general topic "New Developments in Tall Buildings." In the papers that follow, G. Robert Fuller, representing the Committee on Gravity Loads and Technical Effects (CL-1) notes that the NBS report entitled *Probability Based Load Criterion* addressed only ultimate

271

limit states, and that serviceability limit states were not considered. He asks that future research be structured to develop criteria for deflection, drift, rotation, vibration, and other failures affecting functional use, durability, and the like.

Toshio Shiga discusses the June, 1978, earthquake centered off of the east coast of Miyagi prefecture, Japan. In that prefecture, some 1,400 dwellings were completely destroyed, 27 persons were killed, and about 11,000 people were injured. He notes that more than half of the deaths were due to falling walls of cinder blocks or stone—all nonstructural elements. His findings did not surprise most knowledgeable engineers. The impact of structure deformations on the performance of nonstructural elements will receive increasing attention in the years ahead. This attention will result in improved serviceability criteria for the deformations of buildings under seismic conditions.

The Sixth International Conference on Wind Engineering was held in Australia in March of 1983. That conference focused on the issues of the serviceability of building structures as they related to cladding, pedestrian-level winds, the structural system, and so forth. It is likely that the findings of this conference, as they become reorganized so as to respond to the needs of the readers of the Monograph, will provide an important input into the development of criteria for the wind-resistance of structures.

Duiliu Sfintesco, as always a most thoughtful engineer, opens his remarks by noting that the successive updates of the Monograph will bring new "life into this unique reference work by periodically reflecting both new developments and new perspectives in all fields covered by the various chapters." His words, however, are particularly relevant to that of fire in tall buildings. New studies are leading to the conclusion that arbitrary fire ratings for structures may not be defensible—that fire ratings may more properly be related to the fire-related criteria that need be met by the given structure. Almost surely the further developments in the various Monograph updates will speak with ever-increasing concern both to the fire safety of existing buildings and to the need to control the installation of combustibles into existing structures.

The chapter on accidental loading is not represented in this update both because of the high quality of the material contained in the Monograph and because of the overlap of interest with the chapter on fire; that is, fire is the dominant form of accidental loading.

The Monograph, in speaking of quality criteria, cites the need to begin the process of quality control in the planning stages. The text, however, deals almost exclusively with the control of the quality of materials, workmanship, and the like. It is clear, however, that the entire process—planning, design, tendering, and construction—needs to be governed by a homogeneous quality control document. A comprehensive quality assurance approach from the initial conception, through design, construction and operations, and up to demolition is sorely needed.

Again, because of the high quality of the material in the Monograph, the chapter on structural safety and probabilistic methods is not represented in this update. However, the material is not without need for further study. We see a particular need both to provide material that can be assimilated by a wider audience and to better correlate that material with the committees on loading and on quality assurance.

Gravity Loads and
Temperature Effects (CL-1)

Introduction

G. Robert Fuller

A revision to the American National Standards Institute (ANSI) Standard A58 *Building Code Requirements for Minimum Design Loads in Buildings and Other Structures,* was approved in April 1982.

This Monograph update report also presents a synopsis of related activities at the U. S. Department of Commerce, National Bureau of Standards (NBS), to develop a "Probability Based Load Criterion." NBS Special Publication No. SP 577, published in June, 1980, contains a design methodology and a set of load factors for "limit states" design for all types of building structural materials. A "load and resistance factor" design is presented that identifies both load and resistance factors based on a probabilistic safety analysis that will provide desired uniform safety levels.

FUTURE OUTLOOK

The NBS "Criterion" only addresses "ultimate limit states." "Serviceability limit states," which affect the function of buildings, are not considered. Therefore, future research and studies should consider developing factors, such as deflection, drift, rotation, functional use, water drainage, excessive local damage affecting appearance, use or durability, and excessive vibrations.

The "Criterion" also only emphasizes life/safety aspects similar to building codes. Therefore, economic loss factors and life cycle costs (maintenance, repair, and retrofit) should be considered.

Gravity Loads and
Temperature Effects (CL-1)

Report on
New Developments

G. Robert Fuller

The standard for design loads most often referenced in the United States, namely the American National Standards Institute (ANSI) — Standard A58.1 *Building Code Requirements for Minimum Design Loads in Buildings and Other Structures,* was revised in 1982. Major revisions were made in criteria for wind, snow, earthquake, and abnormal loads. Substantial increases in design snow loads and revised considerations for wind effects on snow load were provided.

As a corollary to ANSI A58.1, the National Bureau of Standards (NBS) of the U.S. Department of Commerce developed a "Probability Based Load Criterion." This was published in June, 1980, as NBS Special Publication No. SP 577. The authors were Bruce Ellingwood of NBS; Theodore V. Galambos of Washington University, St. Louis, Missouri; James G. MacGregor of University of Alberta, Canada; and C. Allin Cornell of Massachusetts Institute of Technology, Cambridge, Massachusetts.

The primary objectives of SP 577 were as follows:

> To recommend a methodology and set of load factors for "limit states" design and provide load definitions for ANSI A58.1 that are appropriate for all types of building materials (structural steel, reinforced and prestressed concrete, heavy timber, engineered masonry, cold-formed steel, aluminum, and so on); and

To provide a methodology for selection of resistance factors consistent with the load factors, for various material specification groups.

Appropriate limit states are defined in the proposed design process so that the designer can consider several different modes of possible structural behavior. The particular method outlined identifies resistance factors and load factors, and therefore, it is termed "load and resistance factor design."

Recommendations in the report are confined solely to "ultimate limit states," since these are of particular concern for standards and specifications, which are written to protect the public from physical harm caused by a failure. "Serviceability limit states," which primarily affect the function of the building, are not considered.

Basic design procedures to achieve the stated objectives consist of a probabilistic safety analysis to guide the selection of load factors that provide desired levels of uniformity in safety:

Step 1: Estimate the level of reliability implied by various design standards and specifications (for example, ACI 318, AISC Specification, and the like, and loads from ANSI A58.1) for various members and elements (for instance, beams, columns, fillet welds, and so on). Use realistic best estimates of distribution types and parameters and identify the "reliability index" factor.

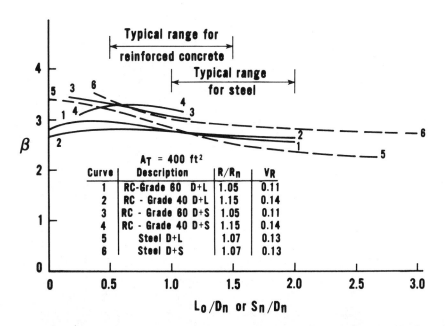

Fig. 1 Reliability index for steel and reinforced concrete beams conforming to current criteria—gravity loads *(NBS, 1980 and Ellingwood, 1982)*

Step 2: Observe the reliability index levels over ranges of material, limit states, nominal load ratios (for example, live/dead, wind/dead, snow/dead), load combinations, and geographical locations. For example, see Figs. 1–7 (Figs. 4.1–4.7 in SP 577 (NBS, 1980)) (Ellingwood, 1982).

Step 3: Based on observed reliability index levels, determine load factors consistent with the implied safety level and selected safety-checking format.

Step 4: Display relationships between implied reliability index levels for these load factors and nominal loads for material statistics (mean resistances and coefficients of variation) against alternate resistance factors. Typical resistance factors are shown in Tables 1–3 (Tables 5.3, 5.6, and 5.8 in NBS-SP 577 (NBS, 1980)) (Ellingwood, 1982).

The load criterion and methodology proposed have not yet been adopted by ANSI. However, discussion of the recommendations and their probable effect on structural design practice are underway. Extensive study of this methodology will also have to be achieved by material-specification writing groups prior to adoption of the load criterion in their standards.

One deficiency of the criterion is that, as already noted, it ignores serviceability limit states, although several are identified as being important, such as the following:

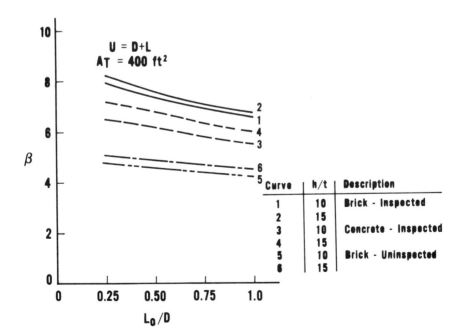

Fig. 2 Reliability index for nonreinforced brick and concrete masonry walls conforming to current criteria *(NBS, 1980 and Ellingwood, 1982)*

Table 1 Optimal load and resistance factors for gravity loads *(NBS, 1980)*

Material	Combination	Optimum values $\emptyset$	Optimum values γ_L, γ_S	Optimum $\emptyset$ for $\gamma_D = 1.2, \gamma_L = 1.6$
Steel beam	D + L	0.96	2.10	0.78
$(\beta_o = 3)$	D + S	1.05	2.32	0.79
R/C beam, Gr. 60	D + L	0.87	1.83	0.81
$(\beta_o = 3)$	D + S	0.93	1.93	0.84
R/C beam, Gr. 40	D + L	0.82	1.61	0.81
$(\beta_o = 3)$	D + S	0.85	1.56	0.86
Glulam beam*	D + L	0.59	1.38	0.66
$(\beta_o = 2.5)$	D + S	0.59	1.08	0.77
Brick masonry Wall* $(\beta_o = 7.5)$	D + L	0.38	4.10	0.22
Brick masonry Wall* $(\beta_o = 5.0)$	D + L	0.52	2.45	0.41
Concrete masonry Wall* $(\beta_o = 6.5)$	D + L	0.41	3.28	0.27
Concrete masonry Wall* $(\beta_o = 5.0)$	D + L	0.49	2.38	0.40

*$\bar{R}/R_n$ assumed to equal to 1.0 for illustration.

Table 2 Resistance factors for metal structures *(NBS, 1980)*

Type element	L_o/D_n	Target β	$\bar{R}/R_n$	V_R	$\emptyset$
Compact steel beam	1	3	1.07	0.13	0.82
Tension member, F_y	1	3	1.05	0.11	0.83
Tension member, F_u	1	4	1.10	0.11	0.71
Continuous beam	1	3	1.11	0.13	0.85
Elastic beam, LTB	1	3	1.03	0.12	0.80
Inelastic beam, LTB	1	3	1.11	0.14	0.83
Beam-Columns	1	3	1.07	0.15	0.79
Plate Girders, Flexure	1	3	1.08	0.12	0.84
Plate Girders, Shear	1	3	1.14	0.16	0.82
Composite Beams	1	3	1.04	0.14	0.78
Columns, $\lambda \leq 0.5$	1	3	1.08	0.14	0.83
Columns, $\lambda > 0.5$	1	3.5	1.08	0.14	0.75
Fillet welds	1	4.5	1.47	0.18	0.71
HSS bolts, A325, tension	1	4.5	1.20	0.09	0.73
HSS bolts, A325, shear	1	4.5	1.00	0.10	0.59
HSS bolts, A325, shear	1	4.0	1.00	0.10	0.65
CF beams, stiffened flanges	5	3.0	1.17	0.17	0.77
Aluminum beams	5	3.0	1.10	0.08	0.82

- Excessive deflection, drift, or rotation affecting appearance, functional use, or drainage of water or causing damage to nonstructural components;

- Excessive local damage (cracking, splitting, spalling, or local yielding, or slip) affecting appearance, use, or durability of the structure; and

- Excessive vibration affecting comfort of occupants or operation of equipment.

Similar to building codes, the criterion emphasizes only life/safety and health aspects. Economic loss factors, and maintenance, repair and retrofit costs are ignored. Failure of a building to function properly is a failure of the building, even though collapse is not involved.

Table 3 Values of resistance factors for reinforced concrete members *(NBS, 1980)*

Action	Type of member	$\bar{R}/R_n$	V_R	Range of ϕ for $L_o/D_n = 0.25 - 2.0$
Flexure, reinforced concrete, $\beta = 3.0$				
Beam, Grade 40, $\rho = 0.35\rho_b$		1.14	0.14	0.82 — 0.84
Beam, Grade 60, $\rho = 0.57\rho_b$		1.05	0.11	0.80 — 0.85
Beam, Grade 60, $\rho = 0.73\rho_b$		1.01	0.12	0.76 — 0.80
Two way slabs, Grade 60		1.16	0.15	0.83 — 0.86
Continuous, one-way slabs		1.22	0.16	0.85 — 0.88
Flexure, plant produced pretensioned concrete, $\beta = 3.0$				
Double T $\omega_p = 0.054$		1.06	0.057	0.86 — 0.95
Beam $\omega_p = 0.228$		1.06	0.083	0.83 — 0.90
Beam $\omega_p = 0.295$		1.04	0.10	0.80 — 0.86
Flexure, cast-in-situ post-tensioned concrete $\beta = 3.0$				
$\omega_p = 0.228$		1.03	0.11	0.78 — 0.83
$\omega_p = 0.295$		1.05	0.14	0.76 — 0.79
Tied columns, compression failures, $\beta = 3.5$				
3000 psi concrete, short		1.05	0.16	0.65 — 0.69
5000 psi concrete, short		0.95	0.14	0.61 — 0.66
5000 psi concrete, $l/h = 20$		1.10	0.17	0.66 — 0.70
Spiral columns, compression failures, $\beta = 3.0$				
3000 psi concrete, short		1.05	0.16	0.74 — 0.76
5000 psi concrete, short		0.95	0.14	0.69 — 0.72
Shear, $\beta = 3.5$				
Beams without stirrups		0.93	0.21	0.50 — 0.52
Beams with minimum stirrups		1.00	0.19	0.60 — 0.64
Beams with $\rho_v f_y = 150$		1.09	0.17	0.66 — 0.70

Note: *1 psi = 6895 N/m²*

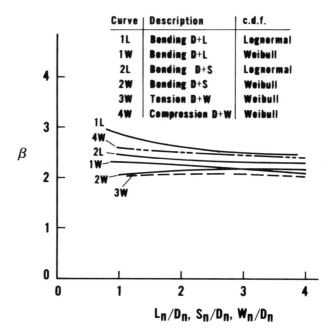

Fig. 3 Reliability index for "Glulam" members conforming to current criteria *(NBS, 1980 and Ellingwood, 1982)*

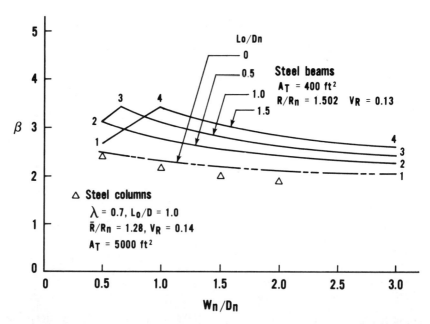

Fig. 4 Reliability index for steel members conforming to current criteria—gravity plus wind loads *(NBS, 1980 and Ellingwood, 1982)*

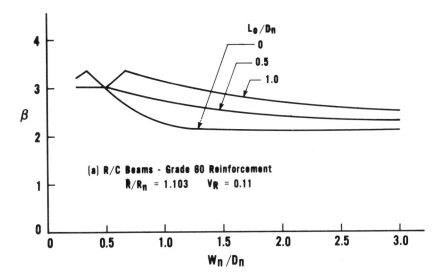

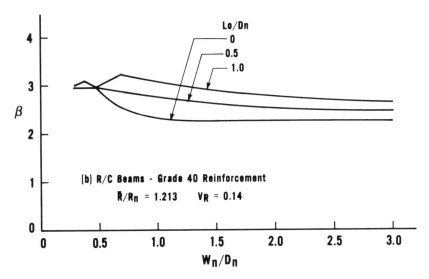

Fig. 5 Reliability index for reinforced concrete beams conforming to current criteria—
gravity plus wind load *(NBS, 1980 and Ellingwood, 1982)*

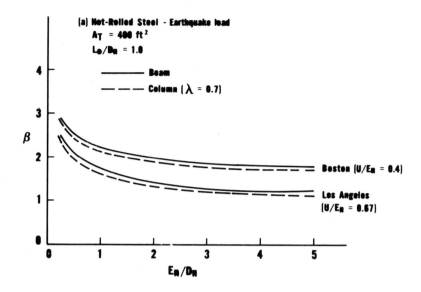

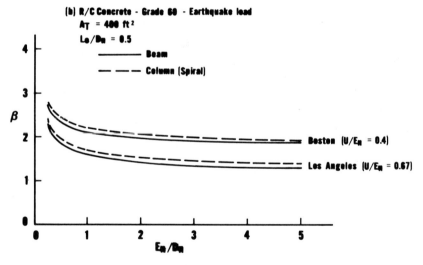

Fig. 6 Reliability index for steel and reinforced concrete beams—gravity plus earthquake load *(NBS, 1980 and Ellingwood, 1982)*

CONDENSED REFERENCES/BIBLIOGRAPHY

The following is a condensed bibliography for this article. It includes all articles referred to or cited in the text. The full citations will be found at the end of the volume, with additional citations for further reading. What is given here should be sufficient information to lead the reader to the correct article: the author, date, and title. In case of multiple authors, only the first name is listed.

ACI 1977, *Building Code Requirements for Reinforced Concrete*
AISC 1978, *Specification for the Design, Fabrication and Erection of Steel Buildings*
AISI 1968, *Specification for the Design of Cold-Formed Steel Structural Members*
American Institute of Timber Construction 1974, *Standard Specifications for Structural Glued-*
Allen 1969, *Safety Factors for Stress Reversal*
Aluminum Association 1976, *Specifications for Aluminum Structures*
Ang 1974, *Reliability Bases of Structural Safety and Design*
ANSI 1982, *Building Code Requirements for Minimum Design Loads in Buildings and*

Brick Institute of America 1969, *Building Code Requirements for Engineered Brick Masonry*

Comite European de Beton 1978, *Common Unified Rules for Different Types of Construction*
Comite European de Beton 1976, *First Order Reliability Concepts for Design Codes*
Construction Industry Research & Information Association 1977, *Rationalization of Safety and*
Cornell 1969, *A Probability-Based Structural Code*
Corotis 1977, *Probability Models for Live Load Survey Results*

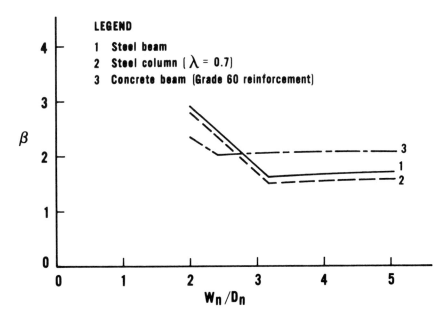

Fig. 7 Current reliability index for steel and reinforced concrete members—counteracting loads *(NBS, 1980 and Ellingwood, 1982)*

Ellingwood 1978, *Reliability Basis of Load and Resistance Factors for Reinforced Concrete Design*
Ellingwood 1982, *Assessment of Current Design Practice*

Ferry Borges 1971, *Structural Safety*
Freudenthal 1966, *The Analysis of Structural Safety*

Galambos 1978, *Load and Resistance Factor Design*

Larabee 1979, *A Combination Procedure for a Wide Class of Loading Processes*
Lind 1978, *Risk Analysis Procedure II*

MacGregor 1976, *Safety and Limit States Design for Reinforced Concrete*
Mirza 1976, *A Statistical Study of Variables Affecting the Strength of Reinforced Normal Weight*

NBS 1980, *SP 577—Probability Based Load Criterion*
National Concrete and Masonry Association 1968, *Specifications for the Design and Construction of*
National Research Council of Canada 1977, *National Building Code of Canada*

Rackwitz 1976, *Note on Discrete Safety Checking When Using Non-Normal Stochastic Models*
Rackwitz 1977, *An Algorithm for the Calculation of Structural Reliability under Combined Loading*

Simiu 1975, *Statistical Analysis of Extreme Winds*

Turkstra 1972, *Theory of Structural Design Decisions*

Wen 1977, *Statistical Combination of Extreme Loads*

Damage to Buildings in the 1978 Miyagi-Ken-Oki Earthquake

Toshio Shiga

EARTHQUAKE

A destructive earthquake, with Richter magnitude of 7.4, occurred at 5:14 P.M. on June 12, 1978, off the east coast of Miyagi prefecture on the mainland of Japan. The epicenter was located at 38°09′ N latitude, 142°13′ E longitude, and the depth was about 40 km.

The earthquake caused severe damage, primarily in the Miyagi prefecture. Damage in and around Sendai City was most significant. Sendai City has a population of 630,000 and is the center of governmental and commercial activities in the northeast area of Japan. This "direct hit" on a modern city has become a matter of great concern in various social and technical fields. Figure 1 is the map showing locations of the epicenter, Miyagi prefecture, and Sendai City.

In Miyagi prefecture, 1,377 wooden dwellings were completely destroyed, 6,213 dwellings were partially destroyed and dwellings with little or moderate damage amounted to 125,375. Twenty-seven people were killed by the earthquake and 10,962 people were injured. It should be noted that more than half of the dead were victims of falling walls made of cinderblock or stone used as fences, privacy walls, and so on.

Fires took place at several chemical laboratories but were extinguished immediately.

GROUND MOTIONS

Strong-motion accelerographs mounted in the basements of buildings in the central part of Sendai City where the ground is hard diluvium (Fig. 2) recorded the maximum acceleration of 250 gals to 440 gals (1000 gals = 1 g). Table 1 shows the maximum ground accelerations measured in Miyagi prefecture.

One measurement was taken at the top floor of a nine-story concrete encased steel-frame building that houses the department of civil and architectural engineering of Tohoku University. At this building, located on the top of a hill about 4 km west of the city center, the maximum acceleration of 1,040 gals was observed, which is the largest building response

Fig. 1 Location of epicenter and distribution of ground motion intensity (I~V: intensity scale of Japan Meteorological Agency)

ever recorded. Despite this high-response acceleration, the damage to the building frame was minor. Figure 3 shows the whole view of the building. Simulation analysis of the response behavior of the building will be shown in a later section.

STRUCTURAL DAMAGE

In Sendai City five reinforced concrete buildings completely collapsed and ten were severely damaged, requiring considerable repair. More than ten steel frame buildings collapsed or were heavily damaged. Figures 4–11 show examples of structural damage.

Collapsed buildings were all low-rise buildings of less than three stories and had the minimum of columns, walls, and braces. They were considered

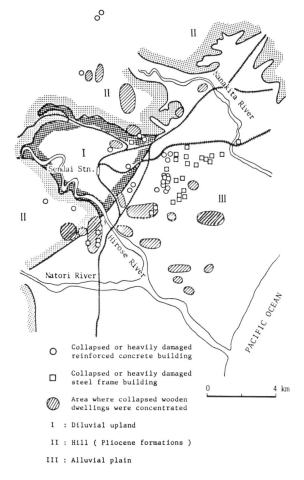

○ Collapsed or heavily damaged
   reinforced concrete building

▢ Collapsed or heavily damaged
   steel frame building

▨ Area where collapsed wooden
   dwellings were concentrated

0   4 km

I   : Diluvial upland

II : Hill (Pliocene formations)

III : Alluvial plain

Fig. 2 Soil condition and the distribution of damaged buildings in the Sendai area

to be lacking in enough redundant strength or ductility for energy absorption to prevent collapse.

Heavy damage to prestressed concrete piles was found in two buildings. One was an 11-story apartment house and the other was a 14-story apartment house. Damage to the upper structure was minor in these two buildings. There were several other buildings in which piles were damaged to some extent. The possibility of pile damage had not been fully recognized before this earthquake.

It was observed that most buildings that suffered severe structural damage were concentrated in the soft alluvial area in the eastern part of Sendai City. On the other hand, many buildings located in the central part of the city on a hard diluvial upland formed by the Hirose River suffered only minor structural damage such as small cracks in walls.

There were seven high-rise buildings over 45 m in height in the center of the city. Their damage was quite minor.

The close correlation of local soil conditions to earthquake damage is one of the very important factors observed in this earthquake. Figure 2

Table 1 Maximum ground accelerations in the 1978 Miyagi-ken-oki earthquake

Site	(numerals indicate number of stories)	Instrument location	Direction	Max. acceleration (gals)
Ishinomaki City	Kaihoku Bridge	Ground Level	LG	191
			TR	273
			UD	116
Shiogama City	Shiogama Harbour	Ground Level	NS	265
			EW	273
			UD	166
	Bldg. of Sumitomo Life (18) Insurance	B2F	NS	251
			EW	241
			UD	91
	Bldg. of Shichijushichi (14) Bank	B1F	NS	295
Sendai			EW	146
City			UD	90
	Bldg. of Japan National (6) Railway Office	B1F	NS	432
			EW	233
			UD	95
	Bldg. of Tohoku Univ. (9)	1F	NS	258
			EW	203
			UD	153
Natori City	Tarumizu Dam	Gallery	LG	235
			TR	185
			UD	79

LG: Longitudinal direction   TR: Transverse Direction

Fig. 3 Faculty of engineering building, Tohoku University, Sendai City: the peak acceleration of 1,040 gals was recorded at the ninth floor of the building.

Fig. 4 Collapse of a three-story reinforced concrete building: Taiyo Fishery Company building, Sendai City

shows the correlation between soil conditions and the distribution of damaged buildings in the Miyagi-ken-oki earthquake.

The principle of earthquake-resistant design adopted for ordinary buildings in Japan is that we might tolerate some repairable damage to structural frames, but no injury to people should be allowed. In view of this principle of earthquake-resistant design, it is expected that the majority of buildings in the area of strong-shaking could withstand earthquake forces fairly well, and the damage to buildings in Sendai City in this earthquake was acceptable in general, although several buildings collapsed or were heavily damaged in the areas of unfavorable geological and soil conditions.

NONSTRUCTURAL DAMAGE

Other topics for consideration are the damage to nonstructural elements such as secondary walls and finishings, the damage to building equipment, and the overturning of furniture, machines, and computers. This kind of damage caused serious loss of function in many buildings, even if structural damage was slight. For example, frightening experiences were reported by the residents in the upper floors of a high-rise apartment house in which doors to corridors had been jammed because of the failure of secondary walls adjacent to the doors. Examples of nonstructural damage are illustrated in Figs. 12–20.

Fig. 5 Collapse of a three-story reinforced concrete building: Obisan building, Sendai City

Fig. 6 Failure of a column of a three-story reinforced concrete building: Maruyoshi Building, Sendai City

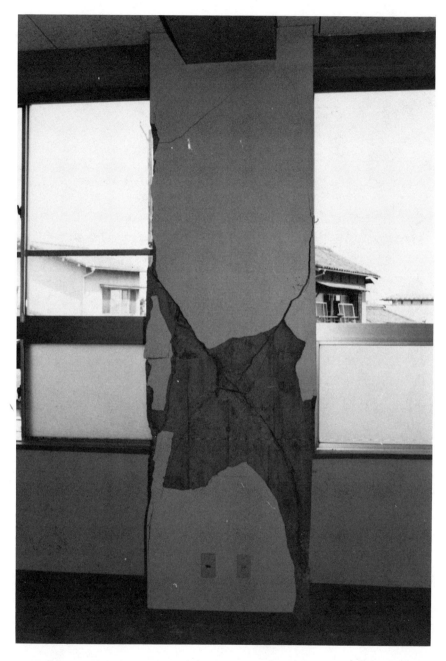

Fig. 7 Shear failure of a column of a three-story reinforced concrete building: Tonan High School, Sendai City

Fig. 8 Shear failure of a column of a three-story reinforced concrete building: Izumi High School, Izumi City

Fig. 9 Collapse of a two-story steel frame warehouse: Sendai Unyu Soko warehouse, Sendai City

Fig. 10 Collapse of an older wood frame house: Sendai City

Fig. 11 Failure of a prestressed reinforced concrete pile of an 11-story steel frame reinforced concrete building: Koriyama Public Apartment house, Sendai City

Fig. 12 Shear failure of nonstructural walls of a six-story reinforced concrete building: Maruhon building, Sendai City

Fig. 13 Shear failure of a nonstructural wall of a 14-story steel frame reinforced concrete building: Sanii Haitsu Takasago apartment house, Sendai City

Fig. 14 Falling off of precast concrete curtain walls of a four-story steel frame building: Sasaki building, Izumi City *(Courtesy: Kahoku Sinpō-Newspaper)*

Fig. 15 Falling off of exterior finishing tiles of a steel frame reinforced concrete building: Toho building, Sendai City

Fig. 16 Breakage of window panes of a nine-story steel frame reinforced concrete building: Tohoku Electric Company building, Sendai City

Fig. 17 Failure of a fiber reinforced panel of a water tank on a roof: Sendai City

Fig. 18 Overturning of radiators: Izumi High School, Izumi City

Fig. 19 Failure of a concrete block wall: Sendai City

An important lesson from this earthquake is that "structural safety" and "functional safety" must be considered in parallel in the earthquake-resistant design of buildings.

SIMULATION ANALYSIS

Nonlinear response analysis of the 9-story building of Tohoku University was conducted, and the calculated response waveforms were compared with the observed accelerograms. Analysis considered the inelastic properties of constituent members such as beams, columns, and walls acting separately. Each member was represented by the linear member model having inelastic bending hinges at both ends and an inelastic shear spring at its midspan. Response calculation was made for transverse and longitudinal directions separately.

Figure 21 shows the plan and section of the building. The main resistance to seismic force is provided by two side-walls in the transverse direction and two staircase cores. Figure 22 shows the observed accelerations during the earthquake at the first floor of the building. Figure 23 shows the comparison of calculated and observed acceleration waveforms at the ninth floor. The agreement between the analysis and the measurement seems to be good.

Fig. 20 Overturning of bookshelves on the seventh floor of the faculty of engineering building: Tohoku University, Sendai City

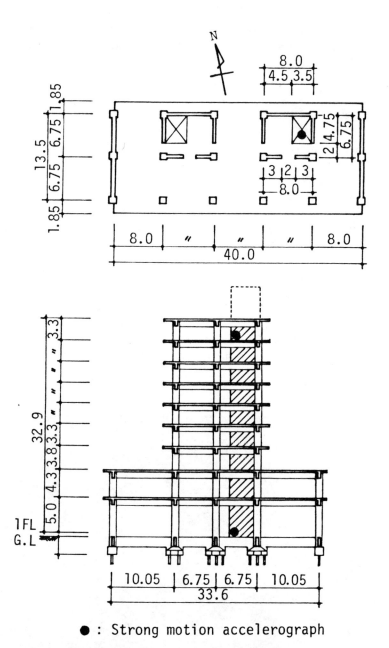

● : Strong motion accelerograph

Fig. 21 Plan and section of the building of the faculty of engineering: Tohoku University

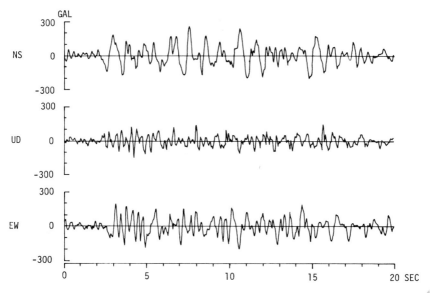

Fig. 22 Observed ground motion at the first floor of the building

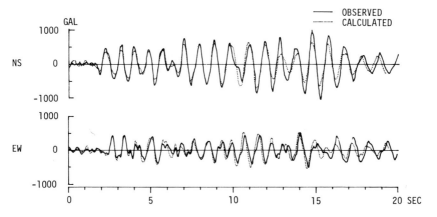

Fig. 23 Comparison of observed and calculated response at the ninth floor of the building

CONDENSED REFERENCES/BIBLIOGRAPHY

The following is a condensed bibliography for this article. It includes all articles referred to or cited in the text. The full citations will be found at the end of the volume, with additional citations for further reading. What is given here should be sufficient information to lead the reader to the correct article: the author, date, and title. In case of multiple authors, only the first name is listed.

Shibata 1980, *Prediction of the Probability of Earthquake Damage to Reinforced Concrete Building*
Shibuya 1980, *Effects of Local Site Conditions on Damage to Buildings during an Earthquake*
Shiga 1980, *Performance of the Building of Engineering*

Update on Wind Loading

A. G. Davenport

The original chapter identified the following wind-associated problems:

1. Structural loading.

2. Structural movements caused by wind.

3. Cladding pressures.

4. Pedestrian wind climate.

5. Air leakage and mechanical systems.

The methods of solution identified for these problems (having varying degrees of effectiveness) include:

Simple static code loads for 1 and 3.

Detailed equivalent static loads using dynamic gust response factors for 1 and 2.

Detailed wind tunnel studies involving 1 through 5.

The verification of these design approaches, generally through full-scale testing, represents an additional area of activity and concern.

The original report summarized various areas of research need and some of these have progressed further and other new needs have been identified. There are a few further developments.

WIND CLIMATE

This area continues to be of primary importance. The systematic calibration of the topographic and terrain influence on the exposure would be advantageous. A special aspect of climatic prediction concerns severe storms such as hurricanes and tornadoes (Georgiou et al., 1983; McDonald, 1980). There is now progress in prediction of these storms in a statistical climatic sense. Monte Carlo simulation of hurricane wind fields based on historical statistics of the large-scale features (tracks, central pressures, and the like) are now well developed. The description of tornado wind fields and statistical prognosis is being actively investigated.

STRUCTURAL INTERACTION WITH WIND

The advent of a new architectural vocabulary for building geometry, away from simple geometric form, gives rise to the greater need for aerodynamic response data. A greater need for information on torsional response is a by-product of the trend to new geometries with aerodynamic centers frequently remote from either mass or stiffness centers of the structure. Suggestions for estimation of the torsional motions are emerging (Davenport, 1981; Evans, 1981).

FULL SCALE STUDIES

The completion of several full scale studies has now given credence both through wind tunnel experiments and gust factor approaches, to the predictions of structural motion.

Other studies—in particular the Commerce Court, Toronto studies by Dalgliesh (1982)—have added further confirmation of the measurement of wind pressures on buildings through wind tunnel testing. Experiments indicate that the wind tunnel tests fall well within the bracket of full-scale scatter—a scatter that reflects not only the difficulty of full-scale experiments, but also the intrinsic variability of full-scale conditions.

CLADDING

Developments in the description of fluctuating wind pressure have raised detailed questions concerning the interaction of wind pressures with glass, as well as with rain screens and other cladding systems (Dalgliesh, 1980; Beason, 1981). Much needed work on the behavior of large windows of glass under high rates of loading and aging are currently underway in Canada and the United States and this should aid in the development of suitable criteria. The other areas, like the treatment of rain screening, probably deserve more study.

PEDESTRIAN-LEVEL WIND

The question of pedestrian-level wind has become important and is a conspicuous detraction of tall buildings. Techniques are now well developed for defining pedestrian-level winds. In several U.S., European, and Canadian cities this matter has become a subject of city by-laws regulating the permissible changes in windiness. It has also been the subject of a special issue of the *Journal of Industrial Aerodynamics* (Lawson, 1978). A special model study of wind conditions in Ottawa, Canada, is underway at the National Research Council 10-m-by-10-m low-speed wind tunnel.

CONFERENCES ON WIND ENGINEERING

Several major conferences on wind engineering have taken place since the publication of the chapter for the Monograph, among them, the following:

1. Fifth International Conference on Wind Effects on Buildings and Structures, July 8–14, 1979, Fort Collins, Colorado.

2. CIRIA Conference, Wind Engineering in the Eighties, November 12–13, 1980, London, England.

3. CWOWE III, Third Canadian Workshop on Wind Engineering, Design Against Wind, April 13–14, May 7–8, 1981, Vancouver, B.C.

4. Centre Scientifique et Technique du Bâtiment Colloquium, Designing with the Wind (Construire avec le Vent), June 15–19, 1981, Nantes, France.

5. Fourth U.S. National Conference on Wind Engineering Research, July 26–29, 1981, Seattle, Washington.

6. International Workshop on Wind Tunnel Modeling Criteria and Techniques in Civil Engineering Applications, April, 1982, Gaithersburg, Maryland.

CONDENSED REFERENCES/BIBLIOGRAPHY

The following is a condensed bibliography for this article. It includes all articles referred to or cited in the text. The full citations will be found at the end of the volume, with additional citations for further reading. What is given here should be sufficient information to lead the reader to the correct article: the author, date, and title. In case of multiple authors, only the first name is listed.

Beason 1981, *Window Glass Research at Texas Technical University*

CIRIA 1981, *Wind Engineering in the Eighties*
CWOWE 1981, *Third Canadian Workshop on Wind Engineering, Design Against the Wind: The 1980*
Centre Scientifique et Technique du Bâtiment 1981. *Design With the Wind*
Cermak 1980, *Wind Engineering*

Dalgliesh 1980, *Assessment of Wind Loads for Glazing Design*
Dalgliesh 1982, *Comparison of Model and Full-Scale Tests of the Commerce Court Building in Toronto*
Davenport 1981, *The Response of Tall Buildings to Wind: Effects of Wind Detection and the Direct*

Evans 1981, *The Assessment of Dynamic Wind Loads on A Tall Building: A Comparison of Model*

Georgiou 1983, *Design Wind Loads in Regions Dominated By Tropical Cyclones*

Lawson 1978, *The Wind Content of the Built Environment*

McDonald 1980. *Tornado and Straight Wind Hazard Probability For Ten Nuclear Power Reactor Sites*

Reinhold 1982, *Wind Tunnel Modeling For Civil Engineering Applications*

University of Washington 1981, *The Fourth U.S. National Conference on Wind Engineering Research*

Fire (CL-4)

Introduction

Duiliu Sfintesco

The updating of the Monograph on tall buildings by means of successive additional volumes is intended to put life into this unique reference work by periodically reflecting both new developments and new perspectives in all fields covered by the various chapters.

The chapter on fire is doubtless one for which such frequent information is most justified by current developments in research and in code provisions, and by real needs in construction practice. The most striking development is the progress away from traditional empiricism toward the recently born fire engineering science.

There are several precise reasons for this update:

1. The wealth of findings and guidance provided by very active, world-wide theoretical and experimental research.

2. The increasing recognition in many codes of the advancement of knowledge.

3. The economic concern for more rational use of means of protection and for their effects on construction and insurance costs.

4. The social concern about rare but still occurring spectacular fires, in spite of the statistically proven low rate of casualties in tall buildings.

The contents of this chapter have been collected by means of both an

311

inquiry conducted by the vice-chairman among the committee members and the chairman's action within the Fire Committee of the ECCS. The resultant contributions are either given below, as separate papers, or are incorporated in these introductory comments.

It is noteworthy that four substantial papers deal with the fire safety of steel structures, thus demonstrating the lively interest in the subject throughout the world and the considerable progress in knowledge related to it. Moreover, much of the information is equally relevant for other forms of construction.

Witteveen describes the design method developed within the ECCS Fire Committee for the calculation of the fire resistance of steel structures exposed to the standard fire. The method is a result of systematic international cooperation in research, both theoretical and experimental. This achievement represents a major step forward in scientific treatment which, of course, leads on to the assessment of natural fires as a function of the building characteristics and use—one more ambitious objective to be attained. This second objective is specifically dealt with, for internal fires, in the paper of Magnusson and Pettersson, describing the Swedish approach to calculating the fire behavior of steel structures exposed to natural fires in compartments. These two papers reflect one of the major and most fundamental aspects of modern fire engineering.

Law gives a comprehensive picture of relevant new developments in the treatment of safety for steel structures, including the calculation of fire exposure external to the building facade. Particular reference is made to the conditions allowing reduced or nil cladding, either because fire resistance is not needed for public safety or because the fire exposure is low. Water-cooling systems are illustrated by characteristic examples. Objectives for further research on a multitude of relevant safety parameters are listed. Moreover, this paper gives a broad view of the present state of the art worldwide.

As a representative of the steel construction industry, Troup argues convincingly against irrational excess in structural fire protection and suggests more logical use of the resulting savings. This argument is illustrated by reference to actual fire incidents. However, the demonstration is solely related to American code provisions and methods and their bibliography. To extend its utility it would be highly desirable to establish a formal exchange of such information internationally and to encourage the dissemination of international work and its results in all countries.

In addition to the contributions just mentioned, a survey was made by Fitzgerald of members of the Tall Building Council's Fire Committee (8A) with regard to their most recent experience. Excerpts of the correspondence he received are contained within his article.

The contribution received from Marryatt offers most interesting and convincing data about the beneficial effects of sprinklers from results recorded in a field in which Australia apparently plays a leading role.

Direct observation and analysis of actual fire incidents are invaluable sources of factual, objective information. So are Degenkolb's comments on the recent fire disaster at Las Vegas, which has shown that considerable fire damage—however exceptional it may be—can still happen even in a highly developed country. The author reviews all weaknesses discovered in this particular instance and draws many practical hints from his study.

Thomas mentions recent developments in fire studies on the international scene, including studies of the early stages of fire development and spread, and quotes several CIB publications that he recommends. Japanese and Swedish work is also mentioned. Various research needs are listed.

Kruppa gives brief information on some results of French tests concerning the heating of protected steel members and the behavior of external columns.

The vice-chairman's inquiry has stimulated several disparate but note-worthy remarks and suggestions, among which are the following:

Gewain, from the AISI, notes advanced work at Worcester Polytechnic Institute in further developing engineering methods to compute the fire resistance of structural steel frames. He also notes work at Ohio State University on the development of smoke- and heat-release testing equipment in conjunction with an ASTM standard.

Bresler, of Wiss, Janney and Elstner, quotes a computer program for the fire response of three-dimensional steel and concrete structures.

Coe, of the Melbourne Research Laboratories, Australia, indicates that they are currently undertaking a complete review of the research and design techniques relevant to the fire engineering design of both steel and reinforced concrete structures.

Another interesting comment concerning special provisions for the safety of handicapped persons in case of fire in tall buildings has been presented by Cowan, of the University of Sydney. A thorough study of this pertinent question should be the subject of needed research.

In conclusion, this chapter brings together condensed information and practical suggestions on aspects specially relevant to fire safety in tall buildings and also gives hints on topics for research.

The great interest in further progress toward defining still more efficient and cost-effective fire protection and the legitimate, continuing quest for a more scientific (that is, more objective) approach mean that further significant progress will be made, justifying another update in the very near future.

Steel Structures Exposed to the Standard Fire — An Introduction to the European Recommendations

Jelle Witteveen

INTRODUCTION

During the last ten years important progress has been made in the development of analytical methods for the design of fire-exposed steel structures. As a consequence, more and more countries are permitting a classification of load-bearing steel elements and structural assemblies under the effect of fire on an analytical basis. This method comes as an alternative to classification based on the results of standard fire-resistance tests. To have a reference document for national codes of practice and with the final aim toward a single European Code, the European Convention for Constructional Steelwork (ECCS) recently finalized the "European Recommendations for the Calculation of the Fire Resistance of Load-Bearing Steel Elements and Structural Assemblies Exposed to the Standard Fire" (ECCS, 1980). In this paper the author, who is the chairman of the ECCS committee responsible for the "Recommendations," summarizes the background and the content.

STANDARD FIRE-RESISTANCE TEST VERSUS
AN ANALYTICAL FIRE ENGINEERING DESIGN

Internationally, the generally accepted method for the design of load-bearing structural elements under fire action is based on a classification system connected to the standard fire-resistance test according to ISO-834 (ISO, 1975). The temperature of the furnace is controlled to vary with time as follows:

$$\nu_t - \nu_0 = 345^{10} \log (8t + 1) \tag{1}$$

where t = time of test in minutes
ν_t = furnace temperature in °C at time t
ν_0 = initial furnace temperature in °C

The fire resistance of a load-bearing element is defined as the time, expressed in minutes, from commencement of the test to occurrence of failure for the applied loading. Normally, the test load is the design load at service state. In Fig. 1 the design procedure according to the standard fire-resistance test is illustrated (ECCS, 1980; ISO, 1975; Pettersson, 1976).

According to the relevant characteristics of the building and its environment the codes and regulations require a time of fire duration t_{fd} for which the structure or structural element must fulfill its load-bearing function. This period is also related to the standard fire exposure and referred to as *fire-resistance time.*

The design implies a proof that the structure or structural element has a fire resistance t_{fr}, determined in a fire-resistance test, that is equal to or exceeds the required time of fire duration t_{fd} (Fig. 1).

Although the fire-resistance test is based on a standard of long standing, it has some serious weaknessess:

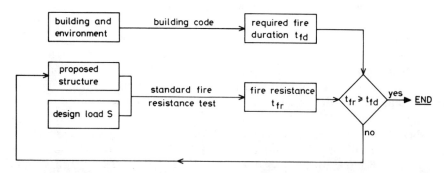

Fig. 1 Fire engineering design based on a classification system connected to the standard fire-resistance test

Due to the dimensions of most furnaces, the size of the test pieces is limited.

The test procedure is insufficiently specified with respect to the heat-flow characteristics of the furnace and the restraint conditions of the test specimen. This may give rise to a considerable variation in fire resistance for the same structural element.

A fire-resistance test only gives information on the behavior of the test piece in question. It is difficult, if not impossible to extend the results to other cases.

A fire-resistance test is rather costly.

Because of these problems there is a strong need to move toward analytical structural fire engineering design methods.

The three available design methods can be categorized as follows:

Level (1): Method in which the fire resistance of a load-bearing element or structural assembly under standard fire conditions is determined analytically. The design criterion is that the analytically determined fire resistance is equal to or exceeds the time of fire duration required by the building regulations or codes.

Level (2): Method in which the fire resistance of a load-bearing element or structural assembly under standard fire conditions is determined analytically. The design criterion is that the analytically determined fire resistance is equal to or exceeds the "effective fire duration", a quantity that relates a nonstandard or natural fire exposure to the standard fire.

Level (3): Method characterized by a direct analytical design of a load-bearing element or structural assembly on the basis of a nonstandard or natural fire exposure.

SCOPE OF THE RECOMMENDATIONS

The "Recommendations" concentrate on the analytical design methods according to levels (1) and (2), that is, on methods for an analytical determination of the fire resistance of load-bearing steel elements and structural assemblies under standard fire conditions, providing an alternative for the standard fire-resistance test.

A design procedure according to level (1) corresponds to a vast majority of national building codes, in which the requirements are expressed as a required time of fire duration, that is, the fire-resistance time, directly related to the standard fire. This design procedure is illustrated in Fig. 2 (ECCS, 1980; Pettersson, 1976).

It is necessary to appreciate that the required time of fire duration does not necessarily signify the duration of an actual fire. In addition, factors such as the building's type of use, its height, and its situation are taken into account, leading to a required time of fire duration that is often greater than the actual fire duration. In circumstances where a rather low fire-load density is present and the above factors do not lead to additional requirements, it is appropriate to design fire-exposed structures on the basis of a nonstandard or natural fire exposure (levels (2) and (3)).

For level (2) the nonstandard or natural fire exposure is related to the standard fire by the concept of effective fire duration. The effective fire duration is a function of the fire load and the geometry and ventilation conditions of the fire compartment, and replaces the time of fire duration stipulated in the building regulations. A level (2) design therefore requires an analytical determination of the fire resistance of load-bearing elements and structural assemblies under standard fire conditions in the same way as for level (1).

Level (3) is characterized by a direct analytical design based on differentiated gas temperature-time curves of the complete process of a natural fire development and is not covered in the present "Recommendations."

In most countries the level (2) and level (3) methods have occasionally been used but, except in Sweden, they are not yet automatically accepted as methods that satisfy the requirements of the building regulations. The design basis given in the "Recommendations" focuses on one basic method, characterized by the following features:

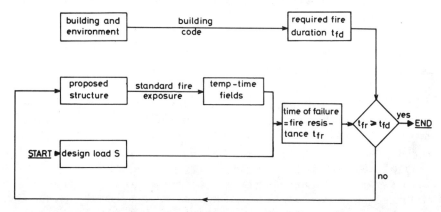

Fig. 2 Analytical fire engineering design based on thermal exposure according to the standard fire-resistance test

- A thermal exposure to the ISO-834 standard fire-resistance test;

- Constant thermal properties of structural and insulation materials assumed to be the average for the temperature range;

- Mechanical properties of steel at elevated temperatures, which are assumed to be independent of time (that is, creep effects are included implicitly);

- A uniform temperature distribution over the height of the cross section and along the members.

These features allow a simplified analytical design procedure in which the structural analysis at elevated temperatures can be dealt with according to conventional methods of structural analysis at room temperature (Fig. 3). In this concept the key factor is the determination of the critical steel temperature T_R at which the structural element collapses under a given load.

STEEL PROPERTIES AT ELEVATED TEMPERATURES

In general a structure under fire action is subjected to a constant load and a temperature increase as a function of time. Depending on the type and thickness of the insulation, the rate of heating can vary. Research reported in Witteveen and Twilt (1975) and Witteveen, et al. (1977) has shown that for practical heating rates and for temperatures not over 600°C, the deformation behavior under constant load can be considered as independent of the heating rate. Consequently a family of stress-strain relationships for different temperatures must exist in which the influence of high temperature creep is implicitly included (Fig. 4).

The gap between the curves applying to 200°C and 300°C results from so-called thermally activated flow (Witteveen and Twilt, 1975; Witteveen et

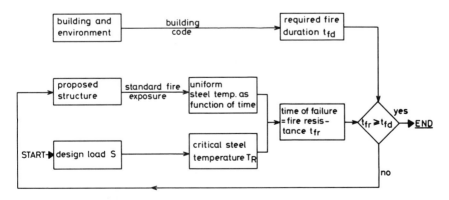

Fig. 3 Analytical fire engineering design using the concept of critical steel temperature T_R

al., 1977). Applying the elementary theory of plasticity, the curved stress-strain diagrams are cut off at certain stress levels. The horizontal plateau is defined as the effective yield stress. In Fig. 5, the effective yield stress variation with steel temperature is given as a fraction of the yield stress at room temperature.

Stress-strain diagrams for other steel grades up to Fe 510 ($\sigma_y = 355 \ N/mm^2$) can be obtained from the stress-strain diagram for steel grade Fe 360 by a simple transformation based on the following assumptions:

> For any grade of steel between Fe 360 and Fe 510 the effective yield stress, as a fraction of the yield stress at room temperature, is the same as for Fe 360 throughout the steel temperature range (Fig. 5).

> For any grade of steel between Fe 360 and Fe 510 the modulus of elasticity in the origin F_o is assumed to be equal to that of Fe 360 throughout the steel temperature range.

STEEL TEMPERATURE AS A FUNCTION OF TIME

The analysis of the temperature distribution within the fire exposed structure or structural element during the heating process (according to ISO-834) is based on the following assumptions:

> Constant thermal properties of structural and insulation materials are assumed to be the average for the temperature range.

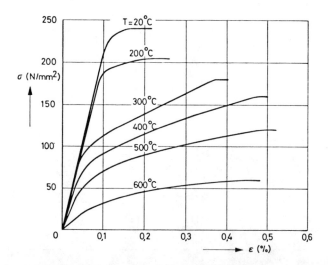

Fig. 4 Stress-strain relationships for Fe 360 at elevated temperatures

The steel is assumed to offer no resistance to heat flow and therefore to be at a uniform temperature.

The resistance to heat flow between the inner surface of the insulation material and the steel is assumed to be zero.

Under these conditions the temperature distribution in the steel can be calculated with classical one-dimensional heat-flow theory (Pettersson et al., 1976; Geilinger and Bryl, 1962; Witteveen, 1965; Lie, 1965; Pettersson, 1976; Centre Technique Industriel de la Construction Metallique, 1976 and 1977).

Under the given assumptions, the resistance of unprotected steel members to heat flow is governed only by convection and radiation. The coefficient of heat transfer caused by convection from the fire to the exposed surface of the steel member a_c is considered to be constant with a value $a_c = 25 \; W/m^2 \, °C$. The coefficient of heat transfer due to radiation a_r is a function of the gas and steel temperatures and can be determined from the Stefan-Bolzmann law of radiation. The resultant emissivity ϵ_r of the flames, gases, and exposed surfaces that appears in this formula is considered constant with a value of $\epsilon_r = 0.5$, giving a conservative solution. The "Recommendations" give tabulated values from which the temperature development of unprotected steel members under standard fire exposure can be obtained as a function of the "section factor" F/A, based on the following formula:

$$\Delta v_s = \frac{a}{c_s \rho_s} \cdot \frac{F}{A} \cdot (v_t - v_s) \, \Delta t \, [°C] \qquad (2)$$

$$\begin{aligned}
\text{in which} \quad & a = a_c + a_r \, [W/m^2 \, °C] \\
& v_t = \text{gas temperature} \, [°C] \\
& v_s = \text{steel temperature} \, [°C] \\
& c_s = \text{specific heat of steel} \, [J/kg \, °C] \\
& \rho_s = \text{density of steel} \, [kg/m^3]
\end{aligned}$$

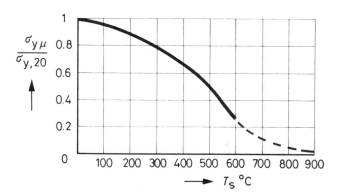

Fig. 5 Effective yield stress $\sigma_{y\nu}$ at elevated temperatures expressed as a fraction of the yield stress at room temperature σ_{y20} (Fe 360-Fe 510)

The resistance to heat flow of insulated steel members is governed by convection, radiation, and the thermal conductivity of the insulation material. For practical applications, however, the influence of convection and radiation can be neglected. Additionally, a distinction is made between lightly insulated members, for which the heat capacity of the insulation material can be neglected, and heavily insulated members, for which the heat capacity of the insulation is taken into account.

The "Recommendations" give tabulated values from which the temperature development of protected steel members under standard fire exposure can be obtained. For lightly insulated materials the formula is:

$$\Delta v_s = \frac{\frac{\lambda}{d}}{c_s \rho_s} \cdot \frac{F}{A} (v_t - v_s)\, \Delta_t\, [°C] \tag{3}$$

in which λ = thermal conductivity of insulation $[W/m°C]$
d = thickness of insulation $[m]$

For heavily insulated members, half of the heat capacity of the insulation is added to the heat capacity of the insulation $c_s \rho_s A$ of the steel.

Finally it is emphasized that the value of the thermal conductivity of the insulation material λ is generally not identical to the conventional value as given in the handbooks on heat transfer. The value of λ will depend on the temperature, as well as on the deformation capacity of the material attached to the steel member. During deformation, cracks or openings may occur. To include these effects, apart from small-scale experiments for determining the thermal conductivity of the insulation material, at least one full-scale test on a loaded member must be performed (Witteveen, 1965; Centre Technique Industriel de la Construction Metallique, 1977).

STRUCTURAL ANALYSIS AT ELEVATED TEMPERATURES

The structural analysis of fire-exposed structures or structural elements is based on the following three assumptions:

- A time-dependent uniform temperature distribution over the height of the cross section and along the members;

- Mechanical properties of steel at elevated temperatures that are assumed to be independent of time (that is, creep effects are included implicitly) (Fig. 4);

- The load that is assumed to be equal to the design load at the service state (for example, dead load + characteristic live loads).

Because of the nonlinear stress-strain relationships of steel at elevated temperatures, the linear theory of elasticity cannot be applied and use has to be made of the theory of plasticity.

Two design methods are available that are identical to those used in structural analysis at ordinary room temperatures:

- A limit-state design according to the elementary theory of plasticity in those cases where a similar design is allowed at room temperature;

- An incremental elasto-plastic analysis.

The first method is suitable when the limit state at elevated temperatures can be defined by structural collapse, that is, where beams in braced frames are present. At a given temperature, the ultimate load can be calculated from the temperature-dependent effective yield stress $\sigma_{y,\nu}$ (Fig. 5). This calculation is illustrated in Fig. 6 (ECCS, 1974; Witteveen, 1965; Kruppa, 1977).

The second method has to be used when the limit state at elevated temperatures is defined by a criterion based on deflections or a rate of deflection. This method must also be applied when geometrically nonlinear effects have a significant bearing on the structural behavior, that is, when columns and unbraced frames are present. At a given temperature, the load-bearing capacity can be determined with the appropriate stress-strain relationship (Fig. 4) by computing the deflection curve. Figure 7 gives an illustration. Application of this method generally requires a computer.

An analytical design based on the specified assumptions in the beginning of this chapter, generally results in a level of fire resistance that is conservative in comparison with the corresponding level in a standard fire-resistance test. The main reasons for this sytematic discrepancy are as follows:

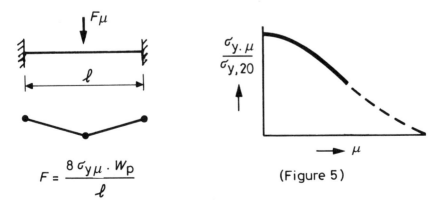

$$F = \frac{8\,\sigma_{y\mu} \cdot W_p}{\ell}$$

(Figure 5)

Fig. 6 Structural design at elevated temperatures according to the elementary theory of plasticity

The analytical method is based on the characteristic values of the material properties at elevated temperatures, whereas fire-resistance tests are performed on specimens, the material properties of which are random samples.

In the computations, the temperature distribution along and across the members is assumed to be uniform, whereas in tests, generally, a nonuniform distribution arises.

For columns, geometrical imperfections play an important role; in tests the specimen has a random imperfection that is generally smaller than that assumed in the analytical design.

It is evident that a similar discrepancy would exist if tests at room temperature were compared with analytical results. Because most structures at room temperature are open for a complete analysis, such tests are exceptions and a discussion on the discrepancy is less relevant. However, it is likely that for years to come, fire-resistance tests as well as analytical methods will be used in fire engineering design. Consequently, there is a need to develop a method for avoiding these discrepancies and obtaining consistency between the analytical and experimental approaches. Pettersson and Witteveen (1979) recently proposed such a method, which has been adopted in the ECCS "Recommendations." The method is characterized by a correction of the design load S to be multiplied by a factor $\kappa \le 1$. The design load S is thereby transformed into a corrected design load S_c. In Fig. 8 the resulting correction factor κ is presented as a function of the design load S divided by the load-bearing capacity at room temperature R_{20} for different structural applications.

TABULATED VALUES OF T_{crit} FOR BEAMS AND COLUMNS

The "Recommendations", as mentioned earlier, concentrate on a design

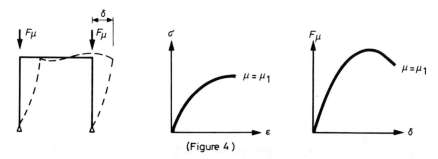

(Figure 4)

Fig. 7 Structural design at elevated temperatures with an incremental elasto-plastic analysis

procedure according to Fig. 3, in which the critical temperature T_R is a key factor. Therefore, for different structural applications, critical temperatures T_{crit} are presented in tables or diagrams.

Beams

The ultimate load-bearing capacity of beams at elevated temperatures is determined by a limit-state design according to the elementary theory of plasticity. As a consequence, no information is obtained about the deformations. However, for practical values of height-to-span ratios of beams, the design criterion of a limiting deflection, $\delta = 1/30$ of the length of the span l is also generally met. In Fig. 9 tabulated values of the critical steel temperatures T_{crit} are given as a function of the corrected design load S_c divided by the ultimate load at room temperature R_{20}.

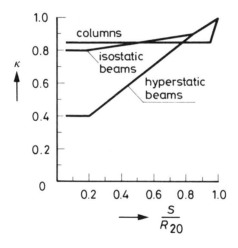

Fig. 8 Resulting multiplier κ for the design load S as a function of the design load S divided by the load-bearing capacity at room temperature R_{20} for columns, isostatic beams, and hyperstatic beams

$\dfrac{S_c}{R_{20}}$	0.7	0.6	0.5	0.4	0.3
T_{crit}	375	450	500	540	580

Fig. 9 Critical steel temperatures T_{crit} as a function of the corrected design load S_c, divided by the ultimate load-bearing capacity at room temperature R_{20}

In cases where an elastic design is used in the structural analysis at room temperature the "Recommendations" provide a conversion table as given in Fig. 10. The table gives values for the critical steel temperature T_{crit} as a function of the corrected design load S_c divided by the ultimate elastic load-bearing capacity at room temperature R_{E20}. Note that the values given in Fig. 9 and 10 are independent of the steel grade.

Columns in braced frames

The ultimate load-bearing capacity of columns at elevated temperatures has to be calculated by an incremental elasto-plastic analysis (Witteveen and Twilt, 1975; Witteveen et al., 1977). In the "Recommendations," results of such calculations are presented for centrally loaded columns (Fig. 11).

At a given design stress level σ and slenderness ratio λ, the critical temperature T_{crit} can be determined. The effect of axial restraint has not been taken into account, and the column is assumed to have a uniform temperature distribution across and along the member. If, in practice, these conditions are significantly different, an incremental elasto-plastic analysis has to be performed for the structural application in question. When the column is subjected to an axial force as well as a moment, for simplicity, the critical steel temperature T_{crit} may be determined as a function of the average stress only.

stat. system $\dfrac{S_c}{R_{E20}}$	0.7	0.6	0.5	0.4	0.3
(simply supported)	440	490	525	560	600
 (fixed-fixed)	520	540	570	590	600
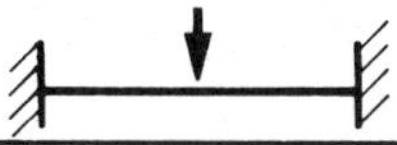 (fixed-fixed point load)	440	490	525	560	600
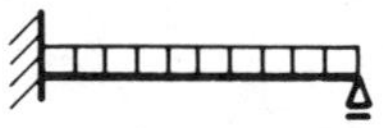 (fixed-roller)	540	570	580	610	650
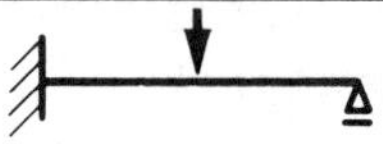 (fixed-roller point load)	480	510	540	575	610
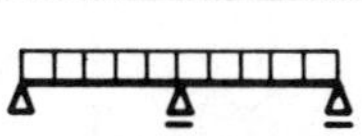 (three support)	540	570	580	610	650

Fig. 10 Critical steel temperatures T_{crit} as a function of the corrected design load S_c divided by the ultimate elastic load-bearing capacity at room temperature R_{E20}

For a low normal force and a considerable moment this condition may lead to extremely high critical temperatures. Therefore, in such cases, the critical temperature T_{crit} may not exceed 500°C.

The slenderness ratio λ, which has to be taken into account, depends on the type of connection to the adjacent members and whether or not they are affected by the fire.

Columns in unbraced frames

The ultimate load-bearing capacity of unbraced frames has to be calculated by an incremental elasto-plastic analysis. In Witteveen et al. (1977) such calculations have been performed; a typical result is given in Fig. 12. The analytical results have been compared with small-scale model tests and, as can be seen, the agreement is quite satisfactory.

Calculations show that the critical temperatures of unbraced frames with more than two stories are rather low compared to those of beams and columns in braced frames. The reason for this is the sensitivity of unbraced frames to nonlinear effects, which is significantly influenced by the decreasing stiffness of the members at elevated temperatures (see Fig. 4). If the critical temperature is not established by experiments or by structural analysis, the critical temperature T_{crit} of the columns in unbraced frames with more than two stories shall be taken equal to 300°C.

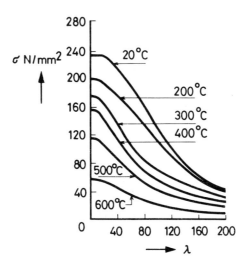

Fig. 11 Buckling curves at elevated temperatures for Fe 360

ACKNOWLEDGEMENT

The "Recommendations" have been prepared by a working group of the ECCS Fire Committee represented by Kruppa, Law, Pettersson, Twilt, and the author. The work presented in this article should therefore be considered a joint effort of this group.

Also, the efforts made by the other members of the ECCS Fire Committee, representing 12 European countries, are acknowledged here.

CONDENSED REFERENCES/BIBLIOGRAPHY

The following is a condensed bibliography for this article. It includes all articles referred to or cited in the text. The full citations will be found at the end of the volume, with additional citations for further reading. What is given here should be sufficient information to lead the reader to the correct article: the author, date, and title. In case of multiple authors, only the first name is listed.

Centre Technique Industriel de la Construction Metallique 1976, *Method of Analytical Prediction of the*
Centre Technique Industriel de la Construction Metallique 1977, *Methodology of Characteristics of*
Communaute Europeene du Charbon et de l'Acier 1974, *Research on the Behavior of Steel Structures*

ECCS 1974, *Fire Safety in Constructional Steelwork*
ECCS 1980, *European Recommendations for the Calculation of the Fire Resistance of Load-Bearing*

Geilinger 1962, *Fire Safety of Steel Structures*

ISO 1975, *Fire Resistance Test—Elements of Building Construction*

effective slenderness ratio	$\dfrac{P}{P_{20}}$	T crit. tests	T crit. analysis	heating rate
120	0.4	310 345	325	10 °C/min
	0.6	260 250	275	
76	0.4	380 390	400	10 °C/min
	0.6	270 260	285	
76	0.2	535		5 °C/min
	0.2	530	505	10 °C/min
	0.2	535		50 °C/min

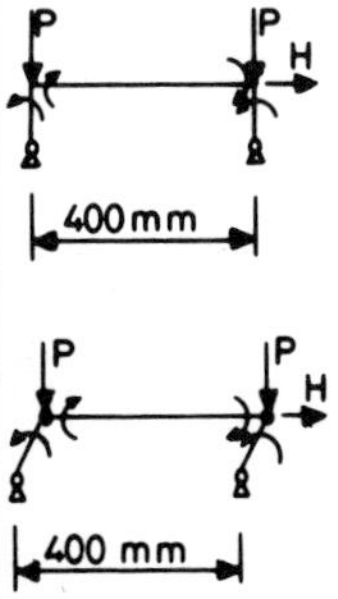

Fig. 12 Analytical and test results of unbraced frames

Kruppa 1977, *Fire Resistance of Structures at Non-Uniform Temperatures*

Lie 1965, *Insulation Materials and Building Structures Under Fire Action*

Pettersson 1976, *Fire Engineering Design of Steel Structures*
Pettersson 1979/80, *On the Fire Resistance of Structural Steel Elements Derived from Standard Fire*

Witteveen 1965, *Fire Safety of Steel Structures*
Witteveen 1975, *Behavior of Steel Columns under Fire Action*
Witteveen 1977, *The Stability of Braced and Unbraced Frames at Elevated Temperatures*

This paper is an edited version of one that appeared as Preprint 81-035, presented at the ASCE Convention, New York, New York, May 11-15, 1981.

Designing Fire Safety For
Steel — Recent Work

Margaret Law

INTRODUCTION

The use of calculation methods for the design of structural fire protection is gaining increasing acceptance. These methods can be expected to take their place alongside other fire safety calculation procedures already well established in, for example, the design of smoke control systems and the provision of adequate space between buildings. There is also more recognition of the need to identify clearly the objectives of providing fire safety, so that building design can be related to the nature of the lives and property at risk and the potential hazards. The desire of architects and engineers to reduce or eliminate the need for cladding on structural steelwork in buildings has meant that these subjects have been of particular interest to the steel industry, which has supported much research in this area. The code authorities are naturally cautious in accepting such methods, but it has been possible to introduce new approaches, to a greater or lesser extent, in a number of recent buildings. This paper reviews the methods and illustrates their use in practice by describing some steel structures completed within the last decade.

STEEL WITHOUT CLADDING

Most unprotected steel elements of construction in common use have a section factor P/A of around 250 m^{-1} (75 ft^{-1}), giving a fire resistance of about 15 min when subjected to the standard test (ISO, 1975). The fire resistance varies inversely with P/A, where A is the cross-section area and P the exposed perimeter; it is thus possible to achieve higher values of fire resistance with the smaller values of P/A that can be provided by large solid sections. For example it is estimated that a solid 360-mm (14-in) square section ($P/A = $ M^{-1} or 3.4 ft^{-1}) could give a fire resistance of the order of 1 hour (Stanzak, 1973). At the moment, such an estimate must be based on calculations of structural behavior related to steel temperature, since fire test furnaces do not have the capacity to fully load these massive sections. These solid sections, however, will rarely be used in buildings. It is more useful to identify the other circumstances where cladding is not needed. These can be listed so far as (a) no requirement for fire resistance, (b) low fire exposure, (c) water cooling are concerned.

No fire-resistance requirement

In a number of circumstances, which follow, the loss of a steel structural element or elements may be acceptable:

When a single-story building is involved that has adequate means of escape and adequate spacing from other buildings.

When the loss involves a roof structure where failure does not adversely affect the behavior of other structural elements required for fire resistance, where the lives of fire fighters are not endangered, and where there is adequate separation from other buildings.

When the loss involves certain elements such as wind bracing, which may be "sacrificed" without endangering the overall stability of the building during the fire.

When the loss involves elements where load can be transferred, as in concrete-filled hollow sections and concrete/steel decks with secondary reinforcement.

It is commonplace for single-story industrial buildings to be of unprotected steelwork, which is accepted provided that there is no adverse effect on escape routes and no undue risk to fire fighters or adjacent buildings. The same approach can sometimes be adopted for structures of more than one story, as described for Building A (Fig. 1). Where property protection is concerned, an automatic extinguishing system is likely to be the appropriate fire safety measure for the contents. As for the structure, it has been suggested, from probabilistic considerations, that structural fire protection is not economically beneficial for low-rise buildings (Lie, 1979), and a study of industrial fires in Sweden has shown that the fire losses were independent of the material of construction, provided it was noncombustible (Thor and Sedin, 1977).

The designation of certain elements as sacrificial in the event of fire, obviously depends on the structural design of the building and the likely pattern of fire behavior. An example is given in the description of Building B (Fig. 2).

The use of concrete filling of hollow sections has been the subject of recent research in Europe (Giddings, 1978); as the steel section is heated, the load is transferred to the concrete core. Tests have shown that the fire performance of steel ribbed floors with concrete topping can be significantly improved by the incorporation of extra reinforcement in the "cool" portion of the concrete (Bryl and Sagelsdorff, 1971).

Low fire exposure

For the following elements fire exposure may be low and there is a very small probability of the steel reaching critical temperatures:

Structural elements in open-sided car parks.

Fig. 1 The Royal Exchange Theatre, Manchester *(Courtesy: Ove Arup & Partners)*

Fig. 2 Centre Pompidou, Paris (side view) *(Courtesy: Ove Arup & Partners)*

Elements in other types of buildings where the fire load is small and calculation or a test shows that the temperatures attained will be low.

External structural elements, free to cool to the ambient air, that are placed at certain positions in relation to windows and other openings of a building.

It was widely believed for many years, with apparently no supporting evidence, that structures housing parked automobiles needed very high standards of fire resistance. Statistical surveys and experiments (Butcher, et al., 1968; Gage-Babcock & Associates, 1973) finally demonstrated that unprotected steelwork is acceptable for open-sided car parks. No similar analysis has yet been carried out for other types of occupancy. Methods of calculating potential fire exposure, taking into account fire load and ventilation, already exist (Law, 1973; Pettersson, et al., 1976). However, they have not so far been used generally to demonstrate circumstances where the exposure is low enough to obviate the use of structural fire protection. The method of calculating fire exposure most commonly adopted (Pettersson et al., 1976) uses assumptions for rates of burning that are not so directly applicable to the low-fire-load/high ventilation condition that favors the use of unprotected steelwork.

The fire exposure outside a building—by emerging flames and radiation from the window openings—is not represented by the standard fire-resistance test, since the exposure is so sensitive to the position of the exposed structural element. At certain positions, the fire exposure is much lower than for the internal elements and cladding is not needed. To avoid costly experiments and to give general guidance to engineers on the use of external steel, a technical study was commissioned by the American Iron and Steel Institute (AISI) and Constrado (Ove Arup & Partners, 1977; Law, 1973). The basis of the calculation has already been accepted by the main U.S. codes. A design manual has been published by AISI (1979) and one by Constrado is in preparation (Law, to be published). In more recent years, the results of some experiments in an apartment building at Lehrte have been reported (Schriftenreihe des Bundesministers fur Raumordnung, 1978) that are consistent with the assumptions for fire and flame behavior contained in the design method, and a study of the structural behavior of fire-exposed external steel assemblies has been carried out (Kruppa, 1980).

It has also been suggested that where automatic sprinkler systems are installed, structural fire protection may be reduced or eliminated. There is certainly a case to be argued on probabilistic grounds for this position. However, if a sprinkler system does not control a fire, the fire severity will be as great as if the system has not been installed—there is no partial protection— while a load bearing element of construction with passive protection, how-ever substandard it may be, is likely to have some degree of fire resistance. Passive fire protection tends to be most unreliable for walls and floors designed as barriers to fire spread, which are often breached by open fire doors or by unsealed openings provided for the passage of services. Thus, sprinklers may be more valuable as an alternative way of providing fire containment than they are as a means of reducing the standard of protection for load bearing capacity.

Water cooling

The heat-absorbing capacity of water can be exploited by filling hollow structural sections with water. Given a constant supply , the cooling effect on the steel can be extended indefinitely. The cooling is particularly marked when water, with its high latent heat, is converted to steam. An early example of the use of water-cooled hollow sections is the U.S. Steel Building in Pittsburgh (Seigel, 1967). For effective cooling the objective is to ensure that water is always in contact with any fire-exposed steel that is acting structurally.

The problems with water cooling are, first, the removal, separation, and release of steam without too much loss of water and, second, the avoidance of stagnant area that would allow the formation of steam traps. There are a variety of systems in use, some circulating the water and others not (Law, 1975). A guide to water cooling has been published by Constrado (Bond, 1975).

Water cooling as a method of keeping steel below critical temperatures has been used mainly for exterior hollow elements, as illustrated by Buildings B (Fig. 2) and C (Fig. 3). In principle, though, it should be acceptable for interior elements as well. Water circulation can be promoted by natural convection or by pumps. The expense of water-storage tanks can be avoided by interconnecting a large number of hollow elements that are not all fire exposed, by connection to the water main, or where the fire-resistance requirement is low, by using simply filled, nonreplenished columns.

Cooling of steel structures by water spray or drenchers has been used in aircraft hangars and for industrial storage tanks. However, this method has not generally been used for the protection of building elements.

STEEL WITH CLADDING

Standard test

The amount of cladding required for various elements of structure is defined in terms of a specified survival time in the standard fire-resistance test. The test is essentially a way of measuring the thickness of cladding required. Because of the size of the specimen, this test can take into account cracks, variations in thickness, effects of expansion, and behavior of joints and fixings in a way that a laboratory test on a small sample could not. However this test has been criticized for the following reasons:

The standard temperature-time curve is different from the temperature-time exposure likely to be encountered in real fires, which will depend on the amount and type of fire load, the ventilation, the size and shape of the building, and the activities of the fire brigade. However, it can be said that given the thermal impedance of a protected steel element, the temperature rise at critical points is not very sensitive to the shape of the temperature-time curve. For many interior building fires, the

Fig. 3 Bush Lane House, London *(Courtesy: Arup Associates)*

heating conditions are not greatly different from those in the furnace. It is the required duration of the test that is more open to criticism. As mentioned earlier, external exposure from building fires is not represented by the standard test.

The loading and end conditions are not well defined.

The structural properties of the test specimen at room temperature are not defined. If the nominal guaranteed values are used to estimate the change in properties during a standard fire test, the calculated critical steel temperatures will normally be lower than those measured (Pettersson and Witteveen, 1979/80).

In these circumstances, methods of calculating the fire resistance of elements of structure should be more readily accepted. Such a method has been adopted in France (Centre Technique Industriel de la Construction Metallique, 1976) and is about to be published by the European Convention for Constructional Steelwork (ECCS).

Design for compartment fires

It has been suggested that rather than meeting the requirements of regulations for a certain arbitrary value of fire resistance, the element should be designed to withstand the assumed "natural" fire conditions. A temperature-time curve for a compartment fire is calculated, assuming burn-out of a certain amount of fire load and taking into account the ventilation, size, shape, and thermal properties of the bounding compartment. The amount of cladding can then be calculated directly, or the compartment fire can be given an equivalent or effective fire duration, meaning that it would give the same effect at a critical point in a structure as that duration of a standard test. This approach could be of benefit for steel structures where is can be demonstrated that because of low fire loads or large heat losses from the compartment, little fire resistance would be needed to withstand the effects of the compartment fire.

Calculated temperature-time curves are already accepted in Swedish Codes (Pettersson et al., 1976) and a similar approach has been published in France (CTICM, 1976). A simple relationship for effective fire resistance t_f has been derived (Law, 1973):

$$t_f = k \frac{L}{\sqrt{A_w \cdot A_T}} \quad \text{min}$$

where L = fire load in wood equivalent in kg (lb)
A_w = window area in m^2 (ft^2)
A_T = area of floor, ceiling, walls (excluding A_w) in m^2 (ft^2)
$k \simeq 1 \, (\simeq 5)$

The design method for exterior steel (AISI, 1979) can also be used to calculate the fire exposure of protected external members, as illustrated for Building D (Fig. 4).

Analytical approach

An analytical approach, in which the steel temperature is calculated, can have the following advantages, whether the standard fire or a compartment fire is assumed:

- Extrapolation of the results of the standard test by scaling methods.

- Estimation of the effects of varying the load acting on the element.

- Estimation of the effects of varying the duration of the standard fire.

- Saving the considerable expense of a conventional fire-resistance test.

EXAMPLES OF THE DESIGN APPROACH AND
THE USE OF WATER FILLING FOR
STRUCTURAL FIRE PROTECTION

Building A. The Royal Exchange Theatre, Manchester, England (Morreau
           and Baldock, 1978), Fig. 1
           Architects: Levitt Bernstein Associates
           Structural Engineers: Ove Arup & Partners

For this building, a fire engineering appraisal was used to demonstrate that cladding of the steel was not essential for the purposes of building regulations. The Royal Exchange Theatre is a concentric auditorium standing within the Great Hall of the Manchester Royal Exchange — formerly used for trading in cotton. There is an open-stage auditorium — seven-sided in plan, with a stage and seating for 450 at the level of the Exchange floor, and two galleries above, each of which seats a further 150 people. The theatre is clad with toughened glass and roofed with metal decking. It was imperative to develop as light a structure as possible which, taken together with the desire to achieve a high degree of transparency, led to a system of tubular steel trusses from which the galleries are suspended; the trusses are supported by existing brick piers. A full fire engineering appraisal was carried out, in cooperation with the city authorities, that led to an agreement that the steelwork could remain unprotected, thus avoiding the cost and additional weight and bulk of fire cladding. The appraisal included an examination of means of escape in which the smoke generation and crowd movements were carefully analysed and a generous number of exits was provided. It was established that should a fire remain unchecked after evacuation, the floor of the Exchange could survive collapse of the structure and consequently there would be no additional hazard to fire fighters. Noncombustible or low-flammability materials were used throughout, and arrangements were made to ensure detection of a fire and for surveillance by the theatre staff whenever the public is present.

Building B. Centre Pompidou, Paris, France (Ahm et al., 1979), Fig. 2
         Architects: Piano and Rogers
         Structural Engineers: Ove Arup & Partners

Much of the structure of this building is exposed externally. Where calculation of the external fire exposure showed protection of the elements to be necessary, protection was provided either by water cooling or by shielding. The Centre Pompidou has a steel superstructure rising above a concrete substructure. The main building has six stories above ground, each 7 m high and 166 m long (23 ft by 544 ft). The main lattice girders span 44.8 m (147 ft) between short cantilevers projecting from the main columns; the outer ends of the cantilever members are restrained by vertical ties. The glazing line generally follows the junction between the lattice girders and the cantilever brackets. The main columns are 1.6 m (5¼ ft) outside this line and are water filled for fire protection; circulation is achieved within each column by pumps. The cantilever brackets are 7.5 m (25 ft) long; thus, the outer line of tension "columns" and associated bracing members are 7.6 m (25 ft) from the windows. Calculations showed that in the event of a fire, all the members on the outer plane are protected by virtue of the 7.6-m (25-ft) distance from the windows; the cantilever brackets are shielded by fire-resistant panels in the facade. There are sprinklers on the external walls and the cantilevers. Horizontal bracing members close to the windows would be lost in a fire, but with each floor divided into two compartments, the loss of a proportion of the bracing does not endanger stability.

Building C. Bush Lane House, London, England (Eatherley, 1977), Fig. 3
         Architects and Structural Engineers: Arup Associates

Prior to the construction of this building, water cooling had only been used for the protection of vertical columns, since its use for beams raises considerable difficulties in ensuring that adequate controlled water flow occurs and no steam pockets develop. In Bush Lane House, water cooling is used for the external structural steel and protects columns, lattice members, and a critical top horizontal member. Bush Lane House provides eight office floors above a first-floor plant room. Each typical floor is approximately 35 m long by 16 m wide, (115 ft by 52 ft) supported by the lift core and three columns set 11 m (36 ft) in from the extremities of the building. The stainless steel lattice that transmits the floor loads is external to the building envelope and leaves the office space uninterrupted. The steel members are water filled and

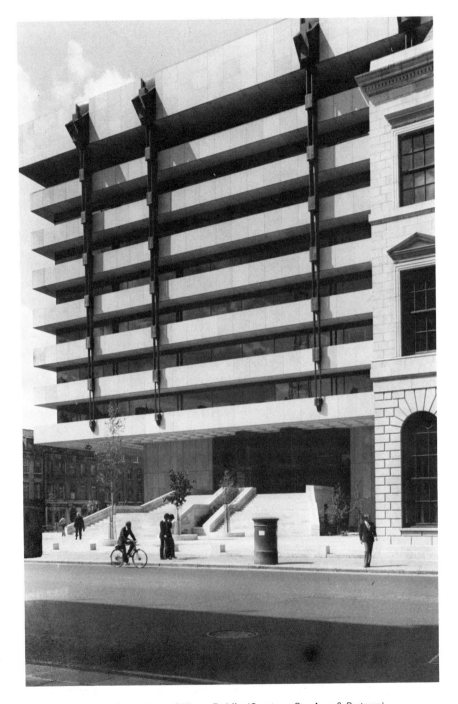

Fig. 4 Central Bank Offices, Dublin *(Courtesy: Ove Arup & Partners)*

interconnected, so that in the event of fire the water circulates and steam is separated in a tank on the roof. This tank also serves as a reservoir to replenish and keep the system full of water. The patterns of water flow, maximum potential steel temperature, and the amount of water storage were all established by calculation.

Building D. Central Bank Offices, Dublin, Eire (McSweeney, 1978), Fig. 4
               Architects: Stephenson Gibney and Associates
               Structural Consultants: Ove Arup & Partners, Dublin

For this building the critical condition for failure of the steel hangers was established by calculation, since no standard test method was appropriate for tension members. In addition, the fire exposure of the hangers, being external, was calculated so that the necessary cladding could be determined. The main building of the Central Bank Offices complex in Dame Street, Dublin, is an eight-story block with 8500 m² (91,400 ft²) of office space. Uninterrupted floor areas and minimal obstruction to windows were considered to be of significant architectural advantage. The floors, measuring 45 m by 30 m (148 ft by 98 ft) are supported at 12 hanger points around the perimeter and on twin reinforced concrete cores. From the hanger points the loads are transmitted directly to roof level through pairs of high tensile Macalloy steel bars. Cantilever frames transmit the vertical reactions to the cores.

The fire protection of the Macalloy bar hangers presented a somewhat unusual problem. They were to be exposed on the facade of the building, and it was of considerable architectural importance that they be expressed as separate bars. It was essential, therefore, to provide a fire cladding that would give adequate protection without being very thick, since each 40 mm bar (1.57 in) was to be encased in an aluminum tube not exceeding 120 mm (4.72 in) in diameter. A research program was necessary to establish the Macalloy steel characteristics, thus leading to a definition of the critical condition for the structure under fire exposure. Fire engineering calculations, based on the method in Ove Arup & Partners (1977), established that the bars would be less severely exposed than internal members and the cladding finally adopted was 20 mm (0.79-in) thick Marinite machined to form interlocking sections round the bars.

CONCLUDING REMARKS

A recent study (Behets and Law, 1980) has identified the following four broad subject areas that need further attention if the use of steel is to be exploited:

A more precise definition by the authorities responsible for building regulations of the objectives of providing structural fire protection.

Such a definition would help engineers to determine more clearly the level of protection needed, if any, and the effect on this level of employing alternative protection measures such as automatic sprinklers.

The development of calculation methods for the fire safety of structures that could be incorporated into the methods for structural design at normal temperatures.

Calculation manuals for the fire behavior of structural steelwork giving methods to engineers that could be accepted by the authorities.

Design guides for architects and engineers that explain when structural fire protection is needed and give information on the methods available for protection of steelwork and their relative costs.

Some of the work already carried out has been described and illustrated in this paper. It is to be hoped this type of work will be followed by general acceptance of the design approach to providing fire safety in buildings.

CONDENSED REFERENCES/BIBLIOGRAPHY

The following is a condensed bibliography for this article. It includes all articles referred to or cited in the text. The full citations will be found at the end of the volume, with additional citations for further reading. What is given here should be sufficient information to lead the reader to the correct article: the author, date, and title. In case of multiple authors, only the first name is listed.

Ahm 1979, *Design and Construction of the George Pompidou National Center of Art and Culture*
AISI 1979, *Fire-Safe Structural Steel. A Design Guide*

Behets 1980, *Study of Research into the Behavior of Structural Steel Elements Exposed to Fire*
Bond 1975, *Water Cooled Hollow Columns*
Bryl 1971, *Fire Resistance of Concrete Panels, Steel Sheeting, and Reinforced Concrete Panels*
Butcher 1968, *Fire and Car-Parking Buildings*

Centre Technique Industriel de la Construction Metallique 1976, *Method of Analytical Prediction*

Eatherly 1977, *The Design and Construction of Bush Lane House*
ECCS (to be published), *European Recommendations for the Fire Safety of Steel Structures Part 1.*

Gage-Babcock 1973, *Automobile Burn-out in an Open-air Parking Structure*
Giddings 1978, *Fire Resistant Construction in SHS — Today and Tommorrow*

ISO 1975, *Fire Resistance Tests — Elements of Building Construction*

Kruppa 1980, *Behavior of External Steel Columns in Fire*

Law 1973, *Fire Safety of External Building Elements — The Design Approach*
Law 1975, *Exposed Steelwork*

Law 1978, *Fire Safety of External Building Elements — The Design Approach*
Law (to be published), *Fire Safety of Bare External Structural Steel*
Lie 1979, *Safety Factors for Fire Loads*

McSweeney 1978, *New HQ for Central Bank*
Morreau 1978, *Royal Exchange Theatre, Manchester*

Ove Arup & Partners 1977, *Design Guide for Fire Safety of Bare Exterior Structural Steel. Technical*

Pettersson 1976, *Fire Engineering Design of Steel Structures*
Pettersson 1979/80, *On the Fire Resistance of Structural Steel Elements Derived from Standard*

Schriftenreihe des Bundesministers fur Raumordnung, Bauwesen and Stadtebau 1978, *Fire Safety*
Seigel 1967, *Water-Filled Tublar Steel Columns — Fire Protection without Coating*
Stanzak 1973, *Fire Resistance of Unprotected Steel Columns*

Thor 1977, *Some Results of Industrial Fires in Sweden*

This paper is an edited version of one that appeared as Preprint 81-055, presented at the ASCE Convention, New York, New York, May 11–15, 1981.

Fire-Resistant Design of Interior Structural Steel

Emile W. J. Troup

STRUCTURAL FIRE EXPERIENCE

During a span of less than three months (November, 1980—February, 1981), nearly 250 occupants have died in nine well-publicized fires in residential-type buildings and places of public assembly. Probably all of these fatalities have been directly or indirectly caused by smoke and other products of combustion. This experience has been similar to previous building fires in the United States, throughout this century, in which there has been large loss of life.

Certain "deficiencies" in building construction and fire safety are often cited in these tragic fires, namely the following:

- highly combustible finishing and furnishing materials;

- inadequate or inoperative exits;

- unobstructed movement of combustion products;

- late fire detection or alarm;

- absence of sprinklers;

- understaffed inspection and code enforcement agencies;

- combustibility of construction;

- inadequate fire separation;

- poorly designed air-handling system.

Conspicuously absent from any such list is "inadequate ASTM E119 (ASTM, 1980) fire endurance of the structural steel frame."

The susceptibility of steel's strength at temperatures of 538 to 1093°C (1000 to 2000°F) is well documented (Fig. 1). It is to be expected that prolonged exposure to these temperatures will cause severe distress in unprotected structural steel under load. One can certainly find examples of destruction of unprotected steel frames in the low-rise, industrial-building fire records. And, occasionally, the dramatic, fire-induced structural collapse of a major building, such as the Livonia, Michigan, auto assembly plant (1953) and McCormick Place, Chicago (1967), exposed a basic flaw in the "state-of-the-art" approach to structural fire protection.

And yet, the reader is hard-pressed to find, during this century, one instance in which the distress of any structural steel member during a fire has been fatal (or even injurious) to the occupant of any building. This is a remarkable record; two reasons for it are that (1) structural steel is truly noncombustible; and (2) unprotected structural steel has far greater resistance to fire than do occupants of the building.

The implication from the second reason is that by the time distress in the steel member can occur, the fate of the occupants in that area has long since been sealed; they have either escaped, been rescued, or expired.

Moreover, the overall performance of unprotected structural steel exposed to short-term, intense fires in buildings has been commendable; even if severe, damage may be localized such that the integrity of the entire frame is

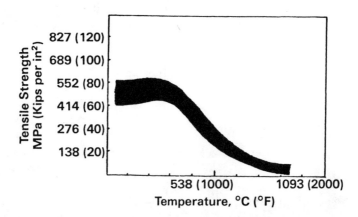

Fig. 1 Tensile strength of A36 Steel at elevated temperature

not jeopardized and repair is easily accomplished (Corbit, 1950; AISC, 1953; Dill, 1960; Canadian Steel Industries Construction Council, 1971).

For the short term, the ASTM E119 test fire exposure can be less severe than the actual event in a building with contents typical of the 1980s. Over the long term, however, there is a tendency for the average gas temperatures at a given location in a building during a fire to be far below those sustained within the E119 test furnace (Fig. 2). For one thing, the typical building space does not have an infinite supply of fuel. Also, compared to the E119 test furnace, there must be an enormous capacity within a building's volume and structure (even when subdivided) to dissipate heat. Maintaining a steel temperature of, say, 816°C (1500°F) over a long period of time at any location would require direct, intimate exposure to the intense fire's radiative and/or convective heat (Troup, 1974).

Another reality in buildings is that unrated, "unprotected" structural steel may be enclosed or encased within an assembly or membrane that does have some insulation or protective value. In other words, the steel will often be isolated from the direct heat of the fire for at least some period of time. This advantage, not considered in rating the fire resistance of a steel structure, is very real, but probably impossible to evaluate.

To summarize, structural steel, in spite of a reduction in strength at high temperatures, has a great deal to recommend it in the real building fire environment, even when unprotected. There is no other way to account for its remarkable, historical lack of involvement in fire fatalities during this century.

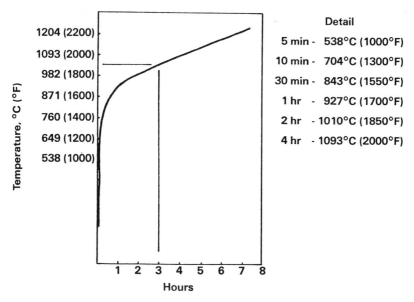

Fig. 2 ASTM E119-80 time-temperature curve

HIGH-RISE AND LOW-RISE

Fire endurance of the structural steel frame in the high-rise building is a necessary element of the total fire safety program. Rapid, safe egress during a fire has not always been a viable alternative for occupants of upper stories. And the effectiveness of the attack and rescue efforts of ground-based fire services diminishes as buildings get higher. Because of the incredible harm, both to large numbers of occupants and to the community, that would result from the collapse of a high-rise building during a fire, the structural frame must have some minimum fire resistance, regardless of the sophistication, expense, or potential effectiveness of other fire safety measures provided.

The low-rise building, up to ten stories high, is an entirely different situation. Three-hour fire resistance of structural steel columns cannot contribute to the life-safety program in these buildings and is therefore an excessive requirement, even for institutional occupancies (Troup, 1975).

To meet fire-resistance ratings, building owners and designers have often had to conform to excessively detailed and inflexible structural assemblies that may not represent the best, safest, or most economical construction. Fortunately, engineering methods, recently available and increasingly accepted, are easing this part of the problem.

ENGINEERING COLUMN ASSEMBLIES

Fire testing of structural assemblies according to a standard procedure, ASTM E119, has been going on for much of the twentieth century. Fire-resistance ratings for structural steel in the early 1900s was achieved primarily by encasement with materials such as concrete, clay tile, and plaster. Ratings for beam and column assemblies in old steel frames are still being determined from listings that date back to World War I (NBS, 1942; BOCA, 1970; NBS, 1931; National Board of Fire Underwriters, 1917–1919; Singleton, 1929; National Board of Fire Underwriters, 1964). The most often referenced listing of current E119 fire-resistance ratings is published annually by Underwriters' Laboratories, Inc. (UL). Some listings of W-section columns are summarized in Table 1 (UL, 1980).

The idea of calculating fire resistance is apparently quite old. As early as 1942, formulas were presented to estimate the fire endurance achieved by the use of tested materials (NBS, 1942). However, the key study that produced a calculation for fire resistance of protected structural steel was that of Lie and Stanzak in early 1970 (Lie and Stanzak, 1973). It is their work that the steel industry used as a basis for developing relationships currently published and in use (AISI, 1980).

The temperature rise (and hourly fire rating) of the structural steel column in a given assembly is a function of the column's *shape* and *mass*. Shape is expressed by the parameter "heated perimeter" D, defined as the inside perimeter of the fireproofing material through which heat enters the space occupied by the steel column. Mass is simply the weight per foot W of the column. The heavier the column, the higher the rating; the larger the heated perimeter, the lower the rating, since there is greater opportunity for heat to enter the column space. For fireproofing materials evaluated thus far, the following column formulas are currently published in English units (AISI, 1980):

(a) Gypsum wallboard (GWB)

$$R = 130\left[\frac{h\,(W'/D)}{2}\right]^{0.75} \quad \text{where } W' = W + \left[\frac{50\,(hD)}{144}\right] \quad (1)$$

(b) Spray-on mineral fiber or cementitious

$$R = \left[C_1\,(W/D) + C_2\right]h \quad (2)$$

Where R = fire resistance (minutes)
$\quad W'$ = weight of steel column and GWB (lb/ft)
$\quad W$ = weight of steel column (lb/ft)
$\quad h$ = thickness of protection (in)
$\quad D$ = heated perimeter of steel column (in)
C_1 & C_2 = material-dependent constants determined for specific spray-on products by the ASTM E119 fire test.

To refine and substantiate the GWB calculation, 15 tests on 7 different columns were conducted in accordance with ASTM E119: W4X13, W6X15.5, W10X49, W12X190, W14X142, TS4X4X3/16, TS8X8X1/4. AISI (1980), in addition to comparing predicted and test fire endurance for these tests,

Table 1 Number of hourly ratings listed by UL (1980)

Column size	Gypsum wallboard	Spray-on cementitious	Spray-on mineral fiber
W4X13	6	—	—
W6X16	7	3	5
W8X28	8	7	7
W8X35	—	5	—
W10X49	18	98	5
W14X228	9	26	12
Total	48	139	29

tabulates GWB thickness required for 1-, 2-, 3- and 4-hour ratings of 35 typical column sections.

The calculation for spray-on assemblies was refined and substantiated by 27 tests on W, TS (tube), and pipe sections. Again, calculated thicknesses of the cementitious and mineral fiber material for 1-, 2-, 3- and 4-hour ratings of 35 W-shape columns are tabulated.

BEAM ASSEMBLIES

Although in an actual building fire the ceiling level is most severely exposed (Troup, 1974), E119 fire tests are conducted so that the column assembly, being totally immersed in gases at the furnace temperature, probably sees a more severe exposure. The floor/ceiling has a built in "heat sink" that draws some heat from the steel beam up through the assembly toward the unexposed surface. Often, the top flange itself is shielded from furnace gas temperatures. For an insulated roof in which the heat sink may be negligible, the exposure severity to beams protected by spray-on material will approach that of a similarly protected column. Thus, calculations used for steel columns should generally yield a conservative (low) fire-resistance rating for the same sections used as beams.

Substantial savings in framing costs can be realized by using the minimum beam size in the protected assembly. In one case, a multistory nursing home, the owner saved $15,000 in framing cost by substituting W10X17 for W8X28 beams in the UL D840 assembly. The spray-on mineral fiber protection was increased from 19 to 25 mm (3/4 to 1 in) on the W10X17 to compensate for the lighter section.

The heat sink effect, or thermal conductance of the floor or roof system, is a factor in the hourly fire rating of protected steel beams supporting such assemblies. For example, UL does not recommend the substitution of higher-insulating lightweight structural concrete for normal-weight concrete in a floor slab (UL, 1980). And yet, of 17 listed assemblies in the N700 series (beam ratings), all but one specify that either concrete may be used without any change in beam protection thickness or hourly rating. One listing (N706) specifies greater beam protection with lightweight concrete for some ratings, but even here the differences in thickness amount to only 3 mm (1/8 in). This is hardly within the control of field applicators of spray-on material.

If the type of concrete is of questionable significance in the controlled test environment of E119, its effect would probably be washed out in the real fire. If the effect of lightweight concrete is only to raise steel temperatures by 5 or 10% in the E119 test, perhaps it should not influence beam or floor/ceiling assembly ratings. Or a "rule of thumb" could be established, for example, add 10% to the beam protection thickness when lightweight concrete is substituted for normal weight. Prohibiting this kind of rational design adjustment increases the cost of fire resistant construction unnecessarily.

EXISTING BUILDINGS

The recycling or adaptive use of existing buildings constitutes a major and growing construction market in the United States. However, some worthwhile projects have been stymied or shelved because of the prohibitive cost of upgrading to current life-safety codes.

Some minimum degree of life safety must be provided in these old buildings. Indeed, recycling is often an opportunity to upgrade what clearly is or could be a very dangerous environment for the occupants. Nevertheless, existing buildings, which are not completely rebuilt, should not necessarily have to meet, to the letter, the same code requirements as new construction. To make the best use of many fine old buildings requires some flexibility, short of dangerous compromise, on the part of the code enforcement officer. One such example involved an existing six-story office building being recycled for residential use. The elaborate fire separations required for a new building would have made the project unfeasible. The code authority judiciously adjusted the requirement for separations, and called for increased smoke detection, which was easily installed and probably resulted in a safer building.

Two of the structural problems associated with older buildings are that (1) the existing steel member is enclosed or confined within an assembly for which no listed fire rating exists; or (2) the existing steel member is "obsolete" and has never been fire tested with modern fireproofing materials. For the second case, if the steel member is essentially unprotected, the information now exists to design a viable fire-resistant assembly for whatever section is encountered. Among the *Fire Resistance Directory* (UL, 1980) and other listings, the calculation methods (AISI, 1980), and the historical fire resistance data, a design that is acceptable to the architect, owner, and building official should be achievable.

For the first case above, again using all available current and historical fire-resistance data, an attempt should be made to squeeze the most value out of the existing material protecting the steel member. If the estimated fire resistance resulting from this analysis is judged deficient, the assembly must be upgraded with additional listed material. If the existing assembly is judged unprotected, the new material will either replace it or encapsulate it.

STRUCTURAL FIRE RESISTANCE AND SPRINKLERS

Large loss of life in building fires almost always relates back to the effects of combustion products, not to the high temperatures. However, the spread of the fire area and the speed with which combustion products are able to move laterally and vertically up through the building interior are heavily dependent on the heat-release rate of the fire.

It is the buoyancy of combustion products, or the difference between fire gas and ambient air temperature/density, that gives them mobility. The fire itself can be thought of as a giant fan propelling the various products of combustion through the building. The higher the thermal energy generated at the fire scene, the more mobile the products are likely to be. Thus, a reduction in the burning rate will mean a reduction in the speed and extent of the movement of the combustion products.

A sprinkler system will not always extinguish the fire that actuates it. But sprinklers, adequately designed and operating in the relatively early stages at the fire scene, will almost always establish some degree of fire control; that is, they will greatly reduce the burning rate. In a tall building, this can be a critical factor in minimizing the threat to the life safety of occupants located in areas remote from and above the actual fire.

Although cost is the real obstacle to the installation of sprinklers in buildings, "reliability" is the most frequently noted technical objection. Like any mechanical system, and like any fire safety measure in buildings (passive or active), sprinkler systems can and do fail. Organizations keeping detailed records of sprinkler performance, however, report a very high percentage of successful performance (Marryatt, 1981). Sprinklers are very effective in controlling fires in most occupancies with ceiling heights of about 6.1 m (20 ft) or less (Troup, 1970). Atrium spaces notwithstanding, this description fits most new, multistoried, nonwarehouse building space.

Most of the excessive structural fire resistance is tied up in low-rise buildings one to ten stories high. The high probability of fire control by sprinklers and the ineffectiveness of structural steel fireproofing as a life-safety measure should be reflected in code requirements. There are few instances in which more than 1 to 2 hours of fire resistance would be of any value in the low-rise buildings. In fact, unprotected steel construction, in conjunction with complete sprinkler protection, would satisfy life-safety needs in most of these low-rise buildings. It should be noted that the impact of the cost of sprinkler protection, up to $10.76 to $21.52 per m² ($1 to $2 per ft²), can be substantially eased if accompanied by elimination of structural fire resistance.

In general, "trading off" basic life-safety measures for sprinklers in buildings is not recommended. In the low-rise building, however, structural fire resistance, in terms of life safety, is not "basic". In fact, it is most often not a life-safety measure at all.

CASE STUDY—EXISTING NURSING HOME

The structural fire resistance required for nursing homes is perhaps the most excessive of any occupancy (Troup, 1975). A 3-hour E119 fire rating is usually required for steel columns supporting more than one floor. Although an uncontrolled fire burning for 3 hours in a two- or three-story steel frame nursing home is conceivable, such a fire could never sustain an average temperature of 982°C (1800°F) for 2½ hours at a single location. (This would be roughly equivalent to the 3-hour E119 fire). There is simply insufficient fuel in the low-rise, steel frame, residential-type building.

An existing nursing home was undergoing renovation and was found to have numerous life-safety deficiencies according to the code then in force. The existing columns were structural tube sections, TS6X6X3/16 and TS8X8X1/4, protected by 28 mm (1 1/8 in) of a listed spray-on mineral fiber. At the time, there were no E119 fire test ratings for protected steel tubes, but a 3-hour rating was required. The architect convinced the code authority to allow use of engineering methods to upgrade the fire resistance.

The first task was to estimate the existing E119 fire resistance using equation (2), developed for use with English units:

$$R = \left[63\,(W/D)+42\right]\ h \quad \text{where } C_1 = 63 \text{ and } C_2 = 42 \tag{3}$$

For the TS6X6X3/16: $W = 14.4$ lb/ft; $D = 24$ in; $W/D = 0.60$

For the TS8X8X1/4: $W = 25.4$ lb/ft; $D = 32$ in; $W/D = 0.79$

Solving these equations for fire resistance R yields 90 minutes for the 6-in tube and 103 minutes for the 8-in tube. The designer elected to supplement the mineral fiber with external layers of "firecode" GWB properly fastened around the existing assembly. Two layers of 5/8-in GWB were evaluated by the governing formula, equation (1), for the 6-in tube, assuming no mineral fiber present:

$$W' = W + \left[\frac{50\,(hD)}{144}\right] = 14.4 + \left[\frac{50\,(10/8)(24)}{144}\right] = 24.8 \text{ lb/ft} \tag{4}$$

W' is the weight of the tube column plus the wallboard.

$$R = 130\left[\frac{h\,(W'/D)}{2}\right]^{0.75} = 130\left[\frac{(10/8)(24.8/24)}{2}\right]^{0.75} \tag{5}$$

$$= 93.7 \text{ minutes}$$

Total $R = 93.7$(GWB) + 90 (mineral fiber) = 184 > 180, OK

Since the W/D ratio for the TS8X8X1/4 is larger than that of the TS6X6X3/16, no calculation is needed to determine that the same protection provides at least the same fire resistance for the larger column.

Rather than condemning the structure as "unprotectable" because the column assemblies were unlisted or requiring outrageously expensive supplementary or replacement fire protection, the code authority enabled the designer and owner to provide an acceptable, economical solution that met the intent of the code.

CASE STUDY—NEW MECHANICAL PENTHOUSE

The owner of an 1896 ten-story downtown office building is building a mechanical penthouse on the roof (Fig. 3). Fire resistance is being engineered for new structural steel in the penthouse, all the existing columns, and certain beams in the existing structure. Only columns in the ninth and tenth stories will have to be reinforced to carry additional roof loads (Fig. 4).

Figures 5, 6, and 7 show the existing columns consisting of four Z-bars joined by two rows of rivets and a plate and encased in concrete fill and 101-mm (4-in) clay tile. This configuration was a common fire-rated column assembly during the period. National Board of Fire Underwriters (1917–1919) lists the assembly for 3 hours (actual test: 3 hours, 33½ minutes). A 3-hour rating is likewise required by the code authority for the renovated building.

Fig. 3 Structural steel framing for a new mechanical penthouse atop an 1896 ten-story office building

All the existing columns will be stripped of their fireproofing and "recycled" with a durable cementitious spray-on material to achieve the rating. Since protected Z-bar columns have not recently been tested by ASTM E119 with current fireproofing materials, the column calculation was used to determine required thicknesses.

The smallest column was a 152-mm (6-in) Z-bar, 159 by 270 mm (6 1/4 by 10 5/8 in) out to out, using a 152-by-6-mm (6-by-¼-in) plate. The weight of the column per foot is 14.38 kg (31.7 lb). The heated perimeter, contour protected, is 1410 mm (55½ in) (Jones & Laughlin Steel Co., 1906) (Fig. 4).

Equation (2) was used for this calculation, as shown below, even though the specific constants were developed for a different cementitious product. Examination of 1980 UL listings indicates that efficiencies of the two products are very similar.

For $R = 3$ hours or 180 minutes, and using the English units,

$$h = \frac{R}{69\,(W/D) + 31} = \frac{180}{69\,(.57) + 31} = 2.56, \text{ say } 2\frac{1}{2} \text{ in (64 mm)} \qquad (6)$$

Where $W = 31.7$ lb, and $D = 55\frac{1}{2}$ in
$C_1 = 69$, and $C_2 = 31$

Fig. 4 Existing tenth story after removal of steel columns encasement and suspended ceiling

The W/D ratio of the other Z-bar columns will be checked, and if they are all greater than 0.57, then 64 mm (2½ in) will be the maximum thickness of cementitious fireproofing required. This thickness will be reduced where columns are reinforced, as the mass of the column and its heated perimeter will be favorably altered.

In the existing elevator shafts, there are unprotected separator beams of 305 mm (12 in), 59.53 kg/m (40 lb/ft) (Fig. 8). Because the new elevators will be larger than the existing ones, only 13 mm (1/2 in) of clearance around these beams will be available for fireproofing. Thus, a highly efficient intumescent mastic, 13 mm (1/2 in) thick, will be applied to achieve fire resistance.

The rooftop penthouse will be 5.49 m (18 ft) high and 18.29 m by 54.86 m (60 ft by 180 ft), and will contain 100 tons of new structural steel, most of which will be protected by cementitious spray-on material for 1 or 2 hours (Fig. 9). Some of the steel, notably beams supporting the upper elevator machine room or other heavy equipment, will be encased in concrete.

The architect wanted to select a roof assembly requiring 1 hour, similar to UL P801 (UL, 1980), but that listing specifies a spray-on mineral fiber of insufficient durability for this application. The architect then proposed an alternate roof assembly made up of the listed materials shown in Fig. 10. This proposal was accepted by the code authority when presented with supportive test data from the product manufacturer, even though the exact roof assembly

Fig. 5 Existing Z-bar column and underside of terra-cotta floor system

had not been tested by the ASTM E119 method. Because of increased durability, the alternate roof system will have a more reliable, long-term fire resistance.

SUMMARY AND CONCLUSIONS

Recent tragic fires are accelerating realization that hard-core fire resistance of noncombustible structural steel frames does not, and cannot, contribute to occupant life safety in most buildings. In low-rise buildings, up to about ten stories, the emphasis on fire protection should be shifted from the noncombustible structural frame to occupant life safety. Structural fire resistance is essential in high-rise buildings, but even here its proper role must be appreciated to achieve an effective, economical fire safety program.

Fig. 6 Typical splice at Z-bar column

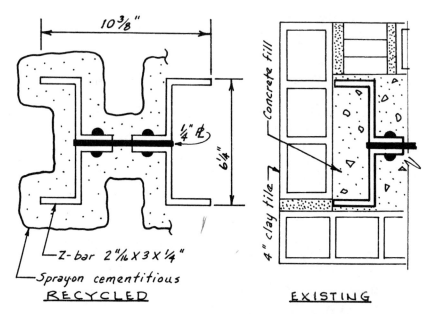

Fig. 7 Protected 6-in Z-bar column

Fig. 8 Existing, unprotected 12-in separator beam in elevator shaft

Fig. 9 New mechanical penthouse framing to be protected by an engineered system of spray-on fireproofing

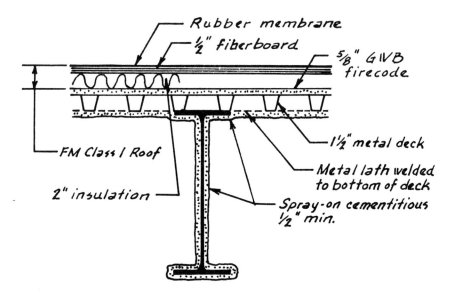

Fig. 10 Penthouse roof detail—1-hour rating

In view of its high probability of early fire control, and the minimal value of structural fire resistance, a completely sprinklered "unprotected" steel frame building is substantially safer for occupants than a building just like it that is stucturally fire resistant but unsprinklered.

The ASTM E119 Fire Test Method will continue to serve a vital function as a relative, large-scale indicator of the fire resistance of different products and assemblies. In the future, however, E119 testing should mostly be reserved for establishing new data bases as products and assemblies are introduced or significantly refined, or as application and installation methods are modified. The shifting role of the rigorous, large-scale fire test is emerging through increased acceptance by code enforcement authorities of *engineered* fire-resistant steel frames for new and recycled buildings. Case studies have been presented to illustrate the techniques and their acceptance and the kinds of economic and functional benefits to be derived therefrom.

Specifically, the writer concludes or recommends the following:

1. Type 2A and 2B (protected) and Type 2C (unprotected) steel-frame construction should be specified for low-rise buildings up to about ten stories high (BOCA, 1981). Type 2A construction provides structural protection for the 1½- to 2-hour ASTM E119 fire exposure (roughly 816 to 871°C average temperature). This exposure is, in fact, very severe in the context of the real building fire, and is excessive in low-rise buildings for the purpose of life safety.

2. Where structural fire-resistance requirements are clearly excessive, the presence of a complete, supervised sprinkler system should permit substantial reduction in these requirements.

3. The fire resistance of any structural steel column, past or present, can now be engineered using listed materials for which ASTM E119 Fire Test data is published or available.

4. In general, column fire-resistance formulas can be applied to steel beams in floor/ceiling or roof assemblies when box or contour type protection of individual beams is used.

5. A study should be made to determine which of the variables in floor/ceiling and roof assemblies have a truly significant effect on the fire endurance of protected steel beams.

CONDENSED REFERENCES/BIBLIOGRAPHY

The following is a condensed bibliography for this article. It includes all articles referred to or cited in the text. The full citations will be found at the end of the volume, with additional citations for further reading. What is given here should be sufficient information to lead the reader to the correct article: the author, date, and title. In case of multiple authors, only the first name is listed.

AISC 1953, *Salvaging Fire Damaged Steel*
AISI 1980,*Designing Fire Protection for Steel Columns*
ASTM 1980, *Standard Methods of Fire Tests of Building Construction and Materials*

BOCA 1970, *Approved Fire Resistance Ratings of Assemblies of Construction Materials*
BOCA 1981, *The BOCA Basic Building Code/1981*

Canadian Steel Industries Construction Council 1974, *Fire-Damage and Repair*
Corbit 1950, *Structural Steel After a Fire*

Dill 1960, *Structural Steel After a Fire*

Jones 1906, *Safe Load Tables: 8-Inch & 6-Inch Z-Bar Columns*

Lie 1973, *Fire Resistance of Protected Steel Columns*

Marryatt 1981, *Sprinkler Trade-Offs and the Australian Experience*

National Board of Fire Underwriters 1917-1919, *Fire Tests of Building Columns*
National Board of Fire Underwriters 1964, *Fire Resistance Ratings*
NBS 1931, *Recommended Minimum Requirements for Fire Resistance in Buildings*
NBS 1942, *Building Materials and Structures*

Singleton 1929, *Fireproofing Structural Steel*

Troup 1970, *The High-Challenge Fireball—A Trademark of the Seventies*
Troup 1974, *New Developments in Ceiling-Level Protection for the High-Challenge Fire*
Troup 1975, *Fire Endurance for Steel Frame Nursing Homes*

UL 1980, *Fire Resistance Directory*

This paper is an edited version of one that appeared as Preprint 81-125, presented at the ASCE Convention, New York, New York, May 11–15, 1981.

Fires in High-Rise Buildings

Joseph F. Fitzgerald

The recent spectacular fires in Las Vegas have again sparked controversy on high-rise fires and the fire safety of new and existing high-rise buildings. The emphasis this time is on existing high-rise buildings that do not meet the latest fire safety standards used by the larger cities and for model codes. There has been a lot of talk about retrofitting existing high-rise buildings, and there have been numerous opinions as to what should be done on a retrofit basis.

That there is talk of mandatory retroactive requirements has acted as a deterrent to voluntary improvement of fire safety systems in existing buildings. Owners logically do not want to voluntarily spend money on improvements when there is the threat of mandatory requirements that very possibly would be different from the improvements they would make. This reluctance holds especially true when there are so many divergent opinions as to what to do to existing buildings. It is a classic problem and one that should be addressed.

The problems that have surfaced relative to the recent spectacular fires have not revealed anything not previously known about the peculiarity of high-rise fires. If the presently known areas of concern had been properly addressed in Las Vegas, the fires would not have ended in such disaster. Even if the basic fire safety provisions required at the time the MGM Grand was built were properly adhered to, the fire would not have caused the problem that it did in this instance. As Rolf Jensen says, " Nothing new was learned from the Las Vegas fire." Any properly trained analyst could easily have detected the obvious deficiencies before the fire occurred.

However, the major area of concern lies in the proper construction of buildings and the inspection of that construction, rather than in the design per se. It also lies in the continual inspection process necessary to maintain the integrity of the original design through the life span of the building. This process is especially important when the fire protection system relies so heavily on mechanical and electrical equipment, much of which it is hoped will never be used except on a test basis.

This concern has been recognized on a national basis by the various code organizations, the American Institute of Architects, and the National Institute of Building Sciences, among others. The lack of qualified inspection personnel and their proper deployment must be addressed.

A complicating element in this inspection process is the overlap, or underlap, as the case may be, of Fire Department and Building Department inspections. It is an element that needs attention.

The following are excerpts from comments made by professionals in the field of fire safety as it relates to tall buildings. They were obtained as a result of a correspondence survey.

AUSTRALIAN EXPERIENCE WITH SPRINKLERS
Harry W. Marryatt

The case for built-in fire protection in high-rise buildings appears to have been underlined by the fires in recent years in Las Vegas (two), New York, and Sao Paulo, but it is essential that such protection be complete. Also, the disturbing increase in arson indicates the strong desirability of providing electronic supervision of all operating gear and water supplies. . . .

Two points will be made in this connection. The first is the necessity for external exposure protection by external sprinkler heads or water curtains on the lower floors of a high-rise building where there is an exposure hazard from a lower building, within at least 30 feet, that does not have automatic sprinkler protection. The second point concerns shallow concealed spaces between ceilings and the floor slabs above them. As these spaces are normally exempt from internal sprinkler protection, they should be subdivided into small areas with noncombustible material.

The report on the Australian experience . . . is an analysis of the results of the 1245 fires involving automatic sprinkler systems in Australia and New Zealand from March 1, 1973, to December 31, 1980.

Tables 1, 2, 3 and 4 give the experience in the light hazard occupancies. These figures are important because they concern buildings in which safety to life is a prime consideration, and they demonstrate that complete light hazard automatic sprinkler systems, correctly designed and maintained, can control fires in these occupancies very efficiently. The word "complete" should be emphasized, as partial protection may be worse than useless.

The average number of sprinkler heads in operation for all light hazard occupancies in 526 fires from 1886–1980 was 1.26. . . . Loss of life was two persons (one in a hospital and one in an institution). . . . Both deaths were from contact burns caused by igniting clothing when smoking. There was no danger to other residents. One hundred percent of the fires were extinguished or controlled.

Table 1 Overall experience in all occupancies

	1866–1968	1968–1973	1973–1980*	1886–1980*
Satisfactory	99.76%	99.36%	99.44%	99.65%
Unsatisfactory	.24%	.64%	.56%	.35%
	100.00%	100.00%	100.00%	100.00%

*The 1973–1980 period covers 1245 fires, and the 1886–1980 period covers 8193 fires.

Table 2 Fires in light hazard occupancies 1973-1980

Smoking	57 = 39%
Arson	39 = 26.7%
Electrical	12 = 8.2%
Electrical appliances	3 = 2.0%
Furnace sparks	11 = 7.5%
Overheating	14 = 9.6%
Hot ashes	2 = 1.4%
Flame	1 = .7%
Spontaneous ignition	1 = .7%
Welding	1 = .7%
Not recorded	5 = 3.4%
	146

Table 3 Floors on which fires occurred in multistory buildings (lowest floor listed is fourth) 1973-1980

4th floor	32 fires
5th floor	29
6th floor	12
7th floor	9
8th floor	1
9th floor	1
15th floor	1
20th floor	1
22nd floor	1
23rd floor	1
26th floor	1
44th floor	1
Total	90 fires

Table 4 Fire record in light hazard occupancies

Occupancy	Number of fires			
	1886–1968	1968–1973	1973–1980	1886–1980
Clubs	1	4	7	12
Apartments	7	12	12	31
Hospitals	48	31	44	123
Hostels	2	3	2	7
Hotels	46	18	24	88
Institutions	7	13	9	29
Office buildings	118	56	46	220
Schools	3	3	1	7
Universities	6	2	1	9

LAS VEGAS MGM GRAND FIRE
John G. Degenkolb

The Las Vegas MGM Grand was built under provisions of the 1970 UBC. The failure to adhere to those requirements is difficult to explain. The building official responsible at the time of construction was later indicted by a grand jury for actions on two buildings — but not for those on the Grand. The failure to meet the 1970 code requirements were extreme. . . .

One significant area concerns the establishment of the 75-foot figure . . . a raw number developed in 1971–1972. In the code, if possible, the height limit should probably be based on the capability of the local fire department and the number of men immediately available. A fire on the upper stories of a high-rise building requires that 40–50 men respond *immediately* and two or three times that number very shortly thereafter. If there are not 100 men available within 15 minutes, built-in protection, that is, sprinklers, becomes essential. . . . Research might be done by contacting fire departments who have fought fires in high-rise buildings to determine the number of men first responding and the rate at which more were added. Los Angeles used 300 men on the Occidental Building fire, which involved two stories around the 30th floor.

Stairway doors that are locked from the stairway side should be unlocked automatically upon actuation of any sprinkler in the building. . . . They must *not* be unlatched, simply unlocked, since they are fire doors. Possibly, the doors should be unlocked automatically on power failure. It would be quite inexpensive to implement such a system for new construction but quite costly to convert existing buildings. People did die in stairways in the Grand Hotel because they could not get out through locked doors.

The separation of elevator lobbies from the remainder of the building has been discussed. We have agreed that *all* lobbies, including the ground floor, should also be separated. Then there is the question of venting the elevator hoistways. In the Grand, the vents were blocked off and there was no place

| Average and greatest number of sprinklers in operation | | | | | | | |
| 1886–1968 | | 1968–1973 | | 1973–1980 | | 1886–1980 | |
Av.	Gtst.	Av.	Gtst.	Av.	Gtst.	Av.	Gtst.
2.00	2	1.25	2	1.14	2	1.18	2
1.10	2	1.00	1	1.08	2	1.06	2
1.14	3	1.23	3	1.20	2	1.19	3
1.00	1	1.00	1	1.00	1	1.00	1
1.18	5	1.39	6	1.33	6	1.28	6
1.00	1	1.31	4	1.67	5	1.21	5
1.24	23*	1.37	8	1.24	2	1.29	23
3.66	8	1.00	1	1.00	1	2.14	8
1.8	4	1.00	1	1.00	1	1.67	4

*Arsonists lit 6 fires

for smoke to go but to mushroom down through the top stories. NBS, the Veterans Administration, and the National Elevator Industry are reportedly doing an investigation of the possibility of pressurizing the hoistways or lobbies. . . . Lobbies will probably turn out to be safe areas of refuge for the handicapped. According to NBS, in a sprinklered building the pressure build-up from a fire will be about .04–.05 in (.10–1.27 mm) of water column. So the lobby would only have to be pressurized to about .07. It should be possible to pressurize a maximum of three lobbies.

On the question of elevator call buttons, research done by Otis indicates that any call button will fail at 450–500°F. But is this serious if the lobby is separated from the remainder of the floor? The MGM Grand did not have smoke detectors in the elevator lobby to initiate recall.

Guest rooms and suites should be posted individually with diagrams showing the location of exits relative to the room . . . maybe on the inside of the bathroom door where such a sign will be noticed.

The Grand—and many other buildings—supplied make-up air via the corridor. This condition has not been permitted for 20 years or more. The proposed revision of NFPA 90A will permit the corridor to serve as a plenum if it is part of an undefined smoke control system. . . . If smoke occurs in the corridor, the pressurization should shut down. The corridor should be separated from the lobby, since the lobby is the most likely place for the fire to originate; consider the Cornell and Ohio State University dormitory fires.

Smoke control requirements must be made more clear. Pressure differentials in thousandths of inches of water column are meaningless in real buildings. A broken window, an open door, or the like, will completely eliminate such minor differences.

Relative to the use of tempered glass in windows to avoid the possibility of flying shards of glass, it seems that tempered glass cannot be depended on to break up into small pieces and that it is likely to fall in a sizable chunk. Apparently there is no standard for tempered glass and its ability to break up into very small pieces. A standard that will assure proper breakup should be developed.

One feature of compartmentation that is very frequently overlooked is the requirement that the fire floor be capable of being vented remotely, that is, without entering the fire floor. The usual result is that sprinkler protection is provided rather than compartmentation.

In general, the current high-rise requirements found in the model codes *are* realistic.

RECENT DEVELOPMENTS IN FIRE STUDIES
Philip H. Thomas

The recent major developments in fire studies relate to the following topics:

1. Preflashover fires.

2. Toxicity.

3. Smoke control.

4. Systems analysis of fire safety.

The latter two areas are especially relevant to the work of the building designer.

The major areas needing research are in the field of active protection systems, reliability of equipment, cost effectiveness of safety systems, and fire modeling. Since the principal causes of fire are man-made, unlike those of earthquake and wind damage, we can do something about the causes as well as alleviate the consequences. There is much to do on the development of safer materials and designs for furnishings.

There is therefore much activity in the field of fire testing and the development of rational methods of assessing performance and validating tests.

RECENT RESULTS OF FRENCH TESTS
J. Kruppa

Tests performed in France since the preparation of the fire chapter in Volume CL have allowed us to draw the conclusions that follow, which represent improvements in the previous knowledge.

First, on the *heating of protected steel members*, tests have shown that

$$\Delta\theta_a = \frac{1}{\frac{1}{K} + \frac{e}{\gamma}} \; \frac{S}{V} \; \frac{1}{C_{pa\rho_a}} \; [\theta_f - \theta_a(t)]\Delta t$$

in which the coefficient γ = insulation, whose thickness is represented by e (equation 4.16 in Chapter CL-4 of the Monograph). Variations of γ with the temperature are obtained using this equation, from heating curves of highly loaded protected profiles. Then it is possible to establish flow charts for stability times giving necessary thickness versus the critical temperature and S/V. This equation is only valid when the thickness of the cladding material is small (about up to 30 mm). For greater thicknesses it is necessary to take into account the thermal capacity of the cladding material which, in some cases, is as high as that of the steel member.

A method of testing for the cladding of structural steel members has been defined recently in France.

Second, on the *mechanical behavior of external columns*, series of tests have been performed with unprotected columns, under static loads, exposed to natural fire. This research has been described in Acier-Stahl-Steel. Its main results are the following:

> Obviously, the effect of the thermal gradient results in a curvature of the pin-ended column towards the furnace and, consequently, in an eccentricity of the initially axial load. However, by comparison with an equivalent internal column, the fire stability of the external column reveals itself as two to three times greater.

> Beam-to-column joints on external columns have an excellent behavior under fire exposure. For the tests with this type of structure, only part of the beam was encased for fire protection. With rigid beam-to-column joints, the structure was able to support the applied static loads for the whole duration of the fire, in spite of heavy stresses and high temperature.

Criteria and Loading

CONDENSED REFERENCES/BIBLIOGRAPHY

The following is a condensed bibliography for this part. It contains bibliographic citations that are in addition to those cited with the articles. The full citations can be found at the end of the volume. What is given here should be sufficient information to lead the reader to the correct article: author, date, and title. In the case of multiple authors, only the first named is listed.

Allen 1977, *Fire Resistance of Reinforced Concrete Columns and Walls*
Allen 1981, *Criteria for Design Safety Factors and Quality Assurance Expenditure*
Atkins 1979, *Averaged Pressure Coefficients for Rectangular Buildings*

Blessmann 1979, *Interaction Effects in Neighboring Tall Buildings*
Blessmann 1979, *Wind Pressures in Neighboring Tall Buildings*

Cruz 1980, *Number of Modes for the Seismic Analysis of Buildings*

Dalgliesh 1978, *Measurements of Wind Inducted Displacements of a 57-Story Building in Toronto*
Dalgliesh 1979, *Comparisons of Wind Tunnel and Fullscale Building Surface Pressures with Emphasis*
Dye 1980, *Comparison of Full-Scale and Wind-Tunnel Model Measurements of Ground Winds*

Everett 1978, *Presentation and Discussion of Results as Performed at University of Bristol, U.K.*

Gandemer 1978, *Aerodynamic Studies of Built-Up Areas Made by C.S.T.B. at Nantes, France*
Georgiou 1979, *Wind Loads on Building Frames*
Gluck 1979, *Dynamic Torsional Coupling in Tall Building Structures*
Griffin 1979, *Universal Similarity in the Wakes of Stationary and Vibrating Bluff Structures*

Holmes 1979, *Mean and Fluctuating Internal Pressures Induced by Wind*

IAEE 1974, *Proceedings of Fifth World Conference on Earthquake Engineering*
IAEE 1977, *Proceedings of Sixth World Conference on Earthquake Engineering*
IAEE 1980, *Earthquake Resistant Regulations—A Word List*
IAEE 1981, *Proceedings of Seventh World Conference on Earthquake Engineering*
Ikenouchi 1979, *Experimental and Numerical Studies on the Aerodynamic Instability of Tower-Like*
Isyumov 1978, *Studies of the Pedestrian Level Wind Environment at the Boundary Layer Wind*

Jeary 1979, *The Determination of Modal Wind Loads from Full Scale Building Response*

371

Jeary 1979, *The Response of a 190 Metre Tall Building and the Ramifications for the Prediction*

Kamei 1978, *Study of Wind Environmental Problems Caused Around Buildings in Japan*
Kareen 1979, *Crosswind Response of High-Rise Buildings*
Kawai 1979, *Characteristics of Pressure Fluctuations on the Windward Wall of a Tall Building*
Kwok 1979, *Cross-Wind Response of Structures Due to Displacement Dependent Lock-In Excitation*

Lam 1979, *Full-Scale Measurement of Wind Pressure Fluctuations on a Bluff Building*
Lawson 1978, *The Wind Content of the Built Environment*
Lawson 1978, *Wind Tunnel Investigations*
Lee 1979, *The Ground Level Wind Environment Around the Sheffield University Arts Tower*
Lopez 1980, *Estimating Shears in Buildings Subjected to Earthquake Motions*

Melbourne 1978, *Wind Environment Studies in Australia*
Melbourne 1978, *Criteria for Environmental Wind Conditions*
Melbourne 1979, *Turbulence Effects on Maximum Surface Pressures—A Mechanism and Possibility*
Melbourne 1980, *Comparison of Measurements on the CAARC Standard Tall Building Model in*
Miyata 1979, *Turbulence Effects on Aerodynamic Response of Rectangular Bluff Cylinders*
Murakami 1979, *Amplification of Wind Speed at Ground Level Due to Construction of High-Rise*
Murakami 1981, *New Criteria for Wind Effects on Pedestrians*
Murzewski 1970, *Structural Safety*
Murzewski 1974, *Structural Safety*
Murzewski 1975, *Stochastic Models of Structural Loads*
Murzewski 1981, *Reliability Consideration of Beam Systems, Developments in Civil Engineering*

Olmer 1980, *Method of Vibration Measurement of Tall Structures*

Perera 1978, *A Wind-Tunnel Study of the Interaction Between Along-Wind and Cross-Wind Vibrations*
Pirner 1977, *Some Results of Model Measurements on Tall Buildings*

Reinhold 1979, *The Influence of Wind Direction on the Response of a Square-Section Tall Building*
Reinhorn 1977, *Dynamic Torsional Coupling in Asymmetric Building Structures*
Riera 1979, *Along Wind Structural Dynamic Response* (In Spanish)
Rosman 1980, *Eccentricity of Earthquake Loads in Regular Multistory Buildings*
Rosman 1980, *Dynamic Characteristics of Nonsymmetric Building Structures*
Rosman 1981, *Buckling and Vibration of Spatial Building Structures*
Roy 1977, *Introduction to Tall Building Structures*
Ruscheweyh 1979, *Dynamic Response of High Rise Buildings Under Wind Action with Interference*
Rutenberg 1975, *Approximations for Natural Frequencies of Interconnected Walls and Frames*
Rutenberg 1975, *Approximate Natural Frequencies for Coupled Shear Walls*
Rutenberg 1975, *Contribution to Earthquake Analysis of Coupled Shear Walls*
Rutenberg 1977, *Dynamic Properties of Asymmetric Wall-Frame Structures*
Rutenberg 1978, *Response Spectrum Techniques for Asymmetric Buildings*
Rutenberg 1978, *On the Dynamic Properties of Asymmetric Wall Frame Structures*
Rutenberg 1979, *Earthquake Analysis of Belted High-Rise Building Structures*
Rutenberg 1979, *A Consideration of the Torsional Response of Building Frames*

Sanada 1980, *Full-Scale Measurement of Environmental Wind in the Shinjuku New Metropolitan*
Sarrazin 1979, *Isolation and Absorption of Seismic Actions in Buildings*
Saunders 1979, *Buffeting Effects of Upstream Buildings*
Sidarous 1979, *An Analytical Methodology for Predicting Dynamic Building Response to Wind*
Sockel 1981, *The Influence of a Parapet on Local Pressure Fluctuations*
Solari 1979, *Dynamic Alongwind Response of a Structural System Including Soil Flexibility*
Sozen 1977, *Introduction to the Behavior of Reinforced Concrete Buildings*
Svojsik 1980, *Seismic Behavior of Macuto-Sheraton Building During the Caracas 1967 Earthquake*

Templin 1981, *Design and Performance of a Multi-Degree-of-Freedom Aeroelastic Building Model*
Topping 1978, *The Client's Question—A Case History of the Use of a Wind Tunnel Investigation*
Tso 1977, *Seismic Spectral Response of Coupled Shear Walls*

Structural Design of Tall Steel Buildings

Introductory Review

William McGuire
Charles N. Gaylord

It is often interesting to predict the course of future events and then, after a time, to compare the predictions with actuality. In Volume SB of the Monograph it was predicted that the future would see "the increased innovative use of steel in tall buildings; the increase of mixed steel and concrete construction; the use of more complex and precise analytical methods; the inclusion of all building elements which have any strength or stiffness in the assessment of structural response; design of integral segments of a structure rather than beam-by-beam and column-by-column; further quantification and allowance for human response; quantification and improved design methods for earthquake loading; and increased recognition of the probabilistic nature of structural phenomena and loadings."

The above was published in 1979. It is still too early to judge these predictions. They relate to evolutionary developments. It will take at least another five years before practice has changed sufficiently to provide the perspective needed to determine how reliable they are. Significantly, however, almost all of the contributions to the steel buildings section of this updated volume pertain to one or more of these developments. They make a useful framework for introducing the section.

INNOVATIVE USE OF STEEL

No changes in the method of employing steel in tall buildings have been as dramatic as the emergence of exposed diagonal bracing and tubular systems in the 1950s and 1960s. But innovation continues. It is clear in the use of a stressed-skin exterior frame on the Dravo Tower in Pittsburgh, which is referred to in the article by Young. It is also clear in Popov and Manheim's report on refinements in the design of eccentric bracing for improved energy absorption in earthquake-resistant structures.

MIXED CONSTRUCTION

The use of mixed steel and concrete construction continues to increase throughout the world. It is a commonplace method of building in many parts of Europe and Asia. Aside from the use of composite beams, the United States has been slow to adopt it. But this method is now receiving increased attention in America. The articles by Winter on proposed design criteria for composite columns and steel-deck reinforced concrete slabs are evidence of this interest. They contain practical guides to design and construction that appear certain to promote the use of this medium.

METHODS OF ANALYSIS

Reference to more complex and precise analytical methods appears in a number of places in this section on steel buildings. Kwieciński points to the desirability of the greater use of plastic design methods and to the need to promote such use through more satisfactory incorporation of these methods in design codes. Rational treatment of stability problems requires more profound analytical treatment than is common today. The papers by Iffland, Khan and El Nimeiri, Nair, and Moy reflect this need in a number of ways. At the core of many of the suggestions and developments found throughout this section is the employment of some form of nonlinear analysis, that is, analysis that includes the effects of geometric nonlinearities, material nonlinearities, or both. This is one of the most active fields of research and development in steel structures today. It is also, at present, a very confusing field. Many methods of treating material nonlinearity are emerging. In the handling of geometric nonlinearities there are schemes that range from approximate "P-Δ" methods to highly refined computer programs. Through the articles in this section, one can get a cross-sectional view of the present state of developments in the nonlinear analysis of tall buildings. It is clear that such work will continue. Among the greatest challenges of the near future will be attaining some sort of stability in these developments and sorting out the methods that are generally useful from those that are of only transitory interest.

TOTAL SYSTEM RESPONSE

A great deal remains to be done on the development of methods for including the actual resistance of all elements of a building system when determining its response to load. In calculations, it is still generally a practical necessity to assume all of a given load to be resisted by the steel or concrete frame. That "nonstructural" components may indeed offer resistance is generally recognized, but only in indirect ways, such as establishing nominal drift indices for wind loading and allowable stresses under combined loads. The research needed to improve this situation continues, however. The contribution by Goodno on the analysis of precast concrete cladding on tall buildings is an example of this ongoing effort. It points to some of the ways for including the resistance of cladding; and of equal importance to the other side of the picture, it clarifies that it may not always be conservative to neglect the interaction between cladding and structure. The paper by Chen on the effective lengths of columns with simple connections calls attention to a commonly neglected fact: connections that are normally assumed to be simple may actually provide sufficient end restraint to offset the effects of a small amount of unavoidable initial crookedness in columns.

MEMBER-BY-MEMBER VERSUS SYSTEM DESIGN

Just as the subject of nonlinear behavior recurs as a refrain in this section, so does the need to see design based on integral segments of a structure, rather than design developed member-by-member. This need is expressed in such places as Khachaturian's article on the optimization of steel frames, Kwieciński's and Popov and Manheim's articles on plastic design, and Goodno's article on cladding. Iffland's paper, and others in the area of stability, review advances in methods for treating the stability of two- and three-dimensional frames. Included in the Iffland report is a recommendation of the American Structural Stability Research Council to the effect that the stability of a structure as a whole be considered explicitly in design practice. Another major challenge for the near future is the refinement of methods for doing this task that are rational, practicable, and reasonably general.

HUMAN RESPONSE

Recognition of human response, which in tall buildings means making the structure stiff enough for human comfort, remains a subject of great interest and active investigation. Since, however, it is a concern in all tall buildings and not just those of steel, recent developments are reported in the section on environmental criteria rather than in this section on steel buildings.

EARTHQUAKE DESIGN

Of the harm that structures can suffer, fire, war, and earthquake are perhaps the most widespread sources and certainly the most alarming in their consequences. Of these, the earthquake is the event that is most amenable to rational structural analysis and design. There is a vast amount of activity in many parts of the world directed toward the improvement of methods for the design of earthquake-resistant buildings. The contributions of Popov and Manheim and Kato and Akiyama are representative of this effort. The relative lack of information on the state of earthquake engineering is a shortcoming of this section that should be corrected in future editions. Fortunately, however, the literature on earthquake design is well documented elsewhere. In the United States, the Earthquake Engineering Research Center at the University of California in Berkeley, is a major repository of information on earthquake effects. Much of this information may be borrowed or purchased, either from the Center or from the U.S. Government-operated National Technical Information Service.

PROBABILISTIC EFFECTS

The prediction that the future would see increased recognition of the probabilistic nature of structural phenomena and loadings was of course a safe one to make. At the time the tall steel buildings volume was published, a number of countries had already adopted limit-states design specifications that were semiprobabilistic in nature and other countries were in the process of considering their adoption. The United States was one of the slower countries in this direction, but its future course now seems fairly well established. In 1981 the American National Standards Institute issued a new edition of its specification for live loads in buildings that is based much more firmly than previous editions were on knowledge of the probability of occurrence of many different types of loads. In 1982, the American Institute of Steel Construction prepared, for trial use, a tentative load and resistance factor design specification. This specification, too, is semiprobabilistic in nature. Standards such as those presently in use in other countries, plus the new American specifications, appear to be the forerunners of an eventual fully probabilistic design methodology.

Two articles that illustrate in passing how far the trends towards limit-states design have progressed are those by Halász and Schulz. The former describes current European practice in treating lateral buckling and the latter summarizes worldwide developments in the specification of column design curves. Both are presented in a limit-states design context.

From the above preview of some of this section's contents, it appears that the original volume's prognostication of things to come for tall steel buildings has, so far at least, not been far off the mark. However, one thing that wasn't noted in the original volume is the rapidly growing interest in computer-aided analysis and design. A recent article in an American construction journal was entitled "Computer-Aided Everything." Although such headlines are certainly journalistic hyperbole, it is clear from them that the engineering of tall buildings is now heavily dependent on the computer and that this dependence will be even greater in the future. The present state of affairs in the use of computerized analysis is referred to in the article by Young. Many of the anticipated future developments in the consideration of nonlinear behavior will necessarily be computerized. The field of computer graphics is emerging as an important adjunct to the description of problems to the computer, the control of computerized analysis, and the interpretation of complex results. Details of the computer-aided design of the future are difficult to predict, but one thing that appears certain is that the computer revolution will continue.

The rapid expansion of computer-aided design is probably a mixed blessing of course. One of the most serious problems in structural engineering is how to retain the essential qualities of good engineering in a time of increasing automation and sophistication in numerical analysis. What is needed is sound knowledge of both theory and structural behavior that is applied with common sense from a background of experience. Among the articles to follow that call attention to these qualities are those in which Lorenz illustrates the central role of connections in determining building performance and Khan and El Nimeiri emphasize the importance of redundancy. Provision of adequate redundancy and proper connections are not things that are apt to be computerized. In recent accounts of poorly conceived structures and actual failures, there is evidence that elementary requirements such as these are not being given the attention they demand. It is appropriate, therefore, to end this generally optimistic report on a sober note of concern for the retention of the high standards of performance that have given the structural engineering profession the respect that it currently enjoys.

Update on Structural
Steel Design

William McGuire
Albert J. Oudheusden

Developments in structural standards are always important, since each
new standard, or major revision of an established standard, influences some
segment of design practice for a number of years. In this article an attempt
will be made to look at what may lie ahead. To do so, the article will cite
typical examples of activity in developing standards since the publication
of Volume SB of the *Monograph on the Planning and Design of Tall Buildings*
in 1979, and it will comment on the potential significance of this activity.

LOAD AND RESISTANCE FACTOR DESIGN

The most widespread activity in standards development has been in the
writing, testing, and refinement of various forms of limit-states or load
and resistance factor design (LRFD) specifications. Specifications of this
sort have been in use in some countries for a number of years. For example,
the first Canadian Standards Association limit-states design specification
was published in 1974. Other specifications of the same type have been in
use in Europe for about the same period of time. There, the recent years
have been a period of gaining familiarity with limit-states design, expanding
its use, and refining some of the earlier provisions.

379

In the United States, progress in this direction has been slower. A committee of the AISC has been engaged for several years in the development of an LRFD specification based on a semiprobabilistic approach. It is anticipated that in 1983 the AISC will have published an LRFD specification as a draft specification allowing one to two years for comment and trial. The intent is that at the end of the trial period a final document will be published that will reflect the experience gained.

Although the pace of progress varies from country to country, there appear to be irreversible trends toward both incorporating the principles of probability in standards and requiring explicit consideration of conditions at both service loads and ultimate loads. It is still too early to predict how far these trends may go toward yielding standards that incorporate sophisticated statistical and probabilistic concepts as well as methods of structural analysis currently considered to be advanced. Such results will depend on whether the emerging methods can be demonstrated to be sensible, reliable, practicable, and economical.

LRFD design specifications have also been developed for cold-formed steel construction under sponsorship of the AISI. These specifications are in final draft form and are being evaluated. It is not clear at present whether the LRFD specifications for cold-formed steel will provide a clear advantage over the conventional allowable stress specifications, because the AISI specification deals mainly with components rather than assembled structures. Also, stability rather than yield stress frequently controls design, so that little advantage can be taken of the inherent ductility of steel.

LOADS AND FORCES

In December 1981, ANSI issued ANSI A58.1-81, *Minimum Design Loads for Buildings and Other Structures* (ANSI, 1981). It is the first revision of this standard since 1972. In defining its scope it is claimed that "the loads specified herein are suitable for use with stresses and load factors recommended in current design specifications for concrete, steel, wood, masonry, and any other conventional structural materials used in buildings." Thus, directly or by implication, ANSI A58.1-81 is trying to do the following things:

1. To make the definition of design loads and forces independent of material type, as in principle they should be.

2. To incorporate the best available knowledge of the statistics and probability of individual load types and of load combinations applicable to the United States.

3. To provide the best statement possible at the present time for the load side of any American load and resistance factor design method.

It is intended that in the future, ANSI A58.1 will be updated at frequent intervals. It is also anticipated that continued study of snow, wind, and other load effects will enable each succeeding edition to have a progressively more solid statistical basis.

SIMPLIFICATION OF STANDARDS

It is clear that, worldwide, steel design specifications are becoming increasingly more complex with the passage of time. Each advance in the understanding of structural behavior and each improvement in analytical capability carries with it the desire to incorporate this knowledge in actual design to promote structural efficiency, versatility, economy, and rationality. Developments such as those reported above will contribute to this trend.

There is justification for complexity. When the design procedures are fully understood and they can be applied economically, they can result in a better structure. On the other hand, it is equally clear that in many common design situations, complex procedures are simply not necessary or economical—they do not lead to a better design than one produced by a competent, experienced engineer using elementary formulas and methods.

In recognition of the continued need for simple, reliable guides, the AISC is preparing a simplified specification. The work is expected to involve the following:

1. a specification for the use of ASTM A-36 steel only;

2. transfer of seldom used provisions to appendices;

3. more orderly arrangement of provisions;

4. simplification of language and format;

5. simplification of provisions; and

6. an illustrated commentary.

COLD-FORMED STEEL CONSTRUCTION

In 1980, a new edition of the AISI, *Specification for the Design of Cold-Formed Steel Structural Members* was published (AISI, 1980). The major revisions from the previous (1968) specification concern material, webs of flexural members, inelastic reserve capacity of flexural members, arc welds, bolted connections, wall studs, channel and z-sections used as beams, and tests for special cases. Supporting information in the form of a commentary, plus charts, tables, and design examples will be issued.

In Europe, ECCS committees have been preparing recommendations for the design of cold-formed steel structures to be submitted as a draft document to ISO/TC 167 on Structural Specifications. As of the present writing it is not clear when this document will be ready. The United States has representation in this work through the AISI and a very close liaison is maintained. As a matter of interest, ISO/TC 167 will also be writing specifications for aluminum and hot-rolled structural steel. However, at present these do not seem to be of primary interest. The AISC represents the United States for hot-rolled structural steel. Norway holds the secretariat.

As previously discussed, load and resistance factor design provisions for cold-formed steel structural members are under consideration by an AISI advisory committee.

Also related to cold-formed steel is the publication by the American Welding Society (1981) of AWS D1.3-81, *Specification for Welding Sheet Steel in Structures*. This specification contains basic strength formulations for arc-welds, as well as qualification requirements for procedures and welders, materials and welding techniques, and workmanship requirements. The welding provisions in the 1980 AISI cold-formed steel specification are based on these AWS recommendations.

MIXED CONSTRUCTION

The past few years have witnessed considerable growth in the use of mixed steel and concrete construction. Much of this activity is reported in other sections of this volume. The development of standards for the various forms of mixed construction has tended to lag behind practice, and some of the standards that have emerged have been narrow in scope, reflecting the limited use of the medium in a particular region. In the United States, for example, mixed construction has been used up to now primarily in composite bridges and composite floors. Only in these areas are there specification provisions in America. There has also been a tendency for those most interested in structural steel to think of mixed construction as being of primary concern to the reinforced concrete industry — and vice versa.

The situation is somewhat better in countries that have taken the lead in the development of general forms of mixed construction for buildings, including slabs, beams, columns, and connections. It is understood that in Japan, for example, there is a general specification for the design of buildings of mixed construction.

Steps have been taken to improve the situation with respect to standards for mixed construction in the United States. Under consideration is a proposal to include composite columns in the AISC specification to match the requirements for beams and columns that are now covered in that standard. Extensive research sponsored by the AISI has resulted in a draft of tentative criteria for the design of composite steel deck slabs. This draft is under consideration by both the AISI and the ASCE for adoption as a standard. At present there appears to be no concerted effort in America to codify the design of connections in mixed construction.

INTERNATIONAL COOPERATION

Direct international cooperation in the development of standards appears, at present, to be most prevalent in the areas of production, materials, and measurements. For example, progress is being made in developing standard (SI-metric) sizes for steel I-beams, channels, wide-flange beams, angles, and other steel products under the auspices of the International Standards Organization Technical Committee ISO/TC 17 on Steel. Sizes for the first two have been approved; others are in various stages of balloting.

Most countries that do not have a long-established tradition of designing to some metric system have in the past ten years reported rapid progress in the change-over to SI (metric) units. For example, they are now used exclusively in Australia, and in Canada the majority of steel structures are now being designed using SI units. The United States continues to be the only major country in which few engineers and constructors have adopted the SI system for internal use. The American Society for Testing and Materials has approved various SI specifications for steel sheets, plates, bars, reinforcing bars, and high-strength steel structural bolts. Generally, these parallel existing ASTM specifications that use inch-pound units. This indicates that some progress is being made in the United States in promulgating SI units.

INDIRECT INFLUENCES ON STANDARDS

There are numerous activities that, although not in themselves making standards, will have a strong influence on the content and direction of future specifications.

One example is in the work of ISO/TC 167. This committee is considering a document, *Steel Structures — Materials and Design.* The document is not intended to be a standard that individual countries will have to adopt. Rather, it will be a guideline from which individual nations can develop their own standards.

In the United States, the Structural Stability Research Council (SSRC) plays a similar sole in influencing the direction and content of specification provisions for the treatment of all aspects of the stability problem. In its Technical Memorandum No. 5 (SSRC, 1981) it noted, "In addition to the material, nonlinearities, geometric imperfections, loading history, large deflections, post-buckling strength and behavior, and connection response may affect significantly the limit of structural usefulness." In consequence of this the memorandum recommends that "Maximum strength, determined by evaluation of those effects that influence significantly the maximum load-resisting capacity of a frame member or element, is the proper basis for the establishment of strength criteria." This is a statement of principle that requires explicit consideration of nonlinearity in analysis and design. It is clear that existing specifications will have to be altered in a number of ways to adapt to this design philosophy. The SSRC is in the process of preparing the fourth edition of its *Guide to the Design of Compression Members*. It can be expected that this guide will contain specific suggestions for the implementation of these ideas in specification form.

As another example of this type of influence, the AISC has sponsored an ad hoc committee charged with the task of reviewing the tall buildings Monograph and suggesting changes to the AISC specification or commentary based on the contents of the Monograph and other world-wide developments. The committee, which was under the direction of the late Dr. Fazlur R. Khan, has completed its work. The items considered were summarized by Lu, Haist, Lin, and Beedle (1980) in a Fritz Engineering Laboratory Report, *Recommendations of the AISC Tall Building Study Committee*. Fifty recommendations were scrutinized. In the final action, few were recommended to the AISC for direct adoption. Most proved to be state-of-the-art items that require further research, development, or extended discussion by standing specification committees. All such questions have been defined and referred to groups capable of taking effective action.

As a final comment on standards, it will be observed that there will always remain some vital aspects of good engineering that will always resist codification or expression in specification language. One of the foremost of these is the precept that a structure should have sufficient effective redundancy to prevent a harmful local event from precipitating a disastrous collapse. How this requirement is accomplished must be determined by competent engineers carefully scrutinizing all details of each structure and judging not only whether each detail is adequate in itself, but also what can happen if for some reason — either foreseeable or unforeseeable — there is a local failure. The ANSI A58.1-81 document states this principle under the heading of General Structural Integrity: "Buildings and structural systems shall possess general structural integrity — the quality of being able to sustain local damage with the structure as a whole remaining stable and not damaged to the extent disproportionate to the original local damage" (ANSI, 1981). If the professional review required to satisfy this principle had been conducted in the design stage of structures that have failed catastrophically in recent years, it is probable that gross failures would have been avoided. Further, it is likely that the deficiencies responsible for the local triggering incidents would have come to light and been remedied prior to construction.

CONDENSED REFERENCES/BIBLIOGRAPHY

The following is a condensed bibliography for this article. It includes all articles referred to or cited in the text. The full citations will be found at the end of the volume, with additional citations for further reading. What is given here should be sufficient information to lead the reader to the correct article: the author, date, and title. In case of multiple authors, only the first name is listed.

AISI 1980, *Specification for the Design of Cold-Formed Steel Structures*
AWS 1981, *Specification for Welding Sheet Steel in Structures*
ANSI 1981, *Minimum Design Loads for Buildings and Other Structures*
Lu 1980, *Recommendations of the AISC Tall Building Study Committee*
SSRC 1981, *Technical Memorandum No. 5*

Introduction

Robert C. Y. Young

Advances in elastic analysis have been largely in the areas of electronic computation and optimization.

Computer-application packages are generally based on elastic analysis, and as technologies have improved, costs have become lower. Thus, any design office should find the computer affordable, and would be remiss if it did not avail itself of this tool. The myriad elastic-analysis programs developed in the early years were generally limited to small structural systems. There are only a handful of comprehensive packages. They are used by the majority of designers and are maintained by vendors, cooperative user groups, and university computer centers. Many of these groups have also developed preprocessing and postprocessing programs to further simplify the use of these packages. Engineers should become familiar with these comprehensive packages to avoid reinventing the wheel.

Considerations of drift and/or flexibility frequently penalize the design of tall buildings by requiring extra material to stiffen them. A structural system consisting of an exterior-framed steel tube with exposed-steel stressed skin has been developed to control drift; the stressed-skin facade interacts with the primary tube. The Dravo tower is an example of this innovative system (Tomasetti, 1981). The core is designed to resist some of the gravity loads, with the primary tube structure resisting the remainder and all of the lateral loads. The estimated drift of this building is 1/250 (sidesway/building height) without the skin, but only 1/500 with it.

Damping devices are being developed to modify the natural frequencies of structural systems.

Progress in optimization of structures is discussed in the following article.

CONDENSED REFERENCES/BIBLIOGRAPHY

The following is a condensed bibliography for this article. It includes all articles referred to or cited in the text. The full citations will be found at the end of the volume, with additional citations for further reading. What is given here should be sufficient information to lead the reader to the correct article: the author, date, and title. In case of multiple authors, only the first name is listed.

Tomasetti 1981, *Development of the Stressed Skin Tube—Dravo Building*

Optimization of Structures

Narbey Khachaturian

Progress in the development of practical methods of optimization is continuing at a rapid pace. Among the several research findings, there are perhaps two developments that can significantly facilitate the application of methods of optimization to the practical design of structures. The first is a better understanding of the physical significance of the various local minima. The second is the development of more expedient methods for discrete optimization of practical structural design problems. In the following paragraphs each of these areas will be discussed briefly.

LOCAL MINIMA
(Khachaturian and Horowitz, 1977)

It has been shown that for a large class of structural optimization problems the feasible region is nonconvex with the possibility of more than one local minimum. The existence of local minima for some situations in structural design poses important problems for structural engineers. One problem is to understand the physical significance of local minima. Another problem is to be able to predict their existence for a given structure.

As a result of recent research efforts, it has been shown that each local minimum corresponds to a specific load carrying mechanism. It is possible that a large frame structure may have several load minima. The global

389

minimum that corresponds to the least volume structure may not necessarily correspond to the most desirable load carrying mechanism.

The following example will demonstrate the existence of local minima and the corresponding load carrying mechanisms.

Figure 1 shows a one-story, one-bay frame with hinged supports made up of prismatic members of square cross section. The frame has a span of 18 ft (5.4m) and a height of 10.8 ft (3.29m) and is subjected to a uniformly distributed vertical load of 1.0 k/f. The objective function is the total volume of the material, and the constraints limit the stresses at the top of the column, the end of the beam, and the midspan of the beam to the allowable value of 1.8 ksi. The variables are x_1 and x_2—the dimensions of each column and the beam respectively. The problem can be formulated as follows:

$$\text{Min } V = 259.6\, x_1^2 + 216.0\, x_2^2 \tag{1}$$

Subject to

$$\begin{aligned}
&\text{(Top of column)} && \frac{9}{x_1^2} + \frac{3{,}240x_1}{3x_1^4 + 1.2x_2^4} \leq 1.8 \\
&\text{(Beam end)} && \frac{(15x_2 + 23{,}328)\, x_1^4}{12x_1^4x_2^3 + 4.8x_2^7} \leq 1.8 \\
&\text{(Beam midspan)} && \frac{(15x_2 - 23{,}328)\, x_1^4}{12x_1^4x_2^3 + 4.8x_2^7} + \frac{2{,}916}{x_2^3} \leq 1.8
\end{aligned} \tag{2}$$

Figure 2 shows the plots of the contours of the objective function and the constraint surfaces.

It can be shown that point A with $x_1 = 2.92$ in (74.2 mm) and $x_2 = 11.72$ in (297.7 mm), as shown in Fig. 2, is a local minimum. At this point both the columns and the beam have at least one point stressed to the allowable limit where the design is defined as fully stressed. The design point A corresponds to a frame in which the cross-sectional dimension of the columns

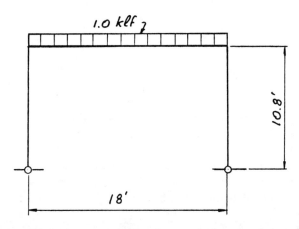

Fig. 1 One-story, one-bay frame (long column) *(Khachaturian, 1977)*

is much smaller than that of the beam, implying that the column is so flexible in relation to the girder that the structure behaves as a simply supported beam resting on the two columns. The design point B, with $x_1 = 9.12$ in (231.6 mm) and $x_2 = 9.71$ in (246.6 mm), is another local minimum. At this point of local minimum the columns induce significant rotational restraint at the ends of the beam, which in turn implies that the structure behaves as a frame.

Since both solutions of this problem are fully stressed, the dimensions of the frame for each point of local minimum can be determined by a simple engineering approach. For point A, if it is assumed that the structure consists of a simple beam resting on two columns, it is possible to begin with the initial point

$$x_1^2 = \frac{9}{1.8} \quad , \quad \text{or } x_1 = 2.24 \text{ in } (56.9 \text{ mm}) \tag{3}$$

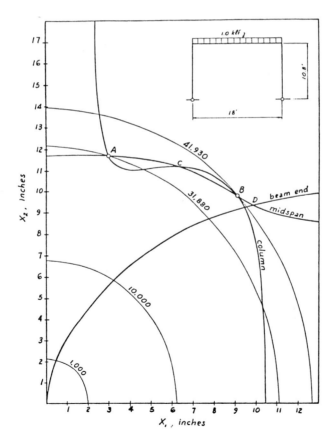

Fig. 2 Local minima for one-story, one-bay frame with members of square section subjected to a vertical load (long column) *(Khachaturian, 1977)*

and

$$\frac{x_2^3}{6} = \frac{486}{1.8} \quad , \quad \text{or } x_2 = 11.74 \text{ in (298.2 mm)} \tag{4}$$

Starting from the point $x_1 = 2.24$ in (56.9 mm) and $x_2 = 11.74$ in (298.2 mm), 12 cycles of analysis and design lead to $x_1 = 2.92$ in (74.2 mm) and $x_2 = 11.72$ in (297.7 mm), which is the optimal point arrived at by mathematical programming.

In a similar way, to arrive at point B, which is the optimal point corresponding to the frame mode of behavior, it is possible to begin with the assumption that the beam is fixed-end and initially to use the following values for x_1 and x_2:

$$\frac{9}{2x_1^2} + \frac{1,944}{2x_1^3} = 1.8 \quad , \quad \text{or } x_1 = 10.34 \text{ in (262.6 mm)} \tag{5}$$

$$\frac{1,944}{2x_2^3} = 1.8 \quad , \quad \text{or } x_2 = 10.26 \text{ (260.6 mm)} \tag{6}$$

The optimal solution, $x_1 = 9.12$ in (231.6 mm), $x_2 = 9.71$ in (246.6 mm) is obtained in 18 cycles of analysis and design.

The structure corresponding to point A has a volume of 31,880 in³, with very slender columns and a heavy beam that may not be an acceptable solution to a structural engineer since it lacks the advantages of frame behavior. On the other hand, the structure corresponding to point B does have the properties of a frame but, with a volume of 41,930 in³, is much heavier than the structure corresponding to point A. The question arises whether it is necessary to design the structure based on point B, which is the mathematical minimum if frame behavior is desired. At any point to the left in the immediate vicinity of B the structure will behave as a frame and have a smaller volume.

DISCRETE OPTIMIZATION
(Liebman, Chanaratna, and Khachaturian, 1977;
Liebman, Khachaturian, and Chanaratna, 1981)

Optimization problems in structural design are predominantly of a discrete type in which the variables can assume only certain predetermined quantities. There are several such problems in structural design, among which is the design of reinforced concrete structures. The amount of reinforcement is determined on the basis of the standard sizes available, and the dimensions of concrete used in practice are usually within the nearest half-inch. Selection of standard steel sections for continuous or frame structures is another example.

One method that is promising as a practical tool is a discrete search technique specifically developed for unconstrained optimization problems. The method has been adapted, using interior penalty functions, to problems of structural optimization, which usually have many design constraints. Before the problem of optimization is solved it is necessary to develop a practical solution space for each of the variables—a task that involves working knowledge of what is done in practice. The actual algorithm can be written in simple and efficient form. Problems with several variables and large solution spaces can be solved. Clearly the method is more readily applicable to practical situations.

CONDENSED REFERENCES/BIBLIOGRAPHY

The following is a condensed bibliography for this article. It includes all articles referred to or cited in the text. The full citations will be found at the end of the volume, with additional citations for further reading. What is given here should be sufficient information to lead the reader to the correct article: the author, date, and title. In case of multiple authors, only the first name is listed.

Khachaturian 1977, *Properties of Optimal Structures*
Liebman 1977, *Discrete Optimization in Structural Design*
Liebman 1981, *Discrete Structural Optimization*

Recent Developments in
Structural Plasticity

Marek Kwieciński

Plastic analysis and design has become a well-established branch of engineering mechanics. At first, attention was mainly focused on the limit-analysis theory, that is, on the incipient new plastic flow of rigid-perfectly plastic structures. Nowadays, new topics attract attention, mostly in connection with the plastic design of the high-rise. These topics are geometrical effects, cyclic and random nonproportional loads leading to low-cycle fatigue or incremental collapse, assessment of deflections, shakedown behavior, yield point load stability, and postyield behavior.

In this note some recent developments in Poland will be surveyed briefly (Sawczuk, 1972a; Szczepinski, 1968). It is commonly felt in that country that plastic design procedures have not found satisfactory reflection in the design codes. Plastic methods should penetrate deeper into suitable recommendations.

LIMIT ANALYSIS

Because of the ductility of structural materials, it is limit analysis that can provide the means for computing intensities of collapse loads and finding the associated fields of internal forces and the mechanisms of incipient motion. One-parameter loading is usually considered. Then an exact solution to the problem of limit analysis of a given structure consists in finding, at the same time, a limit-load multiplier, an associated field of generalized stresses, and an instantaneous, kinematically admissible collapse mechanism. Since the exact solution is rather hard to obtain, suitable limit-analysis theorems have been formulated and proved so as to assess the static, lower bound and the kinematic, upper bound to the actual ultimate load. In other words, the actual load factor is the largest statically admissible multiplier and, at the same time, the smallest kinematically admissible multiplier. In Poland, research focused mainly on the plastic analysis of plates and shells (Sawczuk et al., 1972b). Systems have also been considered that consist of rectangular or skew reinforced concrete slabs resting on two families of beams (Kwieciński, 1979; Kwieciński and Wojewódzki, 1980). In limit-state analysis the following two, usually neglected, effects have been accounted for: the T-beam effect associated with the presence of interacting flanges, and the effect of actual beam widths. Design algorithms have been worked out for a number of slab-beam systems. Extensive tests on full-size structures are going on to verify the design procedures offered.

SHAKEDOWN

All loads are usually imagined to increase slowly and in proportion until collapse of a structure occurs. In reality we are faced with complex loading patterns in which the various loads act randomly and independently within prescribed limits. Two types of failure can take place.

If the loads are basically alternating in character, the yield may occur in turns at some points in tension and compression, leading to eventual failure. Such behavior is referred to as alternating plasticity or low-cycle fatigue.

If some critical combinations of loads follow one another in more or less definite cycles, the plastic strain increments develop in the same sense during each loading cycle. This process leads to incremental collapse (Mroz, 1971).

It is possible, however, that a structure supports all further changes of load in a purely elastic manner. The structure is said to have shaken down to variable repeated loading. The shakedown behavior can be conveniently separated from incremental collapse or alternating plasticity by a shakedown load factor. The known shakedown theorems have been further developed and the shakedown design considered (Brzezinski and Konig, 1973; Konig, 1971; Konig, 1972). Attempts are also made to allow for thermal cycling and temperature-dependent material properties.

GEOMETRY CHANGES

The application of simple limit analysis to the design of the slender frames that are encountered in tall buildings reveals the limitations resulting from the basic assumptions of the theory. Those limitations are that deflections are assumed to be small, so that the equilibrium is not affected by the changes of geometry and the instability phenomena are ignored. Thus, modifications are required to ensure safety in the presence of an ultimate load capacity somewhat reduced by geometric effects and loss of stability (Duszek and Sawczuk, 1974).

It may also happen that when tensile membrane forces are free to develop, a structure can support increased loading. This is rarely the case in framed structures but the effect may be quite significant in plates and in reinforced concrete slabs, especially when they rest on a system of surrounding beams. The real behavior appears still more complex since strain hardening, spread of plastic regions, initial imperfections, and residual stresses enter the picture.

OPTIMUM DESIGN

Particular design is usually selected from a certain class of possible solutions according to some minimum requirement; the criterion ideally is the total cost of the design, erection, use and demolition of a structure. Thus, the optimum design methods constitute an attempt to create safe and simultaneously economical structures by minimizing their total cost. However, the most frequent practice is to minimize the overall weight of a structure with given geometry and specified loads, rather than to look for optimal layout or optimal load patterns. The present-day optimum design is mainly restricted to problems in which the cross-sectional dimensions of particular members are the only design variables. This minimum-weight design provides a basis on which to compare a number of competitive designs against each other or against the theoretical exact solution, if available. Some attempts are being made to work out more sophisticated optimum design procedures.

DEFLECTIONS

It is sometimes necessary to ensure that certain deflections do not exceed prescribed limits, which are usually specified at working loads. An elastic, geometrically linear analysis would seem to be enough under the prevailing circumstances. Unfortunately, it is possible that a considerable increase of displacements can occur under loads just above specified working values and below the collapse load. Thus, we need methods enabling the deflections to be traced up to the collapse point. The deflections will be larger than those justifying the neglect of geometry changes in the equilibrium equations. Deformed configuration must then be considered.

So far as bar systems are concerned, after a complete picture of elastic solution is obtained by standard methods, we know which plastic hinge forms first. A new "elastic" solution can then be found with the full plastic moment being reached at the hinge. This process is repeated step-by-step until a mechanism is formed. Deflections are evaluated assuming that every cross section preserves its original elastic stiffness until the yield moment develops. Then the stiffness drops locally to zero, whereas the bending rigidity elsewhere remains unchanged. Such a neglect of the spread of plastic zones leads to some underestimation of the actual deflections. For simple structures the exact computation of deflections while accounting for true shapes and extents of plastic domains offers no difficulty. For complex structures an approximate method of calculation of displacements at collapse has been proposed in which an equivalent elastic structure of step-wise rigidity is introduced (Bandyszewski and Sawczuk, 1974).

CONNECTIONS

Connections should ensure that the structure can reach the computed collapse load before any undesirable effects have occurred. Having clearly enough stength, a connection must at the same time exhibit adequate rotational capacity to allow for forming a mechanism of the structure as a whole. To produce a good connection, the statical and the kinematical limit-analysis theorems can be suitably employed to find the right shape and dimensions. In Poland these methods have been used for the design of machine parts and structural connections (Dietrich et al., 1970; Szczepinski, 1968). A number of effective solutions concerning bolted connections and optimal design of perforated sheets have been arrived at (Winnicki et al., 1977).

STABILITY AT YIELD POINT LOAD

The yield point load furnished by the limit-analysis theory may happen to be unsafe as a result of prior elastic deformations resulting in changes in geometry. Instability can also occur for perfectly rigid-plastic structures. Any small disturbance at incipient plastic motion results in large changes in geometry. This kind of behavior can be described through a consistent nonlinear approach. Undeformed and deformed configurations must be distinguished for this purpose, and strains must be fully expressed via displacement gradients. The problem is closely related to the P-Δ effect in framed structures.

Nonlinear formulation of plastic analysis problems allows the development of some extremum principles to provide bounds on tractions in the presence of nonnegligible geometric changes. The problem has been studied lately in detail (Duszek, 1973; Duszek and Sawczuk, 1974).

PLASTIC DESIGN IN THE BUILDING CODES

Plastic design is admitted by the Polish Code for Steel Structures in a rather restricted form. The relevant clause states that once the collapse load is established, allowing for plastic hinges to form, the dimensioning must be made elastically. Thus, an additional safety factor is introduced.

There is a lack of recommendations as to the types of structures to be designed plastically and the range of application of particular computational methods in the plastic approach. The following requirements should be formulated in a more precise way: ductility of material; ratio of elastic limit to the fracture point; plastic moduli of sections; ultimate bending moments in the presence of shear, thrust and torque; allowable rigidities; local instability in the neighborhood of plastic zones; global stability of spatial systems; and check on deflections prior to collapse. Unless clear commentaries are worked out, the plastic design philosophy will not find its full application in design practice.

CONDENSED REFERENCES/BIBLIOGRAPHY

The following is a condensed bibliography for this article. It includes all articles referred to or cited in the text. The full citations will be found at the end of the volume, with additional citations for further reading. What is given here should be sufficient information to lead the reader to the correct article: the author, date, and title. In case of multiple authors, only the first name is listed.

Bandyszewski 1974, *Method of Assessing Deflections in Elastic-Plastic Beams and Frames*
Brzezinski 1973, *Deflection Analysis at Shakedown*

Dietrich 1970, *Bearing Capacity of Structural Members*
Duszek 1973, *On Stability of Plastic Structures at the Yield Load*
Duszek 1974, *Stability of Rigid-Plastic Frames at the Yield Point Load*

Konig 1971, *A Method of Shakedown Analysis of Frames and Arches*
Konig 1972, *Shakedown Deflections. A Finite Element Approach*
Kwieciński 1979, *Ultimate Load of Reinforced Concrete Slab-Beam Systems*
Kwieciński 1980, *Ultimate Load Design of Reinforced Concrete Skew Slab-Beam Systems*

Mroz 1971, *On Theory of Steady Plastic Cycles in Structures*

Sawczuk 1972a, *Engineering Methods of Elastic-Plastic Analysis*
Sawczuk 1972b, *Plastic Analysis of Structures*
Szczepinski 1968, *Design of Machine Parts According to the Limit Analysis*

Winnicki 1977, *Numerical Limit Analysis of Perforated Plates*

New Developments in Plastic Analysis and Design

Egor P. Popov
Daniel N. Manheim

In seismic design, much reliance for the safety of a structure must be placed on its ductility. The large ductility required to withstand a major earthquake is illustrated first. This points to the need for simple, rational plastic analyses. Then, bypassing the known procedures for such analyses, the possible occurrence of plastic shear hinges is discussed. Their occurrence and behavior is the principal feature of the paper. A simple example is included that illustrates the rigid-plastic analysis for this kind of plastic hinge.

INTRODUCTION

It is economically infeasible to design conventional static structures to behave elastically during a severe seismic disturbance. For safety, a good deal of dependence must be placed on the ductile behavior of a structure in the postelastic range. Whereas this is recognized by designers, and is implied in the codes, plastic analysis is seldom used in practice to ascertain such behavior. However, the trend toward load and resistance factor design (LRFD) is an indication that plastic analysis and design are slowly gaining acceptance and will become more widely used in the future.

This paper first demonstrates that during a severe earthquake, a structure is likely to behave inelastically, suggesting the need for a plastic analysis. Then it will be shown that in the collapse mechanism in a rigid-plastic analysis of a frame, plastic shear hinges can develop in addition to or instead of plastic moment hinges. This new concept is described in detail. The paper concludes with some remarks on an approximate approach for calculating time-histories of elasto-plastic frames.

THE NEED FOR DUCTILITY IN SEISMIC DESIGN

The magnitude of the lateral forces acting on a building frame during an earthquake is specified by standard codes (ICBO, 1982) and depends on the natural period of vibrations of the structure. Stiffer structures that have shorter periods attract larger forces; the inverse also holds true. The totality of these forces acting on a structure is given by the base shear. For any given building this quantity depends on a number of fixed factors, except for the base shear coefficient C, which brings in the dependence of the base shear on the period of a building.

An example of the variation in C with the period of a structure is displayed in Fig. 1 (Popov, 1980b). The solid lines, established on the basis of dynamic analyses of single-degree-of-freedom systems, are drawn for a very strong earthquake of magnitude 8+. The upper line, identified by $\mu_\delta = 1$, indicates the force levels for which structures with different periods

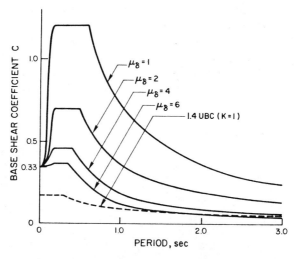

Fig. 1 Base shear coefficient curves *(Popov, 1980b)*

must be designed if they are to remain elastic during this earthquake. On the other hand, the dashed line near the bottom of the graph gives the force levels required by the Uniform Building Code (UBC) (ICBO, 1982). The disparity between the two requirements is very large. By noting that an extremely severe earthquake was assumed in establishing the upper line and by recognizing that the occupancy importance and site characteristic factors may raise the dashed curve, the discrepancy between the two approaches can be narrowed; nevertheless, it is still very large. If, however, the frames can be allowed to act in a ductile manner without any loss in strength, a dramatic decrease in the design lateral force level can be justified. Thus, if a structural frame can safely deflect laterally, say, twice the amount it does at first yield, the appropriate force levels are given by the lines identified by $\mu_\delta = 2$. For frame deflection ductilities μ_δ of 4 and 6, the lateral forces are further reduced.

Based on the above reasoning it appears possible to design a structure elastically using the code forces (the dashed lines in Fig. 1), provided adequate ductility is built into a frame. However, this conventional procedure has some shortcomings. Using only an elastic approach for the design of a frame, the designer remains ignorant of where the plastic activity occurs and its severity. The overall frame ductility μ_δ is usually much smaller than the ductility requirements placed on the individual joints and members. Therefore, granted that inelastic activity in structural frames does take place during a severe earthquake, the rational design of a frame requires plastic analysis. As implied in the introduction, this paper bypasses the known procedures for such an analysis and concerns itself with the occurrence and behavior of plastic shear hinges.

OCCURRENCE OF PLASTIC SHEAR HINGES

The conventional rigid-plastic analysis of frames confines itself to members that form plastic moment hinges. In the presence of axial forces, the moment capacity of members is appropriately reduced. There are situations, however, where plastic hinges may form primarily because of shear. This kind of plastic hinge has not been explored in the past and is discussed herein.

Plastic shear hinges can commonly occur in unreinforced panel zones of beam-column joints or in shear links, which are short sections of beams between columns and bracing in eccentrically braced frames. The possible occurrence of plastic shear hinges in the panel zones of beam-column joints in moment-resisting frames is best clarified by examining the subassemblage shown in Fig. 2 (Bertero et al., 1972). In this diagram l is beam span and h is the story height. All ends of this cruciform model are pinned and, except for the top hinge, are movable in the horizontal direction under the applied lateral force H. The moment and shear diagrams for the column from this subassemblage are shown in Fig. 3 (Krawinkler et al., 1971). The high shear that develops in the panel zone induces large shearing distortions, which may be seen in the photograph shown in Fig. 4(a) or in Fig. 4(b) (Krawinkler et al., 1971) where the deformation of the panel zone is exaggerated for clarity. It is this kind of deformation that gives rise to the plastic shear hinge, which apparently had not been previously recognized.

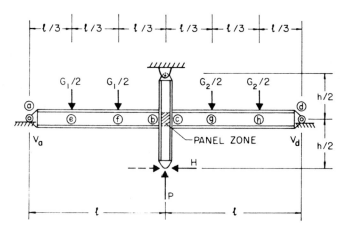

Fig. 2 Idealized model of interior beam-column subassemblages for a multi-bay frame
(Bertero et al., 1972)

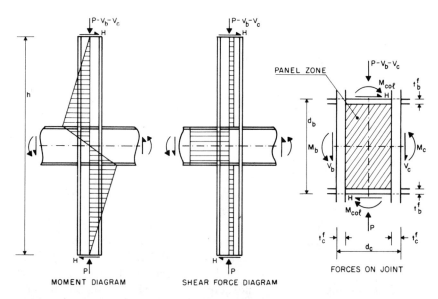

MOMENT DIAGRAM   SHEAR FORCE DIAGRAM   FORCES ON JOINT

Fig. 3 Internal force diagrams for an interior column *(Krawinkler et al., 1971)*

The development of a plastic shear hinge has important consequences. It gives a frame an extra degree of freedom, which results in additional deflections. An increase in story drift due to plastic shear hinges in the panel zones is illustrated in Fig. 5. This additional deformation can significantly increase the P-Δ effect, as has been shown both experimentally and analytically in Krawinkler et al. (1971).

As noted earlier, another instance of plastic shear hinge formation may occur in the beam links of eccentrically braced frames. Recent research on this type of framing indicates that there are many possible schemes of applying this concept in design (Popov and Manheim, 1981b). Several different types of eccentrically braced frames are shown in Fig. 6. In such bracing arrangements if the distances e are kept large, plastic moment hinges would form at the ends of the links under the action of lateral forces. However, if the distances e are small, the webs yield, resulting in plastic shear hinges. For example, for the eccentrically braced frame shown

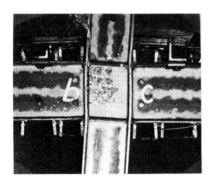
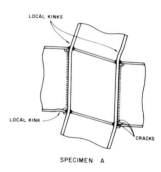

Fig. 4 Shear deformations of a panel zone *(Krawinkler et al., 1971)*

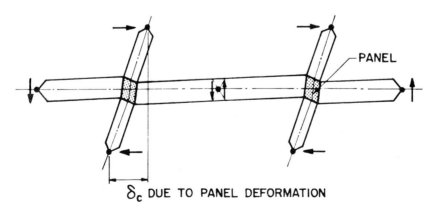

δ_c DUE TO PANEL DEFORMATION

Fig. 5 Story drift caused by panel deformation accentuates the P-Δ effect *(Popov and Bertero, 1980c)*

in Fig. 6(a), if e's are small, plastic shear hinges would form in the right-hand links, as shown in the collapse mechanisms of Fig. 7. The considerable favor designers have accorded recently to eccentric-type bracing for seismic design increases the need for a simple method for rigid-plastic analysis of frames with plastic shear hinges.

BEHAVIOR OF PLASTIC SHEAR HINGE

If two transverse, closely spaced forces forming a couple are applied to a wide-flange or I-beam, the short segment of beam bounded by these forces is a shear hinge at the limit load (Fig. 8). This configuration is an idealization of the conditions found in the panel zones of beam-column joints and in the shear links of eccentrically braced frames. In reality the plastification of the shear links is a gradual process and usually the end moments are not equal (Fig. 9). However, for determining the limit loads for such links, the conditions shown in Fig. 8(b) can be assumed. Then, by applying the lower-

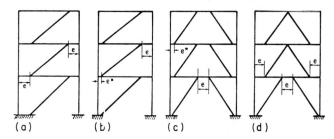

Fig. 6 **Alternative arrangements for eccentric bracing** *(Popov and Manheim, 1981b)*

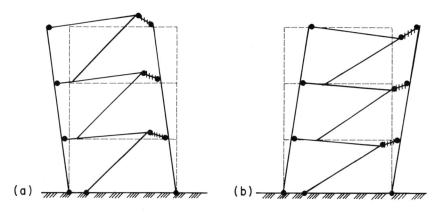

Fig. 7 **Failure mechanisms for a frame in two opposite directions leading to identical conclusions** *(Popov and Manheim, 1981b)*

bound theorem of plastic analysis, an interaction curve between the end moments and shear can be established for the entire link. The results of such an analysis are shown in Fig. 10. In lieu of an upper-bound solution, a two-dimensional elasto-plastic solution for a selected point was obtained with the aid of a computer. Because the two solutions agreed well, no further comparisons were made. Further details on generating the shear-moment interaction diagram may be found in Manheim and Popov (to be published).

The nearly horizontal branch of the curve shown in Fig. 10 corresponds to the useful range for analysis of plastic shear links. Conversely, the essentially vertical part of the curve is the region of the more usually encountered cases, where the effect of shear is small and, for limit loads, the plastic

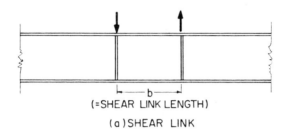

(=SHEAR LINK LENGTH)

(a) SHEAR LINK

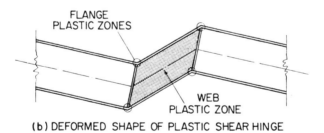

FLANGE
PLASTIC ZONES

WEB
PLASTIC ZONE

(b) DEFORMED SHAPE OF PLASTIC SHEAR HINGE

Fig. 8 Idealized plastic shear hinge

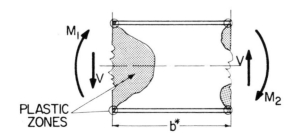

Fig. 9 Gradual plastification of plastic shear link

moment hinges form at the ends of members. An active plastic shear link should be made as long as possible to minimize its ductility requirements. This condition is found by assuming that the full depth of the member resists shear, that is, $V_p^* = \tau_p t_w d$, where τ_p is the yield strength of the material in shear, t_w is the thickness of the web, and d is the depth of a member.

From the above remarks it can be concluded that a constant value of shear may be used for the shear-hinge mechanism, just as a constant value of moment may be used for a moment hinge. An example of a simple plastic shear-link mechanism is shown in Fig. 11. Note how the angle changes along the link. A numerical example corresponding to the mechanism of Fig. 11 is given in Fig. 12.

In the presence of an axial force, the yield stress in the web is found using a yield criterion. In this manner, the limit loads for transversely and axially loaded members have been obtained, [Fig. 12(b)]. A comparison with finite element solutions, which give complete force-deformation paths for several cases of the axially loaded member, shows that the asymptotic values are in agreement with the procedure described above.

SOME PRACTICAL CONSIDERATIONS

Rigid-plastic analytical solutions for frame analysis that were previously developed for collapse mechanisms envisioned only the formation of plastic moment hinges. The behavior of beam flanges at such hinges has been carefully studied and is reflected in the codes (ICBO, 1982). For severe load

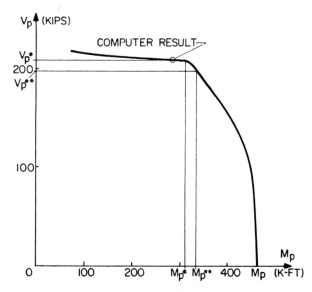

Fig. 10 Interaction diagram between end moments and shear in beam links

reversals, such as may occur during an earthquake, there is some evidence that the plastic moment capacity is retained provided the section is compact. In such applications, the beams transmit small shear and there are no critical problems with the webs. However, in plastic shear hinges the situation is different, since plastically stressed webs can buckle and dramatically reduce the shear capacity of a link. This tendency becomes particularly pronounced during severe cyclic loading.

Based on the experimental evidence to date, it is becoming increasingly clear that the webs of the shear links, at least in seismic-resistant construction,

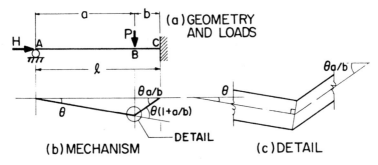

Fig. 11 Kinematic mechanism with a plastic shear hinge for a rigid-plastic beam

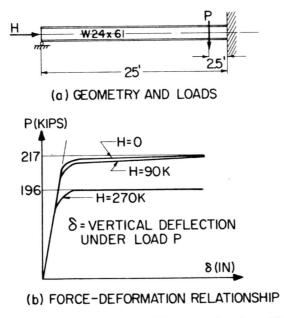

Fig. 12 Example problem for different values of *H*—asymptotic values of *P* by rigid-plastic analysis are nearly the same as by the finite element method

must be stiffened (Popov, 1980a; Popov and Hjelmstad, 1981a). A typical detail for achieving this objective is shown in Fig. 13. The problem of column-web buckling in the panel zone of a beam-column joint also requires attention. However, since transverse beams usually frame into the column web at such locations, the problem becomes less severe.

In implementing the plastic shear hinge in a design, it is important to adhere to the code requirements for plastic design and to provide lateral braces at both ends of a link (ICBO, 1982). In Fig. 13 this support would require lateral braces at the column joint and on line *B-B*.

SPECIAL CONSIDERATIONS IN SEISMIC ANALYSIS

With the exception of monumental buildings, it is customary to perform lateral force analysis using static forces specified in a code. Dynamic analyses, particularly those that include the inelastic behavior of members, are not favored. Perhaps the principal reason is the cost involved in constructing the time-history response of a building. The large number of degrees-of-freedom that are commonly considered for a building makes the computational effort very large. Therefore, there is a great need for the development of approximate methods for calculating the time-histories of elasto-plastic frames. Some attempts have been made by utilizing, for the coordinate functions, the deformed shapes of buildings with plastic hinges. To date the results of this work are inconclusive.

ACKNOWLEDGEMENTS

This paper was motivated by general studies of the seismic behavior of structural components that are in progress at the University of California,

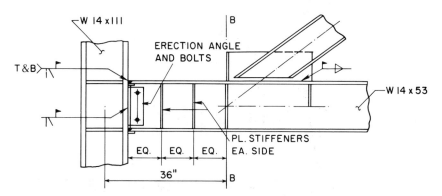

Fig. 13 Web stiffeners along the link and lateral support on line *B-B* are required to assure stability *(Popov, 1980a)*

Berkeley, and was prepared with financial assistance from NSF Grant CEE 81-07217. Any opinions, findings, and conclusions or recommendations expressed in this paper are those of the authors and do not necessarily reflect the views of the National Science Foundation.

CONDENSED REFERENCES/BIBLIOGRAPHY

The following is a condensed bibliography for this article. It includes all articles referred to or cited in the text. The full citations will be found at the end of the volume, with additional citations for further reading. What is given here should be sufficient information to lead the reader to the correct article: the author, date, and title. In case of multiple authors, only the first name is listed.

Bertero 1972, *Beam-Columns Subassemblages Under Repeated Loading*

ICBO 1982, *Uniform Building Code*

Krawinkler 1971, *Inelastic Behavior of Steel Beam to Column Subassemblages*

Manheim (to be published), *Analysis of Plastic Shear Hinges in Steel Frames*

Popov 1980a, *An Update on Eccentric Seismic Bracing*
Popov 1980b, *Seismic Behavior of Structural Subassemblages*
Popov 1980c, *Seismic Analysis of Some Steel Building Frames*
Popov 1981a, *Web Buckling Under Cyclic Loading*
Popov 1981b, *Eccentric Bracing of Steel Frames in Seismic Design*

New Developments in the Stability of Tall Buildings

Jerome S. B. Iffland

INTRODUCTION

Since publication of the Monograph, there have been major advances in the state of the art in the stability of steel buildings. Progress has been made in the stability of individual columns, the stability of two-dimensional frames, the stability of three-dimensional frames, approximate stability solutions for special types of framing, stability under dynamic and repeated load, and the stability of mixed steel-concrete structures. In addition, progress in selected special topics is worth noting. These individual subjects are discussed herein.

STABILITY OF INDIVIDUAL COLUMNS

There has been considerable focus in the past several years on the problem of the maximum strength of individual restrained imperfect columns. Both the European Convention for Constructional Steelwork (ECCS, 1976), and the SSRC (Johnston, 1976) multiple column curves addressed the problems of initial imperfections and residual strengths but avoided the problem of end restraint. The SSRC Technical Memorandum No. 5 (1981) recommended that the column stability and the frame stability problems be separated (see

413

the section following the next one). As a result, research has been directed toward inclusion of the effect of end restraints on individual members. Chen (1979) has summarized current research projects underway in the United States, the United Kingdom, and Italy. There is an indication in the preliminary results of the research that the effect of end restraint may partially cancel out the effects of initial crookedness and residual stresses (Massonnet, 1978). If this finding proves true, then the trend toward the use of multiple column curves could be reversed.

Work on the maximum strength of selected types of individual columns has also continued, and with it the problem of the interactions of local and overall buckling has received a significant amount of attention. The work of Braham et al. (1979; 1980) in the field of tubular columns is an example. Haaijer et al. (1981) have recently presented the results of simulated eccentric load tests on single angle columns. Another example of progress in this area is the work of Scheer and Bohm on ultimate load tests of box columns (Scheer and Bohm, 1978).

STABILITY OF TWO-DIMENSIONAL FRAMES

Technical Memorandum No. 5 (SSRC, 1981) recommends that in design practice, the stability of individual members and elements of the structure and the stability of the structure, as a whole, be considered independently. This recommendation formally states an existing trend throughout the world. The P-Δ design method (Johnston, 1976) is currently in use in many design offices. Use of an amplification factor for computations of the final deflection to use with the P-Δ procedure has been suggested by MacGregor (1972), among others, and has simplified the procedure. Iffland (1981) as well as Beaulieu and Adams (1977) have proposed procedures for generalizing the procedure to cover both gravity loaded only and braced frames. The generalized procedure also includes consideration of erection tolerances. Parallel work in the European community has been summarized by Massonnet and Maquoi (1978). One notable difference is the value of the out-of-plumbness used. Beaulieu and Adams (1977) recommend 1/500 while the ECCS has adopted 1/200 (ECCS, 1976).

Analysis of structures has also been simplified by the increasing use of the Merchant-Rankine formula. The ECCS recommendations for plastic design of steel frames incorporating the Merchant-Rankine formula has been summarized by Massonnet (1976). An approximate theoretical basis for the use of this formula has been provided by Horne (1963). Comparison of experimental failure loads to the Merchant-Rankine formula taken from Horne (1963) are shown in Fig. 1; and comparison of the Merchant-Rankine formula with second-order calculations taken from Massonnet (1976) are shown in Fig. 2. Additional second-order calculations have been prepared by Birnstiel and Iffland (to be published).

Second-order elasto-plastic models have all received recent attention. Birnstiel and Iffland (1980) have formalized the factors influencing frame stability and have suggested how these factors could be considered in a mathematical model. Talaboc (1980) is conducting parametric studies to evaluate the relative importance of some of these factors.

The problem of classification of braced and unbraced frames is also currently being studied. The ECCS (1975) now has rules covering this subject. Biswas and Earwood (1981), have defined the term *threshold stiffness* as the critical stiffness that separates the frame column buckling mode of failure from the frame sidesway buckling mode of failure as illustrated in Fig. 3(a) and (b). These authors are attempting to generalize the solutions for threshold stiffness and to develop an easily applied method to determine its magnitude.

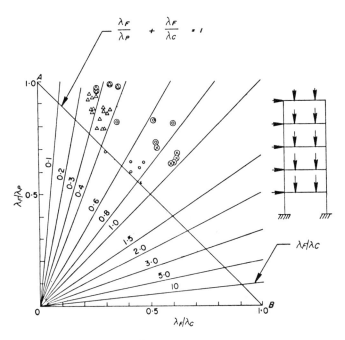

△   THREE STORY FRAMES

O   FIVE STORY FRAMES (NO SIDE LOAD)

×   SEVEN STORY FRAMES

Fig. 1 Comparison of Merchant-Rankine formula with experimental failure loads *(Horne, 1963)*

STABILITY OF THREE-DIMENSIONAL FRAMES

There has been some progress in the problem of the stability of three-dimensional frames. Razzaq and Naim (1980) have recently restudied the elastic buckling problem. Cheng (1977) has discussed procedures for designing three-dimensional frames subjected to dynamic loads. This analysis uses a second-order elasto-plastic model and includes the effect of the floor diaphragm. For the P-Δ design procedure and the Merchant-Rankine formula, extension to three dimensions is lacking.

APPROXIMATE STABILITY SOLUTIONS FOR SPECIAL TYPES OF FRAMING

New approximate frame stability solutions continue to be developed. Four of them will be noted here.

A practical method of second-order design for sway frames has been proposed by Vandepitte (1981). It results from a modification of the horizontal equilibrium equations used in the regular slope deflection method. Such a procedure leads to a noniterative system of linear equations and can be generalized up to the occurrence of plastic hinges. Mortelmans (1980) has presented a method based on distributing story stiffness continuously over the height of the columns so that the sway buckling problem can be treated as a simple differential equation. Nixon et al. (1975) present a method allowing a second-order analysis to be performed using a first-order computer program

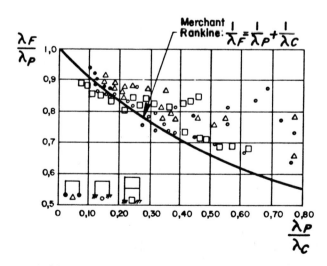

Fig. 2 Comparison of Merchant-Rankine formula with second-order calculation *(Massonnet, 1976)*

without iteration, which is accomplished by including fictitious bracing members in the solution. The fourth method was presented at the SSRC Annual Technical Session and Meeting Panel Discussion in Chicago, Illinois, April, 1981, by Nair (1981). The method utilizes the similarity between approximate frame deflection curves and actual frame deflection curves for both the bending and shear modes of buckling.

STABILITY UNDER DYNAMIC AND REPEATED LOAD

Although there has undoubtedly been considerable research throughout the world in the area of the stability of structures under dynamic and repeated load, only the work of Cheng and Botkin (1972; 1974a) and Cheng

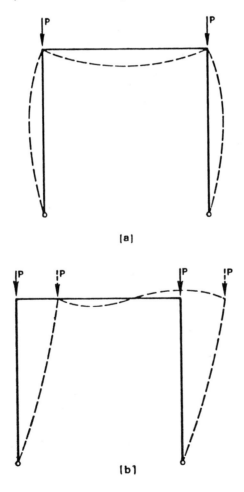

Fig. 3. (a) Symmetrical mode of elastic critical buckling
(b) Sidesway mode of elastic critical buckling

and Oster (1974b; 1976) will be mentioned. This work covers a continuing theoretical study on three-dimensional frames subjected to dynamic and repeated load. The stiffening effect of the floor diaphragm has been included in a second-order elasto-plastic mathematical model developed using finite element techniques. No simplified procedure that design practice can use to study this problem seems to be in the offing.

STABILITY OF MIXED STEEL-CONCRETE BUILDINGS

The principle stated in the Monograph still holds: the behavior of a steel-encased reinforced concrete structure is close to that of a pure steel structure when the amount of steel in the structure is large, and it is close to that of a pure reinforced concrete structure when the amount of steel is small. The Monograph recommended that the methods of checking for stability outlined in Chapter SB-4 be used for the former case and that those given in Chapter CB-8 be used for the latter case. Accordingly, any advances in the state of the art for the stability of both steel and concrete buildings would apply to mixed-steel concrete buildings.

SPECIAL TOPICS

The SSRC multiple column curves (Johnston, 1976) can be transformed into a single equation, as has been done by Rondal and Maquoi (1979). Such a transformation might reduce the practical objection that the use of several curves is not a design-intensive approach. Another special topic of interest is the application of the Merchant-Rankine formula to the problem of member stability by Allen (1978). A final item worthy of mention is a study of the effect of material damage on the buckling of structures by Krajcinovic (1981). The material damage under consideration is that resulting from dynamic loading such as an earthquake.

CONDENSED REFERENCES/BIBLIOGRAPHY

The following is a condensed bibliography for this article. It includes all articles referred to or cited in the text. The full citations will be found at the end of the volume, with additional citations for further reading. What is given here should be sufficient information to lead the reader to the correct article: the author, date, and title. In case of multiple authors, only the first name is listed.

Allen 1978, *Merchant-Rankine Approach to Member Stability*

Beaulieu 1977, *The Destabilizing Forces Caused by Gravity Loads Acting on Initially Out-of-Plumb*
Birnstiel 1980, *Factors Influencing Frame Stability*
Birnstiel (to be published), *Stability Design Procedures*
Biswas 1981, *Criteria Analysis and Design of Braced and Unbraced Frames*
Braham 1979, *Buckling of Thin-Walled Tubular Sections, Specifically Rectangular Sections*
Braham 1980, *Buckling of Thin-Walled Hollow Sections. Cases of Axially Loaded Rectangular Sections*

Chen 1979, *Influence of End Restraint on Column Stability*
Cheng 1972, *Second-Order Elasto-Plastic Analysis of Tall Buildings with Damped Dynamic Excitations*
Cheng 1974a, *P-Delta Effect on Optimum Design of Dynamic Tall Buildings*
Cheng 1974b, *Ultimate Instability of Earthquake Structures*
Cheng 1976, *Effect of Coupling Earthquake Motions on Inelastic Structural Models*
Cheng 1977, *Comparative Studies of Buckling Capacity of Three-Dimensional Building Systems*

ECCS 1975, *Stability Recommendations for Design*
ECCS-EG-76-1E 1976, *Recommendations for Steel Constructions*

Haaijer 1981, *Eccentric Load Test of Angle Column Simulated with MSC/NASTRAN Finite Element*
Horne 1963, *Elastic-Plastic Failure Loads of Plane Frames*

Iffland 1981, *Stability of Tall Structures*

Johnston 1976, *Guide to Design Criteria for Metal Compression Members*

Krajcinovic 1981, *The Effect of the Material Damage on the Buckling of Structures*

MacGregor 1972, *Stability of Reinforced Concrete Building Frames*
Massonnet 1976, *European Recommendations (E.C.C.S.) for the Plastic Design of Steel Frames*
Massonnet 1978, *Recent Progress in the Field of Structural Stability of Steel Structures*
Mortelmans 1980, *Sway Buckling of Multistory Frames*

Nair 1981, *Evaluation of Overall Stability Effects in Tall Buildings*
Nixon 1975, *Simplified Second Order Frame Analysis*

Razzaq 1980, *Elastic Instability of Unbraced Space Frames*
Rondal 1979, *Single Equation for SSRC Column-Strength Curves*

Scheer 1978, *Evaluation of Test Results for Box Columns Made of Thin Unstiffened Steel Plates*
SSRC 1981, *General Principles for the Stability Design of Metal Structures*

Talaboc 1980, *Elastic Plastic Analysis and Design of Multistory Steel Frames by Subassembly Methods*

Vandepitte 1981, *Design of Structures*

Effects of Structural Redundancy and Its Importance on Design Criteria For Stability and Strength

Fazlur R. Khan*

Mahjoub M. El Nimeiri

INTRODUCTION

The traditional tall building structure with a beam and column frame has been designed without any special consideration for the probability of failure of its members. Designing the column and checking against its load carrying capacity is no different for a high-rise building than for normal low-rise construction. This traditional approach assumes that the vertical members of a tall building and those of a short building have the same levels of importance in the overall structure. It also assumes that within a tall structure, the lower-floor columns are of the same importance as the columns in the upper floors. From a probability point of view, it would be more appropriate to

---

*Deceased

adjust the level of reliability of members according to their importance in the overall structure. Therefore, the effective factor of safety for the upper-level columns of a tall building can be decreased slightly compared to the effective factor of safety for the lower-level columns.

Similar questions should be raised when one considers the different performance probabilities of altogether different types of systems for tall buildings. The recent development of the closely spaced framed tube construction for tall buildings provides a large amount of redundancy against total collapse when compared to a traditional beam and column frame with columns spaced far apart (Fig. 1). Since an individual column in a framed tube cannot by itself initiate a progressive collapse or an incipient failure of the entire structure, it would be reasonable to question why the effective factor of safety of columns in framed tube construction should be the same as for a traditional beam and column framing system.

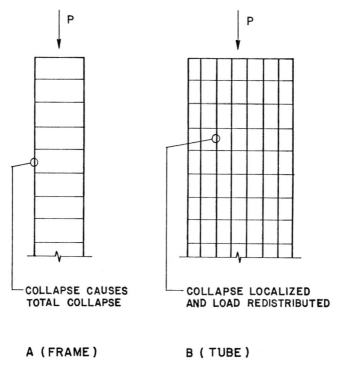

COLLAPSE CAUSES   COLLAPSE LOCALIZED
TOTAL COLLAPSE   AND LOAD REDISTRIBUTED

A (FRAME)   B (TUBE)

Fig. 1 Effect of local collapse on (a) frame and (b) tube

PERFORMANCE OF A SINGLE STRUCTURAL MEMBER VERSUS RELIABILITY OF THE TOTAL STRUCTURAL SYSTEM

The general principle of reliability against possible failure is normally achieved by the use of a factor of safety in designing each element of a structure. In the present AISC specifications it is assumed that each structural member in any type of structural system will require the same level of reliability. Since all structures ultimately relate to the concept of probability of failure, it is interesting to make a qualitative illustration of the point raised above by drawing three normal distribution curves for a given compression member (Fig. 2) . For a given design force and conditions of restraint, the curve for a one-story frame column will have a normal distribution curve marked *A* on the basis of idealized tests. However, if the same member exists on the ground floor in a tall steel structural frame with wide column spacing, then this member takes a very special importance because its collapse or instability will cause possible progressive failure and collapse of the entire structure. Adding that importance factor in a qualitative way, this column is expected to have its normal distribution curve shifted somewhat downward as shown by curve *B*. To give an example for this case, the diagonal members or the vertical columns at the ground level in the 100-story John Hancock Center (Fig. 3) are much more critical for the entire structure than its interior columns are. From a safety point of view, they should have a higher level of reliability than other compression members in the building. Conversely, in a

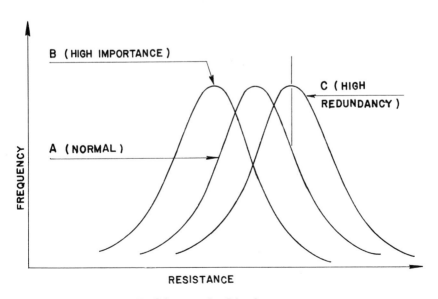

Fig. 2 Comparative *R* for three cases

framed tube structure such as the World Trade Center in New York, or in a
bundled tube structure such as the Sears Tower in Chicago, the individual
column elements and their performance have a lower impact on the overall
stability and reliability of the total structure. Redistribution of load will
occur in case of any unforeseen premature instability of a single column
element. Therefore, in such a case the normal distribution curve in Fig. 2
should be moved upward, as shown qualitatively in curve C, to take into
account the high redundancy of such a structural system.

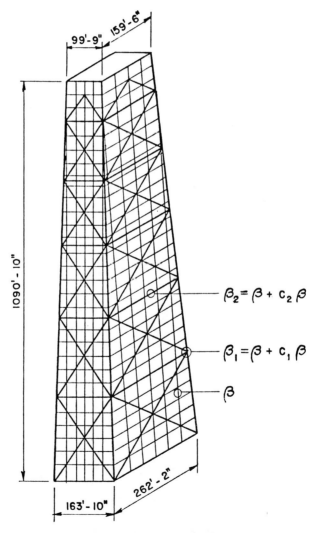

Fig. 3 The 100-story John Hancock Center

ADJUSTMENT FOR REDUNDANCY OR UNIQUENESS
THROUGH THE LRFD DESIGN METHOD

The load and resistance factor design (LRFD) method, which is being widely discussed for possible acceptance for steel structural design, is based on the need to provide a safe margin between the normal distribution curve for the resistance and the normal distribution curve for the load and its effects, as shown in Fig. 2. The reliability index β is expressed as:

$$\beta = \frac{R_m - Q_m}{\sqrt{\sigma_R^2 + \sigma_Q^2}}$$

where R_m and Q_m are the mean resistance and the load effects, and σ_R and σ_Q are the standard derivations for the resistance and the load effects. The LRFD method accommodates the reliability index β by the use of the resistance reduction factor ϕ and the load effect increment factor γ_D, for dead load, and γ_L, for live load. As shown in Fig. 4, the LRFD method provides for the adequate safety margin between the resistance and the load effect by moving the normal distribution curve for resistance downward with a multiplier ϕ

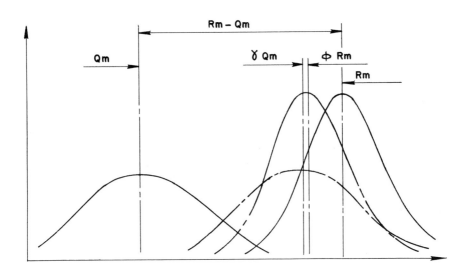

$$\beta = \frac{R_m - Q_m}{\sqrt{\sigma_R^2 + \sigma_Q^2}}$$

$$\phi\, R_m \geqq \gamma\, Q_m$$

Fig. 4 LRFD design basis

and moving the normal distribution for loads upward by multiplying them by appropriate factors γ. This is shown by the second set of curves in Fig. 4.

At present, the effects of redundancy or uniqueness of structural elements are not considered or incorporated in the concept of factors of safety. Nor are they represented in the proposed LRFD method, where the reliability index β is used without regard to the location or importance of any individual structural member. The authors recommend that the effect of redundancy or uniqueness of a structural member be taken into account by adjusting the ϕ factors, but not the load factors. Thereby, present practice would accept the philosophy of a shift upward or downward for normal distribution curves for resistance only. This approach would be consistent with the general design methods used at this time.

SUGGESTED DESIGN APPROACH

In quantitative terms, the upward or downward shift of the ϕ factor can be looked at in the same way as allowing column load reductions for tall buildings to be based on the number of floors above any level. However, in the absence of a detailed research program on this subject, the design engineer may be allowed to adjust the normal ϕ factor upward or downward on the basis of a probabilistic analysis showing the effect of the redundancy or the uniqueness of a certain member in relation to the total structural system.

CONCLUSIONS

This paper has been presented to stimulate discussion on the importance of any structural member's redundancy or uniqueness to the total structural system. The stability and strength of individual elements should consider the type of structural system used and the location of individual members within the overall structure. A rational approach to redundant systems will undoubtedly result in savings in construction costs. At the same time, it will recognize the need to provide a higher level of safety for those structural elements that may cause greater damage and loss of life in the event of an accidental structural collapse.

Design of Laterally Unsupported Beams— East European Practice

Otto Halász

INTRODUCTION

Similar to the effort of West European experts to summarize, in the form of international recommendations for the design of metal structures, the latest results of coordinated international research projects were launched in the East European Countries to prepare common specifications in the field of structural design, including steel and aluminum structures. This work has already resulted in issuing international standards defining the fundamental features of design philosophy—the basic data of analysis (Council of Mutual Economic Aid, 1976), and so on. As far as metal structures are concerned, the work is halfway to its goal: provisional recommendations were proposed for aluminum structures (CME Aid, 1975), and alternative proposals were collected in the form of design guidelines (Dalban et al., 1977). Based on this preparatory work, common standards are expected to be issued in the next few years. Thus, the present paper can report only on design practice as codified by the existing national specifications (Moscow, 1974; Berlin, 1972; Prague, 1976; Warsaw, 1976; Bucarest, 1976; Budapest, 1975) reflecting different approaches that result from different design traditions and development. This report, however, may reveal the debated problems as well, which seem to show close resemblance to those exposed in publications summarizing similar work elsewhere (Galambos, 1977; Kato and Akiyawa, 1976; Lindner et al., 1977).

A numerical comparison of the effects of different countries' design rules is difficult because of differences in the basic design concepts. East European countries adopted a method very close to that referred to as load and resistance factor design in the North American literature. (This method was first introduced by the Soviet Building Code in 1946.) Thus, only a qualitative comparison is possible which, because of the differences in safety factors, may not reflect the situation quite realistically.

The design practice to be discussed in the paper is related to lateral-torsional buckling. This phenomenon terminates the load carrying capacity of beams loaded in the plane perpendicular to the weak axis of their double- or monosymmetric cross section. It takes place because of lateral displacement and torsion as a result that lateral supports are lacking or inadequately spaced. Similar problems arise with segments of plate girders, where the above mentioned phenomenon is combined with simultaneous deformation of the web. Finally, practical cases, where small lateral loads (such as lateral forces of crane girders) are acting, may be regarded as closely related problems.

LATERAL-TORSIONAL BUCKLING CURVES

Specifications convey the condensed results of theoretical and experimental studies in the form of one or more buckling curves which, strictly speaking, refer to some "basic" problem (for example, a simply supported beam loaded by equal end moments). To make extrapolation for more general cases possible, buckling curves are presented in special ways, as shown in Fig. 1.

In specifications where "plastic design" is not dealt with [Fig. 1 (a)], presentation is based on introducing an "equivalent slenderness ratio":

$$\lambda = \sqrt{\frac{\sigma_y}{\sigma_{cr,e}}} \quad ; \quad \sigma_{cr,e} = \frac{M_{cr,e}}{S_x} \tag{1}$$

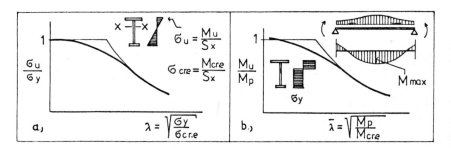

Fig. 1 Definition of equivalent slenderness ratio

where $M_{cr,e}$ denotes the critical value of maximum bending moment causing bifurcation of equilibrium in case of a geometrically perfect, unlimitedly elastic beam under the actual loading conditions and end restraints (Vlasov, 1940);

S_x is the cross-sectional modulus, and

σ_y denotes the yield stress.

Load carrying capacity is defined by the value σ_u/σ_y, where σ_u denotes the ultimate value of extreme fiber stress in the cross section of maximum bending moment (Fig. 2).

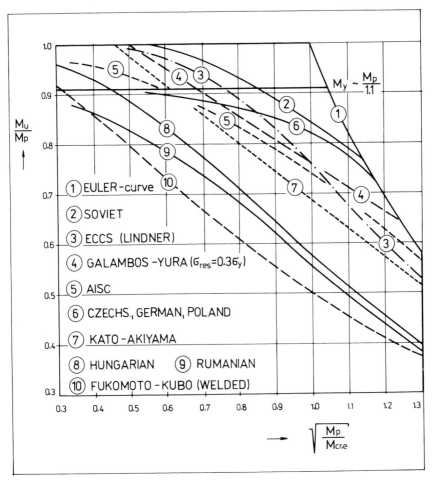

Fig. 2 Lateral-torsional buckling curves

Specifications dealing with plastic design also prefer the presentation M_u/M_P versus $\bar{\lambda}$ with

$$\bar{\lambda} = \sqrt{\frac{M_P}{M_{cr,e}}} \tag{2}$$

where M_P denotes the full-plastic moment of the cross section, and M_u denotes the ultimate value of maximum bending moment [Fig. 1 (b)].

For the sake of comparison, in what follows the second presentation is always selected. In cases where conversion between the two modes was necessary, a shape factor 1.1 was adopted.

In Fig. 2 the buckling curves of different East European and Western national specifications are reproduced, showing considerable differences in their approach. To make the background more evident, the categories that follow can be set up.

Category A: Ultimate moment can be identified with the value of M_{cr}, the critical moment that causes bifurcation of equilibrium of a perfect beam, that is, the start of lateral displacements and torsion in the response of the beam previously deflected in the plane of loading only (Fig. 3). This approach is based on the assumption that M_{cr} coincides with reasonable accuracy with the mean value of test results: initial imperfections have but a limited influence on the carrying capacity, and their probable deteriorating effect can be covered by using a reasonably chosen "resistance factor." This concept is the background of most existing East European design curves (curves 2 and 6 in Fig. 2). It means also that in the elastic region, the curves correspond to the simple Euler-curve; in the inelastic region two different solutions are adopted.

Category A(1): Reduction caused by inelastic behavior can follow the concept used in the case of "perfect" columns: the tangent-modulus or reduced-modulus theory based on an appropriately selected stress-strain diagram (see curve 6 in Fig. 2), usually in the form of

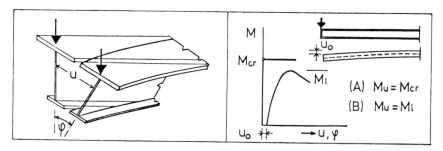

Fig. 3 Basic approaches for ultimate moment

$$\sigma = E \bullet \epsilon \quad ; \quad \sigma \le 0.8 \, \sigma_y$$

$$\sigma = 0.8 \, \sigma_y + 0.2 \, \sigma_y \bullet \tanh \frac{E \bullet \epsilon - 0.8 \, \sigma_y}{0.2 \, \sigma_y} \quad ; \quad 0.8\sigma_y \le \sigma \le \sigma_{y'} \tag{3}$$

originally proposed by German standards. This way of reduction can be regarded as conservative and no attention is paid to the effect of strain-hardening.

Category A(2): The inelastic region can be represented by some approximate formula derived from comparative calculations regarding residual stresses, inelastic behavior (Galambos, 1963), and so on, and from experiments. Soviet specifications (curve 2 in Fig. 2) offer a method similar to that adopted in plate buckling by applying reduction factor $\sqrt{E_t/E}$ where E_t is the tangent modulus and E is the Young's modulus. The value of E_t is derived from a so-called Tetmajer formula, an approximation previously used for column curves:

$$\sigma_u/\sigma_y = 1.2 - 0.32\lambda \tag{4}$$

Thus, the curve in the inelastic range is to be computed by the following equation:

$$(\sigma_u/\sigma_y)^2 - (2.4 + 0.1024\lambda^4)\sigma_u/\sigma_y + 1.44 = 0 \tag{5}$$

As is seen in curve 2 in Fig. 2, it results with good approximation in a straight line.

Category B: The second basic approach—adopted by the minority of East European specifications—rejects the basic role of critical moment and defines the ultimate moment, at least in principle, as the peak value in a load-deflection diagram (Fig. 3) of a beam with initial imperfections (curvature, residual stress, and so on). The curve in this case should be based on numerical and test results. The two specifications in this group follow different patterns.

Category B(1): Curve 9 in Fig. 2, the Rumanian specification, substitutes the σ_u/σ_y versus λ relation with one of the multiple column curves used for the design of centrically loaded columns, which is actually very close to curve b in the ECCS "Recommendations" (Schulz, 1977). This proves to be the most conservative approach.

Category B(2): Curve 8 in Fig. 2, the Hungarian specification, introduces a special interaction equation

$$x = \frac{x \bullet y}{m} + y = 1 \quad ; \quad x = \frac{M_u}{M_P} \quad ; \quad y = \frac{M_u}{M_{cr,e}} \tag{6}$$

This curve can be regarded as an alternative to that adopted by the ECCS

"Recommendations" (Lindner et al., 1977) which, using the above notations, can be written in the form of $x^n + y^n = 1$. By appropriate choice of parameters m and n, the two curves can be brought into fair closeness; that is, the Hungarian curve can be approximated by the ECCS formula, using $n = 1, 5$, instead of $n = 2.5$, in the ECCS "Recommendations" (curve 3 in Fig. 2). As a matter of fact, the conservative attitude of the Hungarian specification—besides some comparative approximate calculations (Hunyadi, 1958)—are to be attributed to the fact that—lacking a large enough assortment of rolled sections—mainly welded shapes are used and measurements on domestic products showed very high residual stresses.

COMPARISON OF THE BUCKLING CURVES

Independently of their background and regarding the quantitative results only, the conclusions that follow may be drawn.

For rolled sections the Soviet specifications seem to furnish reliable approximations. They are verified theoretically (Broude, 1958) and experimentally (Chuvikin, 1958) and are in fairly good agreement with the ECCS "Recommendations" and North American proposals. It is worth mentioning, that the proposal given in connection with load and resistance factor design (Yura and Galambos, 1978) would practically coincide with the Soviet curve, assuming residual stresses as low as $0.15 \, \sigma_y$.

Very little evidence exists concerning the role of residual stresses. The low values of curves 8 and 9 in Fig. 2 reflect the fear of their major effect; and although they agree well with the Japanese test (Fukumoto and Kubo, 1977), curve 10 in Fig. 2, they are not sufficiently verified. This question needs further experimental investigation. Such work has been launched in the TU Budapest recently.

Some results of the investigations may raise the question of using more than one design curve. Putting aside the unsettled problem of residual stresses that could justify this tendency, the differences in loading conditions have similar effects. Although the "equivalent slenderness" can bring together different loading conditions in the case of a perfect, elastic beam, the considerable differences in the effect of these conditions in the inelastic region are well known (Galambos, 1963; Potapkin, 1977), and comparative studies (Broude, 1958) prove that initial curvature has different influence depending on the level of load application (upper flange, neutral axis, lower flange). Some results that assume an eccentricity $e/L = 0.001$ are reproduced, according to Broude (1958), in Fig. 4. (I_D denotes St. Venant's torsion; C_w represents the warping moment of inertia). The same conclusions can be drawn from experiments in Chuvikin (1958); their results are reproduced in Fig. 5 in two different representations, proving that even the "equivalent slenderness" doesn't bring sufficiently coincident curves.

Arguments against the multiple-curve approach are that all previous conclusions refer to single-span beams. The restraining effect of adjacent parts and the possible redistribution of moments as a result of lateral displacements and torsion in a continuous system are still unclarified, making an "overrefinement" illusory.

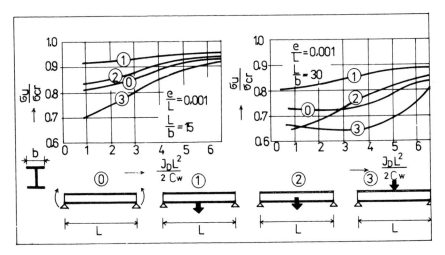

Fig. 4 Effect of imperfections

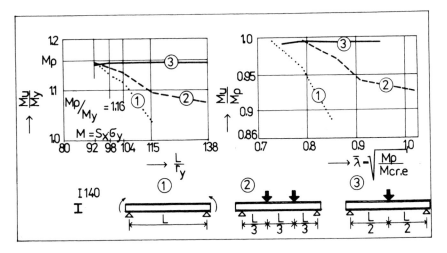

Fig. 5 Effect of the shape of the bending moment diagram

RESEARCH NEEDS

In addition to those dealt with previously, some further problems are worth mentioning.

The very intensive theoretical research in the field of nonlinear buckling analysis of elastic structures by Thompson and Hunt (1973) and their interesting findings may give impetus for some reconsideration concerning design tradition. Three related questions can be mentioned.

1. The elastic post-buckling behavior after lateral-torsional buckling of a simply supported beam seems to be similar to that of an axially loaded column (Fig. 6). The bifurcation is "stable", but the increase in load is of minor practical importance. As pointed out in Bolotin (1959), this increase may be much stronger in continuous systems, revealing a possible favorable effect to be counted on if elongation of the whole beam is totally or partially prevented.

2. The interaction of different buckling modes—mainly that of web buckling and lateral-torsional buckling—has been investigated long since. From numerical examples and tests (Broude, 1958; Iványi, 1981; Lindner et al., 1977), it seems that if investigation is limited to "perfect" systems and pays no attention to post-buckling phenomena, the neglected interaction furnishes unsafe but still tolerable results. On the other hand, in the case of thin-walled beams, the high post-buckling reserves of plate elements have to be counted on and, similar to the methods used for thin-walled compression members, appropriate design procedures need to be worked out (Wang and Wright, 1977).

3. The above problem is connected to optimum design, as well. Nonlinear buckling theory draws attention to the fact that beams designed to have two coincident buckling modes (for example, if the bending moment causing

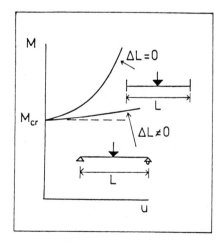

Fig. 6 Post-buckling effect

local buckling of the flange and that causing lateral-torsional buckling of the beam coincide) may be very sensitive to imperfections (Reis and Roorda, 1977; Thompson and Hunt, 1973). The practical consequences need some further investigation, first of all in the inelastic range.

Many practical questions emerge concerning the effect of partial restraint against lateral displacements and torsion, like the effect of purlins (if connected to the tension flanges), rails, cladding, and the like, which have to be checked by tests (Hálasz and Iványi, 1979; Sochor, 1977; Tuma, 1977).

In many cases (for example crane girders) besides those in which heavy vertical loads cause bending moments about the strong axis, some small horizontal loads also have to be reckoned with. This situation results in a problem related to lateral-flexural buckling that must be checked by a second-order analysis, taking into account changes in geometry. As proved by comparative calculations (Goeben, 1977), this procedure often cannot be replaced by buckling analysis, even if higher safety factors are adopted. Although general computational methods are available (Tarnai, 1978a; Tarnai, 1978b), some practicable procedures are needed for everyday praxis.

Finally, design rules for plastic design including adequate spacing of lateral supports—based mainly on North American research—are dealt with in specifications with small differences (Iványi, 1974); research for further refinement seems possible by complex models describing interaction of lateral-torsional buckling and plate buckling (Fig. 7) (Iványi, 1981).

This paper is an edited version of one that appeared as Preprint 81-011, presented at the ASCE Convention, New York, New York, May 11–15, 1981.

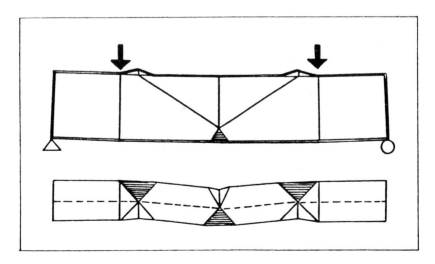

Fig. 7 Yield mechanism for combined buckling modes

APPENDIX

Regional Standards and Recommendations

CMEA (Council of Mutual Economic Aid) "Structural Design of Load Bearing Elements of Buildings. General Requirements. Loads and Effects," *Standard 384-76 and 1407-78,* 1976.

CMEA "Design of Aluminum Structures," *Recommendations RS 5239-75,* 1975.

Dalban, C., et al., "Remarks on the ECCS Recommendations and on the Draft on CMEA Specifications," *Final Report of the Regional Colloquium on Stability of Steel Structures,* Budapest, 1977, pp. 13–24.

National Specifications

"Design Specifications for Steel Structures" (in Russian), *SNiP-V.3-72.* Moscow, 1974.

"Design of Steel Structures. Stability Conditions" (in German), *TGL 13503,* Berlin, 1972.

"Design of Steel Structures" (in Czechoslovakian), *CSN 731401,* Prague, 1976.

"Design of Steel Structures" (in Polish), *PN-76/B-03200,* Warsaw, 1976.

"Design of Steel Structures" (in Rumanian) *STAS 20108/0-76,* Bucarest, 1976.

"Design of Steel Structures" (in Hungarian), *MSZ 15024/75,* Budapest, 1975.

CONDENSED REFERENCES/BIBLIOGRAPHY

The following is a condensed bibliography for this article. It includes all articles referred to or cited in the text. The full citations will be found at the end of the volume, with additional citations for further reading. What is given here should be sufficient information to lead the reader to the correct article: the author, date, and title. In case of multiple authors, only the first name is listed.

Bolotin 1959, *Postbuckling Deformation of Beams*
Broude 1958, *Stability of I-Beams with Initial Curvature and Eccentric Loads*
Broude 1959, *A More Accurate Solution of Prandtl-Timoshecko Problem*

Chuvikin 1958, *Experimental Investigation of Lateral-Torsional Buckling of I-Beams in the Inelastic*

Fukumoto 1977, *A Survey of Test on Lateral Buckling Strength of Beams*

Galambos 1963, *Inelastic Lateral Buckling of Beams*
Galambos 1977, *Laterally Unsupported Beams*
Goeben 1977, *Contribution to the Stability of Crane-Beams*

Halász 1979, *Tests with Simple Elastic-Plastic Frames*
Hunyadi 1958, *Lateral-Torsional Buckling of Steel Beams with Constant and Variable Cross-Sections*

Iványi 1974, *Experiments on Plastic Buckling of Steel Beams*
Iványi 1981, *Interaction between Strength and Stability Phenomena*

Kato 1976, *Advanced Design Formula for Lateral Buckling of H-Sections*

Lindner 1977, *Laterally Supported and Unsupported Beams*
Loos 1953, *Contribution to the Combined Buckling Phenomena*

Potapkin 1977, *Up-to-date Methods in Stability Analysis of Steel Bridge Structures*

Reis 1977, *The Interaction Between Lateral-Torsional and Local Plate Buckling in Thin-Walled Beams*

Schulz 1977, *The Role of Multiple Column Curves in the ECCS Design Concept*
Sochor 1977, *Bearing Capacity of Roof Purlins*

Tarnai 1978a, *Lateral Buckling of Elastic Beams with Initial Stresses and Initial Deformations*
Tarnai 1978b, *Lateral Buckling Analysis of Beams by the Theory of Quadratic Operator Pencils*
Thompson 1973, *A General Theory of Elastic Stability*
Tuma 1977, *Lateral Buckling of Steel Girders*

Vlasov 1940, *Thin-Walled Elastic Bars*

Wang 1977, *Torsional-Flexural Buckling of Locally Buckled Beams and Columns*

Yura 1978, *The Bending Resistance of Steel Beams*

Ductility of Members and Frames Subject to Buckling

Ben Kato
Hiroshi Akiyama

INTRODUCTION

The spectral acceleration response of a structure against an earthquake is approximately inversely proportional to the fundamental period of vibration of the structure. Consequently, the stiffer, and thus stronger, the structure, the larger the horizontal shear force on the structure becomes. On the other hand, if the structure has a sufficient plastic deformation capacity after yielding, it may survive a major earthquake by absorbing the earthquake input energy by the plastic work of the skeleton.

The steel structure is not always ductile and the evaluation of its plastic deformation capacity is rather complicated because of the occurrence of buckling. If one wants to design a structure with sufficient stiffness and strength, the width-to-thickness ratio of member sections tends to become larger, which leads the structure to be brittle. On the other hand, if one wants to design a structure with sufficient ductility, one must select stocky members with compact sections to avoid buckling, which leaves the structure too flexible and uneconomical.

To develop a safety criterion for steel structures against the severest credible earthquake in this context, it will be reasonable and practical to assess the

439

ultimate resisting capacity of steel structures with conventional geometrical dimensions, taking the post-buckling behavior into consideration. Note that the drop in resistance caused by the occurrence of buckling does not immediately cause the collapse of the structure in the dynamic response problem, which is quite different from the gravity-loading problem.

This paper first formulates the moment-rotation relationships of members with various cross sections subject to antisymmetrical bending with and without axial thrust. The formulations are carried up to collapse stage based on the available test results. Then the load-deformation relationship of the moment frame is related to the moment-rotation relationships of individual members. Finally, the dynamically equivalent ductility ratio (plastic deformation capacity) of the moment frame, which is directly applicable to the ultimate limit-state design for an earthquake (Kato, 1981), is evaluated by reducing the actual load-deformation relationship to the elastic-perfectly plastic relationship.

MOMENT-ROTATION RELATIONSHIP OF MEMBERS

A rule to relate the hysteretic moment-rotation relationship of structural members to their monotonic moment-rotation relationship had been proposed (Kato, 1973b); and it was demonstrated that this hysteretic rule also applies to members subject to buckling (Inowe, 1972). Therefore, from the viewpoint of seismic design, it is necessary and sufficient to know the monotonic moment-rotation relationship of structural members until their collapse stage.

In this section, the monotonic moment-rotation relationships of structural members with H-sections, square-hollow sections, and circular hollow-sections are formulated based on the available test results. All the test results are interpreted to the moment-rotation relationships of the members that are subject to antisymmetrical bending with and without axial compressive force, as shown in Fig. 1. These relationships have a general configuration as depicted in Fig. 2(a), namely, when the maximum moment of a member reaches its full plastic moment at its member ends, the curve shows a clear knee (point A). This point is defined as the yield moment M_y, and the corresponding elastic rotation is defined as the yield rotation θ_y. After the general yielding, resistance increases almost linearly as a result of the strain-hardening (segment A to B), and the maximum resistance is attained at, point B when the local buckling of the member section occurs. The member loses its resisting force at point C. This moment-rotation relationship is nondimensionalized by taking $\tau = M/M_y$ in the vertical axis and $\Phi = \theta/\theta_y$ in the horizontal axis; and the relationship is idealized by three linear segments, as shown in Fig. 2(b). In this nondimensional expression, the slope k_p is defined by the ratio of the stiffness of the strain-hardening region to the elastic stiffness, and the slope k_d is defined by the ratio of the negative stiffness of the collapse region to the elastic stiffness.

H-Section Members (Kato, 1977)

On the basis of reported test results on beams (Fukuchi, 1969; Kato, 1976; Lukey, 1969), beam-columns (Kato, 1973c), and stub-columns (Suzuki, 1974), the moment-rotation relationships of H-section members subject to strong axis bending with and without axial thrust were nondimensionalized and best-fitted by three linear segments. In this study, it was postulated that flexural-torsional buckling was prevented by appropriate restraining members, and it was assumed that the maximum strength was governed by the local

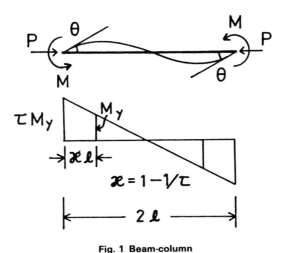

Fig. 1 Beam-column

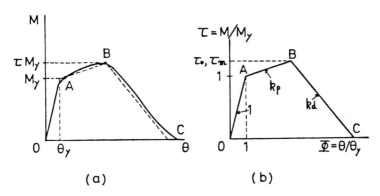

Fig. 2 Moment-rotation relationship

buckling of the plate elements of the section. In fact, the flexural-torsional buckling does not cause drastic reduction in resistance under present loading conditions. Furthermore, it is practically feasible to prevent the flexural-torsional buckling by providing the restraining members.

The nondimensional moment-rotation relationship is defined by τ, k_p and k_d, as shown in Fig. 2(b). The empirical formulae for these key parameters were developed in terms of material property ϵ_y, axial stress ratio $p=P/P_y$, and geometrical parameters b/t_f, d/t_w and λ_y (Fig. 3). The half wave length of flange local buckling is approximately equal to $2b$, and the spread of the plastic region for a given value of τ is proportional to the member length $2l$, as was illustrated in Fig. 1. Therefore, the parameter b/l, or its equivalent parameter λ_y (slenderness ratio about weak axis), becomes an important measure of the plastic deformation capacity.

The following equations are applicable to H-section members with dimensions that satisfy

$$\frac{b}{t_f} \leq \frac{0.52}{\sqrt{\epsilon_y}} \qquad \frac{d}{t_w} \leq \frac{2.4}{\sqrt{\epsilon_y}} \tag{1}$$

(a) Maximum strength index τ_0 for beams ($p=0$)

$\tau_0 = M_{max}/M_y$ ($p = 0$) is given by Eq. 2 or Eq. 3, whichever is larger, but should not be less than unity.

$$\tau_0 = 1 + [(0.043 - 0.0744\frac{b}{t_f}\sqrt{\epsilon_y})^2 - (0.0024\frac{d}{t_w}\sqrt{\epsilon_y} - 0.00025)] \frac{1}{\epsilon_y} \tag{2}$$

$$\tau_0 = 1.46 - [0.63\frac{b}{t_f} + 0.053\frac{d}{t_w} + 0.02(\lambda_y - 50)]\sqrt{\epsilon_y} \tag{3}$$

(b) Maximum strength index τ_m for beam-columns with axial stress ratio p

$$\tau_m = M_{max}/M_y(p=p) = (Z'_p/Z_p)\tau_0 \tag{4}$$

in which Z_p = plastic section modulus with axial stress ratio p, and Z'_p = plastic section modulus with axial stress ratio p/τ_0.

(c) Stiffness ratio of strain-hardening region k_p

$$k_p = 0.03 + 0.04p \tag{5}$$

(d) Stiffness ratio of negative slope region k_d

k_d is given by Eq. 6 or Eq. 7, whichever is smaller.

$$k_d = -0.355 \frac{d}{t_w} \epsilon_y \tag{6}$$

$$k_d = -[-1.33 + (10.6 \frac{b}{t_f} \sqrt{\epsilon_y} - 2)(0.63 + 0.33 \frac{d}{t_w} \sqrt{\epsilon_y})] \sqrt{\epsilon_y} \tag{7}$$

In case of $p > \dfrac{2A_w}{3A}$, the term $\dfrac{d}{t_w}$ in Eqs. 2, 3, 6, and 7 should be factored by 2, and in case of $\lambda_y > 100$ and $p \leq \dfrac{2A_w}{3A}$, the term $\dfrac{d}{t_w}$ in Eq. 2 should be factored by 1.5.

In the above equations,

$M_y(p=0)$ = full plastic moment without axial stress;
$M_y(p=p)$ = full plastic moment with axial stress;
$p = P/P_y$ = axial stress ratio;
P_y = yield axial force of section;
b = half-width of flange;
t_f = flange thickness;
d = inside depth of web plate;
t_w = web thickness;
λ_y = slenderness ratio about weak axis;
ϵ_y = yield strain of material;
$A_w = dt_w$ = area of web; and
A = area of section.

Some examples of the comparison between test results and their predictions by Eqs. 2 through 7 are shown in Fig. 4.

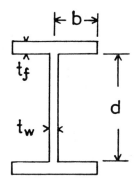

Fig. 3 H-section dimensions

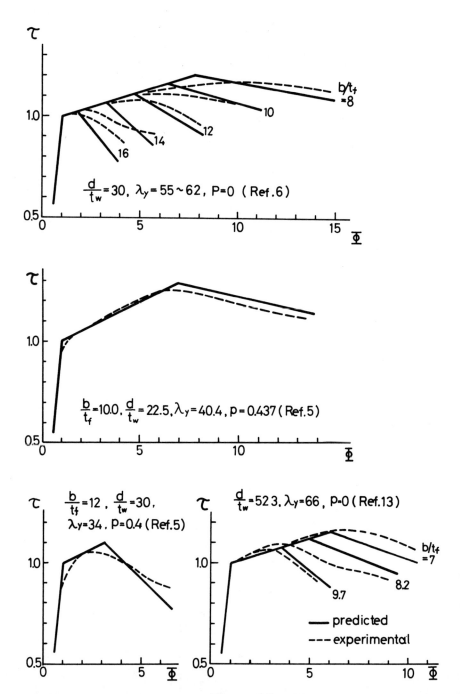

Fig. 4 Comparison between tests and prediction for H-section members *(Kato, 1976; Kato, 1973c; Lukey, 1969)*

Square Hollow-Section and Circular Hollow-Section Members

Experimental moment-rotation relationships of beams and beam-columns with square hollow- and circular-hollow sections were approximated by three linear segments for each by the approach similar to that for H-section members. The developed empirical formulae are shown below.

Square Hollow-Section Members (Kato, 1978c)

The following equations are applicable for square hollow-section members with dimensions

$$\frac{B}{t} - 2 = \frac{b}{t} \leq \frac{1.6}{\sqrt{\epsilon_y}} \tag{8}$$

in which B = outside width of square hollow-section;
b = inside width of square hollow-section; and
t = wall thickness (Fig. 5).

(a) Maximum strength index τ_0 for beams ($p = 0$)

τ_0 is given by Eq. 9 or Eq. 10, whichever is larger, but should not be less than unity.

$$\tau_0 = 0.98 + 0.0202 \left[\left(2.624 \frac{B}{t} \sqrt{\epsilon_y} - 5.79 \right)^2 - 1.368 \right] (1.81 - \lambda \sqrt{\epsilon_y}) \tag{9}$$

$$\tau_0 = \frac{1}{0.526 + 0.341 \frac{B}{t} \sqrt{\epsilon_y}} \tag{10}$$

in which λ = slenderness ratio with respect to principal axis.

(b) Maximum strength index τ_m for beam-columns with axial stress ratio p

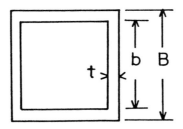

Fig. 5 Square hollow-section dimensions

$$t_m = M_{max}/M_y(p = p) = (Z_p'/Z_p)\tau_0 \tag{11}$$

(c) Stiffness ratio of strain-hardening region k_p

$$k_p = 0.03 + 0.04_p \tag{12}$$

(d) Stiffness ratio of negative slope region k_d

k_d is given by Eq. 13, but should not be larger than zero.

$$k_d = -0.1377\,[(2.674\frac{B}{t}\sqrt{\epsilon_y} + 0.4)^2 - 3.76](\lambda\sqrt{\epsilon_y} - 0.1906)\sqrt{\epsilon_y} \tag{13}$$

In case of $p \geq \dfrac{3A_w}{5A}$, the term $\dfrac{B}{t}$ in Eqs. 9, 10, and 13 should be factored by 1.25, in which $A_w = 2bt = $ total area of two web plates.

Some examples of the comparison between test results and their predictions by Eqs. 9 through 13 are shown in Fig. 6.

**Circular Hollow-Section Members
(Kato, 1973a; Kato, 1978b)**

The following equations are applicable to circular hollow-section members with dimensions

$$\frac{D}{t} \leq \frac{1}{8.8\,\epsilon_y} \tag{14}$$

in which D = diameter of circular hollow-section.

(a) Maximum strength index τ_0 for beams ($p=0$)

τ_0 is given by Eq. 15 or Eq. 16, whichever is applicable, but should not be less than unity.

For seamless tubes,

$$\tau_0 = \frac{0.072}{\sqrt{\epsilon_y}} - 0.0225\frac{D}{t} \tag{15}$$

For cold-formed and welded tubes,

$$\tau_0 = 1.30 - 0.00375\,\frac{D}{t} \tag{16}$$

(b) Maximum strength index τ_m for beam-columns with axial stress ratio p

$$\tau_m = M_{max}/M_y \, (p = p) = (Z'_p/Z_p)\tau_0 \tag{17}$$

(c) Stiffness ratio of strain-hardening region k_p

For seamless tubes,

$$k_p = 0.03 + 0.04p \tag{18}$$

For cold-formed and welded tubes,

$$k_p = 0.045 + 0.03p \tag{19}$$

(d) Stiffness ratio of negative slope region k_d

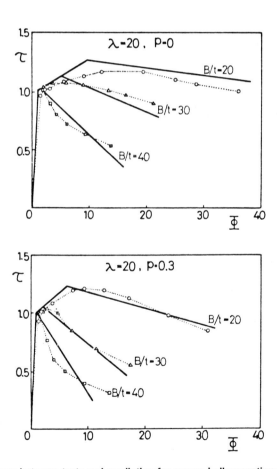

Fig. 6 Comparison between tests and prediction for square hollow-section members *(Kato, 1978c)*

For seamless tubes,

$$k_d = k_{d1} = -\frac{0.011}{\pi^2(1-p^2)}\left(\frac{L}{D}\right)[1 + \cos\pi p + \cos(1-p)\frac{\pi}{2}, \sin\pi p] \qquad (20)$$

For cold-formed and welded tubes:

$$k_d = 0.2\left(\frac{D}{t} - 10\right)k_{d1} \qquad (21)$$

in which L = member length.

ANALYTICAL MODEL OF MOMENT FRAMES

In Fig. 7(a), beams and column-to-beam joint panels at i^{th} floor level carry the stresses resulting from the shear forces acting at i^{th} and i-1th stories, and it can be assumed approximately that one-half of the bending moments and shear stresses of beams and joint-panels at i^{th} floor are due to the shear force acting at i^{th} story. Based on this assumption, the frame is decomposed into a linkage of one-story frames, as shown in Fig. 7(b). Furthermore, this one-story moment frame is simplified to an equivalent "unit frame" as shown in Fig. 7(c). By this simplification, considerable errors are sometimes induced at top and bottom stories, which should be corrected.

The mean yield moment $\overline{M}_y$ and the mean stiffness $\overline{K}$ of member elements of this unit frame are shown in Table 1.

In this table,
$_jK = \mathrm{EI}_j/l_j$ = member stiffness of the original moment frame ($j = c$ or $b, l_j = $ h or l);
$_pK = GV$ = stiffness of joint-panel of the original moment frame; and
V = effective volume of joint-panel.

The average yield shear capacity of the unit frame Q_y is

$$Q_y = \frac{4_j\overline{M}_y}{h} \qquad (22)$$

in which $_j\overline{M}_y$ is $_c\overline{M}_y$ or $_b\overline{M}_y$, whichever is smaller.

The mean stiffness of the unit frame $_r\overline{K}$ is

$$_r\overline{K} = \frac{4}{h^2}\left(\frac{1}{\frac{1}{6_cK} + \frac{1}{6_b\overline{K}} + \frac{1}{_p\overline{K}}}\right) \qquad (23)$$

RELATION BETWEEN FRAME AND MEMBER BEHAVIORS

A procedure needs be developed to evaluate the shear-deformation relationship of the unit frame on the basis of member properties. The deformation of a unit frame consists of deformations of columns, beams, and joint-panels. In general, it is feasible that all these elements be plastified at the ultimate stage of the frame, and for individual building structures it is not difficult to evaluate the frame story deformation on the basis of member properties (Kato, 1978a). However, in this paper, a simple design rule for general use is developed based on the safe-side approximation that one member element of the unit frame (columns or beams) contributes to the plastic deformation of the unit frame. The contribution of joint-panels is considered in a later step.

In the following, the plastic deformation is evaluated in terms of ductility ratios, which are defined as:

For the member element,

$$i^\eta = \frac{\theta_m - \theta_y}{\theta_y} = \frac{\theta_m}{\theta_y} - 1 \tag{24}$$

For the unit frame,

$$_r\eta = \frac{\delta_m - \delta_y}{\delta_y} = \frac{\delta_m}{\delta_y} - 1 \tag{25}$$

Φ in the previous section is related to η as

$$\Phi = \eta + 1 \tag{26}$$

Table 1 Mean yield moment and mean stiffness of member elements of the unit frame

	Yield moment $\overline{M}_y$	Stiffness $\overline{K}$
Column	$_c\overline{M}_y = \dfrac{\Sigma_c M_y}{2}$	$_c\overline{K} = \dfrac{\Sigma_c K}{2}$
Beam	$_b\overline{M}_y = \dfrac{\Sigma_b M_y}{2}$	$_b\overline{K} = \dfrac{\Sigma_b K}{2}$
Joint-panel	$_p\overline{M}_y = \dfrac{\Sigma_p M_y}{4}$	$_p\overline{K} = \dfrac{\Sigma_p K}{4}$

If it is assumed that only columns or beams deform, while other elements remain rigid, obviously the frame ductility $_f\eta$ is equal to the member ductility η. In reality, other structural elements deform elastically. The deformation of the unit frame at yield is given by Eq. 23 as

$$\delta_y = \frac{Q_y}{_f\overline{K}} = \frac{h^2 Q_y}{4}\left(\frac{1}{6_c\overline{K}} + \frac{1}{6_b\overline{K}} + \frac{1}{_p\overline{K}}\right) \tag{27}$$

while the deformation of it under the assumption that only one member element deforms is

$$\delta'_y = \frac{h^2 Q_y}{4}\ \frac{1}{6_j\overline{K}}\ ,\quad (j = c \text{ or } b) \tag{28}$$

Therefore, in an actual unit frame, the ductility ratio should be modified as

$$_f\eta = u\ _i\eta$$

$$u = \frac{\delta'_y}{\delta_y} = \frac{1}{6_jK}\bigg/\left(\frac{1}{6_c\overline{K}} + \frac{1}{6_b\overline{K}} + \frac{1}{_p\overline{K}}\right) \tag{29}$$

in which $_j\overline{K}$ is $_c\overline{K}$ or $_b\overline{K}$, whichever is larger.

Since it was assumed that only one member element deforms plastically, the strength characteristic of the unit frame is identical to that of the member element. In short, the nondimensional $Q/Q_y - \delta/\delta_y$ relationship of the unit

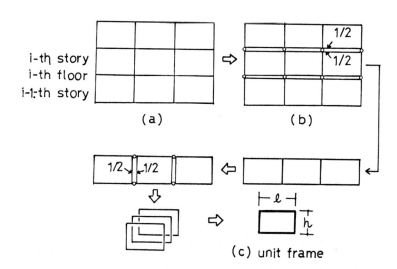

i-th story
i-th floor
i-1-th story

(a)   (b)   (c) unit frame

1/2   1/2

1/2 1/2

ℓ h

Fig. 7 Analytical model of steel frame

frame can be obtained by transforming the τ - Φ relationship of the member element with respect to the horizontal axis in the manner demonstrated in Fig. 8. In this figure, $\eta_m = (\tau_m - 1)/k_p, \eta_u = (\tau_m - 1)/k_p + \tau_m/|k_d|, _Rk_p = k_p/u,$ and $_Rk_d = k_d/u.$

Thus the shear force-deformation relationship of the unit frame is clearly defined.

EQUIVALENT ELASTIC-PERFECTLY PLASTIC RELATIONSHIP

In the ultimate limit-state design against the severest credible earthquake, it is convenient to replace the Q/Q_y - δ/δ_y relationship of the unit frame, such as that shown in Fig. 8(b), by the dynamically equivalent elastic-perfectly plastic relationship (Kato, 1981). The outline of the procedure to develop the equivalent elastic-perfectly plastic relationship is as follows:

(a) Until the restoring force τ goes down below unity, the equivalency of the restoring force characteristics could be assessed by the condition of the equivalency of plastic work. Equating the area $ABCHI$ to the area $AEGI$ in Fig. 9(a), the equivalent ductility ratio $u\eta_0$ is

$$u\,\eta_0 = \frac{\tau_m^2 - 1}{2}\left(\frac{1}{_Rk_p} + \frac{1}{|_Rk_d|}\right) \tag{30}$$

The corresponding equivalent ductility ratio of the member element is

$$\eta_0 = \frac{\tau_m^2 - 1}{2}\left(\frac{1}{k_p} + \frac{1}{|k_d|}\right) \tag{31}$$

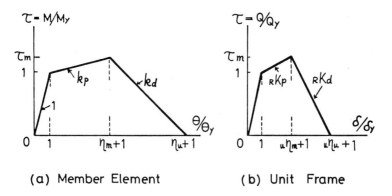

(a) Member Element   (b) Unit Frame

Fig. 8 Shear-deformation relationship

(b) When a particular story of a multistory building deforms farther into the negative slope region in Fig. 9(b), the hysteretic plastic deformation will be concentrated in this weakened story and the residual plastic deformation accumulates in one direction after buckling. A series of dynamic response analyses were carried out to assess this behavior (Kato, 1978d). The occurrence of local buckling at a particular story of a multistory building was assumed. The yield shear Q_y was evaluated with which the cumulative plastic deformation response reached point F in the figure in a given earthquake. Then the restoring force characteristic was replaced by the elastic-perfectly plastic relationship with identical yield shear capacity at this particular story, and the dynamically equivalent cumulative plastic deformation was evaluated by applying the same earthquake to this replaced system. The result of this study is illustrated in Fig. 9(b); let the equivalent plastic deformation be $AU = \eta_{eq}$, the incremental ductility ratio $\Delta\eta$ can be defined by the critical reduction g, which is independent of the negative stiffness k_d/u, and g is defined for the first story since, for practical design, evaluation of g is necessary only for the first story (Kato, 1981):

$$g = \frac{3 + a}{1 + a}, \quad a = \frac{\sum\limits_{i}^{N} s_i \bar{d_i}^{12}}{s_1 \bar{d_1}^{12}} \tag{32}$$

in which s_i = energy distribution ratio at i[th] story relating to the distribution of mass, spring constant, and yield shear coefficient of the structure;

N = the number of stories of the structure; and

d_i = coefficient at i[th] story reflecting the inevitable discrepancy between the optimum and actual yield shear coefficient distribution.

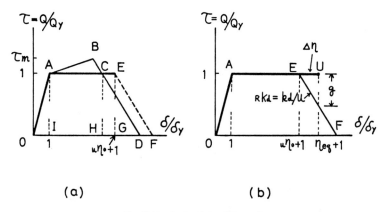

Fig. 9 Equivalent ductility ratio

Then the equivalent ductility ratio η_{eq} is expressed as

$$\eta_{eq} = u\eta_0 + \Delta\eta = u(\eta_0 + g/|k_d|)$$
$$= u\left[\frac{\tau_m^2 - 1}{2}\left(\frac{1}{k_p} + \frac{1}{|k_d|} + \frac{g}{|k_d|}\right)\right] \tag{33}$$

FRAME DUCTILITY RATIO FOR DESIGN USE

The frame ductility ratio given by Eq. 33 is rather conservative, since the plastic deformation of only one member element (columns or beams) is considered. To give a more realistic relationship that is feasible for practical design, Eq. 33 was modified by the AIJ committee for steel structures in the following manner:

(a) The parameters u, g, and k_d were evaluated for the practical variation of properties of steel buildings, and the following values were adopted as the safe-side estimation:

$$u = \frac{1}{3} \quad \text{and} \quad \frac{ug}{|k_d|} = 2 \tag{34}$$

At this step, Eq. 33 is reduced as

$$\eta_{eq} = \frac{1}{3}\eta_0 + 2 \tag{35}$$

(b) A series of repeated and reversed loading tests on column-to-beam sub-assemblages and on moment frame models were carried out up to the average deformation level of point C in Fig. 9(a), and it was demonstrated that more than one-third of the structure's plastic work was carried by the joint-panels at this limited deformation amplitude (Naka, 1981).

Since η_0 in Eq. 35 represents the nondimensional plastic work of the whole structure under the assumption that only one member element deforms plastically, the above information indicates that the actual plastic work required for that member element η_0' should be

$$\eta_0' = \frac{2}{3}\eta_0 \quad \text{or} \quad \eta_0 = \frac{3}{2}\eta_0' \tag{36}$$

and introducing this η_0 into Eq. 35,

$$\eta_{eq} = \frac{1}{2}\eta_0' + 2 \tag{37}$$

Removing the prime, the modified relation is

$$\eta_{eq} = \frac{1}{2}\eta_0 + 2 \tag{38}$$

Note that the deformation of the cited tests did not go far enough to the negative slope region, and the second term of the right-hand side of Eq. 35 was not considered in this assessment.

(c) Furthermore, considering the apparent increase of deformability resulting from the Baushinger's effect that appears in hysteretic loading, the first term of the right-hand side of Eq. 38 was multiplied by 4/3 and eventually Eq. 39 was recommended as a practical formula to relate the frame ductility ratio to the member ductility ratio.

$$\eta_{eq} = \frac{2}{3}\eta_0 + 2 \tag{39}$$

Member ductility ratio η_0 can be evaluated by Eq. 31.

SUMMARY AND CONCLUSIONS

To assess structural safety against the severest credible earthquake, the critical deformation capacity of steel moment frames subject to buckling was evaluated.

The principal conclusions of this study are as follows:

(a) Based on a large number of test results, the moment-rotation relationships of structural members subject to bending with and without axial compression were formulated in nondimensional forms up to their collapse stage. They are given by Eqs. 1 through 21.

(b) The steel moment frame was simplified into the unit frame, and the shear force-deformation relationship of the unit frame was related to the moment-rotation relationship of the member element under the assumption that only one member element of the unit frame contributes to the plastic deformation.

(c) The shear force-deformation relationship of the unit frame thus obtained was replaced by a dynamically equivalent elastic-perfectly plastic relationship, and the critical ductility ratio of the unit frame was evaluated in terms of the member ductility ratio, as shown in Eq. 33 or Eq. 39. This critical ductility ratio of the unit frame is directly applicable to the ultimate limit-state design for earthquake.

A = sectional area
A_w = area of web
B = outside width of square hollow-section
b = half-width of flange or inside width of square hollow-section
D = diameter of circular hollow-section
d = inside depth of web plate of H-section
$G = E/2\,(1 + \nu)$ = shear modulus
$\overline{K}$ = mean stiffness of member element of unit frame
$_r\overline{K}$ = mean stiffness of unit frame
k_p, k_d = stiffness ratios of members in plastic region
M_y = full plastic moment of member
$\overline{M}_y$ = mean yield moment of member element of unit frame
p = axial stress ratio
Q_y = yield shear capacity of unit frame
t, t_f, t_w = thickness of plate elements of section
V = effective volume of joint-panel
Z_p, Z'_p = plastic section modulus
ϵ_y = yield strain of material
$_i\eta$ = ductility ratio of member element
$_r\eta$ = ductility ratio of unit frame
η_0 = equivalent ductility ratio of member element
η_{eq} = equivalent critical ductility ratio of unit frame
θ_y = elastic rotation of member end at $M = M_y$
λ_y, λ = slenderness ratio
τ_0, τ_m = maximum strength index

CONDENSED REFERENCES/BIBLIOGRAPHY

The following is a condensed bibliography for this article. It includes all articles referred to or cited in the text. The full citations will be found at the end of the volume, with additional citations for further reading. What is given here should be sufficient information to lead the reader to the correct article: the author, date, and title. In case of multiple authors, only the first name is listed.

Fukuchi 1969, *Flange Buckling and Ultimate Load of Beams under Moment Gradient, Trans. of the AIJ*

Inowe 1972, *Cyclic Behavior of H-Section Members Subject to Combined Bending*

Kato 1973a, *Local Buckling Strength of Circular Hollow-Section Members, Trans. of the AIJ No. 204*
Kato 1973b, *Theoretical Prediction of the Load-Deflection Relationship of Steel Members and Frames*
Kato 1973c, *Strength and Deformation of H-Section Members*
Kato 1976, *Post Buckling Behavior of H-Section Beams*
Kato 1977, *Deformation Characteristics of H-Shaped Members Subject to Buckling*
Kato 1978a, *Safety Assessment of Steel Building Structures Against Most Severe Earthquake*

Kato 1978b, *Seismic Design of Multi-Story Steel Buildings*
Kato 1978c, *Deformation Characteristics of Box-Shaped Members Shaped to Buckling*
Kato 1978d, *Damage Distribution Law of Shear Type Multi-Story Structures under Earthquake*
Kato 1981, *Seismic Design of Steel Buildings*

Lukey 1969, *Rotation Capacity of Beams under Moment Gradient*

Naka 1981, *Contribution of the Restoring Force Characteristics of Steel Beam-to-Column Connections*

Suzuki 1974, *Flange Buckling Strength of H-Section Stub-Columns*

This paper appeared as Preprint 81-100, presented at the ASCE Convention, New York, New York, May 11–15, 1981.

Design Curves for Centrally Loaded Columns in Limit-States Design

Gerald W. Schulz

INTRODUCTION

The centrally loaded, hinged column is probably the most exhaustively investigated case in stability theory. Sufficient theoretical and experimental studies are available for a proper assessment of the column strength. As a result, the development and international acceptance of a uniform design approach would have been expected, particularly if the comparative simplicity of the problem and its obvious solution are considered.

However, if present design practice is compared on a worldwide basis, significant differences still exist. This situation can only be explained by the role that design curves for centrally loaded columns have in the entire design concept.

In a design concept, column curves not only serve as design curves for hinged members, but they can also be used as reference curves for the design of other structural members and of systems. This second application is different for design concepts based on bifurcation theory or for those based on ultimate strength theory.

This paper describes the influence that the present gradual change from allowable-stress design to limit-states design has on column-design philosophy. The application of column curves in a limit states design concept is shown, and present design practice in Europe, the United States, and Japan is reviewed.

THEORETICAL BASES OF DESIGN METHODS

For a realistic assessment of the strength of axially loaded members, present design rules use essentially the two concepts shown in Fig. 1: the tangent modulus concept, which considers the ideally straight bar and therefore can account for a realistic material behavior only; and the more general ultimate strength concept, which is based on an imperfect bar with an initial out-of-straightness and material inhomogeneities.

The tangent modulus method has to be seen as part of a design concept where stability is treated as a bifurcation problem. Through this approach, the design of structural members and systems can be related to the column strength curve of a hinged, ideally straight column by using the effective length method. The lack of accuracy of this analytical model with regard to actual structural behavior is covered through an adequate safety factor. This approach is still used in a number of countries, mainly in the context of allowable-stress design concepts.

The second approach mentioned above, the ultimate strength analysis of imperfect structural members, is the commonly accepted basis of recent research and subsequent code revisions. It is consistent with the requirements

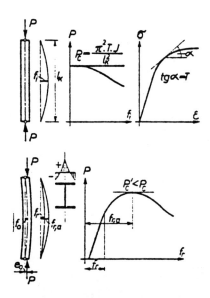

Fig. 1 Tangent modulus and ultimate strength models for column analysis

of the probabilistic safety concepts used in limit-states design, which imply that the analytical model has to recognize realistic assumptions for both material behavior and geometrical properties. Stability is then considered as a problem of divergence of equilibrium and is treated as an inelastic second-order analysis of initially deformed members or systems.

MULTIPLE COLUMN DESIGN CURVES

Based on the ultimate strength concept and considering the imperfect bar as the theoretical model, column-design curves were developed that account for the individual load carrying capacity resulting from column shape and manufacturing processes. Early investigations date back to Karman (1910), Chwalla (1934), and Jezek (1937). In these early studies main emphasis was given to a realistic assessment of the geometrical imperfections, as initial out-of-straightness and eccentric load applications, while the material influence was approximated by a modified stress-strain law.

The closest analytical simulation of the actual column behavior was achieved by recognizing, in addition to the geometrical imperfections, the influence of material inhomogeneities as residual stresses and yield stress scatter. On this basis Batterman and Johnston (1967), Marincek (1965), Young (1971), and Beer and Schultz (1969) investigated the influence of the various column strength parameters. Strating and Vos (1975), Bjorhovde (1972), and in recent times Hawranek (1978), and Fukumoto et al. (1976), extended the deterministic studies by introducing probabilistic principles in the ultimate strength analysis.

Based on a comprehensive program of theoretical and experimental studies (Beer and Schulz, 1970; Sfintesco, 1970), the European Convention for Constructional Steelwork (ECCS) in 1975 published design recommendations for axially loaded members (ECCS, 1975 and 1978). The strength of the most commonly used structural sections is related to the column curves shown in Fig. 2.

In the analytical model used for this ultimate strength determination, the geometrical imperfections are represented by an initial out-of-straightness with the shape of a sine curve and a bow of $l/1000$ at midspan. As shown in the ECCS document (1976), this assumption covers the effects of the main deviations from the ideal geometrical form caused in actual columns through industrial fabrication. These are effects that result from departures in longitudinal direction from the ideal straight axis, as well as effects of eccentric load transfer because of dimensional variations of the cross sections. By taking into account as material imperfections the residual stresses typical for the different cross-sectional shapes and manufacturing procedures, the assignment of the various profiles to the column curves was developed, as indicated in the selection chart of Fig. 3. Distinction is made between steel grades Fe 360 to

Fe 510 and high strength steel with a yield point of 430 N/mm² and above. The more favorable allocation of the high strength steel shapes in the nondimensional column curve system of Figs. 2 and 3 accounts for the beneficial effect of the higher yield point on the residual stress influence on column strength (ECCS, 1976).

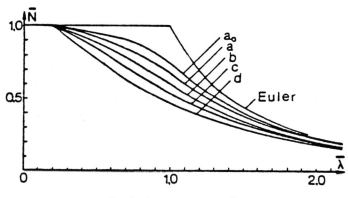

Fig. 2 ECCS column curves

SHAPE OF SECTION	Steel Fe 360, 430,510		Steel σ ≥430 N mm⁻²	
	Column Curve	Yield Stress Reduction	Column Curve	Yield Stress Reduction
rolled tubes / welded tubes (hot finshd.)	a	1.0	a	1.0
	a	0.94	a	0.94
welded	b	0.94	a	0.90
rolled about x-x h/b > 1.2	a	1.0	a	1.0
h/b ≤ 1.2	b	1.0		
about y-y h/b > 1.2	b	1.0	b	1.0
h/b ≤ 1.2	c	1.0		
welded about x-x flame-cut fl.	b	0.94	a	0.90
rolled fl.	b	0.94	a	0.90
about y-y flame-cut fl.	b	0.94	a	0.90
rolled fl.	c	0.94	b	0.90

about x-x	b	0.94	a	0.90	
about y-y	a	0.94	a	0.90	
heat treated	a	1.0	a⁰	1.0	
heat treated about x-x	a	1.0	a⁰	1.0	
about y-y	b	1.0	a	1.0	
	c	1.0			
	c	1.0			

Fig. 3 ECCS column curve selection table

The theoretical investigations of ECCS were accompanied by an extensive experimental program (Sfintesco, 1970). Figure 4 shows, as an example, the statistically evaluated tests for I sections and the corresponding design curve *b*. According to the ECCS safety concept, the characteristic strength of a structural member is defined as the mean value of the test results minus two times the standard deviation.

The concept of multiple column-design curves that led to the ECCS curves, was also the basis for a design proposal of the Structural Stability Research Council (SSRC), (Johnston, 1976a). Figure 5 shows the three design

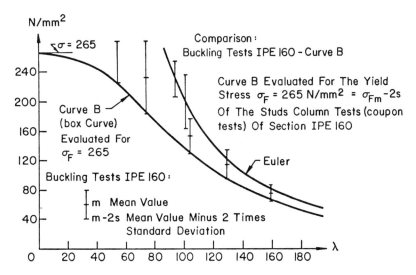

Fig. 4 **Comparison of test results for I sections** *(IPE 160)* **with the corresponding column-design curve *b*** *(ECCS, 1976)*

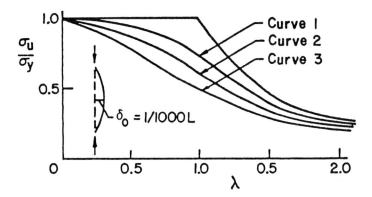

Fig. 5 SSRC column curves *(Johnston, 1976a)*

curves recommended by SSRC, which were selected as arithmetic-mean curves from a wide band of ultimate strength curves that represent different types of cross sections and fabrication processes.

The refined assessment of the column strength dependent on the shape of the cross section and the manufacturing processes, which is done in the multiple column curve approach, makes it necessary to continuously observe technological progress and to correct and update the selection charts. In particular, the role of cold-straightening is not yet properly recognized in the present column design philosophy. In the present concept, the analytical and experimental model for ultimate strength considerations is the column in its as-rolled or as-welded condition and the beneficial effects of cold-straightening are neglected. Frey (1969) and Alpsten (1975) have investigated the increase in column strength that can be expected from straightening procedures. Figure 6 compares theoretical and experimental results for as-rolled and straightened columns. The increase in column strength results mainly from a change of the pattern and a reduction of the magnitude of the compressive residual stresses. In particular, continuous roller-straightening, as used for small and medium sections, gives reliable results that could be utilized in design procedures (ECCS, 1976).

Modifications of column-design practice can also be expected when the theoretical basis of the column-design curves are adjusted to probabilistic concepts. In this area there is a study by Hawranek (1977) of the reliability level of the ECCS column curves. Figure 7 shows the failure probability as a function of the column slenderness for various I sections as related to the ECCS column curve b. The same is shown in comparison to the column curve of the old German code DIN 4114 (1952), which is being revised. Both column curves are derived on a deterministic basis. In the case of the ECCS curves, the deterministic approach results in a fairly constant failure probability over the entire slenderness range.

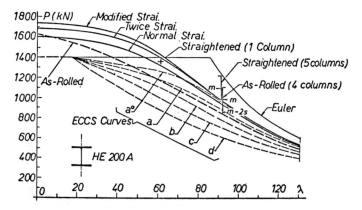

Fig. 6 Ultimate strength curves and test results for columns (I sections) in as-rolled condition and after straightening.

MULTIPLE COLUMN CURVES IN A
LIMIT-STATES DESIGN CONCEPT

The example used in this paper for a limit-states design concept is taken from the "Design Recommendations" of the ECCS (1975 and 1978).

The overall concept of the stability part of the "Recommendations" is reflected in the outline of the *Manual on Stability* (ECCS, 1976), as shown in Fig. 8: Part I of the manual contains general criteria for analysis and design; Part II deals with the design of members; and Part III deals with the design of systems, which are frames, triangulated structures, and shells.

In this concept the safety and suitability of a structure are checked taking into account ultimate and serviceability limit states. The design rules developed are based on the safety concept adopted by the ECCS, which is a semi-probabilistic level-I procedure. This safety concept implies that the structural analysis considers realistic assumptions for material behavior and geometrical properties. Consequently, the design rules given for members and systems are based on the imperfect structural system.

As mentioned before, the imperfections of a steel structure that are relevant for an ultimate strength analysis are deviations from the ideal geometrical form and material inhomogeneities such as residual stresses and scatter of the yield point. In the case of design rules for structural members, the effect of these imperfections is already recognized in the proposed design rules in the form of column curves or simple design formulae.

For the design of systems, analytical methods are proposed that consider the geometrically imperfect system. The material inhomogeneities are

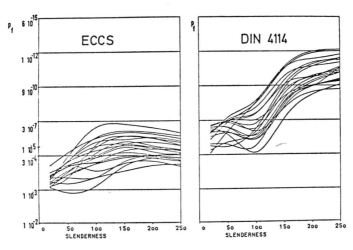

Fig. 7 Failure probability p_f of different I sections as related to the column-design curve *b*
(ECCS) **and to DIN 4114** *(1952)*

recognized by substituting their effect through an additional geometrical imperfection. For instance, in the case of unbraced frames, the analysis is based on a system with a total out-of-plumb of $h/200$ as shown in Fig. 8, and the load carrying capacity is determined by a second-order plastic hinge method.

In such a design concept, the column curves for centrally loaded members are used in various ways. If we consider first the design of members (Fig. 9), the column curves, of course, are used as immediate design curves for all kinds of hinged members: for the design of simple members according to the design chart shown in Fig. 3; for the design of built-up members (Uhlmann, 1977; Finzi, 1977), where the single chords are checked according to the column curves of Fig. 3; and for the design of composite columns, where the column strength is related by means of a modified slenderness ratio to the column curve corresponding to the encased steel section.

For the design of beam-columns, the column curves are used as reference curves. Interaction formulae of the general type shown in Fig. 9 are used as design equations for members in braced frames. In the case of unbraced frames, the overall stability of the structure has to be considered. It is checked by using a second-order plastic hinge method, but the interaction formula in a slightly modified version is used to avoid premature local instability.

In the interaction formula of Fig. 9, the axial load N is multiplied by a term e^*, which is derived from the column curve corresponding to the beam-column section under consideration. The term e^* was introduced to recognize the effects of the various imperfections on the load carrying capacity. Although the influence of imperfections is less important for the typical beam-column case, there remains an important loading range where comparatively high

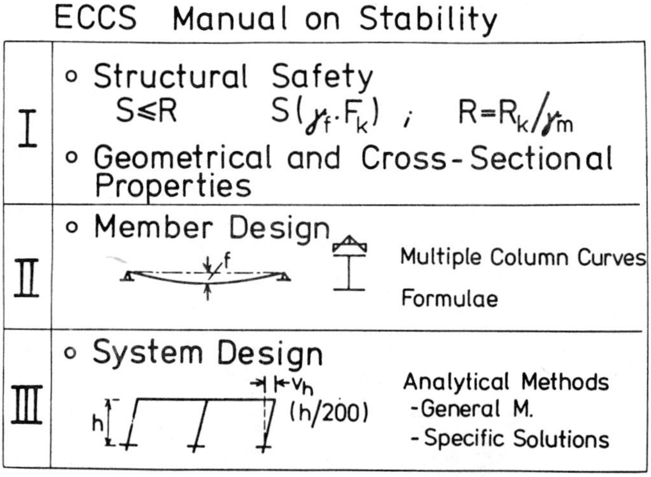

ECCS Manual on Stability

I	○ Structural Safety $\quad S \leq R \qquad S(\gamma_f \cdot F_k) \ ; \quad R = R_k/\gamma_m$ ○ Geometrical and Cross-Sectional Properties
II	○ Member Design Multiple Column Curves Formulae
III	○ System Design $(h/200)$ Analytical Methods -General M. - Specific Solutions

Fig. 8 The ECCS design concept

axial loads are combined with small moments and the influence of imperfections has to be recognized. By referring to the column curve for centrally compressed members through the e^* approach, this reasonably simple design procedure allows one to cover all loading cases quite economically with one formula.

A further, and actually the main, application for multiple column curves is the design of triangulated structures, such as trusses or transmission towers.

For trusses where each panel point is braced normally to the plane of the truss, the stability of the system can be assured by considering the member stability only. In this procedure, it is customary to idealize the members as hinged struts and to account for the eventual restraint supplied at the joints by introducing an effective length.

However, in real structures the members are connected by rigid joints, and the loads applied at the joints not only result in axial forces in the members, but can also cause quite significant bending stresses (Johnston and Dwight, 1976b; Dubas, 1977; Ville de Goyet, 1979). In the context of this paper, the following question shall be discussed: To what extent are results for effective length factors based on inelastic bifurcation theory, and meant for application in an allowable-stress design concept, still valid at ultimate load level?

When the actual conditions are simplified, the behavior of a member in a truss at ultimate load level will depend on the slenderness range, the stiffness ratio of the restraints, and the interaction of the axial forces present in the member with the bending moments caused by local deformation of the member and by global deformation of the truss. The presence of residual stresses, particularly in pronounced zones of compressive residual stresses (for instance at the joints), will lead to earlier plastification and subsequent increase of deformations. It seems obvious that the conventional bifurcation theory does not account for this behavior, and a cautious use of effective length factors derived on this basis seems appropriate.

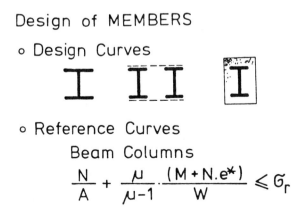

Fig. 9 Application of column curves as design and reference curves

This conclusion is supported by the investigations of Dubas (1977). As a consequence, for buckling in the plane of the truss, the new Swiss code SIA 161 (1979), which is based on limit-states design, allows a K-factor of 0.8 for web members and only $K = 0.9$ for chord members, as compared with $K = 0.8$ for all truss members in a previous edition of the code.

To achieve an economic truss design and to maintain a consistent level of structural safety at the same time, it seems best not only to emphasize the application of effective length factors, but also to make full use of the advantages of multiple column design curves.

DESIGN PROVISIONS IN NATIONAL CODES

The implementation in the various national codes of the new design principles for centrally loaded members has to be seen in the context of a gradual change of the entire design concept from allowable-stress design to limit-states design.

In Western Europe this transition is quite advanced and a number of national codes are presently under revision. However, in some countries, the ECCS multiple column curves have been applied in codes that are still based on allowable-stress design, as in Belgium (NBN 51-001, 1977) and Italy (CNR-UNI 10011, 1979). But the majority of Western European countries have included the ECCS column curves in the original form or in a modified version in their codes or present code revisions that are based on limit-states design:

Belgium	NBN 51-001	(Draft 1979)
France	Recommendations for Plastic Design (Curves *a* and *b* only)	(1975)
German F. R.	DIN 4114 (Simplified selection chart)	(1979)
Great Britain	BS 5400	(Draft 1979)
Switzerland	SIA 161 (Simplified selection chart)	(1979)
Norway	3472 A	(Draft 1979)
Yugoslavia	JUS UE 7081	(1978)

In Eastern Europe, the Council for Mutual Economic Assistance (CMEA) is developing common design recommendations that have adopted the ECCS multiple column curves (Dalban, 1977). Independent of this proposal, a number of countries, such as the Soviet Union (Bridge code), Czechoslovakia

(CSN 731401, 1976), German Democratic Republic (TGL 13503, 1972) and Hungary (MSZ 15024, 1975), use multiple column curves for the design of axially loaded members. The theoretical model is, in most cases, the column with an initial out-of-straightness, where the influence of residual stresses is expressed through an additional geometrical imperfection (SSRC et al., 1981).

In the United States, design criteria are developed by different standard-writing organizations and, in general, are based on allowable-stress design (Fig. 10). In all codes, column strength is related to only one column curve. AISC (Buildings, 1978) and AASHTO (Bridges, 1978) use the column curve originally proposed by the Column Research Council (now SSRC) in the first edition of its guide (1960) and based on tangent modulus theory. AREA codes (Bridges, 1978) use a straight line to approximate the tangent modulus curve in the inelastic range (SSRC et al., 1981). One reason for the continued use of the tangent modulus concept can certainly be seen in its consistent applicability to member and system design. As Galambos pointed out (SSRC et al., 1981) with the gradual transition of North American design practice to limit-states design, the adoption of ultimate strength column curves such as those proposed by the SSRC (Johnston, 1976a) and shown in Fig. 5 will certainly develop.

In Japan column design is based on the allowable-stress concept. The AIJ *Standards for Steel Structures* use a column curve based on tangent modulus theory. The JRA *Specifications for Highway Bridges* are based on an ultimate strength curve calculated for I sections, with weak axis buckling, and considering geometrical ($l/1000$) and material imperfections. The JSCE *Specifications for Steel Railway Bridges* use a straight line in the inelastic range that simulates the strength of columns with high residual stresses (SSRC et al., 1981).

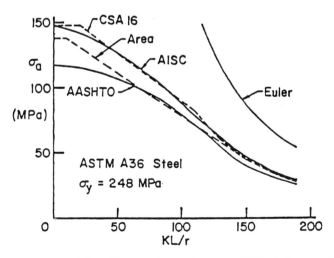

Fig. 10 Column curves (allowable stress) used in present U.S. design practice *(SSRC et al., 1981)*

CONCLUSIONS

In evaluating the role of multiple column curves in a design concept, one has to consider the present change to a new generation of design rules and codes.

In the "old" codes that mostly correspond to the theoretical findings of the first half of the 20th century, stability is treated as a bifurcation problem. The design of systems could thus be related to a column curve based on the tangent modulus concept. In these codes, the column curves, whether single or multiple, had a central role as reference curves and were regarded as a universal design tool.

In an ultimate strength concept, as that of ECCS, stability is considered as a problem of divergence of equilibrium and treated by inelastic second-order analysis of initially deformed systems. Here, the column curve is only one particular design tool among others and is meant for a particular design case.

In summarizing the results of available research and experiences with recent code revisions, there seems to be general agreement that the ultimate strength analysis of columns with geometrical and material imperfections is the proper basis for the development of design rules. There also seems to be broad agreement on the advantages of multiple column-design curves. Whether these principles are actually implemented in the various national codes depends not so much on the state of the art of column design itself as it does on the readiness of code-writing organizations to adopt similar principles for the design of other structural members and of systems.

CONDENSED REFERENCES/BIBLIOGRAPHY

The following is a condensed bibliography for this article. It includes all articles referred to or cited in the text. The full citations will be found at the end of the volume, with additional citations for further reading. What is given here should be sufficient information to lead the reader to the correct article: the author, date, and title. In case of multiple authors, only the first name is listed.

Alpsten 1975, *Residual Stresses, Yield Stress and Column Strength of Hot-rolled and Roller-*

Battermann 1967, *Behavior and Maximum Strength of Metal Columns*
Beer 1969, *The Maximum Strength of Axially Loaded columns with Imperfections*
Beer 1970, *The Theoretical Basis of the New Column Curves of the European Convention for*
Bjorhovde 1972, *Deterministic and Probabilistic Approaches to the Strength of Steel Columns*

Chwalla 1934, *Theory of Compressed Steel Members*

Dalban 1977, *Remarks on the ECCS Recommendations and on the Draft of the CMEA Specifications*
Dubas 1977, *Ultimate Strength of Laterally Braced Trusses*
Dwight 1971, *Comparison of European and British Column Curves*

ECCS 1975 and 1978, *European Recommendations for Steel Structures*
ECCS 1976, *Manual on the Stability of Steel Structures*

Finzi 1977, *Built-up Members, General Report Conclusions*
Frey 1969, *Effect of Cold-straightening on the Strength of Rolled Wide-Flange Shapes*
Fukumoto 1976, *Evaluation of Column Curves Based on Probabilistic Concept*

Hawranek 1977, *Reliability Calibration for Steel Columns*
Hawranek 1978, *Optimization of Strength Computations, Particularly for the Ultimate Strength of*

Jezek 1937, *Stability of Compressed Steel Members*
Johnston 1976a, *Guide to Stability Design Criteria for Metal Structures*
Johnston 1976b, *Study of Struts in Welded Steel Trusses*

Karman 1910, *Investigations on Column Strength*

Marincek 1976, *Ultimate Strength of Metallic Columns*

Sfintesco 1970, *Experimental Basis of the European Column Curves*
SSRC-ECCS-CRA-CMEA 1981, *Stability of Metal Structures, A World View*
Strating 1975, *Computer Simulation of the ECCS Buckling Curve Using a Monte-Carlo Method*

Uhlmann 1977, *Some Problems Concerning Design Recommendation for Centrally Compressed*

Ville de Goyet 1979, *Contributions to the Ultimate Strength Analysis of Trusses*

Young 1971, *Axially Loaded Steel Columns*

A Simple Method of Overall Stability Analysis For Multistory Buildings

R. Shankar Nair

INTRODUCTION

Accurate linear analysis with a digital computer is, nowadays, a standard part of the structural design process for multistory buildings. Several computational techniques and computer programs are available to the designer for this purpose. In general, the results of the linear analysis will include the lateral displacements caused by lateral loadings (such as wind). As explained in this paper, these results from the linear analysis can be used to obtain a very good estimate of overall lateral stability effects in the building. The proposed technique, which is very simple and straightforward and requires no additional computer analysis, is sufficiently accurate for use in the final design of most multistory buildings.

DEVELOPMENT OF PROCEDURE

The proposed method of analysis takes advantage of the fact that most multistory buildings have lateral load-displacement characterstics that are similar to those of either a "flexural cantilever" or a "shear cantilever."

In this context, a flexural cantilever is defined as a structure in which the curvature of the longitudinal (vertical) axis of the structure is proportional to the bending moment on the cross section of the structure. A shear cantilever is a structure in which the slope of the longitudinal axis is proportional to the shear force on the cross section of the structure. In either case, the constant of proportionality (flexural stiffness or shear stiffness) may vary over the height of the structure.

FLEXURAL CANTILEVER

Buildings with braced frames or shear walls and very tall buildings with unbraced frames (in which lateral displacement is caused primarily by column shortening and column elongation) usually have lateral load-deformation characteristics that approach those of a flexural cantilever.

For a flexural cantilever of height H and constant stiffness EI, the uniformly distributed vertical load, p_c per unit height, that will cause lateral buckling is given by the equation

$$p_c = 7.84 \, EI/H^3 \qquad (1)$$

If the stiffness of the cantilever varies with height in accordance with the equation, $EI = (a/H) \, EI_0$, where EI_0 is the stiffness at the base and a is the distance from the top, the critical load is given by

$$p_c = 5.78 \, EI_0/H^3 \qquad (2)$$

If the stiffness varies with the equation $EI = (a/H)^2 EI_0$, the critical load is

$$p_c = 3.67 \, EI_0/H^3 \qquad (3)$$

These equations for critical load (Eqs. 1, 2 and 3) can be found in basic texts on elastic stability.

If a uniformly distributed lateral load of f per unit height is applied on cantilevers with each of the three stiffness configurations described above, the lateral displacement Δ at the top of the three structures is given by the following:

$$\text{For constant } EI: \quad \Delta = 0.125 \, fH^4/EI \qquad (4)$$

$$\text{For } EI = (a/H)EI_0: \quad \Delta = 0.167 \, fH^4/EI_0 \qquad (5)$$

$$\text{For } EI = (a/H)^2 EI_0: \quad \Delta = 0.250 \, fH^4/EI_0 \qquad (6)$$

By combining Eqs. 1, 2 and 3 with Eqs. 4, 5 and 6, respectively, EI can be eliminated and p_c can be expressed in terms of f/Δ, as follows:

For constant EI: $p_c = 0.98\,fH/\Delta$ \hfill (7)

For $EI = (a/H)EI_0$: $p_c = 0.96\,fH/\Delta$ \hfill (8)

For $EI = (a/H)^2 EI_0$: $p_c = 0.92\,fH/\Delta$ \hfill (9)

Equations 7, 8 and 9 cover the range from constant stiffness to a more extreme stiffness variation than is normal in real multistory buildings. It is obvious that the relationship between p_c and f/Δ is not very sensitive to stiffness variations over the height of the structure. Regardless of the distribution of stiffness, the following equation is sufficiently accurate for purposes of design:

$$p_c = 0.95\,fH/\Delta \hfill (10)$$

Thus, if the lateral displacement caused by lateral loading is known, the critical load for lateral buckling can be accurately and easily estimated using Eq. 10. (See Fig. 1 for a definition of symbols and a summary of the procedures).

ANALYSIS AND DESIGN PROCEDURE

The following procedure is suggested for the overall stability analysis and design of buildings that approach the behavior of flexural cantilevers.

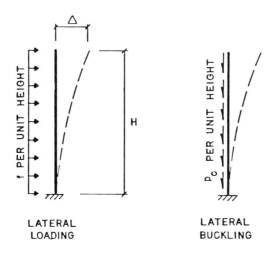

$$p_C = 0.95\ fH/\Delta$$

Fig. 1 Lateral loading and buckling of flexural cantilever

1. Analyze the structure for wind loading (or other lateral loading). Denote the lateral deflection of the top of the building as Δ. If the wind load is uniform, denote the wind load per unit height as f. If it is not uniform, define f as the uniform lateral load that would produce the same base moment as the wind loading used in the analysis. Let H be the total height of the building.

2. Compute the critical load per unit height p_c from Eq. 10, above.

3. Compute the magnification factor μ, as follows:

$$\mu = \frac{1}{1 - \dfrac{\gamma p}{\phi p_c}} \tag{11}$$

where p is the actual average vertical load per unit height on the building, γ is the load factor, and ϕ is the strength reduction factor. (*Note:* p must include the load on *all* vertical members, including those that are not part of the lateral load-resisting system. Thus, p is the total vertical load on the entire building divided by the height H.)

4. For design of structural members, multiply all lateral load effects (that is, all moments, shears, and axial forces caused by lateral loading) by the factor μ. If gravity loads cause lateral displacement of the building, the "sidesway" component of the moments and forces due to the gravity loading should also be magnified by the factor μ.

5. Design structural members for the magnified forces and moments, with all floors assumed to be restrained against lateral displacement (or "braced against sidesway").

In the procedure outlined above, no distinction has been made between the effects of moment on the overall building and the effects of shear on the overall building. (The effects of moment include axial forces in columns, moments in independent shear walls, and moments and axial forces in coupled shear walls. The effects of shear include shear forces in shear walls, axial forces in bracing diagonals, and moments and shear forces in beams and columns.) The magnification factor computed in step 3, above, is strictly applicable only to the effects of moment on the overall structure. Application of the same factor to the shear effects represents an approximation.

SHEAR CANTILEVER

Buildings of low or moderate height with unbraced framed (in which column shortening and column elongation do not contribute significantly to lateral displacement) usually have lateral load-displacement characteristics similar to those of a shear cantilever.

If a portion of a vertical shear cantilever undergoes lateral deformation δ over height h when subjected to a shear force V, the critical vertical load for lateral buckling of that portion of the cantilever is given by

$$P_c = Vh/\delta \tag{12}$$

Equation 12 is also applicable, as an approximation, to framed structures (as opposed to theoretical shear cantilevers). When Eq. 12 is applied to a story of a building, h is the story height, δ is the lateral deformation of the story caused by a shear force of V in the story, and P_c is the total vertical force that would cause lateral buckling of the story (see Fig. 2).

The accuracy of Eq. 12, when applied to a story of a framed structure, depends on the relative stiffness of beams and columns and on the way in which gravity loads are distributed among the columns in the story. The source of error in Eq. 12 is the nonlinearity of the stiffness matrix of individual columns in the story; the flexural stiffness of each column is influenced by the vertical load on the column. If most of the vertical load in the story is in columns that are not part of the lateral load-resisting frame, Eq. 12 will be very nearly exact, since the flexural stiffness of these columns has no influence on the lateral stiffness or stability of the structure. If most of the vertical load is in the lateral load-resisting frame, the error in Eq. 12 can be between 0% and about 20%, depending on the relative stiffness of beams and columns. (The error is greatest for stiff beams and slender columns).

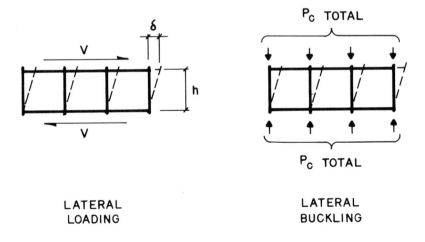

$$P_c = Vh/\delta$$

Fig. 2 Lateral loading and buckling of story in shear-cantilever type building

ANALYSIS AND DESIGN PROCEDURE

The following procedure is suggested for lateral stability analysis and design of buildings that approach the behavior of shear cantilevers. Note that since lateral buckling of this type of structure is largely a one-story phenomenon, the magnification factor must be computed specifically for the particular story that is being considered; it may be different in different stories.

1. Analyze the structure under wind loading (or other lateral loading).

2. For the story being considered

   h = height of story;

   V = total horizonal shear in story due to loading used in step 1; and

   δ = lateral deformation of story (from the results of step 1).

3. Compute the critical load P_c for the story from Eq. 12.

4. Compute the magnification factor μ for the story:

$$\mu = \frac{1}{1 - \dfrac{\gamma P}{\phi P_c}} \tag{13}$$

   where P is the actual total vertical force in the story, γ is the load factor, and ϕ is the strength reduction factor.

5. Apply the magnification factor μ to the moments and shears produced in beams and columns by lateral loading. If gravity loads cause lateral displacement of floors in the building, the sidesway component of moments and shears due to gravity loading should also be magnified by the factor μ.

6. Design the members for the magnified forces and moments, with floors assumed to be restrained against lateral displacment (or braced against sidesway).

Note that in step 5 above, the magnification factor is applied only to the effects of shear on the building. (These effects are moments and shears in beams and columns.) Lateral stability effects will also cause some magnification of the column axial forces produced by lateral loading. This effect is usually unimportant in a shear-cantilever type of structure and can usually be neglected. Alternatively (as a conservative approximation, in most cases) the μ factor computed using Eq. 13 can be applied to all lateral load effects in the story, including column axial forced caused by lateral load.

TORSIONAL STABILITY

The techniques that have been developed for planar stability analysis can easily be extended to allow analysis of torsional stability. In this case, torsional displacements indicated by linear analysis under torsional loading are used to obtain estimates of critical loads for torsional buckling.

If a multistory building's torsional stiffness is provided by braced frames, shear walls, or tall unbraced frames (in which lateral displacement are caused primarily by column length changes), and if these stiffening elements are *not* arranged in the form of a closed tube, the building will have torsion-rotation characteristics that are similar to the lateral load-displacement characteristics of a flexural cantilever. The formula for torsional buckling of such a building (analogous to Eq. 10) is as follows:

$$r^2 p_c = 0.95 \, tH/\theta \tag{14}$$

in which t is an applied torsional load, per unit height, on the building; θ is the rotation of the top of the building, in radians, caused by load t; H is the height of the building; p_c is the critical vertical load, per unit height, for torsional buckling of the building; and r is the polar radius of gyration of the vertical loading, about the vertical axis of the building.

For a doubly symmetrical structure with uniform loading on rectangular floors of plan dimensions a and b:

$$r^2 = (a^2 + b^2)/12 \tag{15}$$

If a building's torsional stiffness is provided by unbraced frames in which lateral displacements are caused primarily by "shear wracking" deformations, or if the stiffening elements of the building are arranged in the form of a closed tube, the building will have torsion-rotation characteristics that are similar to the lateral load-displacement characteristics of a shear cantilever. The formula for torsional buckling of a particular story of such a building (analogous to Eq. 12) is as follows:

$$r^2 P_c = Th/\theta \tag{16}$$

in which T is an applied torsional load on the story; θ is the torsional deformation of the story, in radians, due to torque T; h is the height of the story; P_c is the critical load for torsional buckling of the story; and r is the polar radius of gyration of the vertical load.

With critical loads for torsional buckling computed using Eq. 14 or 16, as appropriate, the magnification factor concept can be used for design.

EXAMPLES

Figure 3 shows six 20-story buildings on which complete and rigorous stability analyses and large-deformation lateral-load analyses have been performed. The methods of analysis and selected results from the analyses are described in Nair (1975). These buildings have also been analyzed using the simple methods of stability analysis proposed in the present paper. Agreement between the simple and rigorous analyses has been found to be excellent, as illustrated below for north-south loading of buildings V and VI from Fig.3.

BUILDING V (BRACED FRAMES)

A linear analysis was performed on this structure under a wind load of 25 psf on the south face (which is 138 ft wide). The resulting displacement at the top of the building was 0.729 ft. The critical load can now be determined from Eq. 10 as follows:

$$H = 240 \text{ ft} \tag{17}$$

$$f = 0.025 \,(138) = 3.45 \text{ k/ft} \tag{18}$$

$$\Delta = 0.729 \text{ ft} \tag{19}$$

$$p_c = 0.95 \,(3.45)(240)/0.729 = 1079 \text{ k/ft} \tag{20}$$

This critical load of 1,079 kips per foot corresponds to 12,948 kips per floor or 1,360 psf on each floor. The actual gravity load on this building was taken as 130 psf on each floor. The corresponding magnification factor (computed without load factors or strength reduction factors) is as follows:

$$\mu = 1/(1 - 130/1360) = 1.106 \tag{21}$$

and the magnified lateral displacement at the roof is given by:

$$\mu \Delta = 1.106(0.729) = 0.806 \text{ ft} \tag{22}$$

The rigorous stability analysis of this building indicated a critical load for north-south buckling of 1,369 psf on each floor (compare with 1,360 psf from the simple analysis). The complete large-deformation analysis under combined gravity load and north-south wind loading indicated a roof displacement of 0.805 ft (compare with 0.806 ft from the simple analysis).

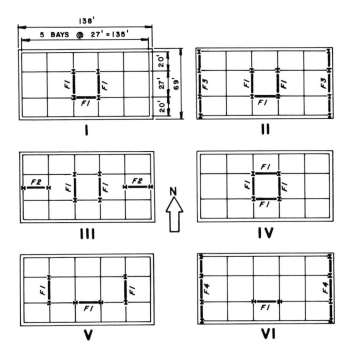

PLAN OF BUILDINGS

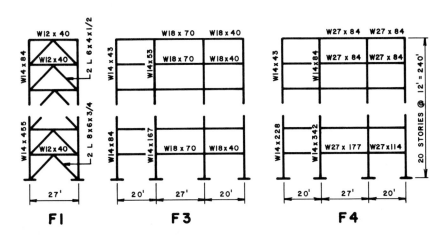

ELEVATION OF FRAMES

Fig. 3 Buildings analyzed in Nair *(1975).*

BUILDING VI (UNBRACED FRAMES)

The behavior of this building, in the north-south direction, can be expected to be closer to that of a shear cantilever than to that of a flexural cantilever. Since instability of a shear cantilever is essentially a local or one-story phenomenon, critical loads and magnification factors must be computed separately for each story. The 5th, 10th, and 15th stories will be considered in the discussion that follows.

A linear analysis was peformed on the building under a wind force of 25 psf on the south face. The resulting story deformations (relative lateral displacement of floors at the top and bottom of the story) were 0.0522 ft, 0.0609 ft, and 0.0582 ft in the 15th, 10th, and 5th stories, respectively. The corresponding shear forces in these stories were 228 kips, 435 kips, and 642 kips. Each story is 12 ft high. Critical loads for lateral buckling of these stories can be determined from Eq. 12, as follows:

$$\text{15th story: } P_c = 228(12)/0.0522 = \ \ 52{,}414 \text{ kips} \tag{23}$$

$$\text{10th story: } P_c = 435(12)/0.0609 = \ \ 85{,}714 \text{ kips} \tag{24}$$

$$\text{5th story: } P_c = 642(12)/0.0582 = 132{,}371 \text{ kips} \tag{25}$$

The actual gravity load was taken as 130 psf on each floor. The corresponding total vertical force in the 15th, 10th, and 5th stories is 7,427 kips, 13,616 kips, and 19,806 kips, respectively. The magnification factors (computed without load factors or strength reduction factors) are as follows:

$$\text{15th story: } \mu = 1/(1 - 7{,}427/52{,}414) = 1.165 \tag{26}$$

$$\text{10th story: } \mu = 1/(1 - 13{,}616/85{,}714) = 1.189 \tag{27}$$

$$\text{5th story: } \mu = 1/(1 - 19{,}806/132{,}371) = 1.176 \tag{28}$$

and the magnified lateral story deformations are as follows:

$$\text{15th story: } \mu\delta = 1.165(0.0522) = 0.0608 \text{ ft} \tag{29}$$

$$\text{10th story: } \mu\delta = 1.189(0.0609) = 0.0724 \text{ ft} \tag{30}$$

$$\text{5th story: } \mu\delta = 1.176(0.0582) = 0.0684 \text{ ft} \tag{31}$$

The complete large-deformation analysis of this building under combined gravity load and north-south wind loading indicated story deformation of 0.0607 ft, 0.0723 ft, and 0.0686 ft in the 15th, 10th, and 5th stories, respectively.

SUMMARY AND CONCLUSIONS

Procedures have been developed for the inclusion of overall lateral stability effects in the design of multistory buildings. These procedures, which are very simple to use, are applicable to the framing systems of most high- and medium-rise buildings. The accuracy of the proposed techniques has been demonstrated by comparing the results yielded by these procedures with the results of complete and rigorous stability and large-deformation analyses.

CONDENSED REFERENCES/BIBLIOGRAPHY

The following is a condensed bibliography for this article. It includes all articles referred to or cited in the text. The full citations will be found at the end of the volume, with additional citations for further reading. What is given here should be sufficient information to lead the reader to the correct article: the author, date, and title. In case of multiple authors, only the first name is listed.

Nair 1975, *Overall Elastic Stability of Multistory Buildings*

Presented at the 1981 SSRC Technical Meeting, April 7, 1981, Chicago, Ill., *SSRC 1981 Annual Proceedings*, Structural Stability Research Council, Bethlehem, Pa., pp. 78–87.

P-Δ Effect in Frame Design

Francois Cheong-Siat-Moy

COLUMN INTERACTION EQUATIONS

The American Institute of Steel Construction (AISC) specification provides the following interaction equation for proportioning slender columns by the load resistance factor design (LRFD) approach:

$$\frac{P}{P_{cr}} + \frac{C_m M}{(1 - \frac{P}{P_e})M_m} \leq 1.0 \tag{1}$$

in which the critical axial load, P_{cr}, and the Euler load, P_e, are based on the effective column length factor K, and $C_m = 0.85$ for sway frames. AISC (1978) defines the other symbols used. When using the above equation, K-values are generally obtained from the alignment chart.

Studies have shown that the AISC interaction equation can be unsafe in many cases, particularly when the P-Δ effect is large, such as when it originates from the axial loads on columns pinned at both ends (Cheong-Siat-Moy and Downs, 1980). To overcome this deficiency, it has been suggested that Eq. 1 be modified. LeMessurier proposed that C_m be made equal to 1.0 and that a more exact K-value be determined (LeMessurier, 1977):

$$K^2 = \frac{I_i \pi^2}{P_i} \frac{\Sigma P + \Sigma(C_L P)}{\Sigma \theta I_i} \tag{2}$$

An equation not involving the C_m term was also postulated:

$$\frac{P}{P_{uk}} + A_F \frac{M}{M_m} \leq 1.0 \qquad (3)$$

in which the K-factor is obtained by Eq. 2, and A_F is an amplification factor equal to the ratio of elastic second-order deflection to first-order deflection. Equation 3 suggests that the second-order bending moment be evaluated directly rather than empirically by means of the C_m-factor.

A comparative study has been made between Eq. 3 and "exact" computer solutions that take into account the P-Δ effect and yielding of the column cross section. It has been found that Eq. 3 agrees well with the computer solutions when the P-Δ effect is small. It becomes over conservative when the P-Δ effect is large (see Fig. 1). Design examples have shown that in the latter case, a larger column section always results (Chen and Cheong-Siat-Moy, 1980).

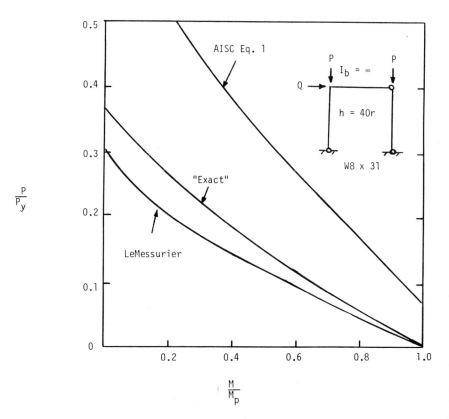

Fig. 1 Comparison of interaction formulas

Attempts have also been made to derive column interaction equations that do not rely on the K-factor. For the combined load case, not including gravity moments, Cheong-Siat-Moy derived Eq. 4 by curve fitting the "exact" computer interaction charts (Cheong-Siat-Moy and Downs, 1980).

$$\frac{P}{P_{ul}} + \beta A_F \frac{M}{M_m} \leq 1.0 \tag{4}$$

in which P_{ul} = critical axial load based on $K = 1.0$
  A_F = amplification factor = ratio of second-order deflection to first-order deflection

$$\beta = 0.9 + 0.1\, A_F \quad \text{when } A_f \leq 4.5 \tag{5a}$$
$$\beta = 1.2 + A_{F/30} \quad \text{when } A_F > 4.5 \tag{5b}$$

DEFLECTIONS

When applying Eq. 1, there is no need to evaluate the second-order deflections in the structure since first-order moments M are used. Consequently, it suggests that it is unnecessary to include deflection calculations when using the LRFD approach. When using Eq. 4, however, an explicit determination of the second-order deflections is generally required for defining A_F. Such a scheme proves to be very valuable in LRFD since deflections rather than strength may often govern the design. Simple cases of beam-columns are used to illustrate this fact. In Fig. 2, it is seen that at the ultimate load, deflections are small and strength will control the design. However, in Fig. 3, the deflections in the column are extremely large, making any strength design meaningless. In fact, for the case shown in Fig. 3, the deflection at working loads ($P = 18$ kips, $Q = 0.65$ kip) is 6.5 inches.

GRAVITY LOADING

It was stated in Cheong-Siat-Moy and Downs (1980) that Eq. 4 is not applicable to gravity loading. However, study shows that Eq. 4 can be successfully applied to gravity loading if a story eccentricity equal to 1/500 of story height ($h/500$) is assumed to exist. Very good results have been obtained using this approach, which ensures that the moment M in Eq. 4 is never equal to zero. Table 1 shows a comparison of the results obtained by Eq. 3 and 4. The structures used are shown in Figs. 4 and 5. To illustrate the calculations involved, an example is given below. A simple frame in which the P-Δ effect is excessively large is chosen to demonstrate the accuracy of Eq. 4 (see Fig. 5).

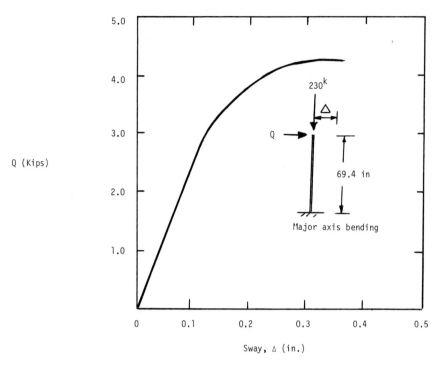

Fig. 2 Small deflections at ultimate load

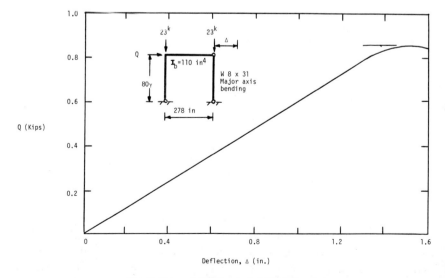

Fig. 3 Large deflections at ultimate load

LeMessurier's Approach—K-Factor (Fig. 5)

Given $h = 74.4$ inches, find P_{cr}. Use A36 and W8×67.
Solution: From LeMessurier (1977),

$K = 3.72$

$\dfrac{Kh}{r} = 74.4$

$Fa = 16.0$

$P_{uk} = 1.7\,AF_a = 1.7 \times 19.7 \times 16 = 536$ kips

Cheong-Siat-Moy's Approach (Fig. 5)

Try $P_{cr} = 525$

$\dfrac{h}{r} = \dfrac{74.4}{3.72} = 20$

$F_a = 20.6$

$P_{ul} = 1.7AF_a = 1.7 \times 19.7 \times 20.6 = 690$ kips

$h\sqrt{\dfrac{P_{cr}}{EI}} = 0.162$

Stability function $s = 3.95$

Due to P_{cr}, reduced intertia $I_e = \dfrac{3.95}{4} \times 272 = 268.6$

Alternative form of amplification factor:

$$A_F = \frac{1}{1 - \dfrac{\Sigma P}{sh}} = \frac{1}{1 - \dfrac{\Sigma Ph^2}{3EI_e}}$$

where $s = \dfrac{3EI_e}{h^3} =$ stiffness of structure

$$A_F = \frac{1}{1 - \dfrac{4 \times 252 \times 74.4^2}{3 \times 29{,}000 \times 268.6}} = 2$$

$\beta = 0.9 + 0.1\,A_F = 1.1$

$M = \Sigma P\Delta = (4 \times 525)\dfrac{h}{500} = 312.5$ k-in

$\dfrac{P_{cr}}{P_{ul}} + \beta A_F \dfrac{M}{M_p} = \dfrac{525}{690} + 1.1 \times 2 \times \dfrac{312.5}{2{,}527} = 1.03$

Solution $\quad P_{cr} = 525$ kips

Difference from LeMessurier's Approach $= 2\%$

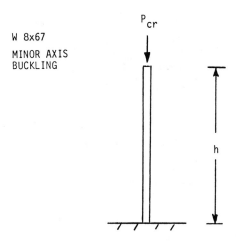

Fig. 4 Determination of critical load—minor axis

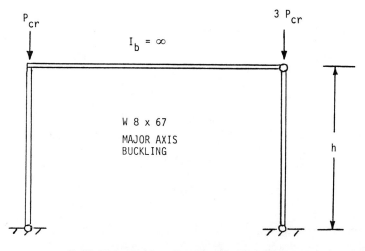

Fig. 5 Determination of critical load—major axis

APPENDIX—SYMBOLS

A_F = amplification factor = ratio of second-order to first-order deflections
C_L = coefficient accounting for the reduction in column stiffness resulting from the presence of axial loads
I_i = moment of inertia of column, i
K = effective column length factor
M = applied moment
M_m = maximum moment that can be resisted by a member in the absence of axial loads
P = applied axial load
P_{cr} = maximum column strength based on K-factor from alignment chart
P_e = Euler buckling load
P_i = axial load on column, i
P_{uk} = maximum column stength based on K-factor of Eq. 2
P_{ul} = maximum column strength based on $K = 1.0$
ΣP = total gravity load on the story
β = function of A_F, Eq. 5
Δ = lateral story deflection

CONDENSED REFERENCES/BIBLIOGRAPHY

The following is a condensed bibliography for this article. It includes all articles referred to or cited in the text. The full citations will be found

Table 1 Critical loads

	Critical axial loads, P_{cr}		
	Frame in Fig. 4—minor axis		
h (in)	Eq. 3 (kips)	Eq. 4 (kips)	Difference %
42.4	643	643	0
84.8	514	525	2
127.2	344	340	1
212	140[a]	140	0
	Frame in Fig. 5—major axis		
74.4	536	525	2
148.8	226	210	7
186	145	142	2

[a]Euler load

at the end of the volume, with additional citations for further reading. What is given here should be sufficient information to lead the reader to the correct article: the author, date, and title. In case of multiple authors, only the first name is listed.

AISC 1978, *Specification for the Design, Fabrication and Erection of Structural Steel for Buildings*
Chen 1980, *Limit States Design of Steel Beam-Columns*
Cheong-Siat-Moy 1980, *New Interaction Equations for Steel Beam-Columns*
LeMessurier 1977, *A Practical Method of Second-Order Analysis, Part-2 Rigid Frames*

Analysis of Precast Concrete Cladding on Tall Buildings

Barry J. Goodno

In the past, designers of tall buildings have accorded little attention to the exterior facade, which is usually treated as nonstructural, despite the fact that cladding may account for 10–20% of the structure's initial cost. The spate of failures of claddings to perform as intended in recent years has focused new attention on the building curtain wall and has forced designers to acknowledge that the facade may not be completely nonstructural, as they had assumed. Rather, the cladding must form a first line of defense for the structure against wind and sonic boom pressures, blowing-missile impact in windstorms, solar thermal loadings, and lateral frame motions caused by wind and earthquake loadings.

Although rarely considered fully in the design process, cladding generally fulfills a dual role: (1) it protects the structure from the environemnt and transfers the resultant reaction forces back to the supporting frame; and (2) it interacts with the primary structure, thereby providing additional lateral stiffness to resist low-level motions. Lightweight claddings, such as those made of glass and light metal or plastic panels, which have been the subject of extensive research, are generally limited to providing a protective facade for the structure. Heavy claddings of precast concrete, brick, and granite, however, are capable of fulfilling both roles and can augment structural stiffness to a considerable degree.

491

The economic advantages of using cladding panels as lateral stiffening elements in high-rise building construction have been pointed out by several investigators, but the actual use of panels as components that intentionally aid in drift control is quite rare. PCI (1977), in fact, recommends that connections for precast concrete cladding panels employ slots and oversize holes to allow for movement to protect brittle facade elements. However, these recommendations are not always followed, in that slots are used for alignment only and, once panels are in place, connection bolts are tack-welded to the connection clip angle. Even in cases where sliding connections are installed properly, connection deterioration with time may negate the intended isolation function.

Results of recent analytical research (Goodno et al., 1980; Goodno and Palsson, 1981) have shown that the stiffness and energy-absorption capacity of heavy claddings can alter the dynamic properties and response of tall buildings substantially. However, before the potential advantages of claddings can be utilized effectively, the forces introduced into panels and connections by lateral frame distortions must be determined for use in design. In addition, practical upper limits for the lateral stiffness contribution of curtain walls need to be established and provided for in the detailing of both panels and connections. A shortage of experimental data on cladding performance, coupled with the wide variety of cladding designs in use in modern structures, greatly complicates the establishment of rational engineering design procedures for cladding.

As a case study, the influence of heavily contoured precast concrete panels (Fig. 1) on the lateral stiffness of a 24-story steel frame office building of core

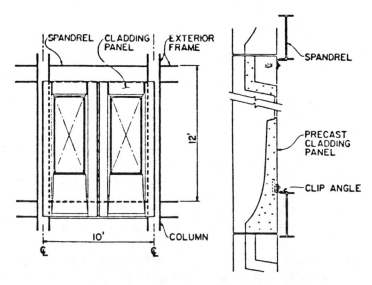

Fig. 1 Typical exterior bay of precast concrete cladding

construction (Fig. 2) was investigated. Finite element models of the structure, the cladding (Fig. 3), and the cladding connections were developed to analytically represent all components contributing stiffness to the structure. The effect of the cladding on the dynamic properties of the structure was studied by varying the cladding panel and connection stiffnesses and by comparing calculated vibration frequencies to measured values from ambient and forced vibration experiments. The translational responses of the model to moderate earthquake ground motions, with and without cladding stiffening effects, were compared. Cladding was found to be particularly effective in altering building torsional frequencies and response; so displacement levels resulting both from accidental eccentricity between centers of mass and rigidity and from partial cladding failure were studied for specified earthquake ground motions. The principal findings are summarized below, but the references should be consulted for further details.

CLADDING MODEL

The cladding panels are highly contoured precast concrete with light reinforcing steel and wire mesh imbedded to prevent cracking. The majority of the panels are 3.7 m (12 ft) high by 1.5 m (5 ft) wide and 0.5 m (1.5 ft) deep with a window cutout measuring 2 m by 0.8 m (6¾ ft by 2¾ ft). There are two panels per bay and each panel is bolted in four places to clip angles that are welded to spandrels in the lightweight exterior frame supporting the curtain wall (Fig. 1).

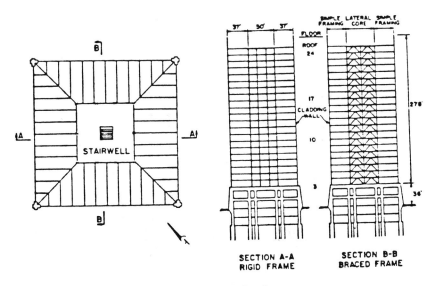

Fig. 2 Structural framing

Initially, the lateral stiffness of the row of cladding panels and connections between story levels was represented by a shear stiffness parameter V, and the entire curtain wall was modeled as a tridiagonal stiffness matrix. Parameter V was adjusted in steps until analytical frequencies for the entire structure matched measured values (Table 1) for the lower modes; V values in the range of 1.1×10^5 kN/m (625 kips/in) to 1.4×10^5 kN/m (800 kips/in) yielded the best match for the composite and noncomposite floor slab models, respectively. Later finite element studies (Will et al., 1979) employing the panel and clip angle model of Fig. 3 revealed that this V value was reasonable but also heavily dependent on the connection details of the cladding to the structure (Table 2).

For cladding-failure studies (Goodno and Palsson, 1981), the simplified cladding stiffness model in Fig. 4 was assumed, in the absence of experimental data. In this model, parameter V is reduced in steps when allowable story-drift level Δ is exceeded on any structure face at any story during a time history dynamic analysis. The allowable drift Δ was taken to be 0.005 times the story height h as specified by the 1979 Uniform Building Code (ICBO, 1979). Beyond 3Δ, all story cladding on the structure face under consideration was considered to have failed, leaving $V = 0$ for that story face. Reverse cycle deflections follow lines of constant slope in Fig. 4.

Two structure models were used for torsional response studies. In the first, the eccentric model, the code-specified 5% accidental eccentricity between centers of mass and rigidity (Fig. 5) was used, and unclad (that is, $V = 0$) and clad model responses were compared to investigate the effectiveness of cladding in altering torsional displacement response to ground motion. In the second, the symmetric model, centers of mass and ridigity were nearly

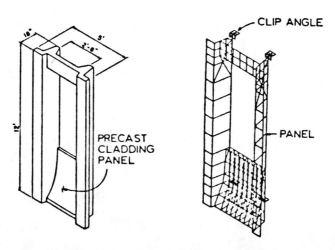

Fig. 3 Finite element model of cladding panel and connections

coincident, as in the actual structure, and cladding failure (described by Fig. 4) was taken to be the source of building torsional response. In the step-by-step dynamic analysis, the state of the cladding at each story on each face was monitored at each time step for horizontal ground motion inputs in the braced and rigid frame directions of the structure. The results are summarized below.

Table 1 Comparison of experimental and analytical frequencies for the symmetric model with composite properties

		Vibraton frequencies, in hertz				
		Analytical			Experimental[c]	
Direction	Mode	Without cladding[a]	With cladding[b]	Percent increase	Ambient	Forced
(1)	(2)	(3)	(4)	(5)	(6)	(7)
Braced	1	0.34	0.40	18	0.40	0.41
frame	2	1.10	1.26	15	1.30	1.30
	3	2.12	2.35	11	2.38	2.35
Rigid	1	0.26	0.34	31	0.31	0.32
frame	2	0.75	1.00	33	0.95	0.96
	3	1.39	1.78	28	1.67	1.66
Torsion	1	0.26	0.41	58	0.42	0.41
	2	0.71	1.17	65	1.24	1.23
	3	1.28	2.00	56	2.14	2.09

[a]Interstory shear stiffness $V = 0$
[b]$V = 1.1 \times 10^5$ kN/m (625 kips/in)
[c]Structure with cladding (average of three tests)

Table 2 Description and results of finite element analyses

Model[a]	Interstory shear stiffness, V in kN/m (kips/in)	
	Case A[b]	Case B[c]
(1)	(2)	(3)
I	1.3×10^5 (741)	$.92 \times 10^5$ (526)
II	$.87 \times 10^5$ (497)	$.63 \times 10^5$ (362)
III	$.64 \times 10^5$ (367)	$.07 \times 10^5$ (41)

[a] I—clip angle and bolt not included.
   II—clip angle and bolt included; clip angle welded on three sides to spandrel.
   III—same as II except clip angle welded on far edge only.
[b]No relative vertical motion permitted between cladding and connection at top of cladding.
[c]Relative vertical motion permitted.

DYNAMIC RESPONSE STUDIES

   The response of the structure model was determined for a number of different model and cladding states and for several different ground motions to study cladding influence on dynamic response. Initially, the linear symmetric model, with 5% modal damping and with floor member properties approaching the noncomposite case, was considered in its clad [$V = 1.3 \times 10^5$ kN/m (725 kips/in)] and unclad ($V = 0$) states. Roof displacement responses in

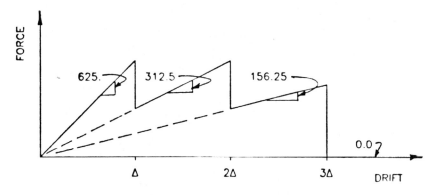

Fig. 4 Cladding-failure model

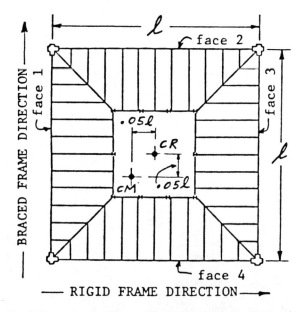

Fig. 5 Floor plan and face numbering for the eccentric model

the braced and rigid frame directions of the building (see Fig. 2) are displayed in Fig. 6 for the 1940 Imperial Valley earthquake (SOOE component) applied separately in each direction. Floor-displacement-response envelopes for both the 1940 Imperial Valley and 1952 Kern County earthquakes are compared in Fig. 7. In both cases, the braced-direction response is virtually the same for

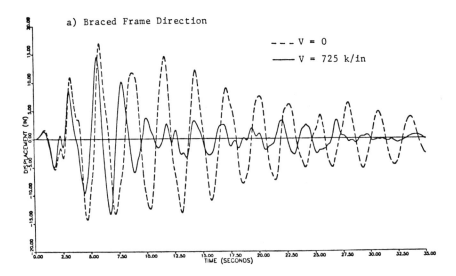

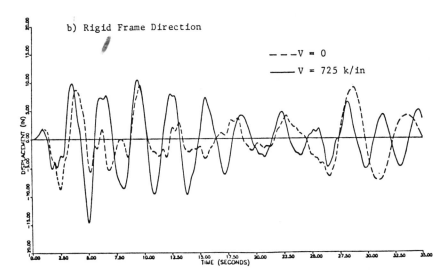

Fig. 6 Roof displacement-time histories for clad (V=725) and unclad (V=0) structures for May 18, 1940, Imperial Valley Earthquake (SOOE component)

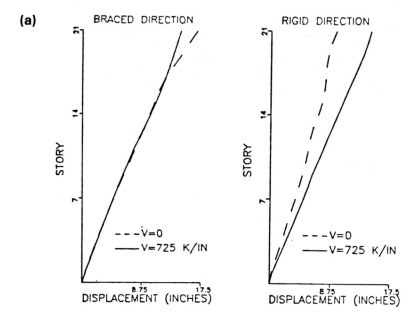

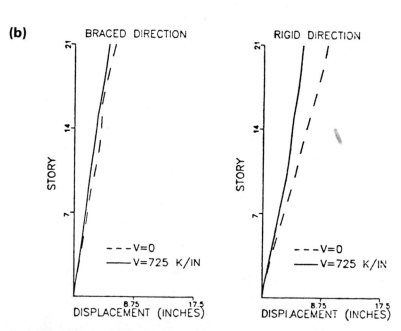

Fig. 7 Floor-displacement-response envelopes

    (a) Floor-displacement-response envelopes for May 18, 1940, Imperial Valley earthquake (SOOE component)

    (b) Floor-displacement-response envelopes for July 21, 1952, Kern County earthquake (S69E component)

the clad and the unclad states, but in the rigid direction the presence of the cladding alters structure frequencies appreciably. This leads to increased rigid-direction response for the structure model with cladding in the Imperial Valley case (Fig. 7a) and to decreased response in the Kern County case (Fig. 7b). The increase or decrease in responses results from the relationship between structure frequencies for the clad model and the frequency content of the ground motions. This response difference suggests that it may not always be conservative to neglect the stiffening effects of heavy claddings.

The influence of cladding on torsional response was studied by comparing the undamped response of the symmetric and the eccentric (Fig. 5) structure models to the first 10 seconds of the N65E component of the 1966 Parkfield, California earthquake (Fig. 8). Composite floor member properties were used resulting in $V = 1.1 \times 10^5$ kN/m (625 kips/in) for the clad structure. For cladding-failure studies employing the progressive failure model in Fig. 4, three allowable interstory-drift (Δ) conditions were considered: (1) $\Delta = 0$ (that is, all cladding fails and $V = 0$); (2) $\Delta = 0.005$ times an average story height of 3.6 m (12 ft) (that is, $\Delta = 18$ mm or 0.72 in), resulting in partial failure of cladding elements as the response progresses; and (3) $\Delta = $ infinity (that is, no cladding fails and $V = 625$). Peak displacement-response values are tabulated in Table 3 for both rigid- and braced-direction inputs, and peak interstory-drift values for each structure face (see Fig. 5) are listed in Table 4. For the eccentric model, the successive states of failure for building face 4 for ground motion input in the rigid frame direction are shown in Fig. 9. In general, the peak response values in Tables 3 and 4 decrease with increasing allowable drift (Δ) but, in several instances, the reverse is true. For example, for ground motion applied in the rigid direction, the braced-direction

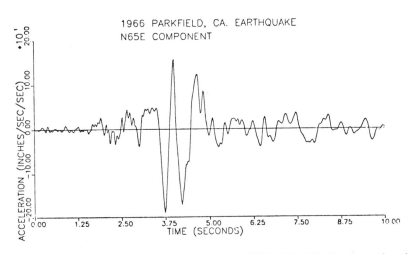

Fig. 8 First 10 seconds of the N65E component of the 1966 Parkfield, California, earthquake

Table 3 Peak displacement response at roof

Model (1)	Cladding state (2)	Peak roof response for ground motion input in braced frame direction		
		Rigid response (in) (3)	Braced response (in) (4)	Torsion response (rad) (5)
Symmetric	Unclad[a]	0.7	28.3	3.4×10^{-4}
	Clad[b]	0.5	27.7	3.6×10^{-4}
Eccentric	Unclad	5.2	27.0	0.017
	PCF[c]	4.4	28.0	0.021
	Clad	7.0	26.3	0.025
Symmetric with partial failure	PCF[d]	0.7	29.1	4.4×10^{-4}

[a] Without cladding ($V = 0$)
[b] No cladding failure ($V = 625$)
[c] Partial cladding failure ($\Delta = 18$ mm, 0.72 in)
[d] Initial state of cladding is shown in Fig. 11.

Table 4 Peak interstory drift values

Model (1)	Cladding state (2)	Peak relative interstory drift (in) for ground motion input in braced frame direction			
		Face 1[e] (3)	Face 2 (4)	Face 3 (5)	Face 4 (6)
Symmetric	Unclad[a]	2.2 (16)[d]	0.09 (24)	2.2 (16)	0.08 (24)
	Clad[b]	2.0 (20)	0.06 (19)	2.0 (20)	0.07 (17)
Eccentric	Unclad	1.9 (18)	1.4 (22)	3.0 (16)	0.9 (19)
	PCF[c]	2.2 (17)	1.4 (16)	2.6 (4)	1.1 (7)
	Clad	2.0 (4)	1.8 (18)	2.3 (20)	1.1 (4)
Symmetric with partial failure	PCF[f]	2.3 (17)	0.2 (7)	2.5 (16)	0.2 (19)

[a] Without cladding ($V = 0$)
[b] No cladding failure ($V = 625$)
[c] Partial cladding failure
[d] Story at which peak drift occurred is shown in brackets.
[e] See Fig. 5.
[f] Initial state of cladding is shown in Fig. 10.

Table 3 Peak displacement response at roof (continued)

Model (1)	Cladding state (2)	Peak roof response for ground motion input in rigid frame direction		
		Rigid response (in) (3)	Braced response (in) (4)	Torsion response (rad) (5)
Symmetric	Unclad[a]	37.1	0.7	0.29×10^{-4}
	Clad[b]	27.0	0.5	0.08×10^{-4}
Eccentric	Unclad	31.4	2.9	0.025
	PCF[c]	26.6	3.6	0.017
	Clad	25.0	5.2	0.015
Symmetric with partial failure	PCF[d]	28.5	0.3	2.8×10^{-4}

[a]Without cladding ($V = 0$)
[b]No cladding failure ($V = 625$)
[c]Partial cladding failure ($\Delta = 18$ mm, 0.72 in)
[d]Initial state of cladding is shown in Fig. 10.

Table 4 Peak interstory drift values (continued)

Model (1)	Cladding state (2)	Peak relative interstory drift (in) for ground motion input in rigid frame direction			
		Face 1[e] (3)	Face 2 (4)	Face 3 (5)	Face 4 (6)
Symmetric	Unclad[a]	0.05 (24)[d]	6.4 (24)	0.05 (24)	6.4 (24)
	Clad[b]	0.04 (11)	2.6 (22)	0.04 (11)	2.6 (22)
Eccentric	Unclad	2.8 (22)	6.3 (24)	2.5 (22)	4.3 (24)
	PCF[c]	1.3 (23)	2.7 (22)	1.2 (22)	3.9 (22)
	Clad	1.0 (1)	1.9 (22)	1.0 (11)	2.9 (22)
Symmetric with partial failure	PCF[f]	0.2 (18)	4.0 (24)	0.2 (18)	4.0 (24)

[a]Without cladding ($V = 0$)
[b]No cladding failure ($V = 625$)
[c]Partial cladding failure
[d]Story at which peak drift occurred is shown in brackets.
[e]See Fig. 5.
[f]Initial state of cladding is shown in Fig. 10.

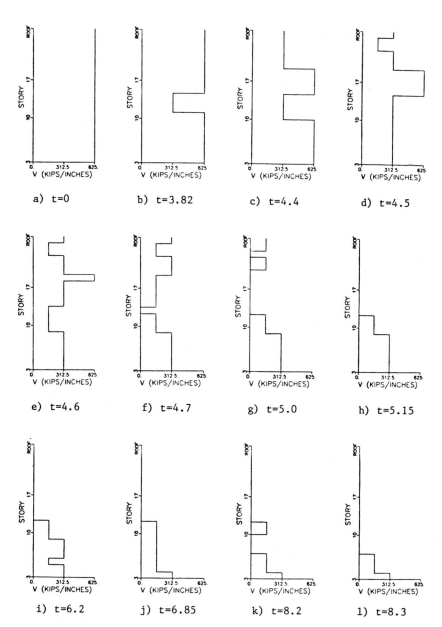

Fig. 9 Progressive failure of cladding on face 4 for ground motion in rigid direction (time *t* in seconds)

roof-response values are larger for the clad than for the unclad or partially clad structures. From Table 4, peak drift values occur in lower stories in the braced direction and in upper stories in the rigid direction.

As a final case, partial cladding failure was imposed on the symmetric model containing no eccentricity between centers of mass and rigidity. Prior structure motion or poor construction practice was assumed to be the reason for the initial failure states shown in Figs. 10 and 11. After 10 seconds of the Parkfield ground motion input, peak translational and drift responses (see Tables 3 and 4) are only slightly greater than values for the fully clad symmetric model. However, rotational response is amplied tenfold by partial cladding failure, even in the absence of imposed accidental eccentricity, as listed in Table 3 and plotted in Fig. 12. Figures 10 and 11 also display the final cladding states in both structure directions.

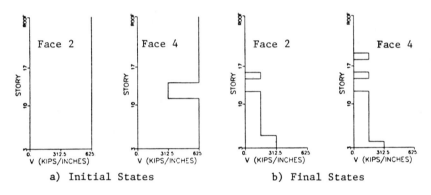

Fig. 10   Initial and final states of cladding for rigid-direction input: symmetric model

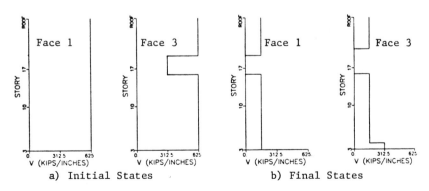

Fig. 11   Initial and final states of cladding for braced-direction input: symmetrical model

CONCLUSIONS

Reported failures of curtain walls in modern high-rise buildings suggest that cladding components are participating structural elements despite design assumptions to the contrary. The results reported above for a heavy precast cladding on a steel frame structure demonstrate that cladding can alter structure frequencies and peak drift and displacement responses appreciably and that it may not always be conservative to neglect cladding-structure interaction effects. When story drifts exceed a certain threshold, cladding stiffness effects are likely to be substantially reduced. In the event of partial cladding failure at different story levels on opposite faces of the structure, the deleterious effects of torsion would be introduced. In the case study discussed above, cladding had a considerable influence on torsional frequencies, and the consequences of progressive curtain wall failure for rotational response of the structure may be significant.

The cladding model used in these studies involves the use of a tridiagonal-stiffness-matrix representation of the panel-connection assembly. This simple model has been found to yield results that are consistent with those obtained by using a finite element model of the panel and clip angle attachments. However, earlier finite element studies have shown that cladding lateral stiffness is highly dependent on the connection details between the panel and the exterior frame. Cyclic laboratory tests of a full-scale panel with a variety of connection conditions are needed to verify analytical predictions and to define the actual hysteretic behavior of the assembly. This information can then form the basis for an improved degrading stiffness model of the cladding to be used in place of the piecewise-linear model introduced here. Such a model would permit follow-up studies of cladding-structure interaction

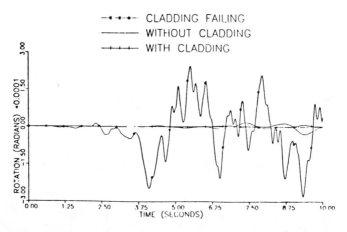

Fig. 12 Roof rotational response, symmetrical case, for 1966 Parkfield Earthquake acting in rigid direction

in which panel degradation occurs at different stories. This interaction would be described on the basis of test data and its influence on building torsional response determined. Ultimately, a more accurate description of heavyweight cladding performance in modern high-rise buildings will lead both to a better understanding of the forces experienced by panels and connections and to development of rational procedures for their aseismic design.

ACKNOWLEDGMENTS

The contributions of Drs. J. I. Craig and K. M. Will and of graduate research assistants H. Palsson, M. Meyyappa, K. Gram, G. Sherwood, G. Saurer, P. LeBoeuf, D. Pless, R. Roglin, M. Ansley, and J. Hopkins to the research work summarized here are gratefully acknowledged. Support for this work was provided in part by the National Science Foundation through grants ENG73-04216 and ENV77-04269.

CONDENSED REFERENCES/BIBLIOGRAPHY

The following is a condensed bibliography for this article. It includes all articles referred to or cited in the text. The full citations will be found at the end of the volume, with additional citations for further reading. What is given here should be sufficient information to lead the reader to the correct article: the author, date, and title. In case of multiple authors, only the first name is listed.

Anicic 1980, *Experiments on Non-Structural Partition Walls Exposed to Seismic Forces*

Beason 1978, *Response of Window Glass to Wind Loads*
Bouwkamp 1960, *Drift Limitations Imposed by Glass*
Bowles 1962, *The Strength and Deflection Characteristics of Large Rectangular Glass Panels under*

Craig 1975, *Wind Pressure Simulation and Response Measurements for Windows*
Craig 1978, *Window and Curtain Performance in Highrise Buildings*
Craig 1981, *Response Measurements for Glass Cladding Panels*

Deo 1978, *Full Scale Measurements of Cladding Pressure*
Deo 1978, *Wind Load Casuality for Dynamic Response of Windows*

Gjelsvik 1973, *Interaction Between Frames and Precast Panel Walls*
Glogau 1977, *Damage Control in New Zealand Public Buildings Through Separation of*
Goodno 1978, *Dynamic Analysis of a Highrise Building Including Cladding—Structure*
Goodno 1978, *Response of Glass Cladding in Highrise Buildings*
Goodno 1979, *Analysis of Cladding on Tall Buildings*
Goodno 1979, *Glass Curtain Wall Elements: Properties and Behavior*
Goodno 1979, *Response Studies of Glass Cladding Panels*
Goodno 1980, *Effect of Cladding on Building Response to Moderate Ground Motion*
Goodno 1981, *Torsional Response of Partially-Clad Structures*
Goldberg 1977, *Provisions for Seismic Design of Nonstructural Building Components and Systems*

ICBO 1979, *Uniform Building Code*

Khan 1967, *Optimum Design of Glass in Buildings*

McCue 1975, *Building Enclosure and Finish Systems: Their Interaction with the Primary Structure*
Minor 1975, *Window Glass Failures in Windstorms*

Oppenheim 1973, *Dynamic Behavior of Tall Buildings with Cladding*

PCI 1977, *PCI Manual for Structural Design of Architectural Precast Concrete*

Robertson 1967, *Glass Design and Code Implications for Extremely Tall Buildings*
Robertson 1974, *Wind Engineering of Tall Buildings*

Sack 1981, *Seismic Behavior of Precast Curtain Walls in High-Rise Buildings*
Sharpe 1972, *Seismic Design of Nonstructural Elements*

Weidlinger 1973, *Shear Field Panel Bracing*
Will 1979, *Dynamic Analysis of Buildings with Precast Cladding*

Notes on Fatigue and Fracture

William H. Munse

Since publication of the Monograph, the Committee on Fatigue and Fracture has assisted in providing guidance for the implementation of their information into codes and specifications. Suggestions have been made to include in such documents precautionary statements concerning the following: the care that should be exercised to protect against lamellar tearing; the need for designers to be aware of the possibility of brittle fracture in buildings with exposed steel members; and the desirability of considering high-cycle fatigue under wind loadings (particularly for the fastenings of cladding in buildings) and low-cycle fatigue where severe earthquake loadings are a possibility.

Introduction

R. F. Lorenz

Current progress in the design of connections in tall steel buildings is being accelerated by many and divergent demands. In all cases, there is an increased interest in the performance of the steel connection, particularly where potential improvements in materials and methods suggest long-reaching economic benefits for steel structures of all types.

Although current studies include investigations on relatively unrelated and diverse connection types, the need for such research usually can be related to the following three basic categories of benefits:

Category I: Improvements in basic connection theory, including effects on structural stability.

Category II: Improvements in the understanding of the performance of specific known types of connections.

Category III: Improvements in connection economics.

The paper by Chen that follows is a noteworthy contribution to category I. This paper verifies from existing test results that "real" columns with some minimum end restraint have measurable improvements in their stability in the nonsway mode. Parallel work in England, at the University of Sheffield, draws similar conclusions and extends the study to include end plate connections.

Other research and studies on steel connections, although not reported in detail here, can be mentioned. A particular development in category I research is the work on semirigid connection theory. Separate studies by Delft University of Technology in the Netherlands and the University of Colorado and the University of Maine at Orono in the United States essentially examine the development of moment-rotation behavior of semirigid beam-column connections. Any forthcoming general design recommendations will give the structural engineer a clearer direction in optimizing framing in steel buildings of modest height.

Category II studies now underway include investigations of coped beam connections, large bracing connections, and beam-to-column web moment connections.

Coped beam connections have already been identified in the AISC (1978) specification as requiring an additional design check for "block shear" in the detailing of connection material near the beam cope. Limited laboratory investigation by Birkemoe and Yura have established conservative design rules, but there still is the need for information about web stability near the cope, as well as any effects on LTB performance. These studies are currently underway at the University of Texas.

Large bracing connections are significant in the tall building and play an important role in its structural performance. As architectural demands have increased the size of these connections, the interplay of the connection parts (framing angles, gusset plates, connectors, and so on) is unknown. It is believed that new studies initiated at the University of Arizona will explain the behavior of these components and make suggestions for meaningful design criteria.

Although moment connections to the weak axia of columns offer no unusual design problem, experimental data has shown that some arrangements can result in low-ductility performance where certain restraint conditions prevail. A study is now underway at Lehigh Univeristy to develop criteria for satisfactory connection details to the column web to provide a reliable design model.

The quest for more economical, but predictable, performance from accepted connection types is continuing in category III research. These studies include examinations of end plate connections, single plate framing connections, column base plate design, and weld repair criteria.

End plate connections to beams are limited to sizes that are dependent on the capacity of the four adjacent fasteners. Initial studies have begun at the University of Oklahoma to investigate the response of stiffened end plates to extend the capacity of this connector type. A corollary study on the effect of end plates on the column compression zone is also continuing.

The economics of shop-welded single shear plates to support field-bolted floor beams has been demonstrated in recent tall building projects. The essential design parameters have been publicized in the research recommendations emanating from the University of Arizona. Further economies have been shown to be possible by extending the work to include the A307 bolt, and this information should be available shortly.

Another general area of proposed reserch includes searching for a more rational criteria for the design of column base plates. The design method historically described in the AISC (1980) *Manual of Steel Construction* is quite conservative, and a more realistic prescription should result in reduced costs for this type of connection.

There seem to be reasonable data to conclude that in many instances, the repair of welds may induce reductions in material performance that exceed those caused by the alleged defect. A new important study sponsored by AISC will be undertaken by the British Welding Institute to investigate the significance of repair work on discontinuities in welds and plain material. Since material repair in such instances can run into prohibitive costs, and even litigation, this study would provide evidence of more reasonable limitations or tolerances in such defects. Such work would provide designers and inspectors with much stronger guidelines as to when repair initiative should be mandated.

It can be expected that steel connection research, as indicated by the broad spectra of these ongoing studies, will eventually arrive at more realistic answers to many conservative and unsubstantiated notions about the role of connections. Particularly in tall buildings, we can expect that research will continue to provide new guidelines to the designer for steel connections that will perform both reliably and economically.

CONDENSED REFERENCES/BIBLIOGRAPHY

The following is a condensed bibliography for this article. It includes all articles referred to or cited in the text. The full citations will be found at the end of the volume, with additional citations for further reading. What is given here should be sufficient information to lead the reader to the correct article: the author, date, and title. In case of multiple authors, only the first name is listed.

AISC 1978, *Specification for the Design, Fabrication and Erection of Structural Steel for Buildings*
AISC 1980, *Manual of Steel Construction*

Effective Length of Columns with Simple Connections

W. F. Chen

INTRODUCTION

In Section 7.6, "Special Topics" of Chapter SB-7, "Connections," in the Monograph, the effect of the stiffness of semirigid beam-to-column connections on the load carrying capacity of columns is evaluated in terms of effective column length. Recent results on the influence of simple shear connections on the effective length of H columns will be summarized here.

Numerical studies have shown that initial crookedness and residual stresses can significantly reduce the strength of hinged-end columns. This finding is reflected most notably in the recent development of multiple column curves. However, the effect of these two factors is not so clearly understood for the most realistic case of columns with partially restrained ends. According to the limited information previously available for columns made of aluminum alloys, the effects of a small amount of initial crookedness can be offset by the introduction of a small amount of end restraint. It is therefore important to study the effect of end restraint on isolated, hinged-end, initially crooked, steel wide-flange-shape columns for which actual data on residual stress patterns are generally known. To this end, the proper end restraint modeling of actual beam-to-column connections is essential in this type of study.

Recently, some studies of the behavior and stength of such columns have been reported using a computer model based essentially on the following three key factors:

1. The initial geometrical imperfections of the column.

2. The magnitude and distribution of residual stresses in the material.

3. The unavoidable end restraints of a column from beam-to-column connections.

Extensive research has been done on the effects of initial crookedness and residual stresses on the behavior and strength of isolated columns without end restraint. As a result, design criteria for columns in in-plane as well as in space have been proposed, refined, and recommended for general use (Chen and Atsuta, 1976, 1977; Chen and Cheong-Siat-Moy, 1980b).

However, the important effect of modest end restraint from simple beam-to-column shear connections on initially imperfect columns has not been systematically studied in depth. The effect of residual stresses and initial crookedness is not so clearly understood for the more realistic case of imperfect columns with modest end restraints, which always exist in an actual framed structure. This important problem has been reviewed in a recent paper by the author (1980a), under the guidance of Task Group 23 of the Structural Stability Research Council (SSRC). (This task group is entitled "Effect of End Restraint on Initially Crooked Columns.")

Recently, Jones et al. (1979, 1980) reviewed over 250 tests on various types of beam-to-column connections and used the spline function to model the end restraint of these connections. Using proper spline functions for the end restraints, the strength and behavior of several cases of nonsway steel columns were investigated by means of a finite-element-type program.

In the following, a brief summary of the results of the study of symmetrically loaded wide-flange steel columns with small end restraint is described. Details of this study are given elsewhere (Sugimoto and Chen, 1981). Further studies on this subject are currently underway at Purdue University.

RESTRAINED MOMENT-END-ROTATION DATA

Moment-rotation data used in the study are shown in Fig. 1 as Type 1 and Type 2. Type 1 data were originally obtained by Batho and Rowan for the members consisting of a 12x5 beam (W12x30) connected to the strong axis of a 12x8 column (W12x65) with a riveted double web angle connection (Steel Structures Research Committee, 1931, 1934, 1936). In this study, Type 1 data are used for the members consisting of a W12x30 beam connected to the weak and strong axis of a W12x65 column. Type 2 data were obtained by Bergquist (1977) for the member consisting of a W10x21 beam connected to the weak axis of a W10x29 column using web cleats fastened with A325 bolts.

Uniaxially loaded columns under study are divided into seven groups. The data used are summarized as follows:

1. Initial imperfection : 0.001L, 0.002L, 0.004L

2. End restraints   : Pinned ends, Restrained ends (Types 1 and 2)

3. Bending axis   : Strong axis (x-axis), Weak axis (y-axis)

4. Columns   : W12x65 with W12x30 beam (Type 1),
                          W10x29 with W10x21 beam (Type 2)

EFFECTIVE COLUMN LENGTH

The term *effective column length* is defined here as that length (slenderness) that on the basic column curve for pinned ends, gives the same strength as the failure load for the actual column with its actual end restraints. The determination of this length is shown graphically in Fig. 2 where a horizontal

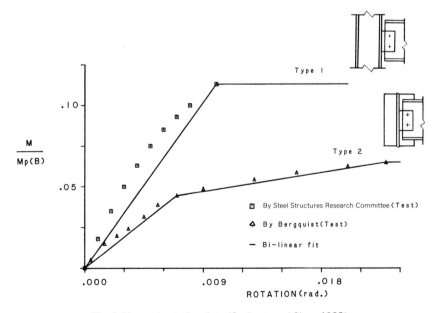

Fig. 1 Moment-rotation data *(Sugimoto and Chen, 1982)*

line is drawn from the restrained column curve with length λ_{ac} until it meets the basic curve with length λ_{ab}. The effective length factor K is then obtained as the ratio of the two values of λ, $K=\lambda_{ab}/\lambda_{ac}$. Values of K obtained in this manner are given in Tables 1, 2 and 3.

In Tables 1 and 2, values of K are shown for strong-axis and weak-axis bending of the W12x65 column with two different initial imperfections, 0.001L and 0.004L, and with Type 1 end restraint. It can be observed that there is no significant difference between and among these cases. This observation is also indicated by the analytical work of Jones et al. (1980) with an initial imperfection of 0.001L. In each case, the effective length factor has a value of around 0.9 and 0.8 for strong- and weak-axis bending respectively. In Table 3, values of K are shown for weak-axis bending of W10x29 column with an 0.001L initial imperfection and with Type 2 end restraint. Again, these values change very little over the range of slenderness considered and are around 0.72. This value is consistent with Jones's results (1980).

COMPARISON WITH DESIGN CURVES

The complete set of results for the W12x65 column in the form of two column curves is shown in Fig. 3 for the pinned-end case, with an initial

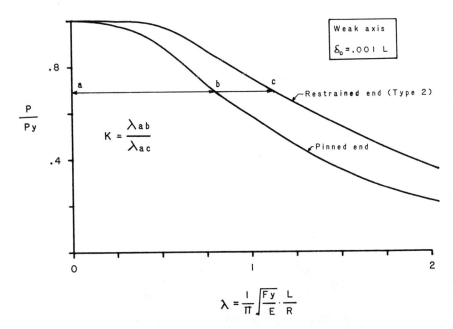

Fig. 2 Calculated column curves *(Sugimoto and Chen, 1982)*

imperfection of 0.001L, and the results are compared with the CRC curve, and two SSRC curves (see Johnston, 1976). The results show that the SSRC curve 2 represents a somewhat average value for both weak- and strong-axis curves.

The column curves corresponding to the end-restrained case (Type 1), with an initial imperfection of 0.001L, are shown in Fig. 4. These curves clearly demonstrate the effects of modest end restraints on the column's maximum load carrying capacity for all values of λ considered. For the end-restrained case the weak-axis and strong-axis column curves fall in a very narrow band, and the CRC curve is seen to be more representative of the present case (Fig. 4).

The ratios of calculated maximum load to the CRC column curve, P_{max}/P_{CRC}, for the W12x65 column are shown in Fig. 5 for restrained ends (Type 1). The ratios for strong-axis bending are in the range of the minimum value of 0.936 at $\lambda=1.155$ to the maximum value of 1.04 at $\lambda=1.755$ for an 0.001L initial imperfection. The CRC curve is more representative for this case. For initial imperfections of 0.002L and 0.004L, it varies from 0.835 at $\lambda=1.28$ to

Table 1 Effective length factor,
K (W12x65, strong axis, Type 1)

$\dfrac{P_{max}}{P_y}$	$\delta_0 = 0.001L$ K	$\delta_0 = 0.004L$ K
.9	.88	.86
.8	.91	.89
.7	.92	.90
.6	.91	.90
.5	.91	.92
.4	.91	.94

Table 2 Effective length factor,
K (W12x65, weak axis, Type 1)

$\dfrac{P_{max}}{P_y}$	$\delta_0 = 0.001L$ K	$\delta_0 = 0.004L$ K
.9	.71	.70
.8	.77	.76
.7	.80	.82
.6	.81	.83
.5	.80	.84
.4	.79	.85

Table 3 Effective Length Factor,
K (W10x29, Weak axis, Type 2)

$\dfrac{P_{max}}{P_y}$	$\delta_0 = 0.001L$ K
.9	.70
.8	.72
.7	.71
.6	.72
.5	.73
.4	.73

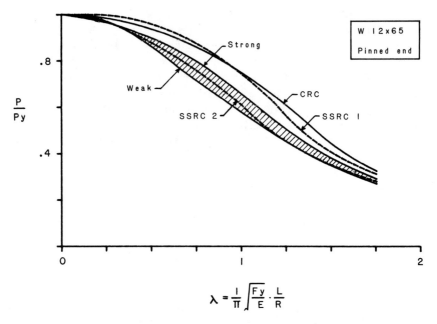

$$\lambda = \frac{1}{\pi} \sqrt{\frac{Fy}{E}} \cdot \frac{L}{R}$$

Fig. 3 Column curves *(Sugimoto and Chen, 1982)*

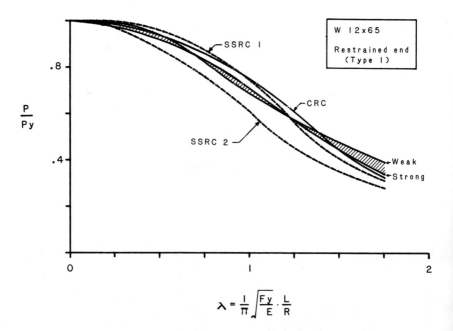

$$\lambda = \frac{1}{\pi} \sqrt{\frac{Fy}{E}} \cdot \frac{L}{R}$$

Fig. 4 Column curves *(Sugimoto and Chen, 1982)*

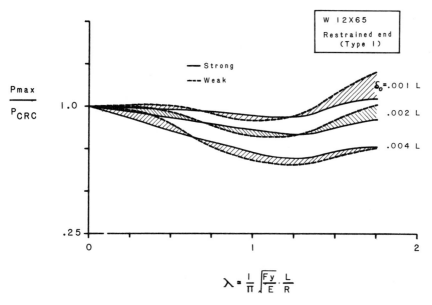

Fig. 5 Ratios of calculated maximum loads to CRC-curve loads *(Sugimoto and Chen, 1982)*

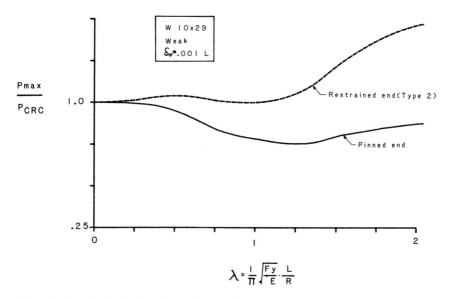

Fig. 6 Ratios of calculated maximum loads to CRC-curve loads *(Sugimoto and Chen, 1982)*

0.923 at $\lambda=1.755$ and 0.693 at $\lambda=1.25$ to 0.761 at $\lambda=1.755$, respectively. For the weak-axis bending case, these values are from 0.916 at $\lambda=1.02$ to 1.205 at $\lambda=1.755$, from 0.819 at $\lambda=1.14$ to 1.005 at $\lambda=1.755$, and from 0.654 at $\lambda=1.23$ to 0.754 at $\lambda=1.755$ for initial imperfections of $0.001L$, $0.002L$, and $0.004L$, respectively.

In Fig. 6, the ratios of the calculated maximum load to the CRC column strength curve are shown for the W10x29 column. The value of this ratio varies from 0.752 at $\lambda=1.25$ to 1.0 at $\lambda=0$ -0.15 and from 1.0 at $\lambda=0$ -1.2 to 1.45 at $\lambda=2.04$ for pinned-end and restrained-end (Type 2) columns, respectively.

For the modest end-restrained case with an $0.001L$ initial imperfection, it can be observed from Figs. 5 and 6 that the CRC curve is a more representative one in the range of slenderness ratio λ up to 1.25.

CONDENSED REFERENCES/BIBLIOGRAPHY

The following is a condensed bibliography for this article. It includes all articles referred to or cited in the text. The full citations will be found at the end of the volume, with additional citations for further reading. What is given here should be sufficient information to lead the reader to the correct article: the author, date, and title. In case of multiple authors, only the first name is listed.

Bergquist 1977, *Tests on Columns Restrained by Beams with Simple Connections*

Chen 1976, *Theory of Beam-Columns*
Chen 1977, *Theory of Beam-Columns*
Chen 1980a, *End Restraint and Column Stability*
Chen 1980b, *Limit States Design of Steel Beam-Columns: A-State-of-the-Art Review*

Johnston 1976, *Guide to Stability Design Criteria for Metal Structures*
Jones 1979, *The Analysis of Frames with Semi-Rigid Connections*
Jones 1980a, *Influence of Semi-Rigid Joints on Steel Column Behavior*
Jones 1980b, *Effect of Semi-Rigid Connections on Steel Column Strength*

Steel Structures Research Committee 1931, 1934, 1936, *Recommendations for Design*
Sugimoto 1981, *Effect of Small End Restraint on Strength of H-Columns*
Sugimoto 1982, *Small End Restraint Effects on Strength of H-Columns*

Proposed New Design Methods For Composite Columns

George Winter*

In regard to the code and specification coverage of steel-concrete composite members and connections, the situation in the United States is as follows: beams and girders and their shear connectors are treated in the AISC Steel Buildings Specification (1978) and composite columns are covered in the ACI Concrete Buildings Code (1977), whereas steel-deck reinforced composite slabs and connections of composite members are not covered in any code or specification. Efforts are now underway to remedy this situation. The present, brief report will deal with a proposal to include composite columns in the AISC specification, to go along with the beams and girders now covered there. The most common forms of composite columns are shown on Fig. 1.

The urgent need for action is illustrated by the fact that composite columns are hardly ever used in this country (see Table 1). For twelve W-shape columns of a great variety of dimensions, the table gives the allowable axial load on a composite column according to the ACI 1971 code and the allowable axial load on the bare steel column according to the AISC specification. In eight of the twelve cases (shown in italics in Table 1) the capacity of the

---

*Deceased

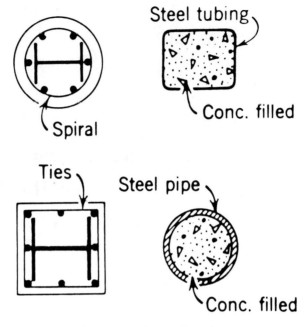

Fig. 1 Types of composite columns

Table 1 Comparison of allowable axial loads

Size of steel shape	Size of column b X d	Axial load, k	
		Composite ACI-71*	Bare steel AISC-68
W 8 X 31	12 X 12	146	148
W 8 X 67	12.5 X 13	*237*	*327*
W10 X 33	12 X 14	160	155
W10 X 122	14.5 X 15.5	*434*	*592*
W12 X 40	12 X 16	*188*	*203*
W12 X 65	16 X 16	366	366
W12 X 190	17 X 18.50	*750*	*1060*
W14 X 53	12 X 18	*226*	*250*
W14 X 87	18.5 X 18	500	492
W14 X 142	19.5 X 19	*716*	*812*
W14 X 246	20.0 X 20.5	*1100*	*1410*
W14 X 426	21.0 X 23.0	*1605*	*2450*

*$\phi = .7, L=1.55$

composite column given by ACI is less than that of the same steel column without concrete given by AISC. In other words, if you want to strengthen an existing bare steel column by converting it into a composite column, more likely than not you will lose allowable carrying capacity. This restriction is the main reason why composite columns are hardly used in the United States.

To deal with this situation, the Structural Stability Research Council (SSRC) requested its Task Group 20, Composite Members, to develop a proposed specification for composite columns that would fit into the present format of the AISC Steel Buildings Specification. This task has been completed and the proposal has been published in Vol. 16, No. 4, of the AISC *Engineering Journal*, Dec. 1979. This proposal will now be discussed briefly. To do so, the ACI treatment of ordinary reinforced concrete columns and the AISC treatment of bare steel columns will first be presented briefly.

For axially loaded reinforced concrete columns, extensive tests show a mean nominal capacity $P_n = 0.85f'_c A_c + f_y A_s$. For design purposes, this mean nominal capacity is reduced by $a\theta$ to the design capacity $P_d = a\phi$ $(0.85f'_c A_c + f_y A_s)$, where ϕ is the usual strength reduction factor and a accounts for possible accidental eccentricities and the like. The values of a and θ for columns with ties and with spirals and the resulting average factors of safety are

Cols. with ties: $a = 0.80$, $\phi = 0.70$, S.F. $\doteq 2.8$
Cols. with spirals: $a = 0.85$, $\phi = 0.75$, S.F. $\doteq 2.4$

The treatment of beam-columns is shown in Fig. 2. The solid line gives the interaction curve for full, unreduced strength. The dashed line gives the design values P_d, M_d obtained from the full strength by the appropriate reduction factors ϕ. The straight horizontal cut-off gives the design load for axially or nearly axially loaded columns, with reduction factor $a\phi$ as explained before.

In the current AISC specification, the design of axially loaded columns is based on the so-called Column Research Council (CRC) column curve shown in Fig. 3. The corresponding equations for the buckling stresses in the two ranges, inelastic and elastic, are

$$\sigma_{cr1} = [1 - \frac{F_y}{4\pi^2 E}(\frac{kl}{r})^2]F_y \tag{1}$$

$$\sigma_{cr2} = \frac{\pi^2 E}{(kl/r)^2} \tag{2}$$

Allowable stresses F_a are obtained by dividing these critical stresses by a variable safety factor S.F.:

$$F_a = \frac{\sigma_{cr}}{\text{S.F.}} \tag{3}$$

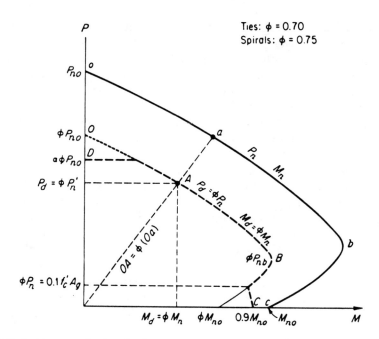

Fig. 2 Typical compression-bending interaction diagram for reinforced concrete columns by ACI code. *(Winter, 1979)*

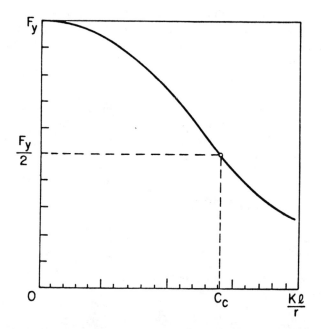

Fig. 3 Strength curve for axially loaded columns on which present AISC provisions are based.

$$S.F. \frac{5}{3} - + \frac{3kl/r}{8C_c} - \frac{(kl/r)^2}{8C_c^2} \tag{4}$$

$$\text{For} \quad kl/r = 0 \quad S.F. = 1.67$$
$$kl/r \geq C_c \quad S.F. = 1.92 \tag{5}$$

Beam-columns are treated by the well-known linear interaction equation

$$\frac{f_a}{F_a} + \frac{Cf_b}{(1 - \frac{f_a}{F_e'}) F_b} \leq 1 \tag{6}$$

$$F_e' = \frac{1}{S.F.} \frac{\pi^2 E}{(kl/r)^2} \tag{7}$$

where f_a and f_b are the simultaneous axial compression and bending stresses and F_a and F_b are the allowable stresses for axial compression alone and for flexure alone.

This brief review shows the completely different treatment of columns and beam-columns in the ACI code, on the one hand, and the ASIC specification, on the other. In addition, the former is in what is now called the load and resistance factor design (LRFD) format, whereas the latter is in the traditional allowable-stress design (ASD) format. This situation illustrates the difficulties in developing realistic design methods for composite columns which, by nature, fall somewhere in between reinforced concrete and structural steel members.

The basic approach of SSRC Task Group 20, based in part on previous work by one of its members, R. W. Furlong, is as follows: the form of the basic AISC equations is adopted without change for axially loaded columns, and with only one simple change for beam-columns. However, the various parameters that enter these equations are redefined in a manner that reflects the influence of the concrete and of the additional reinforcing bars on the member capacity.

Thus, the design equations for concentrically loaded columns become

$$F_a = \frac{1}{S.F.} [1 - \frac{F_{ym}}{4\pi^2 E_m} (\frac{kl}{r_m})^2] F_{ym} \tag{8}$$

$$F_a = \frac{1}{S.F.} \frac{\pi^2 E_m}{(kl/r_m)^2} \tag{9}$$

That is, they are exactly the same equations as in the present AISC specification, except that all quantities with the subscript "m" are modified to reflect the influence of composite action. For beam-columns one basic change in the AISC interaction equation is proposed. Its justification is shown on Fig. 4. That is, for a member made of elasto-plastic material it can be shown that the interaction equation is linear, except for plastic failure of solid rectangular and similar solid shapes, where the first term is squared rather than linear. This condition is in basic agreement with the interaction curves for reinforced concrete beam-columns shown previously, which are also curved rather than linear. For this reason the proposed interaction equation for composite beam-columns is

$$(\frac{f_a}{F_a})^2 + \frac{CF_b}{(1 - \frac{f_a}{F'_{em}})F_b} \leq 1 \tag{10}$$

$$F'_{em} = \frac{1}{\text{S.F.}} \frac{\pi^2 E_m}{(kl/r_m)^2} \tag{11}$$

That is, in contrast to the equation for bare steel columns, the first term of this equation is squared, giving a curve of the shape shown in Fig. 4. For the rest, again all relevant parameters with the subscript "m" are modified to reflect the influence of composite action. These modified parameters will now be described.

Instead of the yield strength F_y of the structural shape, the modified yield strength F_{my} is used:

$$F_{my} = F_y + F_{yr}(A_r/A_s) + 0.85f'_c(A_c/A_s) \quad \text{for hollow shapes} \tag{12}$$

$$F_{my} = F_y + 0.7F_{yr}(A_r/A_s) + 0.6f'_c(A_c/A_s) \quad \text{for encased shapes} \tag{13}$$

This configuration reflects the additional strength contributed both by the longitudinal reinforcing bars of combined area A_r and yield point F_{yr} and by the concrete of area A_c and cylinder strength f'_c. It is seen that reduction coefficients 0.7 and 0.6 are applied to these two terms for encased shapes in contrast to composite pipes and tubes. Based on extensive comparison

Initial Yielding , I and ▨ , $P/P_0 + M/M_0 = 1$

For Complete Plastification , I , $P/P_0 + M/M_0 = 1$

For Complete Plastifications , ▨ , $(P/P_0)^2 + M/M_0 = 1$

$P = f_a A$; $P_0 = F_a A$; $M = 8 f_b S$; $M_0 = F_b S$

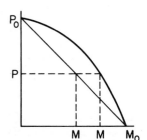

Fig. 4 Compression-bending interaction curves for stocky steel columns

with tests, this application reflects the fact that in tubes and pipes the confined concrete is prevented from spalling, whereas the simple ties used with encased structural shapes are less effective in confining the concrete.

Similarly, the effective modulus of elasticity is modified to reflect the influence of concrete, again separately for the two types of composite columns:

$$E_m = E_s + 0.4E_c(A_c/A_s) \quad \text{for hollow shapes} \tag{14}$$

$$E_m = E_s + 0.2E_c(A_c/A_s) \quad \text{for encased shapes} \tag{15}$$

That is, to the steel modulus E_s is added a term reflecting the stiffening influence of the concrete, based on the ratio of the areas of concrete and steel. The appropriate radius of gyration is simply that of the steel shape, except for an upper limit for encased shapes.

Finally, for beam-columns it is necessary to use a modified section modulus S_m to calculate the bending term f_b.

$$S_m = S_s + \frac{1}{3}A_r(h_2 - 2c_r)(F_{yr}/F_y) + \text{concrete term} \tag{16}$$

where h_2 and c_r are shown on Fig. 5

That is, S_m consists of the modulus S_s for the steel shape, plus a term for the contribution of the reinforcing bars of area A_r, plus another term reflecting the added contribution of the concrete. This last, relatively complicated term, which is mostly of minor importance, is not shown here in detail.

The proposed design equations were verified by comparison with a total of 194 tests published by ten groups of investigators in four countries. A summary of the results is given in Table 2. From the coefficient of variation it is seen that the accuracy of prediction is satisfactory, considering the complex nature of these structural members. The ratio P_{test}/P_{calc} for encased members, slightly larger than 2.0, also appears to be satisfactory. This average ratio is higher for filled pipes—2.26 for axial loading and 2.50 for eccentric loading. (The published tables say tubes, but what actually was tested were

$$\text{e} \cdot \text{g} \cdot M_0 = F_y S_m$$

$$S_m = S_s + \frac{1}{3} A_r(h_2 - 2c_r) \frac{F_{yr}}{F_y} + \text{Concrete Term}$$

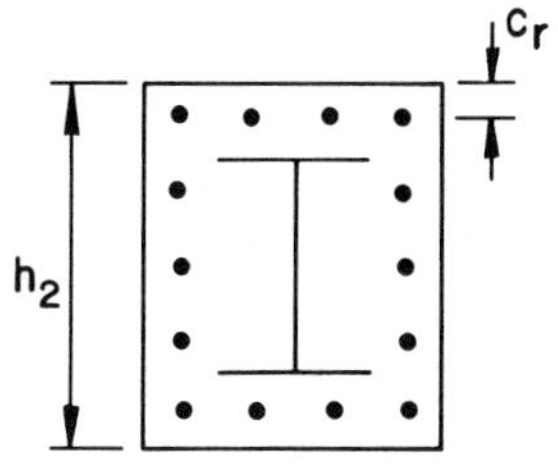

Fig. 5 Modified section modulus S_m

Fig. 6 Architectural elevation of Three First National Plaza, Chicago—a building that used mixed construction *(Courtesy: Skidmore, Owings & Merrill)*

Fig. 7 Three First National Plaza, Chicago—construction sequence showing steel framing proceeding ahead, followed by concrete construction *(Courtesy: Skidmore, Owings & Merrill)*

round tubes or pipes.) The high value for eccentrically loaded composite pipes is fairly easily explained. The proposed formulas, just like those in the AISC specification, are based on an elastically calculated yield stress or critical stress as the failure criterion. However, for simple bending, which enters the interaction equation, the actual plastic failure load of a round tube exceeds the yield load by a much larger percentage than for a two-flanged member. This fact is bound to be reflected in the test comparisons for eccentric tubes, resulting in the high value of 2.50 for the average of P_{test}/P_{calc}. It is possible to make adjustments for that value in the equations before they are incorporated in the AISC specification.

This completes the presentation of the proposed treatment of composite columns within the framework of the present version of the AISC specifi-

Table 2 Comparison of 192 test values with the proposed design method *(Task Group 20, 1979)*

Type of column	No. of tests	$(P_{test}/P_{calc})_{av}$	Coeff. of var.
Filled tubes, concent.	73	2.26	20%
Encased shapes, concent.	29	2.04	17%
Filled tubes, eccent.	32	2.50	15%
Encased shapes, eccent.	60	2.02	15%

Fig. 8 Detail at exterior column of Three First National Plaza, Chicago, during construction *(Courtesy: Skidmore, Owings & Merrill)*

cation. Apart from the present well-established ASD format of the AISC specification, work is proceeding on producing an alternate version in the LRFD format. In this connection the approach for composite columns just presented is also being translated into an LRFD version. Work on a draft of this alternate version of the entire AISC specification is just now in the process of completion. It is expected that it will be published in a future issue of the AISC *Engineering Journal* for comment and trial use.

CONDENSED REFERENCES/BIBLIOGRAPHY

The following is a condensed bibliography for this article. It includes all articles referred to or cited in the text. The full citations will be found at the end of the volume, with additional citations for further reading. What is given here should be sufficient information to lead the reader to the correct article: the author, date, and title. In case of multiple authors, only the first name is listed.

ACI 1977, *ACI 318-77: Building Code Requirements for Reinforced Concrete*
AISC 1978, *Specifications for the Design, Fabrication and Erection of Steel Buildings*
Furlong 1976, *AISC Column Design Logic Makes Sense for Composite Columns*
Iyengar 1977, *State-of-the-Art Report on Composite or Mixed Steel-Concrete Construction for Buildings*
Task Group 20 1979, *A Specification for the Design of Steel-Concrete Composite Columns*
Winter 1979, *Design of Concrete Structure*

Steel-Deck-Reinforced Composite Slabs— Proposed Design and Construction Criteria

George Winter*

Steel-deck-reinforced composite slabs have been used for decades for floors of multistory, steel-framed buildings. Basically they consist of a cold-formed deck made of sheet steel, with concrete of appropriate strength and thickness placed on top of it (Fig. 1). The deck serves a triple function: it constitutes the working platform during steel erection; it serves as formwork during placement of the slab concrete; and it constitutes the tension reinforcement in the completed composite slab. Several of the many current shapes of deck-reinforced slabs are shown in Figs. 2 and 3.

At this time, there is no generally accepted procedure for establishing carrying capacities and allowable loads for such decks. The usual design criteria for reinforced concrete do not apply, because of the different shape of the deck-type reinforcing steel and its peculiar interaction with the concrete. This interaction, through shear-bond, depends strongly on the details of the shape of both the deck and the shear-transfer devices (dimples, ribs, and

---

*Deceased

cross-wires) that determine the shear-bond strength. In consequence, the elaborate load tables provided by all manufacturers of deck-reinforced slabs are based on very elaborate tests for each particular deck shape, depth of deck and of concrete, span range, and so on. Since it is impossible to test every situation that is tabulated in load tables, many of these values have to be obtained by interpolation or extrapolation, for which no generally accepted procedure seems to exist. This situation makes for difficulties of acceptance in local building codes and in other situations affected by lack of standardized approaches.

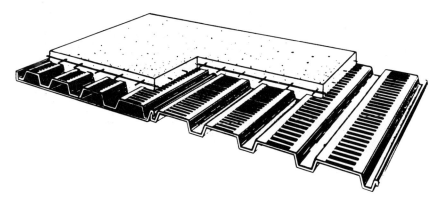

Fig. 1 Typical deck-reinforced slab: transverse ribs increase shear-bond

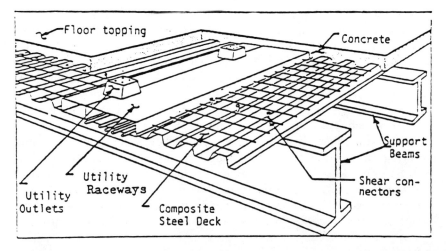

Fig. 2 Another type of reinforcing deck with transverse wires for shear-bond transfer
(Porter and Ekberg, 1976a)

To remedy this situation, AISI sponsored research on composite slabs at the University of Iowa by Profs. C. E. Ekberg, M. L. Porter, and R. M. Schuster (now at the University of Windsor, Canada). This lengthy and extensive research has resulted in a draft of Tentative Criteria for the Design and Construction of Composite Steel Deck Slabs. This draft is now under review by the Committee on Composite Deck Slabs of the ASCE Technical Council for Codes and Standards, for eventual adoption as a standard. In the following, some features of this draft will be presented.

The strength of deck-reinforced slabs is limited either by flexural failure, much as in other reinforced concrete members, or by shear-bond failure of a type peculiar to these deck slabs. Fig. 4 schematically shows such a slab specimen in a laboratory test after shear-bond failure. It is seen that one of the usual flexural cracks has developed into a major failure crack in the concrete. Over the distance from this crack to the nearby end of the slab the bond and interlock between deck and concrete has failed and the two materials have slipped relative to each other. This slippage is clearly observable in the outward end slippage of concrete relative to steel deck, as shown.

The following equation has been established for the nominal shear-bond strength (V_{nb}) of such slabs:

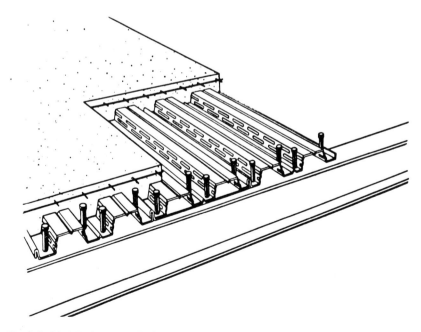

Fig. 3 A third deck type with shear-bond ribs in webs; also shown are stud connections to the supporting beam.

$$V_{\text{nb}} = \left(k\sqrt{f'_c} + m\frac{\rho d}{l'}\right) bd \qquad (1)$$

where l' = shear span, that is, the distance from concentrated load to nearby support, or $l/4$ for uniform load

It will be recognized that this equation is of the same general form as that for the shear strength of ordinary concrete beams with rebar reinforcement. However, while the properties of American bar surfaces are standardized by ASTM, there exists a great variety of types of reinforcing decks, each with its own shape of steel-concrete interface and shear-transfer devices. The shear-bond strength depends greatly on this shape of interface and of transfer device, and can be established only experimentally. For this reason, the equation for the shear-bond strength V_{nb} contains two constants k and m which, for each shape of deck, must be established by test. For this purpose, tests are carried out with two-point loading and results are plotted in the manner shown in Fig. 5.

It has been established by numerous tests that for any given deck shape, test data plotted in this manner give a linear relationship. For this reason, it is sufficient to have two groups of at least two test points each, one at each end of the desired range. Group A represents tests of long-span, shallow specimens, and group B represents tests of short-span, deep specimens. It is easily verified that when so plotted, the equation constant k is the vertical intercept, and the constant m is the slope of that straight line. Once k and m have been established, the strength of any composite slab using the same deck shape, but of different span and/or depth, can be calculated from Eq. 1 for V_{nb}.

The safety condition that must then be met in the actual structure is of the usual LRFD format, that is,

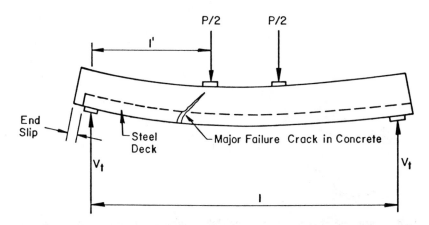

Fig. 4 Deck-reinforced slab specimen after failure in laboratory test *(Porter and Ekberg, 1976a)*

$$\phi V_{nb} = [1.4(D_s + D_{add}) + 1.7L]\frac{bl}{2}$$ (2)

Here D_s is the portion of the dead load of the slab carried in shear-bond, which depends on the conditions of shoring, if any, and D_{add} is the additional dead load in service; L is the live load.

The flexural design stregnth M_d can be determined from the usual ACI (1977) code equation

$$M_d = \phi A_s f_y(d - \frac{a}{2})$$ (3)

provided that the deck is underreinforced and that at failure, the entire deck is at yielding. However, this condition may not be the case for relatively deep steel decks with shallow concrete cover. Also, while the ACI code prohibits the use of overreinforced flexural members, such a rule is not possible for deck-reinforced slabs because the thickness of the deck, and thereby A_s, is often determined by the span of and load on the deck after the placing of concrete but before its setting and hardening. In these two cases the moment strength is best determined by a strain analysis.

The values of the strength reduction factors ϕ that are proposed for composite decks are as follows:

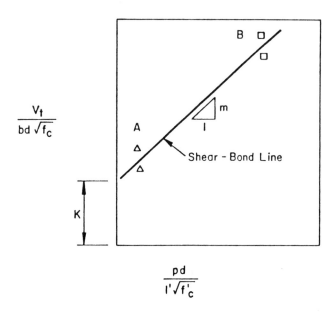

Fig. 5 Plot and evaluation of shear-bond tests *(Porter and Ekberg, 1976a)*

ϕ

Shear-bond	0.80
Flexure	0.90
Flexure when $(F_u/F_y) \leq 1.08$	0.70
Flexure, overreinforced	0.75
Flexure, plain concrete	0.65

That is, a value of 0.80 is proposed for shear-bond, which is somewhat lower than the value of 0.85 for shear in the ACI code. For flexure of underreinforced members the same value, 0.90, as in the code is suggested. However, some steel decks made of higher-strength sheets may show less ductility after forming than decks employing ordinary reinforcing bars do. Such lower ductility is characterized by a ratio of ultimate over yield strength F_u/F_y that is smaller than 1.08. To compensate for possible strength reduction induced by such lower ductility, the ϕ-value for this case is proposed to be 0.70. Further, since overreinforced slabs sometimes cannot be avoided, as was pointed out, a lower value of 0.75, as compared to 0.90, is proposed for such more brittle slabs. Lastly, for bending perpendicular to the ribs of the deck and similar situations, minor bending may sometimes have to be resisted by concrete alone. For this situation, the same value, $\phi = 0.65$, is proposed as in the ACI code. Finally, for calculating deflections at service loads it has been found from many tests that the effective moment of inertia can be calculated simply as the average of the moments of inertia of the cracked and uncracked sections.

This outline presents the most important proposed provisions for deck-reinforced slabs. It should be noticed that because of the variety of current deck shapes, some testing continues to be necessary to establish strength criteria. However, the proposed criteria minimize the amount of such testing. Also, they standardize the type of testing and of test evaluation which, at present, are left to the discretion of manufacturers, building officials, or others. It can be expected that within a reasonable time, the ASCE committee will complete its work and the criteria will be issued as a formal ASCE standard.

CONDENSED REFERENCES/BIBLIOGRAPHY

The following is a condensed bibliography for this article. It includes all articles referred to or cited in the text. The full citations will be found at the end of the volume, with additional citations for further reading. What is given here should be sufficient information to lead the reader to the correct article: the author, date, and title. In case of multiple authors, only the first name is listed.

ACI 1977, *ACI 318-77: Building Code Requirements for Reinforced Concrete*
Porter 1976a, *Design Recommendations for Steel Deck Floor Slabs*
Porter 1976b, *Shear-Bond Analysis of Steel-Deck-Reinforced Slabs*
Schuster 1976, *Composite Steel-Deck Floor Systems*
Schuster 1980, *Mechanical Interlocking of Composite Slabs*

Behavior of Expansion Joints and Filler Masonry Walls During Earthquake Motions: A Case Study

Zareh B. Gregorian

Expansion joints are not desirable in symmetrically shaped buildings that are rectangular, circular, or square in plan, except in cases where the excessive dimension could not be tolerated by the extra construction necessary to overcome the situation. The Federal Construction Council Technical Report No. 65 "Expansion Joints in Buildings," published by the National Academy of Sciences–National Research Council, provides data calling for buildings built in special areas under special environmental conditions to have a maximum dimension of about 600 feet without an expansion joint. In the case of buildings with nonsymmetrical shapes, like L, T, or U shapes, and with parts having different heights, properly located and designed expansion joints may significantly affect or even control the behavior of the structure during earthquake motions. The building observed is the Gameron Hotel in the city of Bandar Abbas on the Persian Gulf (Fig. 1).

The original structure consists of the building's A part, which is an eight-story steel structure and has a rectangular shape with a small appendix on one side that brings the whole structure to an approximately symmetrical shape about its major axis. The structure's extended part B is of the same pattern, except it is two stories taller and was constructed some years later with the same design pattern and framing system as the original building (Fig. 2). The structure is a moment-resisting steel frame with precast, hollow-concrete-block-joist slab floor systems.

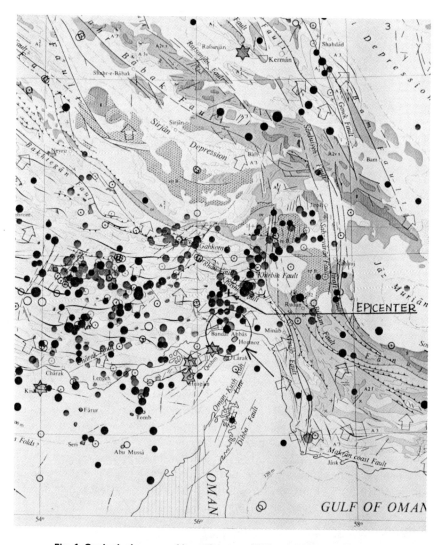

Fig. 1 Geological survey of Iran *(Courtesy: Ministry of Industry and Mines)*

The structural steel columns and beams are embedded in concrete for rust proofing purposes. The interior partitions and exterior facade walls are terra-cotta hollow brick masonry with cement mortar. The facing finish is cement stucco, with windows occupying half the span between columns.

On April 21, 1977, which coincided with the local New Years Eve, an earthquake shook the city of Bandar Abbas, killing 167 people and leaving

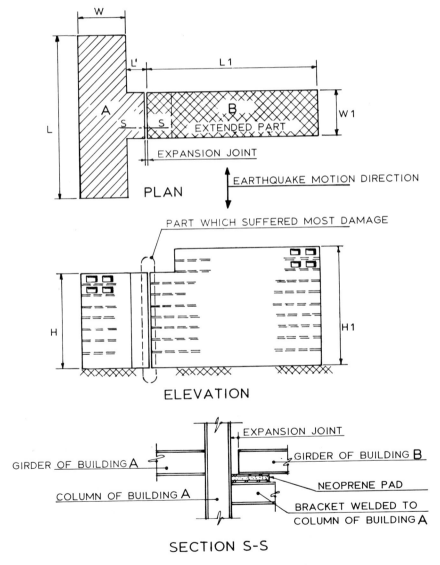

Fig. 2 Gameron Hotel, Bandar Abbas, Iran

556 injured and 7,000 homeless. The magnitude of the earthquake was 7.00 on the Richter Scale and the epicenter of the quake was located on 27-61 N, 56-39 E—approximately 45 kilometers north of Bandar Abbas (Fig. 1). The focal depth was only 29 kilometers. Severe after-shocks were recorded during the following 48-hour period. No fatalities were recorded among the hotel occupants.

The entire building was designed by the author, and a moment-resisting frame was considered for the system. The steel structure and the roofing system were erected with good-quality workmanship (Fig. 3). While adding the extension part B, to avoid double columns at the expansion joint a special detail was developed by using single columns and connecting the girders by means of a neoprene pad, which could withstand relatively large amounts of shear force and elastic deformation (Fig. 2, Section S-S).

The principle axis of the earthquake was in the longitudinal direction of the original structure, building A. The results of the building inspection after the earthquake are discussed below, together with recommendations.

BUILDING PERFORMANCE

The fundamental period of vibration T for the two parts of the structure, acting independently, can be calculated by ISIRI-519 as follows:

$$T_A = \frac{0.09H}{\sqrt{L}} = \frac{0.09 \times 24}{\sqrt{50}} = 0.3055 \text{ seconds} \tag{1}$$

$$T_B = \frac{0.09H}{\sqrt{W}} = \frac{0.09 \times 30}{\sqrt{14}} = 0.7216 \text{ seconds} \tag{2}$$

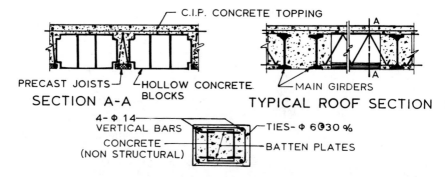

Fig. 3 Typical roof and column sections

That the period of fundamental vibration of building B was larger than that of building A caused building B to undergo larger deformation; but since the end part of building B was partially restrained by the expansion joint detailing and could not move with same period as the rest of the building, torsional forces and severe cracking resulted. The original building A suffered less architectural damage because of its low period of vibration and less severe deformation resulting from its larger dimension being in the direction of the earthquake.

RESULTS

At the time of the earthquake, the building was fully occupied and most bathrooms were occupied by people preparing for evening festivities. Because of the location of the bathrooms in the bay attached to the expansion joint, the tenants evacuated the bathrooms and the rooms and, although nobody was injured, there was a great deal of panic, and a considerable number of ceramic tiles, 4 inches square in size, were detached from the walls. Some water pipes were broken, and power loss occurred in the same area.

The interior partitions, which were full height with only door openings, experienced little damage because they had a larger moment of inertia as a result of the combination of room entrance, closet, and shower-area walls.

The exterior facade walls suffered the most. Cracks developed as a result of shear in building B in the areas that underwent more deflection (Fig. 4).

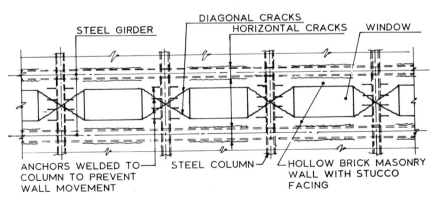

Fig. 4 Typical crack pattern at building facades

INSPECTION

Inspection was performed one month after the earthquake. Several parts of the structure were opened to expose the beam-to-column connections, base-plates, column splices, and particularly the expansion joint construction detail. The damage observed was some cracking, architectural in nature, in the expansion joint region. This damage was repaired after the inspection.

DESIGN RECOMMENDATIONS

1. Avoid nonsymmetrical shapes. Provide expansion joints in proper locations where the building has L, T, or U shapes (Fig. 5).

2. Avoid providing expansion joints at parts where public utilities are located. The optimum location could be a part of the structure that is not in frequent public use, such as storage areas, filing rooms, and the like. The architectural layout should be prepared with this need in mind.

3. Avoid the sliding or sliding-but-resistant types of expansion details used in the case study. Provide full expansion joints to allow the two parts of the structure to act individually during earthquake motions.

4. If the facade of the building is built with masonry, provide frames around openings connected to top and bottom girders and columns to diminish the diagonal cracking due to shear in masonry filler wall facades (see Fig. 6).

5. Although a building can act safely with no structural failures, the excessive deflection might cause psychological effects that are not desirable and could be partly eliminated by reducing the allowable deflections.

6. In bathroom areas, using one piece fiberglass tub and shower enclosures is recommended to prevent the spalling of small pieces of ceramic tile during earthquake motions.

RECOMMENDATIONS FOR THE FUTURE PERFORMANCE OF THE BUILDING

Although the structural behavior of the building was not a problem and the building suffered only architectural damage, to avoid excessive deformations during future earthquakes, two solutions are recommended.

1. Place a new set of columns at the expansion joint, thus eliminating

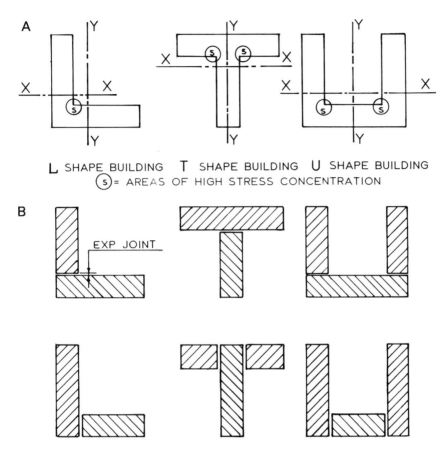

Fig. 5 Recommendations for placement of expansion joints in nonsymmetrical plans. The buildings in part (a) have no expansion joints and consequently stress concentrations might occur at corners during earthquakes. Also, because of the unsymmetrical shape of the building to the y-y axis and the x-x and y-y axes for plan L, torsional forces might be of importance. It is recommended to use expansion joints as sketched in part (b).

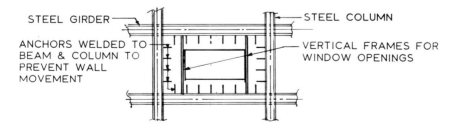

Fig. 6 Recommended detail for exterior walls and window openings

the neoprene pad connection and making the two parts of the building act independently.

2. Leave the expansion joint as it is but reconstruct the end frame that is parallel to the expansion joint at the opposite side of the building. The reconstructed structure should act as a braced frame with proper stiffness, thus minimizing the nonuniform deformation of building B and preventing excessive deformations.

CONDENSED REFERENCES/BIBLIOGRAPHY

The following is a condensed bibliography for this article. It includes all articles referred to or cited in the text. The full citations will be found at the end of the volume, with additional citations for further reading. What is given here should be sufficient information to lead the reader to the correct article: the author, date, and title. In case of multiple authors, only the first name is listed.

Degenkolb 1977, *Earthquake Forces on Tall Structure*

Federal Construction Council 1974, *Expansion Joints in Buildings*

Government of Iran 1970, *Minimum Design Loads in Buildings and other Structures*
Government of Iran 1979, *Geologic Survey Seismotectonic Map of Iran*
Gregorian 1977, *Structural Behavior of Hotel Gameron*

Person 1978, *Bulletin of the Seismological Society of America*

Structural Design of Tall Steel Buildings

CONDENSED REFERENCES/BIBLIOGRAPHY

The following is a condensed bibliography for this part. It contains bibliographic citations that are in addition to those cited with the articles. The full citations can be found at the end of the volume. What is given here should be sufficient information to lead the reader to the correct article: author, data, and title. In the case of multiple authors, only the first name is listed.

Ackroyd 1982, *Behavior of Type 2 Steel Frames*
Allen 1981, *Limit States Design: What Do We Really Want?*

Batten 1978, *Design Studies of Medium-Rise Steel Buildings*
Batten 1978, *Computer-Aided Plastic Design of Unbraced Frameworks*
Beaulieu 1976, *The Effects of Column Out-of-Plumbs on the Stability of Core-Braced Buildings*
Beaulieu 1976, *Stability of Core-Braced Buildings*
Beaulieu 1977, *The Destabilizing Forces Caused by Gravity Loads Acting on Initially Out-of-Plumb*
Beaulieu 1978, *The Effects of Wall Out-of-Plumbs on the Stability of Core-Braced Buildings*
Beaulieu 1978, *The Results of a Survey on Structural Out-of-Plumbs*
Beaulieu 1979, *Probability Considerations in Assessing the Effects of Structural Out-of-Plumbs*
Beaulieu 1980, *Significance of Structural Out-of-Plumb Forces and Recommendations for Design*
Bucheli 1982, *Composite Beams for Buildings* (In French and German)

Chen 1977, *Theory of Beam-Columns—The State-of-the-Art Review*
Chen 1977, *Studies of Axially Loaded Fabricated Tubular Columns*
Chen 1977, *Design of Box Columns under Biaxial Bending*
Chen 1977, *The Axial Strength and Behavior of Cylindrical Columns*
Chen 1977, *Tests of Fabricated Tubular Columns*
Chen 1980, *End Restraint and Column Stability*
Chen 1980, *Limit States Design of Steel Beam-Columns*
Chen 1981, *Static Behavior of Beam-to-Column Moment Connections*
Chen 1981, *Recent Advances on Analysis and Design of Steel Beam-Columns in U.S.A.*
Coull 1975, *Simplified Analysis of Frame-Tube Structures*

Coull 1976, *Torsion of Framed Tube Structures*
Coull 1978, *Deflections of Framed-Tube Structures*

Ha 1978, *Orthotropic Membrane for Tall Building Analysis*

Johnson 1980, *A Simple Design Method for Composite Columns*
Johnson 1980, *Limit State Design of Composite Structures for Buildings*
Johnson 1981, *Shrinkage and Tension Stiffening in Negative Moment Regions of Composite Beams*
Johnson 1981, *Semi-Rigid Joints for Composite Frames*
Johnson 1981, *Analysis and Design for Longitudinal Shear in Composite T-Beams*
Johnson 1982, *Design for Longitudinal Shear in Composite L-Beams*
Johnson to be published, *Cracking in Concrete Tension Flanges of Composite T-Beams*
Joint Committee on Composite Structures 1981, *Composite Structures*

Litzner 1981, *Effect of Residual Stresses on the Carrying Capacity of Composite Columns*

Maeda 1976, *Non-Linear Vibration Analysis of Plane Framed Structures by Finite Element Method*
Maeda 1977, *Stress and Deflection Analysis of Expanded Open-Web Steel Beams*
Maeda 1977, *Effects of Cold-Forming on Mechanical Properties and Weldability of Shear*
Maeda 1978, *Non-Linear Analysis of Cable-Stiffened Structures*
Maeda 1978, *Fatigue Cracks of Deep Thin-Walled Plate Girders*
Maeda 1979, *Structural Behavior of Slabs at Skewed Composite Girders*
Maeda 1980, *Geometrical Non-Linear Behavior of Rib Arches*
Maeda 1980, *An Influence Line Analysis of Arches*
Maeda 1980, *Geometrical Nonlinearity of Stiffening Arch*
Maeda 1980, *Extended Study on Fatigue of Steel Plate in Tension with a Stud in Shear*
Maeda 1980, *Progress Report of Study on Ultimate Strength of Hybrid composite Girders*
Maeda 1980, *Progress Report of Study on Ultimate Strength of Hybrid Composite Girders*
Maeda 1980, *Progress Report of Study on Ultimate Strength of Partial-Composite Continuous Beams*
Maeda 1981, *Finite Displacement Analysis of Thin Plates by Finite Strip Method*
Maeda 1981, *Progress of Preflexed Beam Structures*
Maeda 1981, *Application of Steel-Concrete Composite Constructions*
Maeda 1982, *Finite Out-of-Plane Behavior of Rectangular Plates in Shear*
Maeda 1982, *Study on Finite Out-of-Plane Deformation of Rectangular Plates Subjected to*
Maeda 1982, *Fatigue Strength of Concrete-Filled Grillage Decks*
Maeda 1982, *Influence of Initial Deflection of Plate Girder Web on Fatigue Crack Initiation*
Maeda 1982, *Static and Fatigue Behaviors of Continuous Composite Beams with Preflex Beams*
Marin 1979, *A Vocabulary for Steel Structures*
Marin 1980, *Computing Undimensional Normal Stress Resultants*
Minami 1980, *Hysteretic Characteristics of Beam-to-Column Connections in Steel Reinforced*
Moncarz 1981, *Steel Frames with Nonlinear Connections*
Mortelmans 1981, *Approximate Method for Lateral Load Analysis of High-Rise Buildings*
Murzewski 1979, *Characteristic and Design Values for the Limit States Analysis*

Nakamura 1980, *Shaking Table Test of Steel Frames*

Rentschler 1980, *Tests of Beam-to-Column Web Moment Connections*
Rentschler 1982, *Beam-to-Column Web Connection Details*
Rosman 1981, *Classification of Floor Structures*
Ross 1976, *Design Criteria for Steel I-Columns under Axial Load and Biaxial Bending*
Ross 1980, *Fabricated Tubular Steel Columns*
Rutenberg 1981, *A Direct P-Delta Analysis Using Standard Plane Frame Programs*
Rutenberg 1982, *Simplified P-Delta Analyses for Asymmetric Structures*

Standig 1976, *Tests of Bolted Beam-to-Column Flange Moment Connections*
Sugimoto 1980, *Small End Restraint Effects on Strength of H-Columns*
Sugimoto 1982, *Small End Restraint Effects on Strength of H-Columns*

Taranath 1975, *Optimum Belt Truss Locations for High-Rise Structures*
Toma 1979, *Analysis of Fabricated Tubular Columns*

Wakabayashi 1976, *A Study on the Superposition Method to Estimate the Ultimate Strength of Steel*
Wakabayashi 1977, *Hysteretic Behavior of Steel Braces Subjected to Horizontal Load Due to*
Wakabayashi 1977, *Cyclic Behavior of a Restrained Steel Brace under Axial Loading*
Wakabayashi 1977, *Experimental Studies on the Elastic-Plastic Behavior of Braced Frames under*
Wakabayashi 1977, *A New Design Method of Long Composite Beam-Columns*
Wakabayashi 1977, *Seismic Design of Mixed Steel Concrete Structures in Japan*
Wakabayashi 1978, *Experimental Study on the Elastic-Plastic Response of Steel Frames under*
Wakabayashi 1980, *Experimental Studies on the Elastic-Plastic Behavior of Braced Frames under*
Wakabayashi 1980, *Experimental Studies on the Elastic-Plastic Behavior of Braced Frames under*
Wardenier 1982, *Hollow Section Joints*

Structural Design of Tall Concrete and Masonry Buildings

Introductory Review

Ignacio Martín

Volume CB of the Monograph, *Structural Design of Tall Concrete and Masonry Buildings,* was published in 1978 and contains technical references up to 1977. Since 1977, there has been continuously expanding development in the technology of tall concrete and masonry buildings, especially in the following areas: in properties of material such as high-strength concrete, in creep of concrete, and in anchorage of bars; in the behavior of members and connections; in the methods of analysis of structures subjected to seismic loads; and in the methods of construction of tall concrete buildings such as the use of precast elements.

This update of the Monograph covers the main advances made in the technology of tall concrete buildings since 1977; but this field continues to be in a state of flux, and further developments are to be expected in the future. During the last five years, there has been a substantial amount of published material on tall concrete buildings. This update, authored by leading experts in the field, brings the subject up to date by collecting in one volume information scattered through publications originated in different parts of the world.

Tall concrete buildings have been intensively used worldwide in the last five years and are available not only to highly developed countries but also to emerging countries. In such countries, concrete materials are often native, thereby reducing to a minimum the importation of materials and equipment.

In speaking of technology transfer, we usually think of transfer from a highly developed country to an emerging country. In the case of tall concrete buildings, a reversed technology transfer exists: highly skilled engineers in emerging countries, making use of the limited resources available to them, come up with ingenious and imaginative uses of materials and construction techniques. These innovations can be adopted very successfully by highly developed countries. The Council on Tall Buildings and Urban Habitat is an excellent forum that fosters technology transfer between countries.

The engineering profession is indebted to the generous contribution of talent and time from the authors who have collaborated in the update of the Monograph.

Concrete Framing Systems for
Tall Buildings (CB-3)

Introduction

W. C. Krell

This chapter of the Monograph deals with basic systems. The information is fundamental and, in that sense, is timeless. It deals with a variety of structural systems in the horizontal plane, as well as with lateral load resisting systems.

A combination of structural systems for both floor systems and lateral load resisting systems is an everyday development created by structural engineers who must meet the needs of projects within the economy and competition of today's market.

The chapter remains valid and of practical use to practicing engineers, but it can also serve as an extremely valuable guide to architects, owners, and contractors.

The following article by Gutman introduces a new engineering solution to an old problem by examining the use of precast concrete panels to withstand lateral loads.

Lateral Load Resisting Systems in Concrete Buildings

Abraham Gutman

INTRODUCTION

An owner or a developer often measures successful and economical design in an office building in terms of maximum rental space expressed as the ratio of the net rentable area to the gross building area. To achieve an efficient ratio requires the close integration of all building systems — architectural, structural, and mechanical.

The contribution that the structural system can make to achieving a favorable net-to-gross ratio can obviously be significant. One measurement of a successful office building is an efficient core. An efficient core usually means a core with a very small area. In structural terms, this definition signifies that the shear wall will be very slender and will thus require integration of additional wind-resisting elements. Consequently, the concept of interior shear walls acting alone is set aside, to be replaced by structural concepts that either locate wind-resisting elements completely on the perimeter of the building or combine an interior shear wall system with bracing by perimeter structural elements.

This approach is the direction in which high-rise office design today is going. The following structural configurations represent several new concepts in the design of lateral load resisting systems. Some of the new concepts may lack the ductility necessary when considering seismic designs, although they are adequate for wind-resisting structures. When considering seismic design, special attention should be given to connections.

FRAMED TUBE WITH FACADE SHEAR PANELS

Quite often, the architectural design dictates large spacing of perimeter columns and shallow spandrel beams. A framed tube system consisting of shallow spandrel beams with large spans will be subject to large deflections and large interstory drift that are well beyond code recommendations. This type of framed tube requires considerable stiffening to reduce "shear lag." One of the methods of accomplishing this stiffening is an innovative approach that employs the precast facade as a stress-skin panel. In other words, the principal mode of resistance in the precast facade panel is shear. Depending on the column spacing, the precast facade panels can be two stories high by 6 ft, 10 ft, or 15 ft wide (see Fig. 1) or one story high by 20 ft wide for 20-ft perimeter column spacing. Since the shear panels are attached to the columns (to transfer the wind shear), the axial column strain is transmitted to the panels. If, in addition, the panel is also connected rigidly to the spandrel beam, the entire panel will be subjected to nearly uniform compression as a result of gravity loads, thereby reducing the panel capacity to resist wind shear. Then the shear panels will tend to be quite thick. To reduce panel thickness, a connection to the spandrel beam and the column must be devised that will eliminate the effect of elastic shortening of columns and retain the panel's capability to resist wind shear. To accomplish this configuration, a flexible connection between the shear panel and the spandrel beam must be

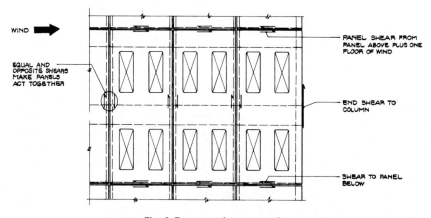

Fig. 1 Forces acting on panels

provided (Fig. 2) that transfers horizontal wind shear only and will not transfer gravity loads. To eliminate boundary strain caused by elastic column shortening entering the panel, a single connection between column and panel must be provided. This connection is located at the center of the panel (Fig. 3). To make the precast panels act together to transmit shear, dowels must be provided at the joints. To prevent the panels from moving in and out requires a flexible connection to the column at the top and bottom of the panel.

Advantages.   This innovative approach produces great savings in concrete and reinforcing. The perimeter columns can be spaced farther apart than in a conventionally framed tube design. The depth of the spandrel beam can be considerably reduced. The spandrel beam does not have to be upset, thus providing more rental space. The shear panels have a dual function; they resist wind shear and they provide an architectural skin. This dual role results in considerable cost savings.

The interior framing can be designed for gravity loads only. This design makes the core very efficient from the rental point of view.

Disadvantages.   The system introduces certain limitations in the architectural design of the facade. Connections to the perimeter frame are structural and require more quality control.

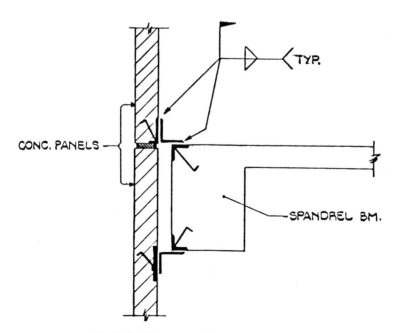

Fig. 2 Flexible connection at spandrel beam

FRAMED TUBE WITH ALTERNATING SHEAR PANELS

In the preceding system, all the facade panels were participating in resisting wind shear. The system to be discussed next introduces an innovative concept in which only selected solid precast concrete panels act structurally to reduce shear lag. The structural panels are so arranged that they stiffen the framed tube in two ways:

      a. Diagonal bracing to reduce deflection.

      b. Shear bracing to reduce interstory drift.

The diagonal bracing of panels can be arranged into K bracing (Figs. 4, 5, and 6) or X bracing. In these cases the panels will be connected to the spandrels with flexible connections (Fig. 7) that can transfer shear only. This arrangement will increase the capacity of the shear panels to resist wind shear. The elastic shortening of the columns will only affect the edges of the panels, which can be locally reinforced. The effect of elastic shortening of the columns on the panels can be further reduced by a proper erection sequencing. The sequencing of erection will have to be fine-tuned in such a way that enough dead load and live load is transferred to the panels to reduce to a minimum the tension they develop when they resist full wind load in truss action.

In very tall buildings, because of high wind shears, the connection between the concrete beam and the precast panel may have to be rigid (Fig. 8). Here again, the erection of precast panels can be delayed to significantly reduce the effect of gravity loads on the panel.

Advantages.   The advantages listed for the first system also apply to this one.

Disadvantages.   This system forces the architect to incorporate the diagonal shear panels into the facade design. The erection sequence of precast concrete panels may increase the cost of construction.

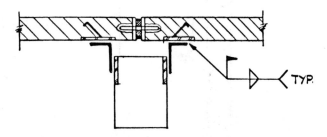

Fig. 3 Connection at column

SHEAR WALLS WITH OUTRIGGERS

When a shear wall is very slender and the building is experiencing excessive drift, it is often desirable to connect the shear wall to the exterior columns at one or more locations. The basic principle involved here is utilization of the core to develop horizontal shears and to provide for vertical shear transfer from the core to the exterior columns to develop the total overturning capacity of the full building dimension.

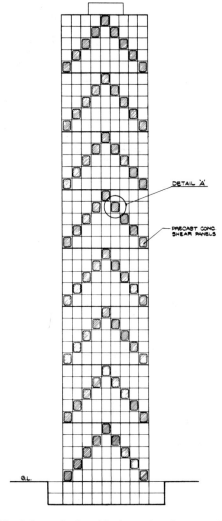

Fig. 4 Framed tube with alternating shear panels

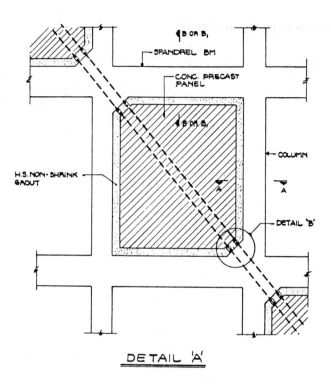

DETAIL 'A'

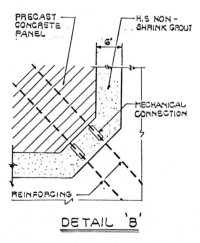

DETAIL 'B'

Fig. 5 Framed tube with alternating shear panels—details

The outrigger system consists of a diagonal strut that often runs through the interior partitions of several floors and connects the shear wall to the perimeter columns (Fig. 9). The diagonal strut will have to be designed for compression and tension because of wind reversal. It will usually be a steel member, and careful attention must be given to the connection at the shear wall, because quite a large vertical shear will have to be transferred. The diagonal strut can also be a concrete member. In this case, the erection sequence will have to be fine-tuned to develop an initial compression in the diagonal strut. The floor will act as bracing elements for the diagonal strut. An outrigger system was utilized on the 55-story Petro-Canada office complex in Calgary, Alberta.

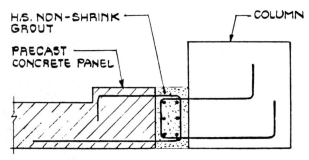

Fig. 6 Section A-A

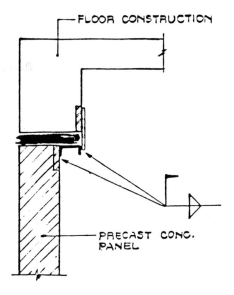

Fig. 7 Section B-B

Advantages.   The outrigger system allows for a very efficient core design and produces considerable economy in terms of reinforcing and concrete.

Disadvantages.   The system affects the office flexibility on several floors. Careful consideration has to be given to the differential elastic shortening between the core and the exterior columns. If the shear wall has larger stresses due to gravity loads than the perimeter columns, the outrigger will load the perimeter columns, thus contributing to design inefficiency. Proper sequencing of erection, or a delayed final connection of the diagonal strut will alleviate this problem. Careful consideration must also be given to the fact that the perimeter columns connected to an outrigger will be subject to greater elastic shortening than the perimeter columns not connected to an outrigger.

SHEAR WALLS WITH LARGE TRANSFER GIRDERS CONNECTING THE SHEAR WALLS TO PERIMETER COLUMNS

Basically, this system is a variation on the outrigger system. Quite often the architect requires open spaces on the lower levels of the building, especially in high-rise hotels. Interior columns may have to be picked up on deep transfer girders. If the transfer girders can be made one floor deep, then they will connect the shear wall with the perimeter columns, thus developing the overturning capacity of the full building plan width (Fig. 10).

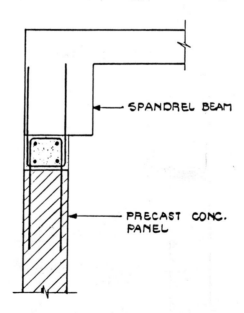

SPANDREL BEAM

PRECAST CONC. PANEL

Fig. 8 Section B₁-B₁

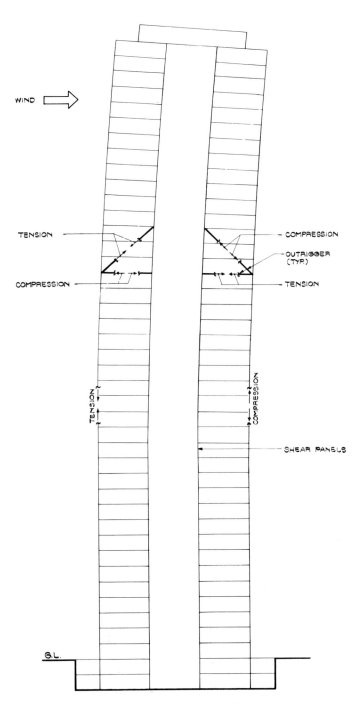

Fig. 9 Shear walls with outrigger

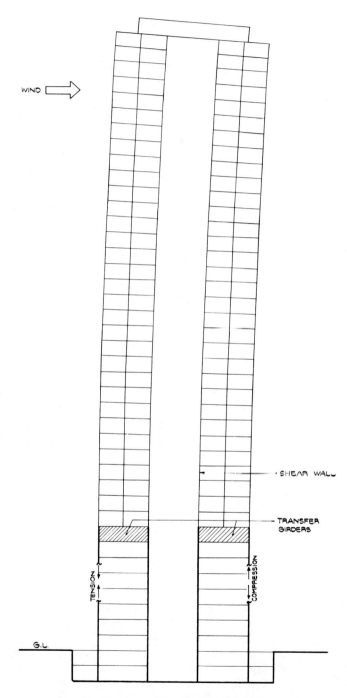

Fig. 10 Shear walls with transfer girders

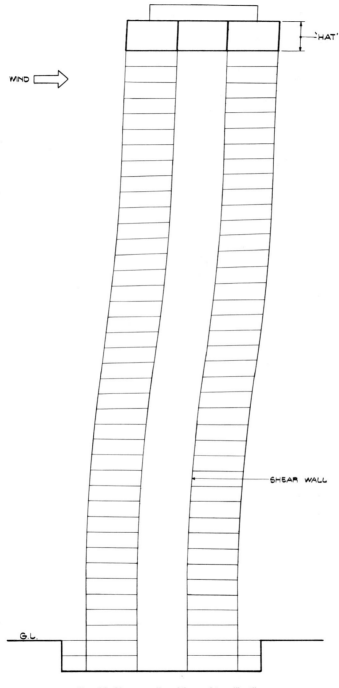

Fig. 11 Shear walls with roof-top "hat"

Advantages. This system allows for very efficient core design and utilizes transfer girders in resisting lateral loads. Deep concrete girders have excellent capacity to resist vertical shear.

Disadvantages. The disadvantages listed for the outrigger system also apply to this system.

SHEAR WALL WITH A ROOF-TOP "HAT"

This system (Fig. 11) has been used successfully on many high-rise buildings. Nevertheless, it deserves to be mentioned again because of its extreme efficiency. If there is room in the top mechanical space or if the building can afford an increase in height, then the shear wall can be connected to the perimeter columns by a structural "hat". This hat may be a grid system composed of reinforced concrete girders, or it may be a space frame. The hat develops the tension and compression capabilities of the exterior columns to help resist lateral movement. The interaction of the hat and the perimeter columns puts a counter-rotational movement into the interior shear wall. Thus, the structure exhibits a reverse curvature, with a point of counter-flexure at approximately the top quarter point. Compared to an unrestrained cantilever, the overturning moment in the core is reduced by about 30–40%, and the drift is also significantly reduced. In addition, if the perimeter columns are exposed, the hat will restrain the columns against excessive movements due to differential temperatures.

CONDENSED REFERENCES/BIBLIOGRAPHY

The following is a condensed bibliography for this article. It includes all articles referred to or cited in the text. The full citations will be found at the end of the volume, with additional citations for further reading. What is given here should be sufficient information to lead the reader to the correct article: the author, date, and title. In case of multiple authors, only the first name is listed.

ACI 1973, *Response of Multistory Concrete Structures to Lateral Forces*
Coull 1966, *Tall Buildings*
Weidlinger 1973, *Shear Field Panel Bracing*

Recent Developments in Elastic Analysis of Tall Concrete Buildings

A. Coull

B. Stafford Smith

INTRODUCTION

In the '60s and early '70s, the evolution of new structural forms for tall buildings gave stimulus to the development of methods of analysis. This stimulus has now diminished. Much of the research has been done, and approximate analytical methods are available for almost all the identifiable regular forms of high-rise structure. More powerful and sophisticated computer programs for general structural analysis are now widely available, as well as some comprehensive programs for tall building analysis. Consequently the designer is usually able to analyze the most complex high-rise structure without recourse to the researcher.

As a result, there have been few radically new developments in the elastic analysis of concrete buildings in the past few years, and this has been reflected by the slower pace of publications. It has been a period of consolidation, with past research work being digested and brought into use in the design office. However, specific techniques have been refined and some gaps in the field of knowledge have been filled.

The continuing evolution of computer systems, and the introduction of the new series of mini- and microcomputers has led to some reappraisal of structural analysis programs. General developments of elastic structural analysis have continued, but much more attention is now being paid to nonlinear problems involving either inelastic material behavior or large displacement conditions. Such developments, of course, apply equally to tall building structures and other structural forms. In recent years, there has also been a greater awareness of the importance of taking account of the soil-structure interaction (Goschy, 1978), rather than dealing with the superstructure as an isolated system, and many analytical models attempt to include more realistic base conditions.

The power of the digital computer, allied with the highly developed matrix-displacement method of analysis using either line or surface finite elements, means that in theory it is now possible to analyze accurately virtually any elastic structure; the only constraint is the capacity of the computer concerned. However, it is rarely economic, or necessary, to analyze exactly the very large three-dimensional structural assemblies encountered in tall buildings, and some simplified mathematical model is normally adopted from which it is anticipated that realistic results may be obtained. The main problem then lies in devising the simplest model that will reproduce the main structural actions of the building, and development work is still underway in this field. Attempts are being made to determine the dominant modes of behavior that must be included in any analysis. It will then be possible to balance the computing time, cost, and accuracy required for a realistic design solution. Different considerations will naturally prevail between the early design stages and the final check calculations.

Since it is generally unnecessary to undertake a comprehensive structural analysis of the complex three-dimensional tall building structure, specific techniques have been devised for common structural forms; the main classification of the problem, and the most appropriate techniques for analysis, were presented in the Monograph (Council on Tall Buildings, Group CB, 1978), and these are still applicable in general terms. However, developments and refinements have occurred in specific area, and these are described in this paper. For conciseness, only a limited set of selected references are given. They have been chosen to be the most appropriate or relevant to a particular topic and, as far as possible, to be the latest in the field, so that they contain adequate reference to earlier work.

Since the Monograph was published, a comprehensive bibliography on load bearing wall systems has been published (Singh, 1976) that covers the period 1928–1976 and contains over 1000 entries. A review of the techniques available for analysis of such structures has also been published recently (Macleod, 1977b).

The present paper restricts itself to a review of the more important developments that have occurred since the Monograph chapter was compiled.

ANALYSIS OF TALL BUILDINGS BY THE FINITE ELEMENT METHOD

The highly formalized finite element method is now firmly established as the most important analytical technique for the analysis of complex structures. By describing a structure as an assemblage of line, plate, and shell elements, including both bending and in-plane actions, the interaction between different assemblies of walls, cores, frames, and floor slabs in different planes may easily be established. With standard programs being readily available, the method may be used for the elastic analysis of virtually any system and may be applied directly to any tall building structure. The method has been well documented in numerous papers and books.

It is rarely necessary to use the technique in the design and analysis of tall buildings, since the simpler analogous frame and continuum approaches are generally sufficiently accurate for practical purposes. The method need generally be employed only to obtain detailed information on local stress fields for specific investigations of localized areas where discontinuities or stress concentrations occur.

However, special elements have been developed that are particularly appropriate for particular building components such as coupled shear walls (Goodno and Gere, 1976; Chan and Cheung, 1979; Kabaila and Edwards, 1979; Weaver et al., 1981). These elements have been specially devised for linking walls to connecting beam elements and for walls containing irregular perforations.

ANALYSIS OF SHEAR WALL STRUCTURES BY THE FINITE STRIP METHOD

Although the finite element method is the most powerful and versatile method of analysis for plane and spatial structures, there is nevertheless scope for the development of other techniques that may have the advantage of greater efficiency or economy for specific forms of structural systems. The finite strip technique can be claimed to fall into this category, as it has particular advantages for structures that are essentially uniform in one direction, which is frequently the case with tall structures containing shear walls and cores. Although the finite strip method was first introduced in 1968, and widely developed for bridge structures, only relatively recently has its extension to tall structures been realized.

In this method, a plane structure is divided into a series of strips running in the vertical direction. By making suitable assumptions regarding the mode of deformation of each strip, stiffness matrices can be formulated, and a solution can be obtained from considerations of equilibrium and compatibility along each strip boundary. The method may be regarded as a combination of the primary features of the classical Levy solution for plate structures with those of the finite element technique. The strip elements may be used in conjunction with the continuum representation of either a set of connecting beams or a rigidly jointed frame (shear cantilever representation) to achieve continuous solutions for planar and nonplanar coupled shear walls and wall frame structures (Fransson, 1977; Cheung and Swaddiwudhipong, 1978). The technique can cope with discontinuities in structural platform throughout the height of the building and can offer significant savings in computer time over the finite element method.

DEVELOPMENTS IN ANALYSIS OF SPATIAL PANEL AND CORE STRUCTURES

At the time of compilation of the Monograph chapter, comparatively little work had been done on the analysis of nonplanar coupled shear walls, spatial panel structures, and beam-connected open-box core structures. The latter are of particular importance in the design of tall buildings, since they may be employed as the sole lateral load resisting element of a suspended building or as major strong points for resisting lateral forces when acting in conjunction with shear walls or columns in cross-wall or flat-plate structures. Consequently, a number of studies have been made of such structures, using both discrete and continuum techniques. Under the actions of lateral forces, such structures are frequently subjected to both bending and torsional actions and, because of the resulting restrained warping stresses, the latter may be of considerable significance in design.

Using Vlasov's warping-torsion theory for thin-walled elements, in conjunction with a continuum representation of the set of connecting beams, explicit solutions have been obtained for standard load cases, leading to the production of convenient design curves (Rutenberg and Tso, 1975). The transfer matrix method (Liauw and Leung, 1975) has been used to include variations in stiffness throughout the height.

Since Vlasov's theory is not well known to many practicing engineers, an alternative approach has been developed from a simpler folded-plate formulation; the two methods yield identical results if the same basic assumptions are made. In this approach, the spatial core structure is assumed to be composed of a number of vertical plate or beam elements, subjected only to in-plane actions and continuously connected along their vertical edges. Considerations of overall and local equilibrium conditions, in conjunction with conditions of equilibrium and compatibility along the edges, lead to a governing third-order differential equation. Explicit solutions may then be obtained for particular load conditions.

The method appears to have been first used for doubly symmetrical rectangular core structures (Kanchi and Dar, 1973) but, based on the concept of a fixed vertical shear center, recent research has shown that the same general expressions apply to a wide range of asymmetrical multicell and multibay cores (Coull and Tawfik, 1981a).

The above techniques, which are suitable for hand calculations, are most appropriate for systems that are uniform through their height or contain only a very small number of discontinuities. For less regular structures, it is necessary to use discrete techniques, and a number of different methods have been proposed for core and nonplanar-wall and spatial-panel structures.

It is generally assumed that because of the high in-plane stiffness of the floor slabs that surround the core, the cross-sectional shape remains undeformed. When subjected to bending or torsional actions, the core cross section undergoes only rigid body movements in any horizontal plane, and the constituent elements are subjected primarily to in-plane actions.

Particular difficulties arise with a finite element analysis in cases where beams connect into the core in the plane of the elements, thus requiring a rotational degree of freedom of the corner in the plane of the element. The problems can be surmounted, even using a basic plane-stress element program, by introducing an auxiliary system of restraining beams, but the increased complexity of the model adds to the time and cost involved, and alternative techniques using analogous line elements are preferable.

In the simplest stiffness-matrix method, the cantilevered core is represented by a series of story-height line elements along the vertical axis. In addition to the conventional six degrees of freedom at each node—three translational and three rotational displacements—an additional degree of freedom is added to represent the warping displacement of the cross section (Taranath, 1976); (Girgis and Stafford Smith, 1979). The total stiffness matrix of each element is then on the order of 14 x 14 and may be derived from the warping theory or folded-plate method. The solution procedure is similar to those used in the matrix analysis of frames.

An alternative technique is a direct extension of the wide-column technique (Council on Tall Buildings, Group CB, 1978) (Macleod, 1977b), devised originally for the analysis of coupled shear walls. In this method (Macleod and Hosny, 1977a), each wall panel is replaced along its centroidal axis by a line element of equivalent bending and shearing rigidity. The width of each wall is represented by flexurally rigid arms, equal in length to the wall width and attached rigidly to the column at each floor level. The rigid arms of adjacent walls are hinged together at the corners to transmit vertical shear and achieve compatibility between the walls. Connecting lintel beams are represented in the usual manner and special diagonal bracing members are employed to prevent distortion of the cross section. The analogous frame can then be analyzed by a stiffness-matrix method, by making special provision to represent the rigid arms, or by using a three-dimensional framework program and assigning very high values of flexural ridigity to the rigid segments. Although the method is attractive in avoiding warping theory, in its present form it appears that it may not represent as accurately as other techniques the behavior of thin-walled cores (Girgis and Stafford Smith, 1979).

An alternative analogous frame module (Stafford Smith and Abate, 1981a) that appears to provide a more accurate representation of nonplanar structures consists of three vertical members, across the ends of which are connected horizontal flexurally rigid beams. The vertical members include a column along the centroidal axis of the wall segment, with a hinge at its mid-height, and a pair of pin-ended links at the edges of the module. In this module, the column provides the required shearing resistance by contraflexure bending, the links provide the bending resistance by a couple resulting from their differential axial resistance, and the combined sectional areas of the three vertical members provide the vertical axial stiffness. Solutions may readily be achieved by any three-dimensional-framework computer program.

A different approach (Kristek, 1979) that has been used successfully makes use of the generalized folded-plate theory developed for roof and bridge structures. To make use of the standard stiffness matrices, a substitute simply supported structure, of twice the true height, is derived by creating a mirror image of the system about the fixed foundation position. Appropriate force systems are superimposed to produce the correct applied loading. The structure stiffness matrix is formed by an assembly of the stiffness matrices of the constituent elements using special elements to describe systems of connecting beams and with floor slabs included as diaphragms of the folded-plate system. The analysis can be carried out by introducing minor adjustments to existing folded-plate computer programs.

OUTRIGGER-BRACED STRUCTURES

An outrigger-braced tall building structure consists of a stiff core, comprised of shear walls or a braced steel frame in the center of the building. The core is connected to exterior columns by flexurally stiff cantilevers at one or more levels throughout the height. When lateral loading acts on the structure, the outriggers and columns resist the bending of the core and hence reduce the drift and base moment that would have resulted with a free-standing core on its own. Outrigger bracing is one of the most efficient and economical systems for controlling drift in tall buildings; the core and columns serve the functional requirements of the building, while the additional outrigger elements are usually incorporated within the plant levels and interfere only minimally with the building's usable space.

The magnitude of the reduction in drift and core moment depends on the relative flexural rigidities of the core, the outriggers, and the columns acting axially about the centroid of the core, as well as on the number and locations of the outriggers within the height of the core.

Based essentially on the application of engineer's beam theory for all elements, it was shown (Taranath, 1975) that the optimum location for a single outrigger was close to the mid-height of the building. Subsequent studies produced generalized results for the optimum locations in multi-outrigger structures for any number of outriggers. These studies assumed the outriggers to be flexurally rigid. A recent investigation (Stafford Smith and Salim, 1981b), which takes into account the flexibility of the outriggers, describes a comprehensive parameter study of the various important structural characteristics, and concludes that four outriggers appear to be the maximum justifiable number for drift control.

FRAMED-TUBE, HULL-CORE, AND BUNDLED-TUBE STRUCTURES

Although framed-tube structures are highly indeterminate three-dimensional frameworks, they can, under certain conditions, be analyzed as effective plane trusses. When they are linked to an interior core to form a hull-core or tube-in-tube system, or when they are combined with interior framed webs to form a modular-tube structure, the analysis requires a further consideration of compatibility and equilibrium between the different elements to achieve a solution (Council on Tall Buildings, Group CB, 1978). In all cases, a considerable computational effort is required.

As a result, simplified techniques have been developed to allow an approximate solution to be achieved. Such a solution gives an assessment of the degree of shear lag and the lateral deflections that occur and is suitable for the early stages of design calculations. The frame panels have been replaced by equivalent orthotropic plates, in which the racking stiffness of the frames is modeled by a reduced shearing stiffness of the plate (Ha et al., 1978). By making simplifying assumptions on the distributions of axial and shear forces in the beams and columns and the corresponding stresses in the equivalent plate, closed-form solutions have been obtained, enabling design curves to be produced for both bending and torsion (Coull and Ahmed, 1978). With the aid of further simplifying assumptions, the method can be used for the approximate analysis of bundled-tube structures (Coull et al., 1982).

PLANAR WALL AND FRAME STRUCTURES

The bulk of the essential work on the analysis of combinations of planar wall and frame structures was completed prior to the compilation of the Monograph, and major new developments are unlikely. A few investigations have been made either to extend and simplify earlier analyses or to fill gaps in the literature.

The continuum technique for coupled walls, allied with the shear cantilever concept for rigidly jointed frames, has been further extended to give
solutions for combinations of walls, coupled walls, and frames, including the
influence of elastic foundations (Arviddsson, 1979). Solutions have also been
achieved for wall frame structures with rigidly jointed connecting beams
(Basu and Nagpal, 1980).

Another generalized approach to tall building analysis, also based on the
continuum technique for coupled shear walls, has proposed that coupled
shear walls, braced frames, and moment-resisting frames are all cantilevers
of the same structural family (Stafford Smith et al., 1980). Each can be
represented by a pair of structural parameters, representing their shear and
flexural stiffnesses, whose values can be substituted in a generalized deflection
equation or in graphs to obtain their deflection behavior. This approach has
the potential of providing a generalized solution for structures combining a
variety of types of bent.

The shear cantilever analogy for the simplified analysis of multistory
multibay frames has been extended (Chan et al., 1975) to include the influence
of axial forces in the columns, which may be of considerable significance for
tall structures. This extension has been achieved by making further assumptions
regarding the distribution of axial deformations of the columns across the
width of the building.

THREE-DIMENSIONAL ASSEMBLIES OF WALLS, FRAMES, AND CORES

Work has continued on the development of suitable methods of analysis of
three-dimensional assemblies of walls, coupled walls, frames, and cores. This
work has followed the general procedures outlined in the Monograph Chapter
CB-5 (1978). In view of the complexity of the complete building structure, the
aim has been to seek simplified models that will represent with sufficient
accuracy the behavior of the prototype structure. To do so, it is generally
assumed that the floor structures are infinitely rigid in plane and infinitely
flexible out of plane, so that horizontal strains in the elements may be
neglected. Further simplifying assumptions may also be made regarding the
mode of action of individual elements in particular structures; the object is
generally to reduce as far as possible the number of degrees of freedom that
must be used in the analysis.

A generalized continuum method (Danay et al., 1974), suitable for the
analysis of asymmetrical multistory structures with uniform cross-sectional
properties, has been developed from techniques described in the Monograph
chapter. The unknowns of the problem consist of three horizontal rigid body
displacement functions, together with an axial displacement function for
each individual wall connected by beams. Using a variational formulation,

an equilibrium system of linear differential equations is obtained, and direct and numerical solutions are presented.

In one discrete technique (Harman and Walker, 1975), a set of nodal floors are selected between which only minor changes in the structure occur. At each floor level, constraints are imposed that permit columns and walls to be treated in the same general manner and a stiffness matrix with a fraction of the natural degrees of freedom is assembled using one component matrix for each "member group" of similar members; this component matrix is based on the member group's average properties between nodal floors. For final analysis, greater accuracy can be achieved by using additional nodal floors.

A simpler more approximate technique (Haris, 1978), suitable for solution on a small computer, uses the cantilever method to derive the flexibility and stiffness matrices for each frame. The lateral load on the building may then be distributed among the components according to the approximate stiffness matrix of each frame, shear wall, or bracing. Both bending and twisting of the building may be considered.

The partitioning of the structure into a series of plane frames forms the basis for a substructure technique (Nair, 1975), which may be employed for the analysis of three-dimensional multistory building frames. The analysis is exact within the limitations that the torsional stiffness of all members is neglected and the floor slabs are assumed rigid in their own planes.

A very simplified technique suitable for long slab-type buildings can be solved on a hand calculator. It has been achieved by the reduction of the framed structure to one built-in column with equivalent bending and torsional stiffnesses (Mortelmans et al., 1981). The discrete actions of the horizontal members on the columns are distributed over the story heights. If the floor systems are treated as rigid in the horizontal plane, the calculation is reduced to the solution of a set of four linear equations. The determination of the internal actions then requires only some further simple operations.

An analysis of staggered wall-beam structures has been produced by replacing the structure by an equivalent plane frame (Mee et al., 1975). Effective stiffnesses of the wall, lintel, and floor slabs are combined to determine the properties of an equivalent uniform beam, taking into account the influence of local deformations at the lintel-web junction.

INTERACTION BETWEEN FLOOR SLABS AND SHEAR WALLS

In tall buildings, the shear walls are designed essentially to resist gravitational forces. However, in some cases the slabs are rigidly connected to the vertical load bearing elements, particularly shear walls, and so are constrained to bend with those elements under the action of lateral forces. In such cases the slabs can play an effective role in resisting the lateral forces as well. Such systems can be analyzed using the techniques developed for beam-connected shear walls, provided the effective width or stiffness of the slab that acts as an equivalent beam can be established.

At the time the Monograph was compiled, the only data available for the designer was a set of curves produced from a finite-difference solution of the plate-bending problem (Council on Tall Buildings, Group CB, 1978). Since then, much research has been carried out to obtain a more comprehensive understanding of the interaction between laterally loaded shear walls and connected floor slabs. Solutions have been obtained by using the finite element approach in particular (Petersson, 1972; Black et al., 1974; Tso and Mahmoud, 1977), but an influence coefficient technique has also been used (Wong and Coull, 1980) and yields accurate results with much less computational effort. The influence of the most important parameters—wall shape and spacing, flange dimensions, and wall depth and thickness—has been examined; and a comprehensive set of design curves, giving the value of the effective width or stiffness for a wide range of practical configurations, has been presented for use in a design office (Coull and Wong, 1981b).

Attempts have also been made to elucidate both the nature of the shear transfer between wall and slab and the distributions of bending moments in the slab (Wong, 1979). Similar problems exist with flat-plate structures, in which the floor slabs interact with laterally loaded columns in a tall building (Vanderbilt, 1979; Elias and Georgiadis, 1979).

However, care must be exercised when using such design curves based on an elastic analysis (Schwaighofer and Collins, 1977). High stress concentrations occur at the inner corridor edges of the walls, particularly with plane walls, and localized cracking of the concrete and a loss of stiffness at the joint may occur, with a consequent redistribution of stresses.

DIRECT P-Δ COMPUTER ANALYSIS OF FRAMED STRUCTURES

A method of computer analysis that combines in a single run the first-order effects of all loading and the second-order P-Δ effects of gravity loading was referred to in Chapter CB-8 of the Monograph. This method merits further reference here because of its simplicity and considerable practical utility (Nixon et al., 1975). In this method, the structural model for a conventional first-order analysis is modified in each story by adding a fictitious negative area bracing member. The bracing members, whose sectional areas are a function of the gravity loading carried in the corresponding stories, soften the sway stiffness of the structure to allow P-Δ additional deflections and actions to be induced. The method is direct and accurate except for small errors in the column shears and axial forces, which may be easily adjusted by statical considerations.

A more recent technique for a direct computer analysis incorporating P-Δ effects (Rutenberg, 1980; Rutenberg, 1981) is as simple to apply and avoids errors in the column axial forces. A fictitious additional column is connected by links in plane with the considered bent. In each story, the column is assigned a negative shear area whose size depends on the gravity load acting through that story. Similar to the negative area bracing, the negative shear area softens the sway stiffness in each story to allow the P-Δ additional deflections and actions to be induced. An alternative method using a fictitious column involves assigning to the column segment in each story a negative moment of inertia, whose size depends on the gravity loading carried through that story. In this case the column rotation must be restrained at each framing level.

APPLICATION OF ELASTIC METHODS OF ANALYSIS TO NONLINEAR ELASTO-PLASTIC ANALYSIS OF STRUCTURES

Although the techniques described in the Monograph Chapter CB-5 and in the present paper have been devised specifically for the elastic analysis of tall concrete building structures, they may be extended in many cases to allow inelastic behavior to be assessed. This extension may be achieved, if the nonlinear behavior is treated in a quasi-linear or piecewise-linear fashion, by assuming that under limiting conditions the cross section of a member becomes fully plastic, and that for further load increments that section behaves as if it were a plastic hinge.

If an analogous frame approach is used, an initial elastic analysis allows the determination of the first plastic hinge position at the most highly stressed cross section. A load increment is added, for which the structure is assumed to behave elastically with the single plastic hinge inserted, and the superposition of the initial and incremental systems enables the position of the next plastic hinge that forms to be established. The procedure is repeated systematically until ultimate conditions are reached when the structure is transformed into a mechanism, or until some other limiting condition, such as a maximum deflection or limit of ductility in a member, is attained. The nonlinear behavior is then represented by a series of linear curves.

If the continuum approach is adopted, a similar procedure is employed, but in this case a "plastic zone" of elements containing plastic hinges is assumed to develop. The problem then consists of determining the boundaries of the elastic and pin-ended "plastic" regions at any load increment. The behavior may again be traced from elastic to limiting conditions on a step-by-step linear basis.

Analyses have generally been restricted to plane coupled shear walls (Gluck, 1973; Nayar and Coull, 1976) and simple core structures (Schwaighofer and Ho, 1980; Coull and Tawfik, 1981c), but there appears to be no intrinsic reason why the techniques cannot be extended to deal with more complex structural forms.

In the particular case of coupled shear walls, it has been demonstrated that the computations may be considerably simplified, with little loss of accuracy, if further assumptions are made regarding the distributions of beam shear forces in the elastic regions (Pekau and Gocevski, 1981).

FUTURE DEVELOPMENTS

In view of the nature of the analysis function, it is likely that the present trends will continue, and levels of activity will reflect the amount of new construction at the time. Developments of analytical techniques for tall building structures will keep pace with those for other comparable structural forms. Emphasis will continue on the development of special techniques appropriate to particular situations.

If radically new forms of tall building structures evolve, a corresponding impetus will be given to the development of appropriate analytical techniques, since theory and analysis tend to follow practice in this field.

Refinements will be made continuously as it becomes possible to build new information into mathematical models simulating, for example, material behavior, joint stiffnesses, soil-structure parameters, and so on. It is likely that the search will continue to provide readily available information, in the form of charts and graphs, that may be applied directly in the early design stages.

More work is also required on the prediction of structural behavior during the construction stages.

CONDENSED REFERENCES/BIBLIOGRAPHY

The following is a condensed bibliography for this article. It includes all articles referred to or cited in the text. The full citations will be found at the end of the volume, with additional citations for further reading. What is given here should be sufficient information to lead the reader to the correct article: the author, date, and title. In case of multiple authors, only the first name is listed.

Arvidsson 1979, *Interaction between Coupled Shear Walls and Frames*

Basu 1980, *Frame-Wall Systems with Rigidly-Jointed Link Beams*
Black 1974, *Stiffness of Flat Plates in Cross-Wall Structures*

Chan 1975, *Approximate Analysis of Multistory Multibay Frames*
Chan 1979, *Analysis of Shear Walls Using Higher Order Finite Elements*
Cheung 1978, *Analysis of Frame Shear Wall Structures Using Finite Strip Elements*
Coull 1978, *Deflections of Framed-Tube Structures*

Coull 1981a, *Analysis of Core Structures Subjected to Torsion*
Coull 1981b, *Bending Stiffness of Floor Slabs in Cross-Wall Structures*
Coull 1981c, *Elasto-Plastic Analysis of Core Structures Subjected to Torsion*
Coull 1982, *Simplified Analysis of Bundled-Tube Structures*
Council on Tall Buildings, Group CB 1978, *Structural Design of Tall Concrete and Masonry Buildings*

Danay 1974, *The Axial Strain Effects of Load Distribution in Nonsymmetric Tier Buildings*

Elias 1979, *Flat Slab Analysis Using Equivalent Beams*

Fransson 1977, *A Generalized Finite Strip Method for Plate and Wall Structures*

Girgis 1979. *The Torsion Analysis of Tall Building Cores Partially Closed by Beams*
Gluck 1973, *Elasto-Plastic Analysis of Coupled Shear Walls*
Goodno 1976, *Analysis of Shear Cores Using Superelements*
Goschy 1978, *Soil-Foundation-Structure Interaction*

Ha 1978, *Orthotropic Membrane for Tall Building Analysis*
Haris 1978, *Approximate Stiffness Analysis of High-Rise Buildings*
Harman 1975, *Analysis of Tall Buildings Using Member-Groups*

Kabaila 1979, *Hybrid Element Applied to Shear Wall Analysis*
Kanchi 1973, *Torsion of Rectangular Shear Cores of Tall Buildings*
Kristek 1979, *Folded Plate Approach to Analysis of Shear Wall Systems and Frame Structures*

Liauw 1975, *Torsion Analysis of Core Wall Structures by the Transfer Matrix Method*

Macleod 1977a, *Frame Analysis of Shear Wall Cores*
Macleod 1977b, *Structural Analysis of Wall Systems*
Mee 1975, *Wall-Beam Frames under Static Lateral Load*
Mortelmans 1981, *Approximate Method for Lateral Load Analysis of High-Rise Buildings*

Nair 1975, *Linear Structural Analysis of Multistory Buildings*
Nayar 1976, *Elasto-Plastic Analysis of Coupled Shear Walls*
Nixon 1975, *Simplified Second-Order Frame Analysis*

Pekau 1981, *Elasto-Plastic Analysis of Coupled Shear Walls*
Petersson 1972, *Bending Stiffness of Slabs in Shear Walls*

Rutenberg 1975, *Torsional Analysis of Perforated Core Structures*
Rutenberg 1980, *A Direct P-Δ Analysis Using Standard Plane-Frame Computer Programs*
Rutenberg 1981, *Simplified P-Δ Analysis for Asymmetric Structures*

Schwaighofer 1980, *Elasto-Plastic Analysis of a Core Subjected to Torsion*
Schwaighofer 1977, *Experimental Study of the Behavior of Reinforced Concrete Coupling Slabs*
Singh 1976, *A Bibliography on Shear Walls*
Stafford Smith 1980, *A Generalized Approach to the Deflection Analysis of Braced Frame, Rigid*
Stafford Smith 1981a, *Analysis of Non-Planar Shear Wall Assemblies by Analogous Frame*
Stafford Smith 1981b, *Parameter Study of Outrigger-Braced Tall Buildings*

Taranath 1975, *Optimum Belt Truss Location for High-Rise Structures*
Taranath 1976, *The Effect of Warping on Interconnected Shear Wall-Flat Plate Structures*
Tso 1977, *Effective Width of Coupling Slabs in Shear Wall Buildings*

Vanderbilt 1979, *Equivalent Frame Analysis for Lateral Loads*

Weaver 1981, *Finite Element for Shear Walls in Multistory Frames*
Wong 1979, *Interaction Between Floor Slabs and Shear Walls in Tall Buildings*
Wong 1980, *Interaction Between Floor Slabs and Shear Walls in Tall Buildings*

Inelastic Dynamic Approach to Earthquake-Resistant Design

Mark Fintel
S. K. Ghosh

SYNOPSIS

This brief report describes an innovative procedure for aseismic design of building structures. The procedure is based on the controlled use of inelasticity in selected structural members. Certain members, not crucial to the stability of the structure and easily reparable (for instance, beams), are deliberately made weaker than other, more vital elements (for example, columns and walls). The corresponding requirements for inelastic deformability in the weak members are determined through inelastic response-history analyses of the structure under carefully selected earthquake input motions. The required deformability is provided for by proper proportioning and detailing. The resulting design assures that structural instability will not occur and that earthquake damage will be confined to designated structural elements. The other elements (columns and walls) need not be detailed for inelastic deformability. Thus, efficiency and economy, in addition to desired structural performance, can be achieved.

BACKGROUND

It was demonstrated some time ago by Veletsos and Newmark (1960) that a specific earthquake excitation causes about the same displacements in a structure whether the structure responds elastically or with any degree of inelasticity. Figure 1 illustrates this phenomenon schematically. If a structure responds elastically to a seismic event, it will be subjected to earthquake forces F_u substantially larger than those specified in all current codes. If the same structure is designed to code-specified earthquake forces F_{el} it needs to deform inelastically from E to U' to reach the amount of displacement computed for the elastic structure subjected to the earthquake forces F_u. Therefore, the code-specified forces are valid only if the corresponding required deformability is available.

A structure can be designed for any level of strength between F_w, corresponding to the design wind forces that must be resisted elastically, and F_u; how much strength to provide is basically a matter of decision. However, the consequence of the chosen strength level is the resulting inelastic deformations. The overall deformations of the structure must not lead to instability, and the damage to the structural and nonstructural elements caused by the inelastic deformations must be within acceptable limits.

Under current design practice, the elements of a structure located in a seismic zone are proportioned to resist the internal forces resulting from an elastic, static analysis of the structure under the code-specified forces F_{el} (distributed along the height of the structure in a specified manner). This procedure does not permit determination of the magnitude and location of inelastic deformations in the individual structural members. Detailing

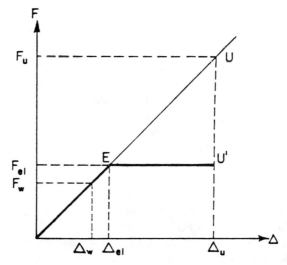

Fig. 1 Idealized earthquake force versus displacement relationship

requirements prescribed in codes are intended to ensure that all elements of a structure will have an amount of deformability commensurate with the force level for which the structure is designed. There is no way to ascertain whether the deformability thus provided will always suffice. More importantly, the need to meet stringent detailing requirements for all portions of a structure, whether actually needed and usable for seismic resistance or not, places multistory concrete structures at a distinct disadvantage in seismic regions.

INELASTIC RESPONSE-HISTORY ANALYSIS

The above problem can be alleviated, and a fairly precise determination made as to how much deformability to provide in which locations, by taking advantage of recent advances that permit dynamic inelastic response-history analyses of structures to be carried out at reasonable costs. Response-history analysis is a step-by-step tracing, in small time increments (say 1/100 of a second), of the response of a structure to an earthquake accelerogram. *Inelastic* response-history analysis implies that some or all of the members are allowed to deform beyond their elastic limits during the earthquake response of the structure. At each time interval a new analysis is carried out for the structure in its deformed state, as determined at the end of the previous time segment. Thus, each second of an earthquake record entails a large number of analyses. The output from these analyses (Fig. 2a) are bending moments, axial forces, shear forces in members, member end rotations, overall deformations, and interstory distortions. Envelope or maximum values of response quantities can be obtained from the output (Fig. 2b). These values are needed for proportioning the members. Additionally, the output in the form of time histories of the various response quantities is useful for in-depth study of the behavior of a structure during an earthquake.

Inelastic response history analysis can serve as a tool that will permit control of the extent and spread of inelasticity in a strucure; such control is related to the concept of the "structural fuse," discussed below.

THE CONCEPT OF STRUCTURAL FUSE

In many fields, provision for failure is engineered into a system, so that it occurs in a predetermined manner and possible catastrophe is avoided. For instance, fuses or circuit breakers are commonly used in electrical circuits. Pressure vessels are routinely protected by rupture disks or safety valves. The same idea can be utilized in the design of earthquake-resistant structures.

There are three big advantages to making provision in advance for planned failure in a system (Civil Engineering-ASCE, 1980):

1. Damage is less than if failure occurred in an uncontrolled manner.

2. In the event of failure or partial failure, the areas needing repair are known beforehand.

3. Repairs are usually simple and inexpensive.

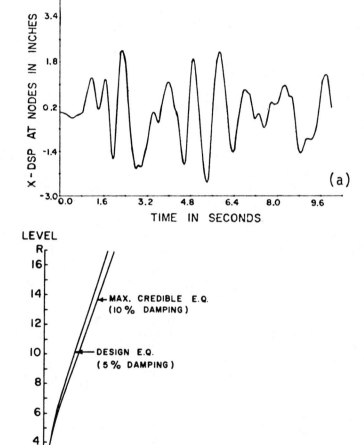

Fig. 2   (a) Time history of top horizontal displacement; (b) envelope values of horizontal displacements from a representative dynamic analysis

In a building structure, the beams are particularly suited for use as structural fuses because they are not crucial to the stability of a structure and are easy to repair. A structure can be designed such that under severe earthquake-induced excitation, all inelastic deformations will be confined to designated beams, while the more vital elements such as columns and walls will remain elastic throughout their seismic response. Earthquake damage will thus be confined to the designated structural elements, and structural instability will not occur.

Control of inelastic deformations in a structure is best achieved by intentionally making certain members weaker in relation to others. Intentionally weakened beams act as structural fuses (Fintel and Ghosh, 1981) which, as shown in Fig. 3, do the following:

1. Preset the commencement of yielding during an earthquake, thus ensuring controlled energy dissipation in selected members.

2. Reduce the moment M_y transferred from beams into columns, thus protecting the columns from hinging.

3. Reduce the seismic axial forces (tension and compression) in the columns or walls $-(M^-_y + M^+_y)/l$.

4. Decrease the congestion of reinforcement, as well as shear stresses, in the joints.

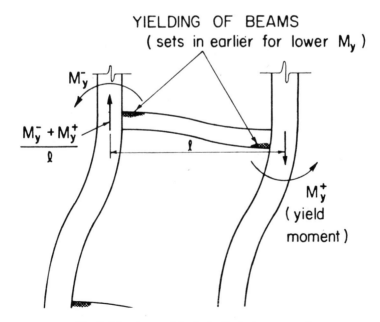

YIELDING OF BEAMS
(sets in earlier for lower M_y)

M^-_y

$$\frac{M^-_y + M^+_y}{l}$$

l

M^+_y
(yield moment)

Fig. 3 Advantages of the inelastic design approach

The strength reductions discussed above can be made only if the corresponding deformations and internal forces (computed from inelastic response-history analyses under earthquake input motions) do not violate any of a set of chosen performance criteria. If the initially chosen strength levels result in unacceptable deformations or shear or axial forces, then both suitable adjustments and structural reanalysis must be carried out until all performance criteria are satisfied. This iteration process can usually be accomplished with a small number (three to five) of analyses and is utilized in the design procedure described below.

EXPLICIT INELASTIC DYNAMIC DESIGN PROCEDURE

The suggested design procedure entails the following (Fintel and Ghosh, 1982):

1. Preliminary layout and design of the structural system for gravity loads and for code-specified wind and earthquake forces.

2. Modeling of the structure for dynamic analysis in each of the two orthogonal directions using multibay, multistory models.

3. Selection of design earthquake accelerograms that will critically excite the structure. The selection must be based on local seismicity, as well as on the dynamic characteristics of the proposed structure.

4. Specifying peformance criteria for serviceability under the design earthquake and for safety under the "hypothetical maximum credible" earthquake.

5. Determination, using inelastic response-history analysis, of forces and deformations under the design earthquake in all preliminarily selected members; and repeat of such analysis with altered strength levels for the structural members until the final member selection satisfies all performance criteria and results in an optimum relationship between strength and ductility demands.

6. Proportioning of members for strength and deformability.

7. Checking that the structure has the needed margin of ductility to meet the chosen safety criteria corresponding to the hypothetical maximum credible earthquake at the site (which will be considerably more severe than the design earthquake).

Some of these items need further elaboration.

Design and Maximum Credible Earthquake

Insofar as intensity is concerned, a design earthquake may, for example, be defined as having a peak acceleration with a 90% probability of not being exceeded in 50 years. This probability is equivalent to a return period of about 500 years. The maximum credible earthquake may, for example, be defined as having a peak acceleration with a 90% probability of not being exceeded in 500 years (or with a return period of 10,000 years).

As to frequency characteristics of earthquake input motion, a methodology has been suggested (Derecho et al., 1977) to guide the selection of accelerograms with the frequency content to critically excite a particular structure. The idea is, for an elastic structure or for a structure with limited yielding (with a correspondingly limited shift in the initial fundamental period), to select accelerograms with their relative velocity response spectra peaking around the initial fundamental period of the structure. For structures that are expected to yield extensively and thus substantially lengthen the initial fundamental period during seismic response, accelerograms should be selected with spectra that remain flat or ascend beyond the initial fundamental period of the structure. The variability of ground motion at a site makes it desirable to consider a number of potentially critical input motions in the design of a structure. The most critical input motion out of such an ensemble can usually be isolated on the basis of a few preliminary analyses (Derecho et al., 1978).

Modeling the Structure

Multistory, multibay models of frame, shear wall–frame, and shear wall structures, and not "stick" models as in some previous investigations, are used for static and dynamic analyses in the proposed design procedure. Modeling of frame–shear wall structures and of coupled wall structures has been discussed in Ghosh and Fintel (1979) and Fintel and Ghosh (1980), respectively.

Dynamic Analysis

A modified version of the computer program DRAIN-2D (Kanaan and Powell, 1975) has been selected for inelastic response-history analyses of structures. The selection was based on a comparative evaluation of this and other available programs. DRAIN-2D detemines the seismic response of plane inelastic structures, with masses lumped at nodal points, through step-by-step integration, based on the assumption of a constant response acceleration during each time step, of the coupled equations of motion. Viscous damping that has both mass-proportional and stiffness-proportional components is used.

Program DRAIN-2D accounts for inelastic effects by allowing the formation of concentrated "point hinges" at the ends of elements where the moments equal or exceed the specified yield moments. The moment versus end-rotation characteristics of elements are defined in terms of basic bilinear relationships that develop into hysteretic loops following certain specified rules. The modified Takeda model (Takeda et al., 1970) (Fig. 4), with unloading and reloading stiffnesses decreasing in loading cycles subsequent to yielding, has been utilized to specify the hysteretic behavior of reinforced concrete elements.

Performance Criteria

For the design earthquake, a set of serviceability requirements needs to be formulated; for the maximum credible earthquake, safety against collapse needs to be assured.

In general, suitable limits on inelastic deformations—shear stresses and so forth—should constitute performance (serviceability and safety) criteria and should be established through correlation with degrees of observed damage in laboratory tests. This aspect has been discussed in Fintel and Ghosh (1982). Much work remains to be done in this area.

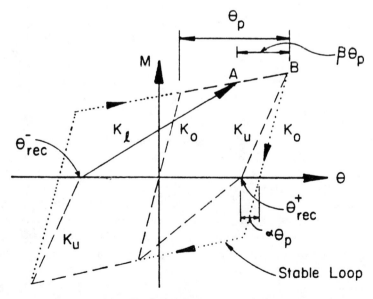

Fig. 4 Takeda model

Proportioning of Elements

The proportioning of elements for combined flexure and axial forces, shear, and inelastic deformability has been discussed in (Fintel and Ghosh, 1982).

CONCLUSION

This paper presents an approach to the design of earthquake-resistant reinforced concrete building structures based on the use of earthquake accelerograms as loading; dynamic inelastic response-history analysis to detemine member forces and deformations; and known resistance for proportioning the members. An important feature of the design procedure is that it enables the designer to establish a predetermined sequence of energy-dissipating mechanisms, and thereby to impose on the structure a desired response, permitting no alternate types of behavior. A structure so designed needs to be detailed for ductility in only the predetermined hinging regions.

A virtual optimization procedure may be employed in determining appropriate strength levels for the various structural elements. Through a numer of analyses, it is usually possible to design into the members a desirable balance among flexural strength, shear capacity, and ductility. This design promotes economy and also enhances structural performance.

CONDENSED REFERENCES/BIBLIOGRAPHY

The following is a condensed bibliography for this article. It includes all articles referred to or cited in the text. The full citations will be found at the end of the volume, with additional citations for further reading. What is given here should be sufficient information to lead the reader to the correct article: the author, date, and title. In case of multiple authors, only the first name is listed.

Civil Engineering—ASCE 1980, *Include Structural Fuse in Design*

Derecho 1977, *Structural Walls in Earthquake Resistant Buildings, Dynamic Analysis of Isolated*
Derecho 1978, *Structural Walls in Earthquake-Resistant Buildings—Analytical Investigation:*

Fintel 1980, *Seismic Resistance of a 16-Story Coupled Wall Structure: A Case Study Using Inelastic*
Fintel 1981, *The Structural Fuse: An Inelastic Approach to Seismic Design of Buildings*
Fintel 1982, *Explicit Inelastic Dynamic Design Procedure for Aseismic Structures*

Ghosh 1979, *Modelling of Frame-Shear Wall Structures for Static and Dynamic Analysis*

Kanaan 1975, *A General Purpose Computer Program for Inelastic Dynamic Response of*

Takeda 1970, *Reinforced Concrete Response to Simulated Earthquake*

Veletsos 1960, *Effect of Inelastic Behavior on the Response of Simple Systems to Earthquake Motions*

Recent Developments Concerning Deflections and Cracking Limitations in the Design of Tall R/C Buildings

Peter Gergely

SYNOPSIS

The developments in the calculation of the stiffness of tall concrete buildings include an increasing emphasis on inelastic behavior, more precise
accounting of secondary effects, and consideration of nonstructural elements.
The emphasis in crack control has switched from the prediction of crack
widths to critical examination of the reasons for crack control, specifically the
study of the relationship between cracking and corrosion.

LATERAL STIFFNESS OF BUILDINGS

Various aspects of drift limitations and several practical guidelines for
estimating lateral deflections were included in Chapter CB-9 of the Monograph
(Council on Tall Buildings, Group CB, 1978). Other chapters have also

discussed methods of elastic analysis (Chapter CB-5) and inelastic analysis (Chapter CB-6). These and other chapters (such as Chapter CB-10 on thermal effects) have proved to be highly useful in determining deformations of tall concrete structures.

The following pararaphs provide a brief summary of the latest developments and trends in the deflection control of tall concrete buildings. The emphasis is on research, rather than on the description of actual projects or on specific examples of drift control.

One of the major reasons for the limitation of horizontal deflections is to reduce secondary moments and avoid instability. In the past, most designers used approximate expressions to estimate the additional forces caused by drift. Several investigations have examined these approximate procedures and compared them with rigorous analyses that are becoming practical as the cost of computer-aided analysis decreases. The results show that in most cases the approximate drift values are conservative and the secondary moments by detailed analyses are smaller.

Since drift limits, such as 1/500, were based on experience and assured satisfactory structures while conservative approximate methods were used, the application of modern approaches may require smaller drift limits. This is especially so in the case of light framed structures with little help from secondary structural elements.

In one study, the effect of out-of-plumb of columns on the P-Δ moments was evaluated (MacGregor, 1979). It was found that these moments could be significant—comparable to the P-Δ effect resulting from lateral deflections.

Recent years have seen growing emphasis on the inelastic behavior of structures. Most of the investigations have been motivated by the needs of earthquake-resistant design. Such problems as local and overall ductility, joint behavior, local sources of nonlinear response, and the inelastic behavior of frames and walls have received increased attention. Several researchers, especially in Japan, have utilized full-scale tests to assess the safety of reinforced concrete under high-level repeated loading.

The interaction of walls and frames has also been studied in recent years, in both the linear and the nonlinear ranges. This work included the development of analytical representations of filler walls, shear walls, and coupled walls at various force levels (Darwin and Pecknold, 1976). The effects of cracks at the wall-frame interface have also been studied, although much more work needs to be done for both earthquake and wind loading.

Measurements of deflections and periods of vibration of actual structures have indicated the accuracy of analytical approaches, as well as the effects of repeated loading and age on stiffness. These comparisons showed that the measured stiffnesses were much greater than the predicted values, mainly because of the greater-than-expected contribution of nonstructural elements. Some researchers have found that the natural period of buildings increases with age by as much as 50%. This increase probably results from a reduction of the connection between walls and frames, severe wind loading, and earthquakes.

Other studies have been concerned with the torsional response of buildings, the effects of in-plane flexibility of floor slabs, the design and effectivenss of outriggers on deflections, slab-column connections, and the problems connected with the use of high-strength concrete columns.

CRACK CONTROL

Most current building codes have provisions that limit the width of cracks at the surface of concrete members. The purpose is to reduce the extent of corrosion of bars. However, in recent years, a number of engineers have questioned the relationship between surface width of cracks and corrosion. Since the surface crack width increased with the concrete cover, larger cover would induce faster corrosion, which is intuitively not correct (Gergely, 1982).

Analytical studies and measurements of the extent of corrosion under various exposure conditions have shown that the width of flexural cracks (cracks normal to the bar in question) has negligible effect on the initiation and rate of corrosion. The electro-chemical action necessary for the corrosion process to continue depends on an electric potential difference that is a function of the permeability of the concrete cover rather than the existence or width of cracks. An exception to this observation is the situation where corrosive chemicals continuously reach the bar. Also, longitudinal cracks (along the bar) rapidly lead to the corrosion of the steel.

The most important factor in corrosion protection is the permeability of the concrete cover. It is necessary to have sound concrete, which is best achieved by low slump, good vibration, and well-graded aggregates.

Therefore, in the design of members in tall buildings, cracking and thus the spacing of bars may be controlled not by corrosion but by the requirements of appearance. Since it is impossible and unwise to recommend crack-width limits to satisfy appearance, the questions of crack control may remain a problem to be settled by the designer and the owner. The crack width that might be troublesome depends on the use of the structure, the type of occupancy, the surface texture of the concrete, and the distance between the concrete surface and the occupants. Clearly this is a complicated problem.

An associated question that will emerge if crack-width limits are relaxed is the effect of cracking on safety. Certain cracks are harmless but other types of cracks (diagonal tension and splitting cracks, for example) may indicate safety problems. The effects of these new ideas on the design of tall building frames and foundations have not been examined to a great extent.

FUTURE WORK

Recent investigations related to deflection, stiffness, and crack control in tall concrete buildings have pointed out the need for further work in the following areas:

(a) Establishment of drift limits for various types of buildings, framing types, and secondary elements. These limits may have to be tied to the accuracy and conservatism of the method of deflection analysis.

(b) Thorough evaluation of the cost of providing stiffness with various types of structural systems.

(c) Additional studies of the nonlinear interaction between walls (including filler walls) and frames. The effects of repeated loading and age on the loss of stiffness should be included.

(d) Further work on the effect of high-strength concrete on the behavior of tall concrete buildings, especially on deflections.

(e) Establishment of guidelines for crack-width limits that address how this problem should be handled if crack width does not affect corrosion protection.

CONDENSED REFERENCES/BIBLIOGRAPHY

The following is a condensed bibliography for this article. It includes all articles referred to or cited in the text. The full citations will be found at the end of the volume, with additional citations for further reading. What is given here should be sufficient information to lead the reader to the correct article: the author, date, and title. In case of multiple authors, only the first name is listed.

Council on Tall Buildings, Group CB 1978, *Structural Design of Tall Concrete and Masonry*
Darwin 1976, *Analysis of RC Shear Panels under Cyclic Loading*
Freeman 1980, *Significance of Stiffness Assumptions on Lateral Force Criteria*
Gergely 1982, *The Role of Cover and Bar Spacing in Reinforced Concrete*
MacGregor 1979, *Out-of-Plumb Columns in Concrete Structures*

Creep, Shrinkage, and
Temperature Effects (CB-10)

An Update

Paul Lew

The development of high-strength concretes with up to 11,000-psi strengths has dramatically changed the range of concrete high-rises. This development has been paralleled by development of "superplasticizers" to make these high-strength concretes workable. The use of high-strength concretes typically results in structures working at higher stress and strain levels. There is also a higher total amount of creep that occurs due to these higher stress levels. However, these effects can be restricted by careful planning.

For typical concrete strengths, the following moduli of elasticity have been found from testing.

Strength psi (28-day)	Modulus of Elasticity ksi (28-day)
9000	5260
7500	4580
6000	4270
5000	4090
4000	3920

Separate laboratory tests for creep and shrinkage were performed. These tests, as shown in Fig. 1, indicate that creep is reduced in high-strength concrete. This finding was confirmed by Perenchio and Klieger of the PCA (1978), who showed that creep strains per psi would reduce with high-strength concrete to 600–700 millionths per psi. Shrinkage remained essentially unchanged, as shown in Fig. 2, although some reduction is to be anticipated with higher-strength concretes.

Water Tower Place, designed by C. F. Murphy, is a 76-story, 859-foot-high

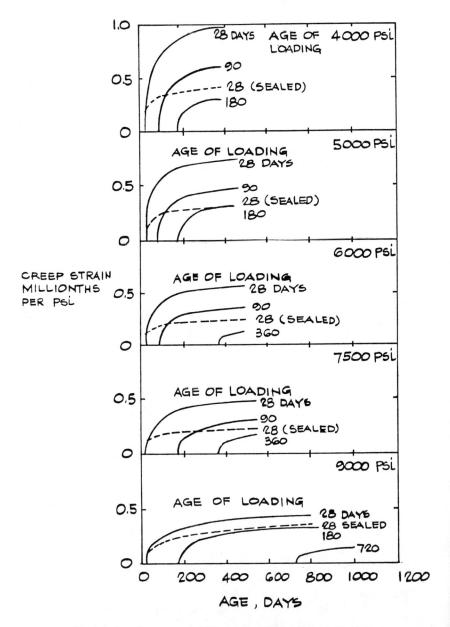

Fig. 1 Laboratory creep data *(Courtesy: Portland Cement Association)*

reinforced concrete building in Chicago. It was instrumented by the Portland Cement Association to investigate the effects of creep and shrinkage on differential vertical shortening of columns and walls. Stress histories were recorded for the tower and are plotted in Fig. 3. Concrete strengths varied with the level in the building as follows:

Levels	Strength
B4–25	9000 psi
25–40	7500 psi
40–58	6000 psi
58–60	5000 psi
60–76	4000 psi

Only in the lower floors, with 9000 psi concrete, was the reinforcing raise above 1% and, in fact, it reached 8% in the columns. Surveys of compressive strain were done and are shown in Fig. 4. As a result of this study, the total compressive strain was found to be relatively constant, reaching a maximum of 1400 millionths between the 57th and 58th floors. This condition is a result both of limiting the use of high-strength concretes to the lower levels, early in the job, so that these concretes receive loads at an older age than the weaker concretes on top, and of using high percentages of reinforcing in the lower floors. Extrapolating these results without taking into account load history and reinforcing could produce a significant understatement of the compressive strain. This study indicated that differential vertical movements of up to an inch are possible at the top of the building. Initial tests of concretes with superplasticizers indicate that reduced creep and shrinkage can result, in general varying with the water-to-cement ratio.

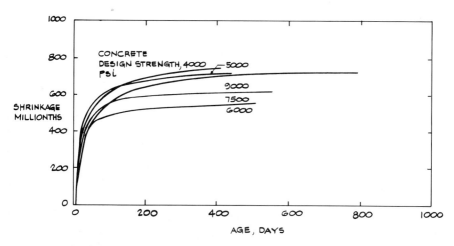

Fig. 2 Laboratory shrinkage data *(Courtesy: Portland Cement Association)*

The key to creep, shrinkage, and temperature effects is restraint. One particular case of interest is transfer girders connected from core shear walls to exterior columns, as shown in Fig. 5. Differential vertical movements of the exterior columns with respect to the core walls will be restrained by the transfer girders. This restraint will cause significant stresses to be induced in the tranfser girders. These forces must be accounted for in the design. This condition, although typical for hotels, is one of the few cases where differential vertical movements have primary structural consequences.

In general, the effects of differential creep, shrinkage, and thermal strains on non-structural elements must be eliminated. One of the more critical elements affected by vertical movement is the facade. This movement must be detailed for in the facade, so that there is no restraint that will result in the

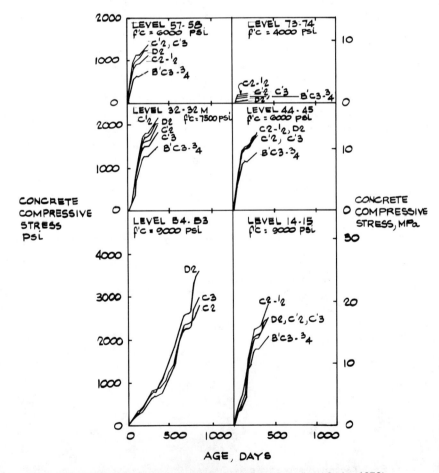

Fig. 3 Calculated stress histories of columns *(Russell and Corley, 1976)*

facade becoming an unintentional bearing wall. If this detailing is not done, the facade will bow and spall, and potentially could fall off. The differential thermal coefficients and temperatures of the concrete and facade must be studied to find the proper size of the pressure-relieving joints to be provided in the facade. The differential temperature effects must be added to the effects of creep, shrinkage, and elastic deformations to determine the amount of

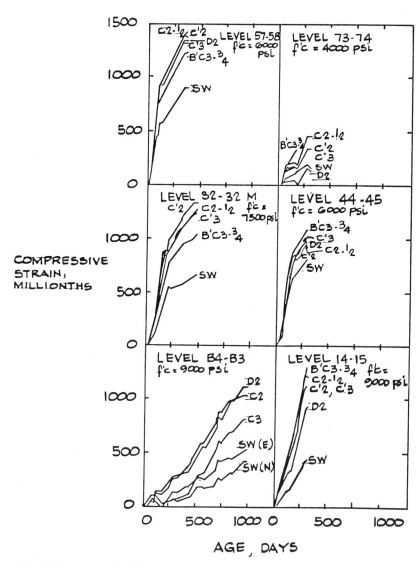

Fig. 4 **Measured vertical shortening of columns and walls** *(Russell and Corley, 1976)*

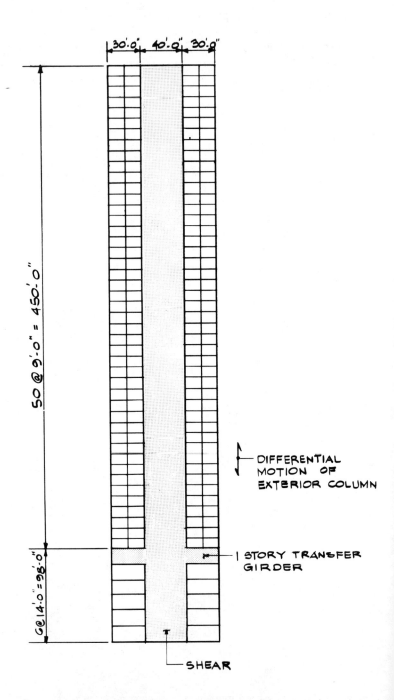

Fig. 5 Typical tower with transfer girder

differential motion that must be accommodated. To prevent sealant failure, these joints must be sized for two or four times the differential movement.

With proper analysis using the techniques provided in the Monograph Chapter CB-10, the movements discussed here can be predicted within design tolerances and detailed for. In summary, by limiting the use of high-strength concretes to the lower levels, the compressive strains can be maintained to be no larger than those typically experienced in ordinary-strength concretes. Differential strains in vertical elements may have significant structural consequences in some special cases, such as transfer guides and facades. The method provided in the Monograph can be used to design for these vertical movements.

CONDENSED REFERENCES/BIBLIOGRAPHY

The following is a condensed bibliography for this article. It includes all articles referred to or cited in the text. The full citations will be found at the end of the volume, with additional citations for further reading. What is given here should be sufficient information to lead the reader to the correct article: the author, date, and title. In case of multiple authors, only the first name is listed.

Perenchio 1978, *Some Physical Properties of High-Strength Concrete*
Russell 1976, *Time Dependent Deformations of Vertical Members in Ultra-High Concrete Buildings*
Zetlin 1971, *An Approach to the Internal Straining of Concrete*

New Developments in the Design of Cast-in-Place Concrete Tall Buildings

Ignacio Martín

INTRODUCTION

The Monograph Volume CB, *Structural Design of Tall Concrete and Masonry Buildings,* was published in 1978 and covers technical information up to roughly 1976. Four years have elapsed since the text of Volume CB was written, and in that time both the ACI (1977) and CEB-FIP (1978) have issued new building codes, the Applied Technology Council has issued its Tentative Provisions for the Development of Seismic Regulations for Buildings (ATC, 1978), and a new issue of the Uniform Building Code (UBC) (ICBO, 1979) was published in 1979.

The technical literature has been enriched with new publications, primarily dealing with the behavior of shear walls, columns, and beam-column connections. The importance of lateral drift of concrete buildings under seismic loading has been recognized. Ultra-high-strength concrete has been used and new knowledge on creep of concrete has been developed.

BUILDING CODES

As noted, both ACI and CEB-FIP have issued new building codes, but there are no drastic changes in the content when compared to previous editions.

ATC has published its tentative provisions, in which Chapter 11 is devoted to reinforced concrete and Chapters 12 and 12A are devoted to masonry. The provisions of these chapters are similar to the equivalent provisions in ACI and UBC. However, ATC has some innovative features applicable to reinforced concrete design.

In the ATC equivalent-lateral-force procedure, the seismic coefficient is inversely proportional to the response modification factor R, that varies from a value of 2 for a reinforced concrete moment frame to a value of 8 for a reinforced shear wall in a dual special moment frame and shear wall system.

The period of moment-resisting frame, reinforced concrete structures is determined by the equation

$$T = 0.025 \, h_n^{3/4} \tag{1}$$

where, T is the period of the structure and h_n is the height in feet above the base to the highest level of the building.

The story drift is determined by applying a deflection amplification factor to the deflections determined by elastic analysis. The deflection amplification factor ranges from 2 for reinforced concrete ordinary frames to 6 for reinforced concrete special frames in moment-resisting frame systems, and from 4 for reinforced concrete shear walls in bearing wall systems to 6.5 for reinforced concrete shear walls in dual systems. ATC requires the consideration of the P-Δ effect using the deflection amplification factor.

METHODS OF ANALYSIS

The traditional one-dimensional cantilever beam and two-dimensional frame and shear wall models are being replaced by both the pseudo-three-dimensional model, which permits the determination of the torsional effects, and the three-dimensional model, which permits the determination of the torsion and rocking motion of the structure, as pointed out by Gates (1978).

Unemori et al. (1980) have shown the importance of the in-plane flexibility of floor slabs on the seismic response of cross-wall buildings.

Selna (1978) has questioned the use of gross concrete sections in elastic analysis for seismic loading. The reduction in stiffness caused by cracking may increase or decrease the seismic response to a given earthquake.

The contribution of the slab to the horizontal member stiffness continues to be a subject of debate, especially in the case of flat-plate tall buildings without lateral bracing or shear walls. Freeman et al. (1980) have proposed

60% of the tributary width for the uncracked condition. For drift consideration of large amplitude motion up to the yield capacity of the structure, a 50% reduction of the gross concrete section is proposed, which lengthens the period of the structure by about 40%. Long and Kirk (1980) recommend the use of 30% of the tributary width of flat plates for the cracked condition.

COLUMNS

Marín and Martín (1979) have pointed out the need for design aids when designing columns with cross sections other than the circle and the rectangle. Interaction diagrams of C-shaped cross sections have shown the lack of ductility of these columns when they are heavily reinforced.

Tests by Uzumeri and Sheikh (1978) have shown that the amount of longitudinal steel, as well as the distribution of longitudinal and lateral steel around the column perimeter, contributes to the confinement of the concrete core and improves the strength and ductility of reinforced-concrete-tied columns.

Selna et al. (1980) have indicated the following considerations in the design of reinforced concrete columns for seismic forces: for ductile frames, the margin of column flexural strength over beam flexural strength that is required has not been resolved; captive spandrel beams in shear wall buildings should be designed using ductile reinforcement detailing; the major issue in flat slab columns is punching shear, and boundary element pilasters should be designed to prevent compression-crushing and longitudinal-buckling failures caused by overturning. Extra ties are inexpensive to place in columns because their weight is low and fabrication problems are minimal.

Ultra-high-strength concrete is being used in tall building concrete columns and it is necessary to have a thorough understanding of the properties and characteristics of this material.

Tests by Ford et al. (1981) indicate that the ultimate compressive strain of tied reinforced concrete columns can be increased when beneficial for the use of higher-strength steels. They also stated that two different moment magnification factors should be usd in the design of slender columns in unbraced frames: one for the moments that do not produce sidesway, and the other for sway-producing moments. Such a two-factor approach can substantially reduce the design moment requirements, hence improving design economy.

Priestley et al. (1981) tested spirally-confined concrete columns and found a substantial increase in flexural strength for high axial load levels, which should be considered when assessing shear forces in columns. Maximum concrete strains in the confined core were greatly in excess of the values predicted by existing formulas. The shear carried by the concrete in the columns generally exceeded the predicted strengths by large margins.

Oliva (1980) has tested reinforced concrete columns and reinforced concrete frames, respectively, with biaxial seismic response. He has found that in the design of rectangular columns, the motion along the strong axis may cause damage that can significantly decrease the weak-axis stiffness, resulting in excessive unexpected deformation in that direction under low loads.

SHEAR WALLS

Oesterle et al. (1980a) tested isolated shear walls sustaining reversing inelastic rotations and found both that their observed hysteretic behavior and load deformation characteristics are similar to those of beams and that the maximum rotational ductility decreases with increasing levels of shear stress.

Wide-flanged shear walls show shear lag in the flanges, which limits the effective width of the flange. Coull and Abu El Magd (1980) have developed a method to assess the degree of shear lag in the flange, the effective width, and the lateral deflection.

Ductility and shear capacity of shear walls can be improved with adequate reinforcement detailing as proposed by Oesterle et al. (1980b). Vertical boundary elements act as dowels to resist shear when inelastic reversals increase the concentration of shear in the compression zone. Transverse hoop reinforcement improves the shear capacity and dowel-action stiffness of boundary elements. It is recommended to provide adequate anchorage of horizontal wall reinforcement in hinging regions of walls subjected to earthquake loading. Such walls develop horizontal cracks in the tension boundary element that propagate into diagonal web cracking. Horizontal reinforcement may be ended in 90-degree or 135-degree hooks.

CONNECTIONS

Recent tests of beam-column connections have shown that a review of the contributions of concrete and steel to the shear strength of connections is in order. Meinheit and Jirsa (1977) have suggested a departure from the additive procedure for determining the shear strength of connections. They suggested expressing the confinement effect of transverse reinforcement as a function of its volumetric ratio, and further suggested that this ratio should not be less than 0.01.

ACI Committee 408 (1979) and Jirsa et al. (1979) have proposed a revision of the development, splice, and standard hook provisions for deformed bars in tension. The proposed revision will require longer development lengths for hooks up to No. 8 and shorter development lengths for No. 9 hooks or larger bars. In the proposed revision the grade of steel of the hook does not influence the stress developed by a standard hook.

Yamazaki and Hawkins (1980) have studied slab-column connections and found that while ACI 318-77 provides a realistic measure of the shear stress on the front column face, it underestimates shear stresses on the sides of the column face.

CREEP AND SHRINKAGE

Creep of concrete is a subject of major concern in the design of cast-in-place concrete buildings, especially if posttensioned slabs are used. The *Conclusions of the Hubert Rüsch Workshop on Creep of Concrete* (ACI, 1979) indicate that the methods to predict creep of concrete can be classified in three levels according to their complexity and expected level of accuracy. The methods suggested by ACI and CEB-FIP can be classified as level-2 (intermediate) methods, in which the following parameters are taken into account:

member size;

relative humidity;

ambient temperature;

age of loading;

consistency of fresh concrete as a measure of concrete composition;

type of cement; and

development of creep with time

FUTURE TRENDS

It is expected that limitation of overall and interstory drift of tall buildings will receive considerable attention. The limitation of drift is intimately related to the ductility that such limitation will require.

Shear walls continue to be the subject of attention and research. The following items are worth mentioning: the ductility of shear walls with arbitrary cross sections; the shear strength, and especially the shear strength of shear walls with boundary elements and interior stiffeners; and the effect of construction joints.

The behavior of connections deserves continued research because more information is needed to provide the designer with more efficient methods of detailing joints.

Research on seismic behavior of reinforced concrete members and structures has been extensive in recent years, shedding light on the response of concrete structures to seismic excitations. This knowledge must be evaluated to simplify the methods of analysis and design.

CONDENSED REFERENCES/BIBLIOGRAPHY

The following is a condensed bibliography for this article. It includes all articles referred to or cited in the text. The full citations will be found at the end of the volume, with additional citations for further reading. What is given here should be sufficient information to lead the reader to the correct article: the author, date, and title. In case of multiple authors, only the first name is listed.

ACI 1977, *Building Code Requirements for Reinforced Concrete*
ACI 1979, *Conclusions of the Hubert Rüsch Workshop on Creep and Concrete*
ACI Committee 408 1979, *Suggested Development, Splice and Standard Hook Provisions for*
ATC 1978, *Tentative Provisions for the Development of Seismic Regulations For Buildings*

CEB-FIP 1978, *Code Modele CEB-FIP for the Structures En Beton*
Coull 1980, *Analysis of Wide-Flanged Shear Wall Structures*

Ford 1981, *Design Indications from Tests of Unbraced Multipanel Frames*
Freeman 1980, *Significance of Stiffness Assumptions on Lateral Force Criteria*

Gates 1978, *The Art of Modeling Buildings for Dynamic Analysis*

ICBO 1979, *Uniform Building Code*

Jirsa 1979, *Rationale for Suggested Development, Splice, and Standard Hook Provisions for*

Kaar 1977, *Stress-Strain Characteristics of High-Strength Concrete*

Long 1980, *Lateral Load Stiffness of Slab-Column Structures*

Marín 1979, *Design Columns with Non-Rectangular Cross Section*
Mattison 1978, *Studies of the Production and Properties of High Strength Concrete*
Meinheit 1977, *The Shear Strength of Reinforced Concrete, Beam-Column Joints*
Mukherjee 1981, *Development of High Strength Concrete Incorporating a Large Percentage of*

Oesterle 1980a, *Hysteretic Response of Reinforced Concrete Structural Walls*
Oesterle 1980b, *Reinforcement Details for Earthquake-Resistance Structural Walls*
Oliva 1980, *Shaking Table Testing of Reinforced Concrete Frames with Biaxial Response*

Parrott 1981, *The Production and Properties of High-Strength Concrete*
Perenchio 1978, *Some Physical Properties of High-Strength Concrete*
Priestley 1981, *Ductility of Spirally-Confined Concrete Columns*

Selna 1978, *Modeling of Reinforced Concrete Buildings*
Selna 1980, *Strong and Tough Concrete Columns for Seismic Forces*
Shah 1979, *High Strength Concrete*

Unemori 1980, *Effect of Inplane Floor Slab Flexibility on the Response of Crosswall Building Systems*
Uzumeri 1978, *Strength and Ductility of Reinforced Concrete Columns with Rectangular Ties*

Wolsiefer 1982, *Ultra High Strength Field Placeable Concrete in the Range 10,000 to 18,000 psi*

Yamazaki 1980, *Finite Element Predictions of the Behavior of Slab-Column Connections*

Seismic Resistance Versus General Structural Integrity

G. Robert Fuller

GENERAL CONSIDERATIONS

Certain design compatibilities exist between seismic considerations and the concept of "general structural integrity" or the resistance of buildings to progressive collapse. Multistory precast concrete bearing-wall systems and precast concrete plank-floor systems have weaknesses with regard to both seismic resistance and progressive collapse. However, there is very little research on the general structural integrity of precast concrete panel buildings, as evidenced by reports of the Research Workshop on Earthquake-Resistant Reinforced Concrete Building Construction held in July, 1977, at the University of California, Berkeley (Bertero, 1978). The state of knowledge of the behavior of precast concrete bearing-wall buildings under seismic loads was also noted as being very limited. The correlation of general design provisions for seismic and progressive collapse, together with state-of-knowledge, and research needs, were discussed at the workshop.

SEISMIC RESPONSE

There is a fundamental difference between the behavior of a cast-in-place concrete building and a precast panel building when each is subjected to dynamic lateral forces. Research at Massachusetts Institute of Technology (Becker et al., 1980) demonstrated a complex mechanism that occurs when a panelized structure is subjected to dynamic oscillatory forces. Analytical studies showed that connections behaved nonlinearly in several different modes when subjected to cyclic loading. Cracking and softening of the cast-in-place concrete joints, yielding of the connection reinforcement, and slippage along the panel-joint interface were all shown as possible effects.

A rocking motion is induced that is peculiar to panelized construction. This rocking motion, plus stress concentrations caused by overturning and lateral shears, could cause failure in either connections or panel corners.

Design forces and force distributions in seismic design codes are based on flexural ductility, which may not be directly applicable to concrete panel buildings. Lowrise structures (under six stories) of precast concrete panels probably have sufficient strength and stiffness to remain in the elastic range during earthquakes. Therefore, buildings of limited height could be designed for strength only. Their energy-dissipating properties would thus preclude behavior in the inelastic range.

However, highrise precast concrete panel structures must be designed with adequate vertical reinforcement and horizontal shear-resistant joints, and with ductile vertical and horizontal connections between all precast elements. In addition, precaution must be taken to prevent degradation or softening of horizontal concrete joints at the edges of wall panels.

Another dissimilarity between the responses of precast and in-place concrete buildings to dynamic cyclic loading is the behavior of floor diaphragms. The relative flexibilities of the two systems are quite different. The overall response of the structure and the distribution of seismic forces within the structure are affected by diaphragm action. Any nonsymmetry or eccentricities in the building could further compound the problem. The need for peripheral and horizontal transverse and longitudinal reinforcement to maintian diaphragm action in precast concrete floor systems is apparent (Fuller, 1978a).

PROGRESSIVE COLLAPSE

Most structures will remain stable under normal gravity loads. They are also designed to withstand normal wind and earthquake loads. But how resistant are buildings constructed in areas of low seismicity and low probable wind forces to abnormal loading conditions such as explosions, vehicular collisions, tornadoes, faulty practice, excessive eccentricities, and so on? Designers generally neglect these low-probability loadings.

Designers also tend to neglect the overall three-dimensional stability of statically indeterminate multistory structures. Engineers in many areas of the country are neither familiar nor concerned with dynamic effects of wind and earthquake forces. Bearing walls and load carrying elements are usually designed only for gravity loads; continuity and ductility are not considered of major import. It is suggested here that this situation demonstrates the need to develop "general structural integrity" in all buildings when life-safety or economic loss are important considerations.

Research sponsored by the U.S. Department of Housing and Urban Development (HUD) at the Portland Cement Association (PCA) consisted of analytical and experimental studies of the behavior of structures subjected to abnormal loads (Schulz, 1979). By considering various load carrying elements that were ineffective to support load, remaining structural elements were tested. Conclusions from this research were that in order to retain general structural integrity, all connections between elements in a precast concrete panel building need tensile continuity and ductility.

Continuity is essential to develop the bridging needed to transmit and redistribute loads around an ineffective or collapsed member. Ductility is necessary not only to sustain deformations that may be associated with conditions in the damaged state, but also to establish some measure of energy absorption under the dynamic effects of either normal or abnormal loads.

PCA determined that the following ties were necessary to prevent progressive collapse:

(a) *Transverse:* Permit cantilever action and beam action in cross-wall panels and assist floor diaphragm action.

(b) *Vertical:* Provide a tie-down for wall panels to prevent overturning; suspend the wall structure from the cantilevered portion above; ensure adequate shear capacity in horizontal connections; and provide a strong column element.

(c) *Longitudinal:* Permit a suspension system (partial catenary or membrane) in floor elements, and tie adjacent diaphragms together.

(d) *Peripheral:* Ensure floor diaphragm action and provide beam action at exterior walls.

RESEARCH ON EVALUATION OF
STRUCTURAL PERFORMANCE

What occurs when a concrete panelized building is subjected to seismic forces or abnormal loadings? To answer this question, research was sponsored by HUD at Drexel University on "The Nature and Mechanism of Progressive

Collapse in Industrialized Buildings Utilizing Established Small Scale Direct Model Techniques." Three-dimensional small-scale physical models of precast concrete bearing-wall buildings were tested and studied analytically (Muskivitch and Harris, 1979).

Attention was focused on various types of connections and their contributions to the mechanism to prevent progressive collapse. Both elastic and inelastic models were used, and assemblies were tested to duplicate prototype behavior of the tests previously conducted at PCA. Small-scale models of components and joints were tested to verify their validity and to verify the PCA tests. This modeling of entire structures, with the addition of testing to evaluate response to dynamic seismic forces, showed interesting results that substantiated conclusions from MIT and PCA research.

DESIGN CONSIDERATIONS

A problem exists in structural design procedures for prefabricated concrete buildings. In many instances, elements of a building are designed individually without viewing the entire structure as a unit. In both monolithic concrete structures and those of structural steel with continuity provided at all connections, general structural integrity is usually provided. Precast concrete buildings, on the other hand, need to have special design considerations for ductility and continuity. This applies not only to buildings in high-seismic zones and high-wind area but also to those in other areas of the country (Fuller, 1978b).

A change in design philosophy is needed for the structural analysis and design of precast concrete buildings. Because the probability of major seismic activity is low or only moderate in most areas of the United States, earthquake resistance is not usually considered. Few structural engineers are conversant with structural dynamics as related to the earthquake design of buildings. General structural integrity needs to be emphasized, and further guidance in the form of criteria needs to be developed for the practicing engineer.

With respect to progressive collapse, a successful design is one resulting in a structure that both limits the extent of failure and bridges over the failed area if an abnormal loading occurs. The capacity to limit the failed area is generally proportional to the structure's continuity and ductility, or general structural integrity. The challenge, then, is to provide an optimum amount of continuity and ductility in all structures.

The easiest way to develop general structural integrity in concrete panel bearing-wall structures is to provide adequate horizontal, vertical, and peripheral ties between all structural elements. At a research workshop held in Austin, Texas, in November, 1975, ductility and continuity similar to that used for seismic and wind design were emphasized as a very important method to avoid progressive collapse (Breen, 1976). The consensus was that most structures designed and detailed to resist high seismic loads would have a low susceptibility to progressive collapse.

However, some structures might satisfy code-specified quasi-static seismic design forces but might not prevent progressive collapse. This condition could be true for buildings under construction, buildings subjected to abnormal vertical loads, or underreinforced structures with low overturning moments. Designing according to the code (static design) may also be insufficient to resist even moderate earthquakes. The structure with adequate lateral shear capacity may have little of the ductility needed to resist dynamic cyclic loading.

Proper floor diaphragm action is required to resist both seismic forces and abnormal loads. This diaphragm action, necessary to distribute lateral loads to vertical bracing elements, is discussed in a *PCI Journal* article, "Considerations for the Design of Precast Concrete Bearing Wall Buildings to Withstand Abnormal Loads" (Speyer, 1976). As noted, "Special consideration should be given to the interconnection of precast floor elements" in seismic zones. Design recommendations were also made for the minimum ties required to develop general structural integrity. Reference was made to the PCI *Design Handbook for Precast and Prestressed Concrete*, which has a design methodology for diaphragm action to resist lateral loads.

In any major earthquake a panelized structure, as well as most other structures, will undergo some damage. It is necessary to guarantee that such a damaged structure retains overall stability. Maintenance of this stability in a damaged state is directly analogous to the maintenance of this stability after damage caused by an abnormal (nonseismic) loading. The strength of the structure must not be so degraded, through seismic reversals, that the structure is no longer capable of supporting gravity loads.

CODE PROVISIONS

Most engineers who are familiar with aseismic analysis realize the shortcomings of code requirements and the difficulty with which design recommendations are incorporated into building codes. Building codes generally have provisions for aseismic construction. However, do current model code provisions assure adequate resistance to seismic forces in prefabricated concrete structures? Conclusions from research at MIT, Drexel, and elsewhere would indicate that they do not.

Improvements are needed in building code provisions for design to resist earthquake forces. We can currently design to prevent collapse, but the mere adoption of a code will not do it. Competent design and suitable materials, backed up by adequate checking and thorough inspection, are also required.

The most important item in earthquake-resistant design is not even mentioned or specified in the codes—the structures must be tied together to act as a unit. Precast panelized structures do not have this inherent ability (Fuller, 1978b).

There have been examples from recent earthquakes, such as the ones in Anchorage and San Fernando, which demonstrate that even though precast concrete buildings complied with building codes, brittle connections failed when they were overloaded. With ductility, buildings survived; without it, they collapsed. It was not so much the magnitude of the lateral force, but the way the designer framed the building to resist dynamic forces. In most parts of the country where forces are known, only strength and force levels need be specified in building codes and specifications. If a structure is strong enough, it is sufficient. In earthquake country, however, ductility is also required. The building must remain stable and act as a unit even when design forces are exceeded. The structure's deformation capability is as important as its strength.

Similar conclusions were drawn in the Workshop on Earthquake-Resistant Reinforced Concrete Building Construction (Bertero, 1978):

> "Those structures which suffered the most distress in the San Fernando Earthquake were frequently found to satisfy code requirements while having deficiencies in continuity, etc., which cannot be remedied by code modifications alone, especially the simple expedient of requiring higher forces. Higher force requirements will result in stiffer structures. As many of the major problems in earthquakes are produced by displacements, designs which produce stiffer structures may be self-defeating, especially for relatively brittle structural materials such as reinforced concrete."

Another problem with code compliance was discussed at the same workshop in reference to the National Building Code of Canada (NBC). This code requires that buildings over three stories, located in Seismic Zones 2 and 3, have certain structural systems. One permissible system is referred to as "continuously reinforced concrete" (National Research Council, 1975a).

The NBC commentary (National Research Council, 1975b) explains that "continuously reinforced concrete" refers to reinforced concrete conforming to CSA A23.3-1973 (CSA, 1973). The commentary also states that precast concrete construction may be used if reinforcing is made continuous by means of lapped or welded splices in accordance with CSA A23.3. Splices also need to be encased in cast-in-place concrete. However, the designer can use a "K" factor of 1.3 in the design and detail the structure in the same manner as for nonseismic areas.

Because the NBC commentary specifically permits precast concrete structures, numerous precast buildings have been erected in high seismic-risk regions of Canada. These buildings may or may not contain adequate provisions for the continuity and ductility required to resist dynamic oscillatory forces. A conclusion of the workshop was that because of the difficulty in accurately predicting the actual magnitude of possible earthquakes, concrete structures with only "nominal ductility" should not be constructed in high seismic zones.

RECENT RESEARCH AND ANALYSIS ACTIVITIES

Professor Mufit Yorulmaz of the Faculty of Architecture, Technical University, Istanbul, Turkey reported on two references by Dr. E. Karaboga of Karadeniz (Black Sea) Technical University, Turkey. Dr. Karaboga's research concerned theoretical and experimental analysis of the strength of horizontal joints in large panel structures (Karaboga, 1974, 1980). He used ultimate load theory, taking into account various eccentricities. As Professor Yorulmaz explained, tall buildings of large concrete panels are not common in Turkey, but because of the governmental policy to foster social (public) housing, this type of construction may be recommended in the future.

The latest activity of interest to Committee 21E of the Council on Tall Buildings and Urban Habitat is the Seminar/Workshop on Design of Prefabricated Concrete Buildings for Earthquake Loads, conducted by the Applied Technology Council of Berkeley, California, and held April 27–29, 1981, in Los Angeles. The seminar, sponsored by the U.S. National Science Foundation, was intended both to develop a resource document for improving the seismic design and fabrication of prefabricated concrete buildings and to identify research needs and priorities. Sixteen papers were presented on the three general topics of moment frames, precast wall systems, and diaphragms. In each category, the subject areas of systems, strength, loads, connections, analytical procedures, test data, and problem areas were covered. Also included in the seminar were papers on the state of practice and current code developments from Japan, New Zealand, Yugoslavia, and the United States. Finally, six summary papers by steering committee members were presented on loading criteria, member capacities, connections, moment frames, precast wall systems, and diaphragms.

CONDENSED REFERENCES/BIBLIOGRAPHY

The following is a condensed bibliography for this article. It includes all articles referred to or cited in the text. The full citations will be found at the end of the volume, with additional citations for further reading. What is given here should be sufficient information to lead the reader to the correct article: the author, date, and title. In case of multiple authors, only the first name is listed.

Becker 1980, *Seismic Response of Precast Concrete Walls*
Bertero 1978, *Proceedings of Workshop on Earthquake-Resistant Reinforced Concrete Building*
Breen 1976, *Summary Report of Research Workshop on Progressive Collapse of Building Structures*

CSA 1973, *Code for Design of Concrete Structures for Buildings, CSA Standard A23.3-1973*

Fuller 1978a, *Seismic Resistance vs. Progressive Collapse of Precast Concrete Panel Buildings*
Fuller 1978b, *Progressive Collapse Provisions for Multi-Story Buildings*

Karaboga 1974, *Strength of Horizontal Joints in Large Panel Structures*
Karaboga 1980, *Internal Horizontal Joints of Large Panel Constructions*

Muskivitch 1979, *Report 2—Behavior of Precast Concrete Large Panel Buildings Under Simulated*

National Research Council 1975a, *National Building Code of Canada*
National Research Council 1975b, *Commentaries on Part IV—National Building Code of Canada*

Schultz 1979, *Report 6—Design Methodology, Design and Construction of Large Panel Concrete*
Speyer 1976, *Considerations for Design of Precast Concrete Bearing Wall Buildings to Withstand*

Recent Developments in the Design of Masonry Structures

Arnold W. Hendry

In the few years that have elapsed since the preparation of Chapter CB-13 of the Monograph, steady development in the field of masonry construction has taken place as a result of continued research and innovations designed in a number of countries. This article draws attention to a number of significant developments.

BASIS OF STRUCTURAL DESIGN

Before proceeding to matters of detail, it is worth noting that new or greatly improved codes of practice for masonry construction have been prepared in several countries and by international bodies. In the United Kingdom a limit-states code for unreinforced masonry was published in 1978 as BS 5628, Part 1. This document is to be followed by Part 2 (1981 — draft), which will deal with reinforced and prestressed masonry. A draft standard for engineered masonry construction has been issued in West Germany (DIN 1053, Part 2, 1981 — draft) and, as in Britain, it will be followed by another part relating to reinforced masonry. In the United States, ACI/ASCE Committee 530 has produced a standard for concrete masonry structures,

ACI 531-79. The British and German codes are in terms of characteristic compressive strengths of masonry and stated safety factors, whereas the ACI/ASCE code is based on allowable stresses.

Recommendations for masonry structures have been published by two international bodies, the International Council for Building Research (CIB) in 1981, and the European Association of Brick and Tile Manufacturers (TBE) in 1978. These documents are intended to be of assistance in the preparation of national codes that are being established or revised.

In terms of safety factors and stated material strengths, there are considerable differences in the treatment of structural safety among the various codes of practice. European practice has moved towards the adoption of limit-states formulations, whereas in North America, design is undertaken in permissible-stress terms. Considerable discussion continues in this area, but attempts are underway to make safety factors more rational. There is a fairly general view that the safety factors for masonry are in many cases higher than necessary. This view takes into account both the greatly improved knowledge of material that has resulted from research work and the improved design and site control methods that have evolved. However, there is some way to go before safety factors for masonry construction are likely to approach the values currently adopted for concrete structures.

VERTICAL LOAD DESIGN

The strength of brickwork compression elements is a fundamental problem in the design of load bearing structures. Its solution requires consideration of a number of aspects, including the following:

1. Basic assumptions concerning material strength and behavior.

2. The theoretical model to be adopted in calculating the strength of the element.

3. The allowance to be made for departures from idealized conditions.

4. Analysis of the structure for determination of structural eccentricity.

5. Determination of slenderness ratio.

Earlier codes of practice dealt with these problems in a simplistic manner that although satisfactory up to a point, could not be expected to lead to the most efficient use of materials or to be consistent with the achievement of uniform, or even known, levels of safety. Recent research has therefore been directed towards the improvement of knowledge relating to all of the above factors.

It has been established (Powell, 1976) that the stress-strain curve for clay brick masonry is accurately represented by a parabola. Referring to Fig. 1, this relationship may be expressed in the form

$$\frac{\sigma}{\sigma'} = 2(\frac{\Sigma}{\Sigma'}) - (\frac{\Sigma}{\Sigma'})^2 \tag{1}$$

where σ' and Σ' are, respectively, the maximum stress and strain in the material.

Various solutions for vertical load bearing capacity have been published (Mann, 1979; Lugez, 1979) and the effect of nonlinearity of the stress-strain curve has been investigated (Burns, 1972). Recent work has included computer simulation (Contaldo, 1979; Sawko, 1980) of masonry compression members. As a result of this analytical and numerical work, it is possible to arrive at a set of capacity reduction factors for slenderness and eccentricity that have an adequate theoretical basis and that are in reasonable accordance with experimental results. One theoretically derived set of curves (Awni, 1981) is compared in Fig. 1 with corresponding results obtained experimentally.

An alternative approach that has been developed in North America is the moment-magnifier method (Turkstra, 1976; Hatzinikolas et al., 1980; Brown, 1980), in which an interaction curve is first derived that defines the strength of a short compression member subject to axial load and bending moment. This curve has the form indicated in Fig. 2, in which the vertical axis is in terms of the applied load divided by the ultimate load in axial compression, P_o. On the horizontal axis, the applied moment M is divided by the moment capacity M_k corresponding to the application of a load at the middle third of the section. Such interaction curves can be derived on the basis of a nonlinear stress-strain curve.

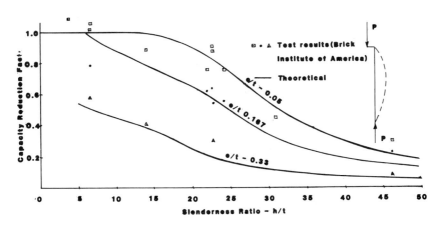

Fig. 1 Theoretical capacity reduction factors compared with test results

End conditions and slenderness are allowed for by multiplying the moment $P \cdot e$ by a factor

$$L = \frac{C_m}{1 - P_{/P_{cr}}} \tag{2}$$

in which C_m is a correction factor depending on the moment distribution in the element and is intended to give the equivalent uniform moment in the column as would lead to the same column strength on the actual moment diagram. P_{cr} is the Euler critical load taking into account the effective height of the compression member. One of the problems in applying this method to masonry elements has been the difficulty of defining the flexural rigidity of the section. However, progress has been made in resolving this matter, and proposals have been put forward (Hatzinikolas et al., 1980) for calculating the effective EI for plain and reinforced masonry. These proposals have shown good agreement with experimental results.

It is necessary to consider the effect of accidental eccentricities in masonry walls. Such eccentricities may arise from differences in materials properties, inaccuracies in construction, or structural eccentricity. Several ways of dealing with this problem have been put forward. Firstly, an initial lack of straightness may be assumed and included in the differential equation from which the

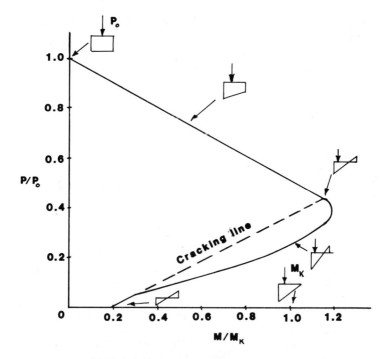

Fig. 2 Axial load—moment interaction curve

column strengths are determined. Alternatively, the estimated accidental eccentricity may be added to the structural eccentricity in determining the appropriate capacity reduction factor or in applying the moment-magnifier method. Tentative values for accidental eccentricities are suggested in the CIB Recommendations, as follows:

Differences in material properties	$e_{a1} = 0.02\,t$
Errors in construction of the wall	$e_{a2} = 0.002\,H$
Error in superposition of walls in successive stories (internal walls only)	$e_{a3} = 5\text{mm}$

These values are not necessarily cumulative [that is, $e_a \leq (e_{a1} + e_{a2} + e_{a3})$] but the total allowance for accidental eccentricity should be not less than $H/300$ and may be increased by a factor of two if execution or control are likely to be poor.

Assessment of structural eccentricity in current practice is rather uncertain, but some progress has been made (Awni, 1979) in developing rational methods of calculation that accord with experimental results. When these methods have been fully verified it will be possible to overcome one of the major uncertainties in the design of masonry structures. However, it is likely that eccentricity will be critical only in outer walls, possibly three to five stories below roof level. Below this level, and in internal walls, eccentricities are likely to be relatively small.

Effective height, used in the calculation of slenderness ratio, is the subject of rule-of-thumb provisions in some codes of practice, whereas other codes indicate that the effective height may vary according to the loading pattern, which may produce single- or double-curvature deflection of the member. Tests on sections of structures (Awni, 1982) confirm that frame action in masonry structures does in fact take place, although full rigidity of the wall-floor slab joint will not generally be achieved. Although double-curvature deflection is possible, it is unlikely to be achieved in very many cases and, in addition, it has been reported (Hatzinikolas et al., 1980) that plain masonry walls tested in double curvature have a tendency to fail in the first mode. It would therefore seem advisable to adopt the story height as the effective height in such construction. In reinforced masonry, however, the development of effective joint rigidity may justify the adoption of a reduced effective height.

Figure 3 shows a recent research project at the University of Edinburgh on wall-floor slab interaction.

Taken together, the developments outlined above represent a significant advance in the theory of masonry structures. However, this progress has yet to be fully exploited in practical design.

Fig. 3 Tests in progress to study wall-floor slab interaction in a brick masonry structure
(Courtesy: University of Edinburgh/Department of Civil Engineering)

SHEAR STRENGTH OF UNREINFORCED MASONRY

The resistance of masonry to in-plane lateral loading has continued to receive attention in several countries. Hendry et al. (1981), have approached the problem by considering the strength of brick masonry under biaxial stresses, taking into account the inclination of these stresses to the bed joints. Criteria of failure have been established experimentally and the implications for the behavior of shear walls have been examined. This work makes it clear that the strength of shear walls is affected by their length-to-height ratio and by loading conditions. Consequently, the use of an average shear stress, calculated on the basis of the plan area of the wall, may be in error. However, if the L/H ratio is between 1 and 2, the error will not exceed $\pm 10\%$ of the shear strength derived from the commonly adopted relationship:

$$\tau = \tau_o + \mu\sigma_n \tag{3}$$

where τ = shear strength of the masonry
τ_o = shear strength with zero precompression
μ = an apparent friction coefficient
σ_n = precompression

Similar studies relating to concrete blockwork have been reported by Hegemeir et al. (1978) and by Hamid and Drysdale (1980).

A different approach has been adopted by Mann (1982), who has produced a theory of shear strength based on consideration of the stresses imposed on single masonry units. A simplified version of this theory gives rise to the following formula for shear strength:

$$\tau = 0.45\,\beta_{RZ}\sqrt{1 + \sigma_n/\beta_{RZ}} \tag{4}$$

where β_{RZ} = tensile strength of units.

Suggested values of unit tensile strengths lie between $0.04\,f_{bk}$ and $0.025\,f_{bk}$ MPa for solid and hollow units respectively; f_{bk} is the compressive strength of the unit.

SEISMIC PERFORMANCE

The need for fuller understanding of the seismic performance of masonry structures has resulted in continued research in this area. A number of studies have been carried out to evaluate the performance of existing structures. Thus Adham (1980) has carried out detailed calculations on a group of reinforced brick masonry structures undamaged by the 1971 San Fernando earthquake. This study has enabled him to identify a number of construction details that were found to be effective in resisting damage. He also recommends the use of more refined shear and biaxial failure criteria for the evaluation of the seismic performance of masonry buildings. A seismic analysis of one of the Park Lane Towers at Denver was carried out by Meadaris (1978) and indicated that the building could withstand an earthquake of about magnitude 7 on the Richter scale with some localized material failure. The dynamic characteristics of a 20-story apartment block at Pittsburgh have been measured by Oppenhiem (1978). This examination showed a somewhat unexpected degree of interaction between shear walls, resulting from the end fixity of lintel beams that had not been considered in the original design. The work indicated that the natural frequencies of the structure could be calculated provided that the coupling was taken into account.

A number of laboratory investigations have also been undertaken in the United States on the seismic behavior of piers (Mayes 1978; McNiven 1980) and on assemblies of elements (Adham 1980; Nachbar 1978). Extensive reports have also been made on shaking table tests on single story masonry houses (Gulkan 1978; Clough 1980). The results of these tests will augment considerably existing information on the seismic resistance of buildings.

REINFORCED AND PRESTRESSED MASONRY

Recent years have seen considerable interest in the use of reinforced and prestressed masonry. Much of this interest has been centered in the Western United States and has been related to the design of earthquake-resistant structures. However, research on the flexural and shear strengths of various types of reinforced masonry has been carried out in the United Kingdom. Sinha (1981) has put forward an ultimate load analysis for reinforced brickwork flexural members. This analysis is supported by tests on a large number of grouted cavity beams. Similar work on reinforced concrete blockwork has been reported by Roberts (1980). Osman and Hendry (1982) have investigated the mechanism of shear failure in this type of beam and have found that compression zone friction accounted for 30–40% of transmitted shear, dowel effect accounted for up to 55%, and aggregate interlock for 7–15%. These authors confirmed Sinha's finding that the stress-strain relationship in the compression zone of grouted cavity beams is parabolic.

Rathbone (1981) has put forward proposals for the shear strength of reinforced concrete blockwork beams for use in design, and Hendry et al., (1981) has outlined the basis of the shear strength values included in the British draft Code BS 5628, Part 2 (1981). In the latter paper, it is shown that the shear strength of bed reinforced brickwork beams is not influenced significantly but the amount of reinforcement present and a characteristic value (that is, 95% confidence limit for strength) is set at 0.35 MPa. The corresponding figure for grouted cavity sections, on the other hand, is dependent on the percentage of steel, and in the draft code it varies between 0.35 and 0.65 MPa as the steel percentage is increased from 0.15 to 2.0.

Tests on shear reinforced masonry beams are rather few in number. Available results certainly demonstrate an increase in shear resistance compared with beams without shear reinforcement; but in many cases failure took place in flexure so that the effect of the shear reinforcement was indeterminate. Grouted cavity beams, however, can be expected to behave similarly to reinforced concrete, and in their case there is greater scope for introducing shear reinforcement.

The design of reinforced masonry walls for combined axial load and bending moment has been studied by Drysdale (1976) and also by Hatzinikolas et al. (1980). Both report the application of the moment-magnifier method to this type of element. The case of biaxial bending of reinforced masonry columns has received little attention but some preliminary work has been published by Davies and El Traify (1982) setting out the basis of a method for deriving moment–axial load interaction curves for this case.

Further applications of post-tensioned brickwork have been described in the past few years and the technique has been used in the two-story office building shown in Fig. 4 which was recently built in England. No examples of the use of prestressed masonry in high-rise buildings are known, but the experience being gained in low-rise construction will be valuable in applying prestressed masonry to tall buildings. Research is in progress on post-tensioned

Fig. 4 Office building of George Armitage & Sons, Ltd., Leeds, England, of reinforced and prestressed brick masonry construction *(Courtesy: George Armitage & Sons, Ltd.)*

brickwork beams, and some initial results have been published by Pedereschi and Sinha (1982). Figure 5 is a view of a 6 m span beam of this type under test.

The problem of corrosion of reinforcement in masonry elements has received attention recently. It has been pointed out by Kropp (1979) and De Vekey (1981) that the mortar in bed joints may offer only very short-term protection because the calcium hydroxide present in mortar, which provides a protective, alkaline environment for the steel, becomes converted to calcium carbonate by the penetration of atmospheric carbon dioxide. This process of "carbonation" results in an acidic environment, and in the presence of water and oxygen the steel will rapidly corrode. However, reinforcement surrounded by well-compacted nonporous concrete will be reasonably protected and can be expected to have satisfactory durability in moderate conditions.

Where very severe conditions of exposure are expected, it may be necessary to resort to austenitic stainless steel reinforcement. In intermediate situations coated steels may be adequate

In England, field information on the durability of reinforced brickwork has been reported by Foster (1981), and in India by Dayaratnam (1981). It would appear from these reports that, with reasonable detailing, a life of at least 40 years may be expected for mild steel bars embedded in dense cement mortar under exposed conditions. In India examples up to 80 years old are still in service.

Fig. 5 Test on a 6-m span, post-tensioned brickwork beam *(Courtesy: University of Edinburgh/ Department of Civil Engineering)*

National and International Codes

Britain

BS 5628 Part 1-1978	Code of Practice for Structural Use of Masonry: Part 1: Unreinforced Masonry
BS 5628 Part 2-1981 (draft)	Code of Practice for Structural Use of Masonry: Part 2: Reinforced and Prestressed

United States

ACI 531-79	Building Code Requirements for Concrete Masonry Structures

West Germany

DIN 1053 Part 2-1981 (draft)	Engineer-Designed Buildings Calculation and Construction

International

CIB Report: Publication 58	International Recommendations for Masonry Structures, 1981
TBE	Recommendations for the Design and Execution of Masonry, 1978

Conference Proceedings and Reference Works (since 1976)

1976   Proc. Fourth Int. Brick Masonry Conf., Brugge.

1976   Proc. First Canadian Masonry Symp., University of Calgary.

1978   Proc. N. American Masonry Conf., Boulder, Col., The Masonry Society, Denver, Col.

1979   Proc. Fifth Int. Brick Masonry Conf., Washington D.C., Brick Inst. America, McLean, Va.

1980   Proc. Conf. on Research in Progress on Masonry Const., Marina del Rey, CA, The Masonry Soc., Denver, Col.

1980   Proc. Second Canadian Masonry Symp., Ottawa, Carleton University, Ottawa.

1981   Proc. Symp., on Reinforced and Prestressed Masonry, London, Inst. Struct. Eng.

CONDENSED REFERENCES/BIBLIOGRAPHY

The following is a condensed bibliography for this article. It includes all articles referred to or cited in the text. The full citations will be found at the end of the volume, with additional citations for further reading. What is given here should be sufficient information to lead the reader to the correct article: the author, date, and title. In case of multiple authors, only the first name is listed.

Adham 1978, *Interaction between Unreinforced Masonry Structures and Their Roof Diaphragms*
Adham 1980, *Investigation of Reinforced Brick Masonry Buildings Undamaged by the San*
Awni 1979, *A Simplified Method for Eccentricity Calculations*
Awni 1981, *The Strength of Masonry Walls Compressed between Floor Slabs*
Awni 1982, *Eccentricity Measurements on Load Bearing Masonry Structures*

Burns 1972, *Unreinforced Brick Masonry Walls under Vertical Loads*
Brown 1980, *An Evaluation of the Moment Magnifier Technique for Design of Unreinforced Masonry*

Clough 1980, *Shaking Table Study of Single Storey Masonry Houses*
Contaldo 1979, *The Numerical Simulation for the Prediction of the Load Carrying Capacity of Masonry*

Davies 1982, *Biaxial Bending of Reinforced Brick Masonry Columns*
Dayaratnam 1981, *Durability of Reinforced Brickwork*
De Vekey 1981, *Durability of Reinforced Masonry*
Drysdale 1976, *Design of Masonry, Walls and Columns for Combined Axial Load and Bending Moment*

Foster 1981, *Aspects of Durability of Clay Masonry*

Gulkan 1978, *An Experimental Investigation on the Seismic Behaviour of Single Storey Masonry Houses*

Hamid 1980, *Strength of Concrete Masonry Under Biaxial Stresses*
Hatzinikolas 1980, *The Analysis of Eccentrically Loaded Masonry Walls by the Moment Magnifier*
Hegemeir 1978, *Behaviour of Concrete Masonry under Biaxial Stresses*
Hendry 1981, *The Shear Strength of Reinforced Brickwork*

Kropp 1979, *Evaluation of Corrosion Resistance of Reinforcement Embedded in Masonry Joints*

Lugez 1979, *With Regard to the Buckling Function of Masonry Walls*

Mann 1979, *Mechanical Treatment of Buckling Behavior of Slender Brick Partitions*
Mann 1982, *Failure of Shear-Stressed Masonry—an Enlarged Theory, Tests and Application to Shear*
Mayes 1978, *Seismic Research on Multi-Storey Masonry Buildings, University of California, Berkley*
McNiven 1980, *Seismic Behaviour of Masonry Piers*
Meadaris 1978, *An Investigation of the Dynamic Response of the Park Lane Towers to Earthquake*

Nachbar 1978, *Stability under Seismic Loading of Buildings with Fully Cracked Wall-Floor Joints*

Oppenheim 1978, *High Rise Building Vibration Properties: An Unexpected Behaviour Mechanism*
Osman 1982, *An Investigation into the Behaviour of Reinforced Grouted Cavity Brick Beams under*

Page 1982, *The In-Plane Failure of Masonry—An Overview*
Pedereschi 1982, *Development and Investigation of the Ultimate Load Behaviour of Post-Tensioned*
Powell 1976, *The Determination of Stress/Strain Relationship of Brickwork*

Rathbone 1981, *The Shear Behaviour of Reinforced Concrete Blockwork Beams*
Roberts 1980, *Further Work on the Behaviour of Reinforced Concrete Blockwork Subject on Lateral*

Samarasinghe 1981, *Behaviour of Brick Masonry Shear Walls*
Samarasinghe 1982, *Strength of Brickwork Under Biavial Stress*
Sawko 1980, *Numerical Solution of Eccentrically Loaded Struts in No-Tension Material*
Sinha 1981, *An Ultimate Load Analysis of Reinforced Brickwork Flexural Members*

Turkstra 1976, *The Moment Magnifier Method Applied in Brick Walls*

Structural Design of Tall Concrete and Masonry Buildings

CONDENSED REFERENCES/BIBLIOGRAPHY

The following is a condensed bibliography for this part. It contains bibliographic citations that are in addition to those cited with the articles. The full citations can be found at the end of the volume. What is given here should be sufficient information to lead the reader to the correct article: author, date, and title. In the case of multiple authors, only the first named is listed.

Coull 1981, *Elasto-Plastic Analysis of Core Structures Subjected to Torsion*
Coull 1981, *Analysis of Core Structures Subjected to Torsion*
Cruz 1980, *Number of Modes for the Seismic Analysis of Buildings*
Canadian Standards Association 1981, *Guidelines for the Development of Limit States Design*

Elias 1979, *Flat Slab Analysis Using Equivalent Beams*

Gesund 1979, *Limit Analysis of Flat Slab Buildings for Lateral Loads*
Gesund 1980, *Local Flexural Strength of Slabs at Interior Columns*
Gesund 1980, *Design for Punching Strength of Slabs at Interior Columns*
Gesund 1981, *Limit Design of Slabs for Concentrated Loads*
Gluck 1979, *Dynamic Torsional Coupling in Tall Building Structures*
Goli 1979, *Linearity in Limit Design of Orthotropic Slabs*
Goli 1980, *Yield Line Analysis of Orthotropically Reinforced Exterior Panels of Flat Slab Floors*
Goodno 1976, *Analysis of Shear Cores Using Superelements*

Ha 1978, *Orthotropic Membrane for Tall Building Analysis*
Harman 1975, *Analysis of Tall Buildings Using Member-Groups*
Hsieh 1982, *A Plastic-Fracture Model for Concrete*

Khan 1976, *A Simple Method of Analysis for Deflections and Stresses in Wall-Frame Structures*
Kristek 1979, *Folded Plate Approach to Analysis of Shear Wall Systems and Frame Structures*

Lamar 1978, *Static Analysis of Structures with Thin Walls Subjected to Horizontal Forces*
Liauw 1978, *Torsion of Multi-Story Spatial Core Walls*
Lopez 1980, *Estimating Shears in Buildings Subjected to Earthquake Motions*

Macleod 1977, *Structural Analysis of Wall Systems*
Macleod 1977, *Frame Analysis of Shear-Wall Cores*
Marin 1974, *Strength and Ductility of C-Shaped Structural Walls*
Marin 1977, *Behavior of Reinforced Concrete in Combined Axial Load and Bending*
Marin 1978, *Charts, Formulas and Criteria for Computing Columns in RC Buildings. Summary of*
Marin 1979, *Design Aids for L-Shaped Reinforced Concrete Columns*
Marin 1979, *Designing Columns with Non-Rectangular Cross Sections*
Marin 1980, *Computing Undimensional Normal Stress Resultants*

633

Marin 1980, *Computation of Reinforced Concrete Columns with Non-Rectangular Cross Section*
Mee 1975, *Wall-Beam Frames Under Static Lateral Load*
Minami 1977, *Seismic Resistance of Reinforced Concrete Beam-to-Column Assemblages with*
Minami 1980, *Seismic Resistance of Diagonally Reinforced Concrete Columns*
Minami 1980, *Earthquake Resistant Properties of Diagonally Reinforced Concrete Columns*
Minami 1980, *Rational Analysis of Shear in Reinforced Concrete Columns*
Minami 1981, *Rational Analysis of Shear in Reinforced Concrete Columns*
Mortelmans 1981, *Approximate Method for Lateral Load Analysis of High-Rise Buildings*
Mukherjee 1975, *Vibrations of Coupled Shear Walls on Framed Supports*
Mukherjee 1977, *Free Vibrations of Open-Section Shear Walls*

Nayar 1976, *Elasto-Plastic Analysis of Coupled Shear Walls*

Pekau 1981, *Elasto-Plastic Analysis of Coupled Shear Walls*

Reinhorn 1977, *Dynamic Torsional Coupling in Asymmetric Building Structures*
Rosman 1976, *Statics and Stability of Partially Restrained Column Systems* (In German)
Rosman 1977, *Design of Open Frames* (In German)
Rosman 1977, *Mechanics of Wallbeam Frames* (In German)
Rosman 1981, *Buckling and Vibration of Spatial Building Structures*
Roy 1977, *Introduction to Tall Building Structures*
Rutenberg 1975, *Approximations for Natural Frequencies of Interconnected Walls and Frames*
Rutenberg 1975, *Torsional Analysis of Perforated Core Structures*
Rutenberg 1975, *Analysis of Spiral Stairs Supported on a Central Column*
Rutenberg 1975, *Approximate Natural Frequencies for Coupled Shear Walls*
Rutenberg 1975, *Torsion of Perforated Core Structures*
Rutenberg 1977, *Dynamic Properties of Asymmetric Wall-Frame Structures*
Rutenberg 1978, *On the Dynamic Properties of Asymmetric Wall Frame Structures*
Rutenberg 1979, *Plane Frame Analysis of Laterally Loaded Asymmetric Buildings—An Uncompleted*
Rutenberg 1979, *Earthquake Analysis of Belted High-Rise Building Structures*
Rutenberg 1980, *Laterally Loaded Flexible Diaphragm Buildings: Planar Analogy*
Rutenberg 1981, *A Direct P-Delta Analysis Using Standard Plane Frame Programs*
Rutenberg 1982, *Simplified P-Delta Analysis for Asymmetric Structures*

Stafford Smith 1981, *Analysis of Non-Planar Shear Wall Assemblies by Analogous Frame*
Sozen 1977, *Introduction to the Behavior of Reinforced Concrete Buildings*
Svojsik 1980, *Seismic Behavior of Macuto-Sheraton Building During the Caracas 1967 Earthquake*

Taranath 1975, *Optimum Belt Truss Locations for High-Rise Structures*
Taranath 1976, *The Effect of Warping on Inter-Connected Shear Wall-Flat Plate Structures*
Tso 1975, *Cyclic Loading of Externally Reinforced Masonry Walls Confined by Frames*
Tso 1977, *Effective Width of Coupling Slabs in Shear Wall Buildings*

Vanderbilt 1979, *Equivalent Frame Analysis for Lateral Loads*

Wakabayashi 1977, *Behavior of Systems*
Wakabayashi 1978, *Effect of Strain Rate on Stress-Strain Relationships of Concrete and Steel*
Wakabayashi 1980, *Dynamic Loading Effects of Concrete and Steel Materials and Beams*
Weaver 1981, *Finite Element for Shear Walls in Multi-Story Frames*
Wong 1980, *Structural Behavior of Floor Slabs in Shear Wall Buildings*
Wong 1980, *Interaction Between Floor Slabs and Shear Walls in Tall Buildings*

Project Descriptions

Headquarters for The Hong Kong and Shanghai Banking Corporation

Norman Foster

The 5000-m² site has been the headquarters location of The Hong Kong and Shanghai Banking Corporation for many years. It is arguably the most important site in Hong Kong, being at the head of Statue Square, the only substantial public open space in the island's central business district. The square itself is a major pedestrian route to the harbor waterfront and ferry services to Kowloon and the New Territories on the mainland to the North. Although now about 400 m from the waterfront, the site was originally on the shoreline at the foot of the steep granite rock formation that lies to the south; successive land reclamation schemes have progressively extended the level ground areas that the site overlooks.

The building is constructed in three bays of 28, 35, and 45 stories in height. Plant, services, and stairs form eight compact towers on the east and west sides, with flexible open working spaces between. Vertically, the floors form groups of varying number, from eight to four, separated by double-height spaces. Vertical transportation is by a combination of high-speed lifts to the double-height spaces and escalators to individual floors. The base of the building at ground level forms an open public pedestrian concourse of 12 m clear height. Above this level is the main banking floor and a central ten-story high atrium. Below-ground accommodation includes a museum, secure area, vehicle servicing, and the central engineering plant.

The main structural frame is of fire-proofed and clad steel. It consists of eight vertical mast assemblies, to which inclined main horizontal structures are attached at intervals. These elements provide lateral stiffness and suspension points for groups of floors. External walls are a purpose-designed system, capable of providing glazed, solid, translucent, or louvered areas. Services, plant, and stairs are of modular construction, designed for off-site fabrication and fitting out. All support services distribution is contained within structural floor voids, with outlets for air, light, power, and communications through a full-access panel floor system.

Demolition of the existing 1936 building commenced in July, 1981, with substructure work started in January, 1982. Completion of the building is targeted for 1985. The project will be carried out under a management contract.

The building is suspended from two lines of steel masts 38.4 m apart, forming three bays, each 16.2 m wide front to back. At five points up the building the masts are connected by a double-height inclined structure from which clusters of floors are suspended; the clusters diminish incrementally from 8 stories at the base to 4 stories at the top. The bays rise to varying heights, three of them to 28 stories, two to 35 stories, and one to 41 stories. This staggered profile provides the benefit of varying width spaces inside, garden terraces outside, a more interesting profile in the cityscape, and a tuneable response to the legislation of light angles and shadow allowances.

Each structural mast is a cluster of four vertical members, and this walk-through zone extends as a 3.5-m-wide movement strip across the building, linking into vertical towers at the edges to provide service modules or escape stairs. These strips are handled in a manner similar to "pavement lights," allowing the penetration of natural light into the deeper floors. A large proportion of the strip is left void to form small-scale atriums through which escalators handle local vertical movement.

The floor units, which span 11.1 m, between the structural edges of the movement strips, are of prefabricated steel construction in 2.4-m-wide elements. As noted, all the support services distribution — air, light, power, and communications — is through a full-access panel floor system. Each unit can be removed without affecting the structural integrity of the whole.

The base of the building is in effect a gateway straddling an extension of Statue Square to allow generous public passage through the site. Elevated 12 m above this passageway is the main Banking Hall level with an atrium that is a vertical ten story extension of the ground level concourse. Natural light is scoped through the top of the atrium from reflectors on the south facade. The concourse is of translucent glass, pavement light construction to pull natural

Fıg. 1 New headquarters for the Hong Kong and Shanghai Banking Corporation—Model of Interior Court

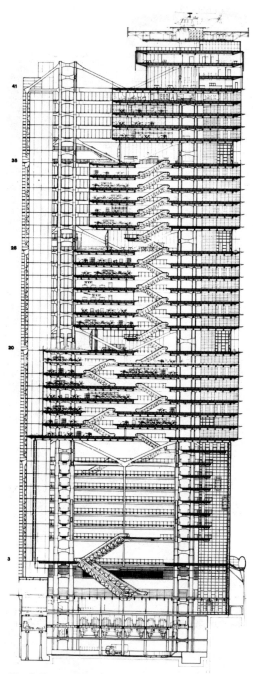

Fig. 2 East-west section *(Courtesy: Foster Associates)*

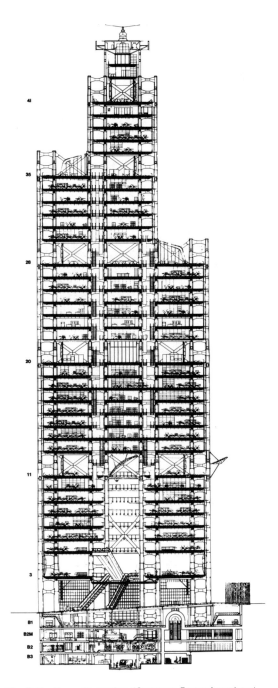

Fig. 3 North-south section *(Courtesy: Foster Associates)*

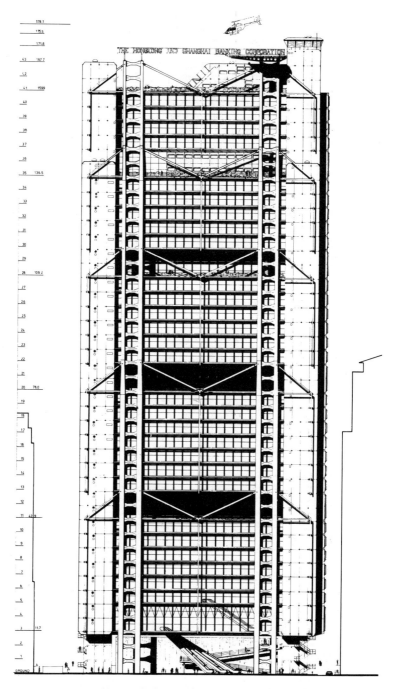

Fig. 4 Harbor-side elevation *(Courtesy: Architectural Design, London)*

light into the levels below ground which, as noted, contain a museum, secure areas, vehicle servicing, and the central engineering plant. At night the base of the building would have a crystalline, glowing appearance from the lighting below ground.

A change in level of 2.4 m across the site is exploited, on the southern edge, to incorporate a vertical wall of water, which provides cool shade for related sitting areas and acts as a visual buffer to busy Queen's Road, in which the sound of water would dominate the noise of traffic. Escalators, walkways, and ramps provide movement to the public areas and also link overhead traffic-free bridges to the primary routes behind the site, which were inhibited by the previous building and the barrier of Queen's Road.

Given Hong Kong's crowds, it is probably impossible to calculate the magnitude of movement through the site, but it has been predicted that daily visitors to the building may exceed 20,000, quite apart from the office population itself. The form of the building reflects the movement and density of use, with the greatest public footprint at the base tapering to the least dense and

Fig. 5 Night-time photomontage of bank model in Hong Kong setting *(Richard Davies; Courtesy: Foster Associates)*

most private areas at the top. Since vertical travel is by a combination of high speed lifts and escalators through a sequence of varied spaces, the scale of the larger organization could be broken down into smaller "village" units—each with its own identifiable reception area served directly by lifts. Movement from these points is by escalator and offers many of the social and operational benefits normally associated with low-rise structures. The double-height spaces, with their related outdoor garden terraces, provide reception areas as well as restaurant, leisure, and training areas.

The concept is also an ideal response to the different use patterns that might follow from subletting parts of the building. Detailed studies have shown that 24 lifts are appropriate in conjunction with escalators, but the proportion could easily be altered without any changes to the structure. Such capability has been used during construction to provide the temporary Banking Hall in an existing annex, which adjoined the main site. It was the intention that when this annex was eventually demolished, the new building and banks of lifts which overhang it would simply grow downward from the masts and occupy the total site. However, such is the pace of change in Hong Kong that plans were accelerated and the annex was removed in the early stages of construction during 1982.

The building is virtually self-erecting; traveling gantries place pieces of the mast in position and then climb up them. Underslung gantries do the same with the floor units, which arrive, like the modules, preplumbed with services. There is the potential within the system to expand the building area by 30% without any modification to the structure.

Fig. 6 Entrance to public concourse *(Birkin Howard; Courtesy: Foster Associates)*

In Hong Kong, each building has to be its own self-contained island in the event of a fire. This requirement means, for instance, that the office population has to be able to transfer to separate protected areas, rather than being allowed to discharge into the street. By the provision of two-hour protective shutters, the roof terraces double up as external protected areas for refuge from fire.

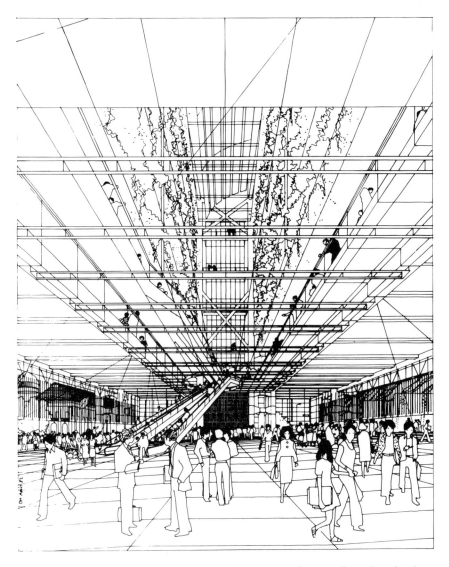

Fig. 7 Public concourse and banking hall *(Birkin Howard; Courtesy: Foster Associates)*

The rich mix of spaces and activities within the varying matrix of the building is reflected in the external envelope, with its diverse infill of translucent, transparent, solid, and grilled panels. External sunshades reduce the energy load, provide maintenance access, and are an integral part of the wind engineering concept.

Although the key design decisions have been argued on a humanistic basis, it did seem important to challenge the traditional office tower on its sacred raison d'etre—namely the net-to-gross argument. The bank commissioned separate space-planning consultants to assess the building performance, and they identified an extraordinarily high 73.5% net to gross overall, with individual floors running as high as 85%. Compared with the usual maximum of 65% for around 40 stories, and given an achieved 18.1 plot ratio, this net to gross effectively provides an additional 7500 m^2, which the Bank has valued as a bonus worth around £40 million.

The difficulties of building rapidly and quietly on a tight site have been resolved by a combination of technologies, drawn from sources ranging from indigenous craft-based family industries to aerospace and other advanced industries. For example, the fastest way to place caissons is to hand-dig them—a locally based technique that also happens to be noise-free. Likewise, the most elegantly efficient structures to be seen in the colony are the spider webs of bamboo scaffolding that mark virtually all construction sites. However, given the amount of imported hardware that buildings contain, as well as an awareness of the very real relationship between weight and performance, the design has been strongly influenced by sources outside the traditional building industry. These sources ranged from the Concorde design team, to military establishments coping with mobile bridges required to take tank loadings, to the world of aircraft subcontractors, particularly those in the United States.

Equally important influences on the design development are the first indigenous impressions of Hong Kong, as well as freely acknowledged source material that has accompanied most board room presentations. In this context, the nineteenth century Galleria in Milan is still a favored example of a handsome public passage. Likewise, the urban gardening of Paley Place in New York has been widely cited and illustrated as a quiet oasis in the midst of metropolitan bustle. Its ingredients of water, greenery, and seating suggest the possibilities of a smaller breakdown of spaces at the public ground levels. The use of color, light, and structure in traditional Chinese and Japanese architecture will certainly leave its mark on the finished building, as will the more intangible aspects of Oriental design such as those seen in Fung Shui. It certainly seems more than a coincidence that the spirit of the first sketch by Koo Pak Ling should have been so strongly echoed in the detail proposals over a year later.

Excerpted (and slightly revised) with permission from *Architectural Design,* London

Tsuen Wan Estates Development— Hong Kong

David Croft

INTRODUCTION

The Tsuen Wan Estates Development which, when complete, will be known as Luk Yeung Sun Chuen (The New Green Willow Village), is to be sited on the 5.5-ha podium deck above the Mass Transit Railway depot at Tsuen Wan, Hong Kong (Figs. 1, 2, and 3). The development consists of residential tower blocks, schools, banks, shops, and other public amenities. It will provide accommodation and facilities for 20,000 people.

There are 17 residential blocks with a total gross floor area of 215,000 m². Each block is of cruciform shape in plan and is between 28 and 30 stories high. The structure of each block consists of reinforced concrete shear walls and floor slabs, supported on a grillage of 2-m-deep beams that transmit the loads onto columns, which pass through the railway depot below.

There are two basic floor arrangements, referred to as type A and type B. Although similar in appearance, the two types show significant differences in the arrangement of the load bearing walls. The two floor arrangements, combined with the variation in the number of stories, result in four basic

Fig. 1 Architectural model *(Courtesy: Neil Famin)*

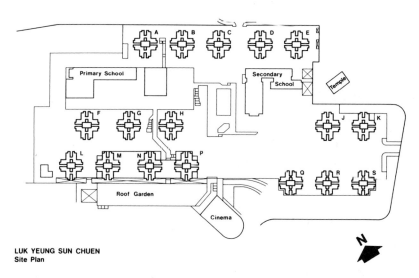

LUK YEUNG SUN CHUEN
Site Plan

Fig. 2 Site plan

block types; and within each block type there are variations in the arrangement of the central lift and stair cores. Figure 4 shows a typical floor plan for a type-A block.

PRELIMINARY DESIGN

Scheme Design

The scheme design for the depot structure was carried out in 1977. At this time no detailed information was available on the residential blocks, as the

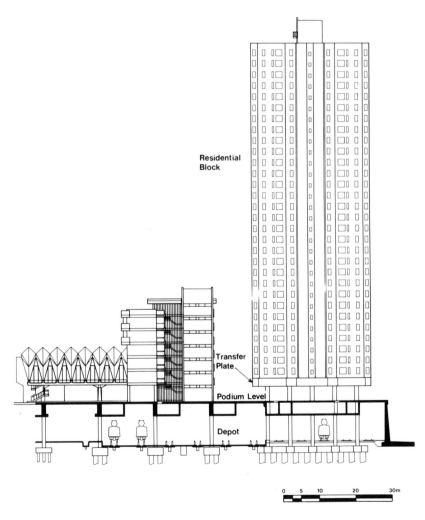

Fig. 3 Typical section

developer had not been appointed. Depot members were sized to be capable of supporting blocks up to 30 stories high, and block loadings were calculated based on experience gained from a previous similar development.

Preliminary Analysis

The initial schemes proposed by the developer in 1978 were similar to the arrangement shown in Fig. 4. The majority of the walls, however, were shown as 150 mm thick, and simple hand calculations showed these to be inadequate in many cases. To determine which walls needed to be thickened, and to what extent a more detailed analysis was necessary to determine the degree of coupling between wall sections provided by the spandrel and lintel beams

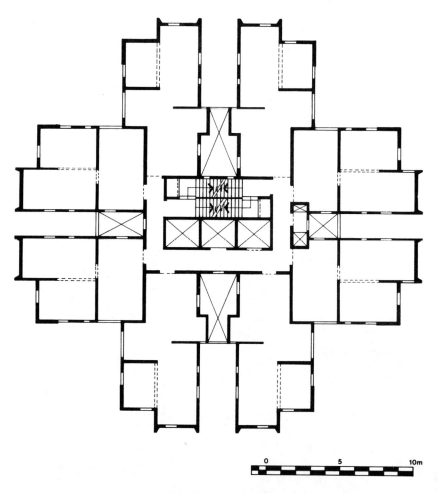

0   5   10m

Fig. 4 Typical floor plan

under wind loading, a three-dimensional, ten-story model was analyzed in which full fixity was assumed at transfer plate level, and horizontal wind loads, calculated in accordance with the Hong Kong Building Regulations (Public Works Department, 1976), were applied. This analysis showed that the stresses in some walls and beams were high, although not excessively so. However, it was recognized that these stresses would be increased as a result of the deformations of the transfer plate and depot structure. It was therefore recommended that the thickness of critical walls should be increased. Additionally, in view of the size and nature of the project, it was recommended that a wind tunnel test should be carried out.

WIND TUNNEL TEST

Hong Kong Wind Climate

Although strong winds in Hong Kong derive from both monsoons and typhoons, the latter almost exclusively govern structural wind loading. A typhoon is a severe tropical cyclone particular to the tropical latitudes of the western Pacific Ocean. It takes the form of a large vortex of air spiraling inwards towards the center, where the barometric pressure is minimal. The incoming air escapes upwards around the central low-pressure area, in which light winds and occasionally calms are experienced.

Typhoons are distinquished from tropical cyclones in other parts of the world mainly by their frequency (average 20 per year) and by their development into very large systems. The season in the South China Sea region extends from May to October, with a peak during the latter part of this period. However, typhoons have occurred in all months of the year. In the peak months, they tend to move towards the Pacific coasts of Asia in a generally north-westerly direction. In the other months, they are more apt to cross the Philippines in a westerly direction towards Indo-China.

The appropriate wind speed for the wind tunnel test was found from the data published by Mackey (1971).

Test Details

The wind tunnel test was carried out in early 1979 by the Department of Aeronautical Engineering at Bristol University. The test model (Fig. 5) was made to a scale of 1:350 and included the 17 tower blocks, the depot roof, and the low-rise Estates Development, as well as the existing buildings in close proximity to the site. All 14 Type-B-blocks were treated as identical, as were the three Type-A blocks.

The low-rise buildings on the depot roof were modeled in a simplified way in view of the fact that their design was not then final. This level of accuracy was sufficient for the purpose of obtaining wind loads on the tower blocks but would not be appropriate for investigating wind effects on the low-rise structures themselves. Similarly, the modeling of the surrounding buildings was also greatly simplified, as these too will obviously change with time.

The model was designed so that each of the tower blocks could be removed and replaced either by one attached to the dynamic balance below (Fig. 6) or by one fitted with pressure tapping points (Fig. 7).

The time scale used in the test was 1:50.

For the design of the residential blocks a return period of 50 years was chosen and the necessary wind parameters were derived using the formulae given by ESDU (Engineering Sciences Data Unit, 1972). The specified mean hourly velocity at 10 m of height was 28 m/sec and the specified mean velocity, turbulence, and power spectral density are shown in Figs. 8–10. These figures also show the values measured in the wind tunnel. As a comparison with the U.K. wind code (British Standards Institute, 1972b), this wind could be equivalent to a basic (3-sec) wind speed of 68 m/sec with ground roughness 3.

The appropriate averaging interval was determined using the formula proposed by Lawson (1976) as follows:

$$T = \frac{4.5L}{V} \tag{1}$$

Fig. 5 Wind tunnel model

Fig. 6 Balance detail

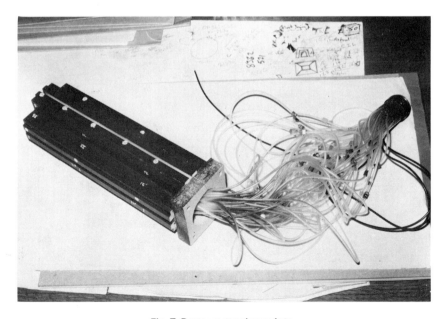

Fig. 7 Pressure tapping points

where T is the averaging interval in seconds
  L is the length or height of the structure (100 m)
  V is the mean wind velocity

This formula gives a value of $T = 10$ sec, based on a mean hourly velocity at mid-height of 45 m/sec. which is somewhat shorter than the 15 seconds suggested by the U.K. code corresponding to Class C structures, and reflects the higher wind speeds in Hong Kong compared with the U.K.

The design values for 10-sec gusts were taken as those values that were exceeded in the wind tunnel test 0.05% of the time.

The specification for the tests originally called for measurements of static and dynamic components of the base shear forces and moments at 15° azimuth intervals for all blocks, together with pressure readings on selected angles on specified blocks. As it happened, however, technical problems were encountered with the dynamic balance that could not be overcome within the time available. It was therefore necessary to determine the 10-sec gust force

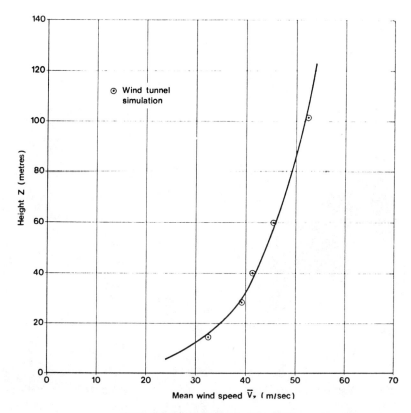

Fig. 8 Upstream wind velocity profile

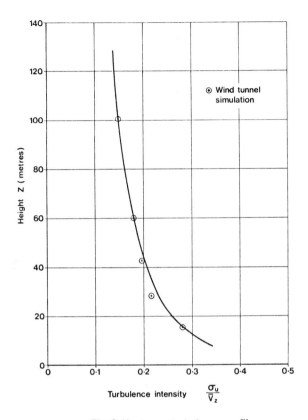

Fig. 9 Upstream turbulence profile

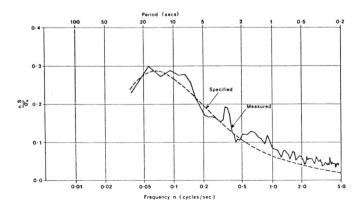

Fig. 10 Upstream power spectral density

and moments for the critical blocks by integrating the pressure readings and for the other cases by factoring up the mean values using relationships derived from the critical blocks.

Results for Block C without and with the surrounding blocks are shown in Figs. 11 and 12 and for all blocks in Fig. 13. Also shown for comparison are the corresponding values given by the Hong Kong and U.K. codes.

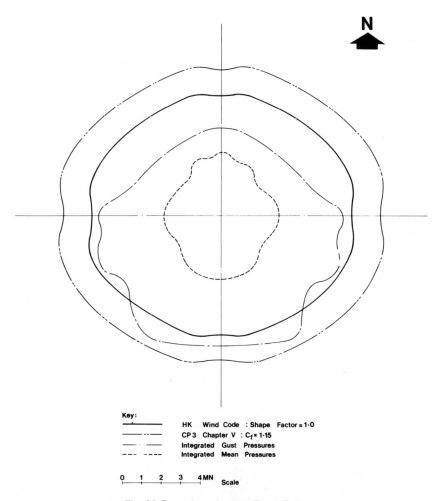

Key:

———•———	HK Wind Code : Shape Factor = 1·0
———··———	CP 3 Chapter V : C_f = 1·15
———·———	Integrated Gust Pressures
——— ———	Integrated Mean Pressures

0 1 2 3 4 MN   Scale

Fig. 11 Base shear forces—Block C alone

Test Results

The pressure readings taken for Block C, in its position on the podium but with the other blocks removed, served as a base run and enabled the effects of the shape of the individual blocks to be separated from the effects of the interaction between them. The base shear force is plotted in Fig. 11, and the corresponding values obtained from the Hong Kong and U.K. codes (assuming a basic wind speed 68 m/sec and roughness 3, Class C) are also plotted for comparison. From these results the conclusions that follow were drawn.

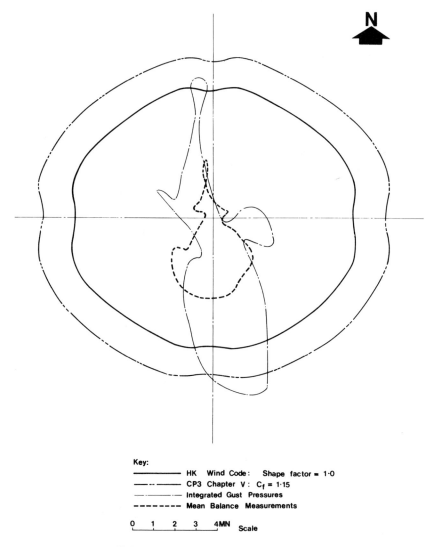

Key:

——————— HK Wind Code: Shape factor = 1·0
—— ·· —— CP3 Chapter V: C_f = 1·15
—— · —— Integrated Gust Pressures
– – – – – – Mean Balance Measurements

0 1 2 3 4MN Scale

Fig. 12 Base shear forces—Block C with other blocks

Although the mean pressures are found to be reasonably constant for all wind directions, the gust pressures are significantly higher for winds from the north, apparently due to the fact that the site is much more exposed to the north than to the south; and that on that side the podium is at the level of the surrounding ground.

The Hong Kong wind code appears to be conservative for south winds but to underestimate the wind loading from the north. As the south direction is more typical of the urban conditions in Hong Kong, these results indicate that the Hong Kong code forms a reasonable basis for design in most cases.

It was found that for any wind direction the pressures on most faces were negative (Fig. 14) and that the resultant forces on the structure were primarily due to these suctions, rather than by positive pressures on the windward side.

Comparing the results for the shear forces and bending moments, it was apparent that the resultant wind force acts at a lower level than implied by the codes of practice, which assume that the pressure at each level is proportional to the square of the velocity at that level in the undisturbed airflow. It would seem to be more realistic to assume that the pressures are, on average, uniformly distributed up the building.

The base shear forces for Block C with the other blocks in place are shown in Fig. 12, and the bending moments show a similar pattern. It is apparent that the shielding effects of the adjacent blocks substantially reduce the wind load in the east-west direction. In the north-south direction, however, the wind forces are increased. This is because the wind has to pass the five blocks in A–E, where the gaps between the blocks amount to less than their width. As a result the airflow tends to pass around the outer blocks, thereby increasing

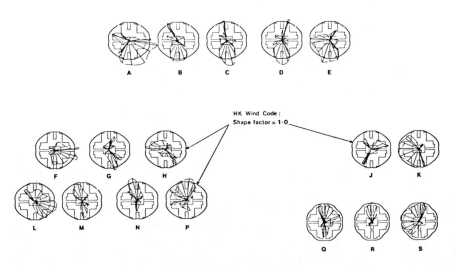

Fig. 13 Base shear forces—all blocks

the suction on the leeward side, and hence the resultant forces. On Block E
the wind force is enhanced for wind from the east because of the presence of
Block D downstream, which increases the suction on the leeward face. In
each case, however, the same relationship between moment and shear forces
as for Block C alone was found.

Design Pressures

As a result of these tests it was proposed, and subsequently agreed with the
Building Ordnance Office (BOO), that each block should be designed for a
uniform pressure on the face of the building calcuated from a basic pressure
at 2.7 kN/m² multiplied by force coefficients, as shown in Table 1.

The value of 1.1 was chosen after discussion with BOO so that the total
shear force on the structure would not be less than that given by the Hong
Kong wind code. Some blocks, therefore, are designed for a greater total
shear force than is necessary, in order to conform with BOO requirements.
However, the test results justify the assumption of uniform pressure up the
buildings, and in most cases the associated total bending moments are reduced.

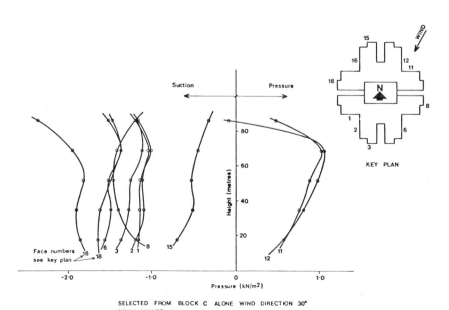

Fig. 14 Typical pressure distributions

FINAL DESIGN

Analysis

The difficulty in the analysis of the residential blocks arises from the complex behavior of the shear walls, which is caused by their irregular plan shapes and the arrangement of the window and door openings. It is not possible to calculate accurately the degree of coupling between the walls by any simple technique. The analysis is further complicated because the blocks are supported by the relatively flexible transfer plate and depot structure, the deformations of which will induce additional shear forces and bending moments in the lower stories.

Initially, the intention was to analyze one three-dimensional computer model, which would include the depot structure, the transfer plate, and the 30 stories of walls and floors. However, although the blocks are essentially symmetrical about both axes, which allows the model to be reduced to one quadrant in plan, the problem was still too large to be analyzed in a single stage. It was therefore decided to carry out the analysis in three stages.

A three-dimensional model (Fig. 15) representing the 30 stories of walls and beams above the transfer plate was analyzed first. This model was fully fixed at transfer plate level and was subjected to vertical dead and live loads and wind loads in two directions.

A second model (Fig. 16) was then produced to represent the depot structure, transfer plate, and 15 stories of walls and beams. Again vertical and wind loading was applied. Member forces were abstracted from the wall elements at the 16th floor of the 30-story model and applied at the top.

In the second model the transfer plate members were stiffened by the structure above so that spandrel beams helped to transfer loads to the columns. It is not reasonable, however, to rely on this contribution during the early construction stages when the transfer plate has been built and depropped and the first few stories of walls have been constructed but have not matured. A third model was therefore analyzed in which the second model was modified

Table 1 Design force coefficients

Block	Type	Stories	N-S	E-W
A–E incl.	B	30	1.25	1.25
FGHL	B	29	1.1	1.15
JK	B	30	1.1	1.1
MNP	B	28	1.15	1.1
QRS	A	30	1.1	1.1

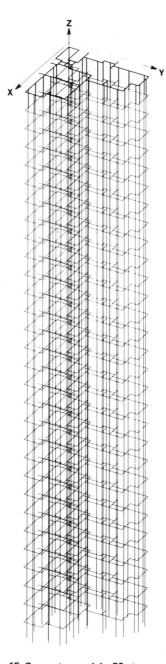

Fig. 15 Computer model—30-story model

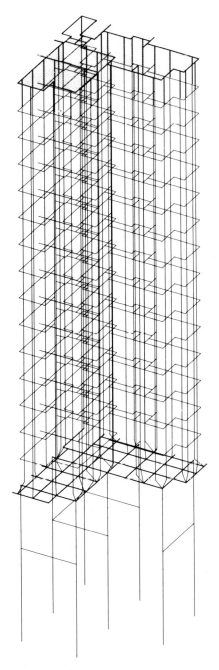

Fig. 16 Computer model—15-story model

to remove the structural contribution of the residential block. This model was loaded with the self-weight of the transfer plate, plus the equivalent of the self-weight of four stories of walls and slabs.

Advantage was taken of the symmetrical plan arrangement of the load bearing walls by modeling only one-quarter of the block and choosing suitable restraints at the two axes of symmetry. These restraints vary for each type of loading and hence three analyses were required for each model. In these models each rectangular wall section was represented by a vertical beam element at the section centroid (Fig. 17). At story height intervals, these elements were connected by horizontal stiff arms, which also connected to beam elements representing the spandrel and lintel beams. To limit the size of the problem, a number of horizontal stiff arms were omitted and the length of the spandrel beams being modeled were increased. Beam properties were adjusted to model the correct effective stiffness of the beam-wall arrangements.

The floor slabs were assumed to act as horizontal diaphragms and this effect was simulated by specifying equal horizontal displacements of the nodes at each floor level. Figure 17 shows relevant element numbers for a typical floor. This single-story model is referred to as the "chasis" model, from which the 15-story and the 30-story models were generated.

In the 15-story models, the transfer plate was represented by a grillage of beams (Fig. 18). The effects of axial and shear deformations of all elements were included, but torsional stiffness were not generally taken into account, except in certain selected members. All loads were applied directly to nodes as point loads and moments, where appropriate. Separate analyses were carried out for each of the four basic block types.

The computer analysis program used was PAFEC 75. There were approximately 3,800 elements and 2,600 nodes required for the 30-story models, and 2,100 elements and 1,400 nodes were required for the 15-story models. To save time and reduce the possibility of error in both data preparation and interpretation of the results, purpose-written computer programs were used to generate the data automatically and to postprocess the results and present them in a comprehensible form.

The input data for the 30- and 15-story models were generated from the data for the single-story chassis model by a special computer program. This program also generated the necessary vertical loading data. Another program was written to extract the analysis results from the required level of the 30-story model and generate loading data for application to the top of the 15-story model.

For the design of the spandrel and lintel beams, a program was written to generate shear force and bending moment envelopes for combinations of dead load, live load, and wind loads acting in the directions of the major axes and at 45°. Allowance was made for live load reduction and permissible overstress under wind loading, and corrections were made for the spandrels, which had been modeled with modified spans, as mentioned above. The results were presented graphically as shown in Fig. 19. Similar envelopes were generated for the transfer plate members.

For the design of the walls themselves, it was necessary to calculate the resultant vertical stresses at critical sections under the various load combinations from the results for the individual axial forces and bending moments in the vertical elements. Where composite walls were modeled by one or more elements (for example, elements 100, 104, 108, and 120 in Fig. 17) it was necessary to combine the forces and moments and apply them to the combined section. These calculations were carried out using yet another program, and the results were again presented in graphical form in terms of the ratio of actual to allowable stress (Fig. 20). These plots indicate where the

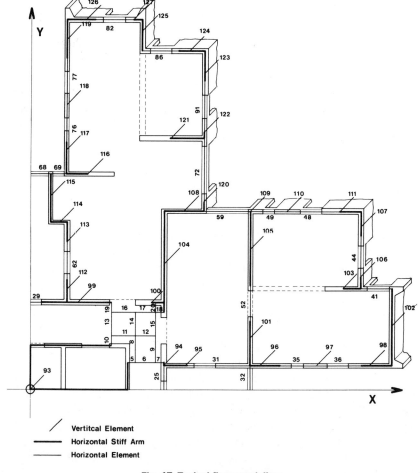

Fig. 17 Typical floor modeling

steel precentage could be reduced or alternatively where grade 40 concrete was required.

Behavior of the Structure

Spandrel and lintel beams are required to transfer shear forces across wall sections under wind loading, so reducing bending moments in the individual walls. The efficiency of a beam providing coupling is governed by the stiffness of the connecting beam relative to the stiffnesses of the connected walls. Figure 21 shows shear force plots for elements numbers 25 and 52 located on Fig. 17. Element 25 is a relatively stiff spandrel beam connecting flexible wall elements, and the plot is almost linear, indicating that the walls

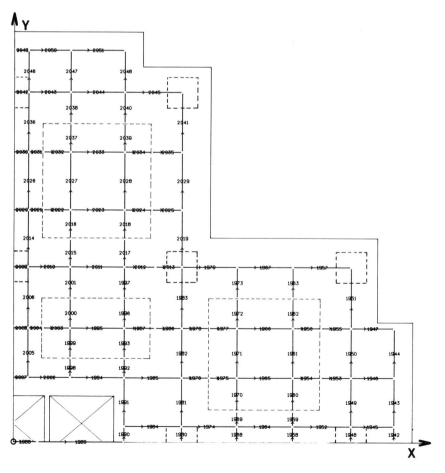

Fig. 18 Transfer plate element modeling

are effectively acting together as a single cantilever. Element 52, in contrast, is a relatively flexible lintel beam, in which the peak shear force occurs at about the eighth floor and the shear force distribution is similar to that normally associated with coupling beams.

The degree of coupling under wind loading can be expressed in terms of the ratio between the actual shear transferred across an axis of symmetry and that which would be transferred with full coupling. The latter force can be expressed as

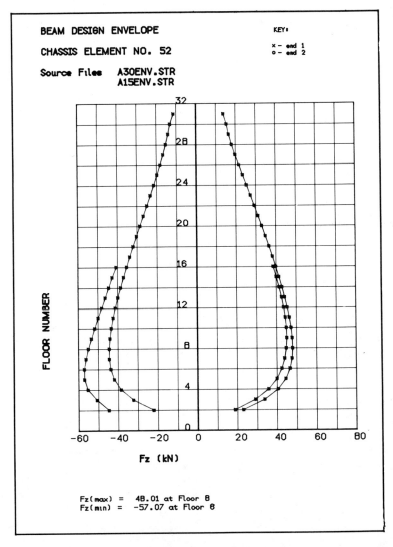

Fig. 19 Typical forces plot

$$P = \frac{MAL}{I}$$

where M = total wind moment

A = area of walls in one-half of the block

L = distance to the centroid of the walls in one-half of the block
from the axis of symmetry

I = total inertia of the block assuming full coupling

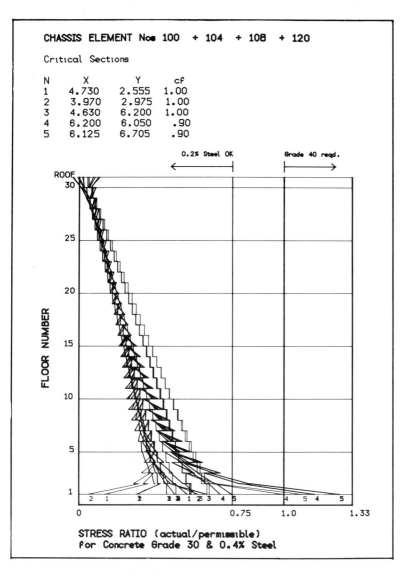

Fig. 20 Typical wall stress plot

On this basis, coupling was found to be approximately 80% efficient in the east-west (*x*-axis) direction and 70% efficient in the north-south (y-axis) direction.

In the 30-story model, axial stresses in the walls due to vertical loading are very uniform at about 4.5 N/mm² at first floor level. In the 15-story model the stress increases to about 7.0 N/mm² in the walls close to the column supports, as a result of the flexibility of the transfer plate. In addition, the rotation of the transfer plate induces local bending in the lower stories. The forces in the beam and wall elements under wind loading are also affected by the deformations of the transfer plate. Figure 22 demonstrates the effect on the shear force distributions for chassis element 44.

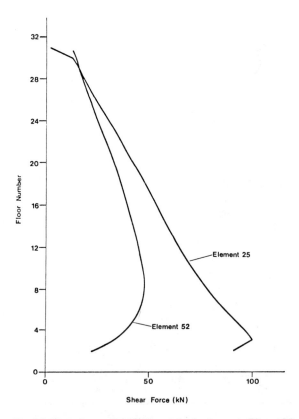

Fig. 21 Shear force distribution—chasis elements 25 and 52

Element Design

The structure was generally designed in accordance with the BOO regulations. Additional checks for shear and vertical tensile stresses were also made to CP110 (British Standards Institute, 1972a).

It was found that compression reinforcement in the walls could be avoided altogether, provided that grade-40 concrete was used for the first lift of walls. Significant tensile stresses as a result of bending in the individual walls only occur in the lower stories, and these were catered for by the provision of 0.4% vertical reinforcement with additional trimming bars at the ends of the walls.

The shear forces in the individual walls are generally small, except in some walls at first-floor level. In these cases it was necessary to check the principal stresses at various positions, and these stresses were found to be acceptable.

Several of the spandrel beams are highly stressed in the lower stories and heavy reinforcement is required. The maximum shear stress is approximately 2.5 N/mm² under working loads.

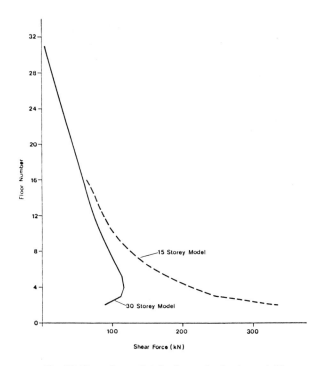

Fig. 22 Shear force distribution—chasis element 44

Reinforcement quantities

Approximately 14,500 tonnes of reinforcement are required for the residential blocks, transfer plates, and columns above the podium deck. This tonnage is equivalent to 68 kg/m^2 of gross floor area.

A breakdown into the various structural elements is as follows:

Slabs	32%
Walls and spandrels	49%
Transfer plates	16%
Columns	3%

Rates for reinforcement weight per unit area of each structural element:

Slabs	20.5 kg/m^2
Walls and Spandrels	23.4 kg/m^2
Transfer plates	255.0 kg/m^2

ACKNOWLEDGEMENTS

The author is grateful for the work carried out by his colleagues within the project team in Ove Arup and Partners, in particular J. Hirst and B. Parkinson, who supplied parts of this text, and also R. Care and P. Cross. Architect: Choa, Ko and Partners in association with Lee and Zee Associates. Client: Mass Transit Railway Corporation of Hong Kong. Developer: Luk Yeung Sun Chuen-Joint Venture.

CONDENSED REFERENCES/BIBLIOGRAPHY

The following is a condensed bibliography for this article. It includes all articles referred to or cited in the text. The full citations will be found at the end of the volume, with additional citations for further reading. What is given here should be sufficient information to lead the reader to the correct article: the author, date, and title. In case of multiple authors, only the first name is listed.

British Standards Institute 1972a, *CP110: The Structural Use of Concrete*
British Standards Institute 1972b, *CP3: Wind Loads, Chap. V*

Engineering Sciences Data Unit 1972, *Characteristics of Wind Speed in the Lower Layers of the*

Lawson 1976, *The Design of Cladding*

Mackey 1971, *Extreme Wind Studies in Hong Kong*

Public Works Department 1976, *Code of Practice on Wind Effects*

Project Descriptions

Hopewell Centre

Samuel Y. S. Kwok

In the history of Hong Kong, Wanchai — the site of the Hopewell Centre — had always been a densely populated residential area on Hong Kong island; whereas Central and Tsim Sha Tsui were regarded as central business districts. However, in 1969 the government announced the plan for a cross-harbor tunnel to link Hunghom on Kowloon Peninsula and Causeway Bay (east of Wanchai) on Hong Kong Island; and the plans for another Lion Rock Tunnel and Aberdeen Tunnel were unveiled a few years later. In light of these plans, Hopewell viewed land in the Wanchai and Causeway Bay area as being of high development potential. Hence, from 1970 to 1972 Hopewell has acquired 13 lots, amalgamated to an area of over 5,200 m², at the site where Hopewell Centre now stands. The cost was around HK$15 million at the time. (HK$5.8 = US$1 in January, 1982).

This site is bounded by Queen's Road East to its north; Kennedy Road to its south; a service lane, a church, and an apartment block to its east; and a derelict garden owned by the government to its west. The levels of Kennedy Road and Queen's Road East differ by 48 m, so the entrance level from Kennedy Road to the centre is at 17th floor (Figs. 1, 2, and 3).

GENERAL DATA

The site area is approximately 5,200 m² (56,000 ft²). Total gross area is

669

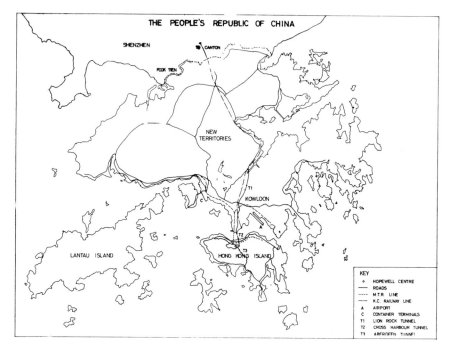

Fig. 1 Map of Hong Kong

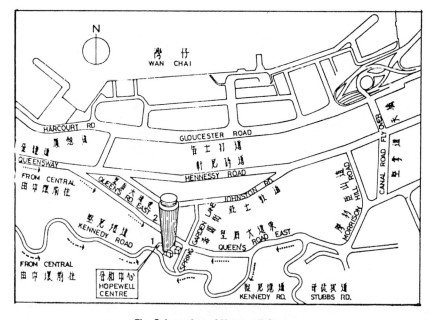

Fig. 2 Location of Hopewell Centre

77,900 m^2 (838,000 ft^2). Actual built area (including car park floors, refuge floors, and other service areas) is approximately 112,900 m^2 (1,215,000 ft^2).

The Hopewell Centre has 64 stories and 1 basement floor, for a total height of 216 m (708 ft) or p.d. (principal datum) 222 m (728 ft). The diameter of the main tower is 44.2 m (145 ft). The diameter of the service core averages 19.8 m (65 ft). The circumference of the main tower is 138.8 m (455.4 ft), divided into 48 structural bays of approximately 2.87 m (9 ft 5 in) wide.

The Hopewell Centre's approximate net rentable spaces are shown in Table 1.

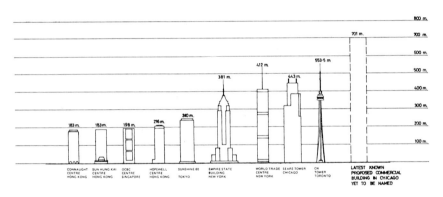

Fig. 3 Hopewell Centre in relation to some of the world's tallest buildings

Table 1 Hopewell Centre's approximate net rentable spaces

Penthouse office on 64th floor	650 m^2	7,000 ft^2
Office on 63rd floor	800 m^2	8,600 ft^2
Revolving restaurant on 62nd floor	910 m^2	9,800 ft^2
VIP lounge restaurant on 60th floor	780 m^2	8,400 ft^2
Office on 59th floor	752 m^2	8,100 ft^2
Typical office floor on floors 18–57 (except 32nd & 45th)	1,208 m^2 (each)	13,000 ft^2
Office on mezz. floor	957 m^2	10,300 ft^2
Shopping arcade on 17th floor (including lobby)	1,208 m^2	13,000 ft^2
Office on 16th floor	1,115 m^2	12,000 ft^2
Restaurant & kitchen on 8th floor	1,580 m^2	17,000 ft^2
Restaurant on 7th floor	1,858 m^2	20,000 ft^2
Shopping arcade on basement to 3rd floor	5,827 m^2	62,700 ft^2

Car Parking

There are 250 private-car parking spaces on floors 9 to 15, accessible from Kennedy Road, and 50 service-car parking spaces on floors 4 and 5, accessible from Queen's Road East via Spring Garden Lane.

E/M Services Room

The main A/C plant rooms are on the 8th floor of the main tower and the 9th and 11th floors of the podium block. Ancillary services rooms are on floors 2, 5, 16, 32, 45, and 58; whereas individual fan and AHU rooms are on each individual floor (Figs. 4 and 5). The building automation control room is on the 3rd floor.

CIRCULAR PLAN SHAPE

There are four main reasons for building the centre as a cylindrical tower of diameter 46 m:

1. Being 216 m high above ground, it is exposed to a very high wind pressure. Allowing for the roughening effects of the protruding columns, a shape factor of 0.8 can be used for a building of circular plan. Hence the wind pressure is reduced by 20% from that which would act on a square building of the same projected width. The wind resistance is up to 90 psf.

2. The circular plan shape helps to eliminate the local stress concentrations that can occur in buildings of rectangular plan.

3. Circular planned structures, such as chimneys and silos, also lend themselves particularly well to slipforming.

4. A columnless and continuous space having an average width of 1.2 m can be achieved around the service core for office space, which can therefore be planned with great flexibility and versatility. The usable floor area is about 87% of the gross floor area on each floor, which is a high efficiency ratio.

STRUCTURE

The structure is a tube-in-tube structural system consisting of an outer shell of diameter 44.2 m (145 ft) and an inner core of 19.8 m (65 ft). The inner core is composed of three concentrated tubular shear walls, which are braced with a deep spandrel beam. The outer shell is then tied to the inner core with 48 radial beams, which support the floor slab also.

The whole building is resting on granite rock that has a bearing load of 5,365 kN/m² (50 ton/ft²). Furthermore, 330 rock anchors of 78 tons to 360 tons stress are installed at designated locations for transfer of load to the rock layer. The horizontal stress is distributed by both the outer shell and the inner core.

The designed highest wind pressure anticipated is 4.3 kPa (90 psf). Horizontal deflection is anticipated at 155 mm.

CONSTRUCTION

The vertical structure of the main tower above the 3rd floor is constructed with the slipform system, except for the lower few floors and the penthouse group from the 58th floor upwards, which are of varying plan shape. The ancillary buildings were constructed with the conventional method using timber shuttering.

The advantage of slipform is savings in time, with a resulting reduction in cost. For this project, a saving in construction time estimated at one year was gained by the use of slipforming.

By December, 1979, the slipforming construction of the main tower structure had been completed up to the 58th floor. The full profile of the 64-story Hopewell Centre emerged on the skyline of Hong Kong at its topping out ceremony in April, 1980.

Each hydraulic jack used in the slipform construction method can exert a pressure of 3 tons psi. For the outer shell, 192 jacks were used and 126 for inner core. The uplifting speed was 300–380 mm per hour. The speed of construction both for the outer shell and the inner core was 4 days per story. The mold formwork for the floor slab is fiber-glass (see Table 2).

Table 2 Construction schedule of Hopewell Centre

Site formation commencement date:	Mid-1976
Superstructure commencement date:	Mid-1978
Tower superstructure completion date:	April, 1980
Whole superstructure completion date:	June, 1980
Phase I occupation (basement to 58th floor):	October, 1980
Full beneficial occupation:	January, 1981
Total concrete volume:	60,000 m³
Total reinforcement weight:	15,033 metric tonnes (14,765 tons) (Reinf./floor area = 200 kg/m²)

SLIPFORMING CONSTRUCTION METHOD

This method of construction has come into increasing use in the last decade, and the Hopewell Group has been its foremost proponent in Hong Kong by setting up Slipform Engineering Ltd.

In Hong Kong, they completed slipforming the 50-story high, HK$500 million head office for China Resources Company, a PRC company located at the Wanchai waterfront, in November 1982. This method is also being used

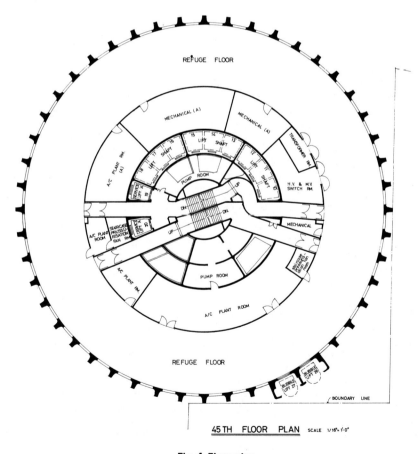

45TH FLOOR PLAN SCALE 1/16"=1'-0"

Fig. 4 Floor plan

for housing blocks of around HK$200 million being built for the Housing Authority at Sheung Shiu.

The China Hotel in Guangzhou was also built by slipforming, as were the chimneys for Singapore's Jurong Power Station, the chimney for Taiwan Steel's Kaoshing plant, and harbor caissons for a Malaysian port.

Another major single residential project to be slipformed will be Broadwood Road Development, worth about HK$2.5 billion. There will be 8 blocks of

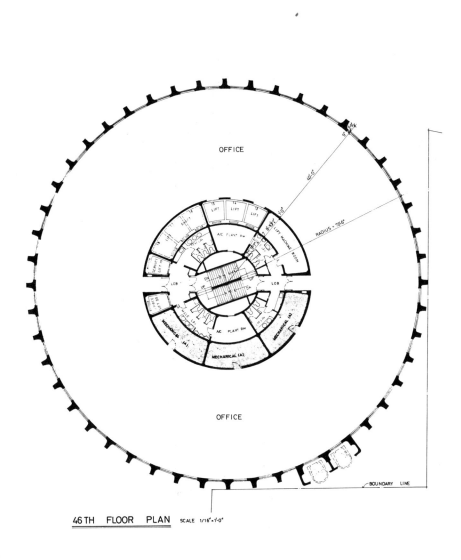

46 TH FLOOR PLAN SCALE 1/16"=1'-0"

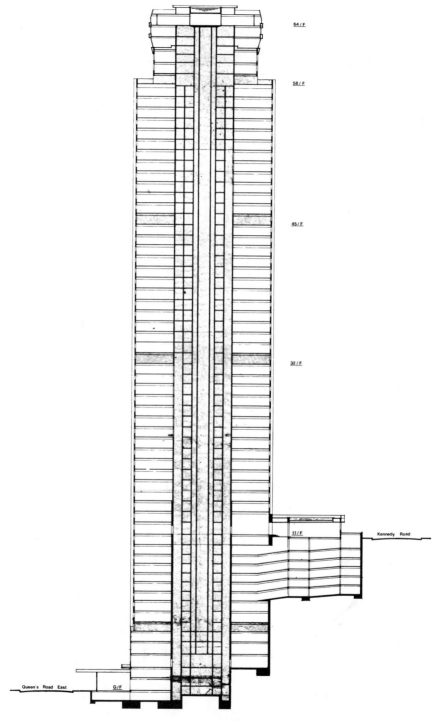

64 / F

58 / F

45 / F

32 / F

17 / F

Kennedy Road

Queen's Road East

G/F

Fig. 5 Floor plan

500 luxury apartments. Each block will be more than 200 m^2. The project will occupy 3 sites of total area 20,000 m^2 along Broadwood Road.

Basically in slipforming, a pair of 1-m-high sliding steel panel wall forms is used and is jacked continuously upwards as the placing of the reinforcement and pouring of concrete proceeds. The 1-m-high form is backed by RST; wales formed into a rigid frame give support to the panels at two levels 600 mm apart. The wales are joined by bolted splice plates or corner posts depending on the structural type. To resist distortion during construction, these forms are firmly braced with steel angle bracing and tubular steel trussing.

Adjustable steel yokes clamp the inside and outside forms together at correct wall thickness. Accuracy and rigidity are essential on any formwork, but an advantage of slipforming is that once set up, it remains the same throughout the process. The constant setting out of the formwork, floor by floor, is completely eliminated. The adjustable steel yokes can also allow adjustment of the top of the steel panel wall forms when there is change in wall thickness.

The rigid slipform is also designed to allow single construction of decking to form a work platform for placing concrete, reinforcement, and all necessary door or window blockouts. Hanging scaffolding can be hung from this deck to allow access to the concrete wall exposed after jacking up the slipform mold for surface treatment and pulling out wall starter bars for the construction of the floor slab.

Continual cleaning and oiling of forms is also minimized. The cleaning can be done by hand scrapers at the end of each day's concreting before the concrete hardens. The panel surface is then lightly oiled with the aid of a sponge.

When slipforming is a continuous operation, the supply and distribution of the reinforcement and concrete plays a major part in the programming of the operation. Hopewell Centre was slipformed on a start-stop basis, because the government restricts construction work from 7 p.m. until 8 a.m. the next day for the sake of noise control. In this case, 70% of the placement of reinforcement was carried out when the form was not moving.

Reinforcement guides are fixed to the yokes to ensure that all vertical bars are placed and held in the right position, leaving only the splice in between bars to be tied. The horizontal steel is then threaded through under the yokes and fixed into position by tying to the vertical bars. The horizontal steel can be fixed as high as the yoke head plates when the form is stationary; the remainder is placed when the form is moving up.

Plumb is controlled by traditional plumb bob and laser devices. The result is an off-plumb dimension of 19 mm maximum (Fig. 6).

BUILDING SERVICES

Operating Cost Efficiency

The aim of the Hopewell Centre project is to have good operating efficiency, maximum flexibility for office layout and subdivision, proper lighting level, a low running-cost air-conditioning system, reliable safety and security systems, and high-quality public address and security maintenance telephone systems. Therefore, great emphasis was placed on the operating cost efficiency in the design of electrical and mechanical services systems. A comprehensive building automation system was employed to manage the various systems.

Building Automation System and Other Service Surveillance Systems

The Building Automation System. The building automation system (BAS)

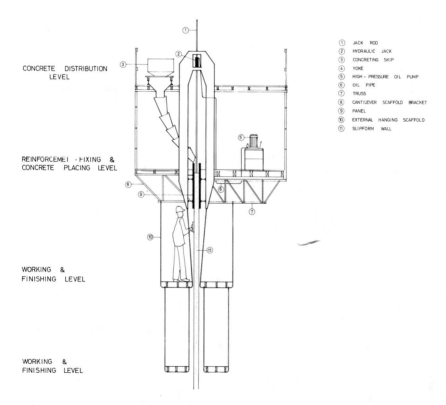

Fig. 6 Slipforming construction method

(Fig. 7) controls all building services automatically and is programmed for energy savings. Functions incorporated in the BAS include security, HVAC, lighting control, the electrical plant, fire fighting control, the potable and flushing water systems, the emergency/evacuation system, and the weather monitoring system.

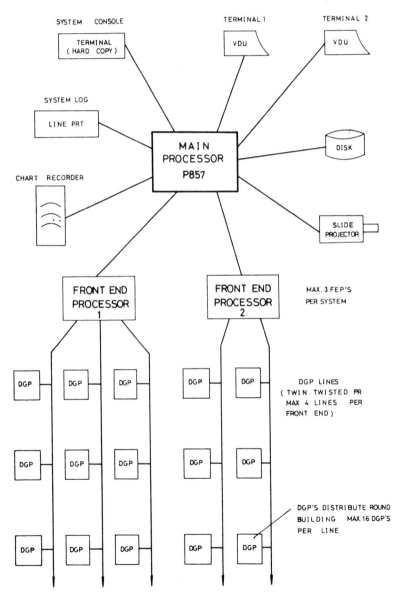

Fig. 7 Building automation system [*Courtesy: Philips (HK) Ltd.*]

The BAS breaks down as follows:

Equipment for central control room: computer with memory, cassette drive unit, cabinet housing, control desk, printer, video display and alpha-memoric display;

Data gathering panel: concentrates all the input and output signals back to the central processing unit;

Data transmission cable: two pairs of standard telephone cables — one pair for input signals, the other for output signals;

Field Points: 1,600 inclusive of digital and analog.

Emergency and Maintenance Telephone System. The emergency and maintenance telephone system ensures immediate contact with all security personnel.

Exchange equipment is comprised of 90 extensions with 8 internal connecting links to serve areas on all floors, including the control room, the elevator machine room, the A/C machine room, and the fire hose system. The facility includes the following: floor numbering extension number; quick single digit dialing; group hunting; and attendant numbering display.

Public Address System. The public address system provides background music and permits public or emergency announcements. The functions include the following:

irregular and emergency announcement microphones within the building;

radio broadcast (as, for instance in the event of a typhoon); and

background music by tape recorder or record player.

CCTV System. The CCTV system enables the building's central control operation to keep watch on the whole system. The system and its functions consist of the following:

to show the various camera positions via a geograhic minic display board (GMD);

to back up the security system;

to permit more reliable supervision in case of emergency;

to give emergency coverage of areas including major escape routes, staircases, fire brakes, lift lobbies, lift cars, and main entrances; and

72 cameras and 12 9-in black-and-white TV monitors.

Master Antenna System. A common antenna for AM, FM, and TV allows users on each office floor to connect their receivers or TV sets. The system is mainly for receiving local CTV channels and AM and FM radio broadcast channels.

Staff Paging System. A staff paging system incorporates a paging induction loop system into the building. The system and its functions consist of the following:

> an inductive loop antenna to be run in a PVC conduit;
>
> a bleeper with its own code number to be carried by each staff member;
>
> each bleeper is designed to receive the message and call tone; and
>
> an absence-indicating light will light should the staff person called not be available.

Security Guard Tour Point/Intercom System. This system enables direct internal maintenance and security communication. The system and its functions consist of the following:

> a visual indication lamp in the central control room (CCR) showing whether positions have been checked;
>
> hardcopy printout recording the exact time the checks are made, the floor number, and the checkpoint number; and
>
> two-way audio communication between the CCR and outstations.

FIRE SERVICE INSTALLATION

The fire service installation includes a sprinkler system (Fig. 8), a smoke-heat detection system, and push button alarms (see Table 3). The fire control panels on floors 3 and 17 will indicate the zone where the fire signal occurs.

Apart from the fire services installation, refuge floors 6, 32, 45, and 58 are provided to eliminate the stack effect of the staircases and to allow refuge areas for people in case of fire or emergency.

AIR-CONDITIONING VENTILATION INSTALLATION

Air-conditioning is centrally controlled through the building automation system but can be adjusted manually at local spots to meet individual requirements.

Four sets of water-cooled hermetic centrifugal units are installed to generate chilled water and have a total capacity of 3,000 TR. The condensing water dissipates the heat through four sets of closed-circuit cooling towers with a total coil area of 631.7 m^2 (6,800 ft^2). Heating water is generated by heat recovery units attached to the chiller units and/or by two sets of gas-fire hot water boilers (Fig. 10).

Table 3 Fire service installation

Type of system	Area protected
Automatic sprinkler system with a 75,000-l tank on the basement floor and four other transfer tanks of about 7,700 l. For the basement to the 17th floors and the 46th to 64th floors the pressure is maintained by sprinkler pumps; for other floors it is maintained by gravity.	Entire building except staircases, mechanical/ electrical rooms, and toilets.
Heat-smoke detection system	Lift lobbies, staircases, mechanical/electrical rooms, and air ducting systems.
Fire hydrant/hosereel system (Fig. 9), with a 36,000-l main tank on the 58th floor and other smaller transfer tanks. The water pressure on the 44th to 64th floors is maintained by pumps; while that on others is maintained by gravity.	Entire building.
BTM or CO^2 gas flooding system. The detection system works on a cross-zone basis; only 2 detectors will actuate the horn for evacuation, stop the ventilation system, and discharge the fire fighting gas after a 30-sec delay.	Hong Kong Electric Co. (local utility co.) transformer rooms, building automation room, and emergency generator room.
Hand appliances: fire extinguishers or fire blankets (kitchen area).	Entire building.
Staircase pressurization system.	The air pressure of the two main staircases in the affected zone of the tower (in between two refuge floors) will be boosted to about 0.25-in water gauge in case of fire, thus preventing smoke from leaking into the staircases and leaving a safe and clear exit to the refuge floors. The pressure is maintained by a pressure detector in the discharge site to adjust the bypass damper.
Direct link with fire control station	Any occurence of fire alarm will automatically be sent to the fire control station through a telephone line.

Since a four-pipe system (that is, separate chilled and hot water piping) is utilized, both cooling and heating facilities are available throughout the year. Basically, the entire building is air-conditioned by means of the systems outlined in Table 4.

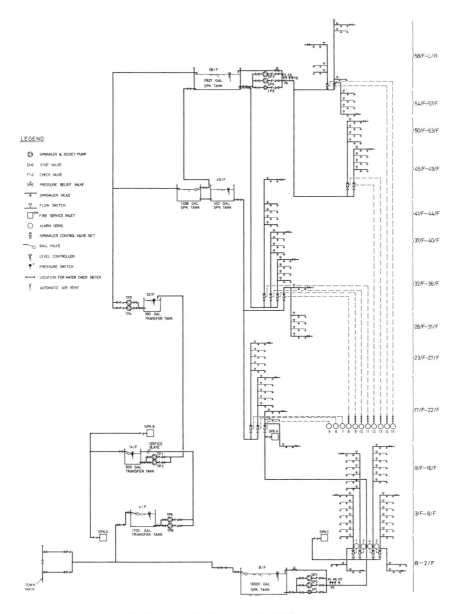

Fig. 8 Schematic diagram of sprinkler system

Table 4 Air-conditioning systems

Shops/arcades, restaurants, coffee shop, and lounge	Fan-coil units and/or a constant air-volume, central air-handling unit.
Offices	A variable air-volume system with reheat for the exterior zones and constant air-volume, central air-handling units for the inner zones.

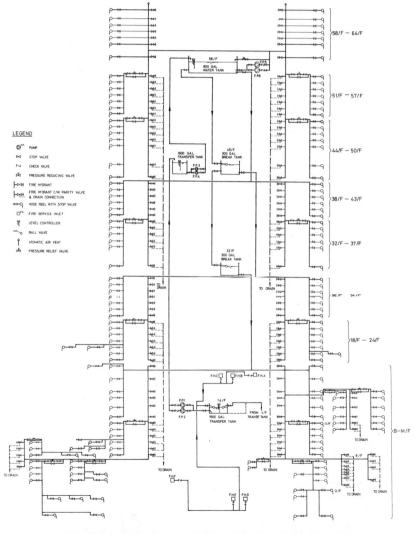

Fig. 9 Schematic diagram of fire hydrant and hosereel system

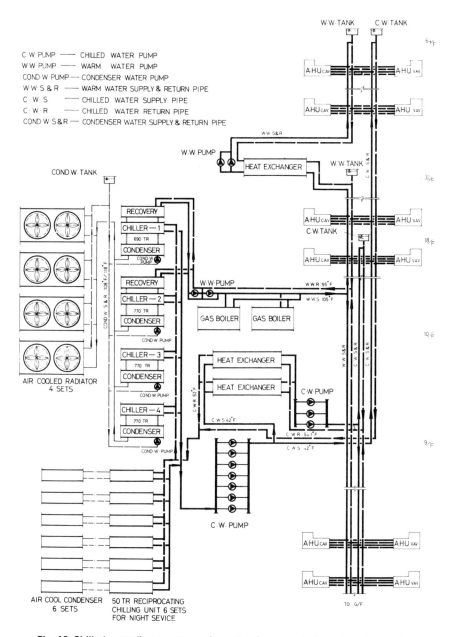

Fig. 10 Chilled water/hot water supply system for central air-conditioning system

Uncooled areas such as toilets, kitchens, pantries, and plant rooms are provided with ventilation.

The advantages and disadvantages of curtain walling in Hong Kong are still being argued. However, a reinforced concrete external wall is an efficiency device that cuts down cooling and heating capacities because of its low heat transmission coefficient and consequent reduced conduction heat load.

The gear-shaped column on the circular circumference also adds to the shading effect and reduces direct sunlight to around 62%, thus reducing solar heat gain through the window pane.

WATER SUPPLY/DRAINAGE SERVICES

Hopewell's plumbing and drainage system is also designed to suit the requirements of such a tall building. The toilets are conveniently located and equipped with high-quality sanitary fittings and finishes.

The total water storage capacities are proposed as follows:

Potable water — 11,570 Imp Gal (52,500 l)
Flush water   — 8,400 Imp Gal (38,000 l)

The supply from the city main (150 mm diameter) is pumped to the top floors by means of a series of transfer pumps. The feed to the fixtures is by gravity from a series of break tanks, except for the 63rd and 64th floors, which are fed through a booster pump. The break tanks act as pressure breaking devices preventing the excessive accumulation of pressure head due to the height of the building. Standby pumps are installed throughout to provide full reliability of the water supply system.

The storm water and sewage are collected by a 380-mm-diameter pipe and a 300-mm-diameter pipe, respectively, and then fall to the existing government drainage systems. However, the sewage from the ground floor and the basement is discharged to the government system through a sewage sump and pump tank station (Fig. 11).

ELECTRICAL POWER SUPPLY SYSTEM

Transformers

The building is powered via three main feeder cables from the Hong Kong Electric Co.'s underground cable networks, at 11 kv, to the main HV distribution panel on the 2nd floor. From this point, there are two high-voltage cables, one running to the 2nd floor for the tenants' supply for the lower block (podium), and the other to the 16th floor for occupants on the office floors of

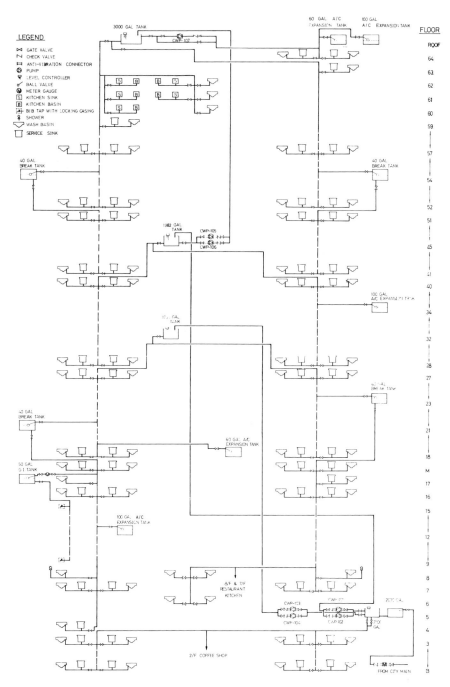

Fig. 11 Schematic diagrams of potable water systems

the tower. Separate high-voltage cables also run from this distribution panel to the 8th floor, where the subdistribution high-voltage panel is located for the general services supply (Fig. 12).

Dividing the supply into two separate systems has the advantage that they are independent and more reliable. Excessive voltage drop can be avoided for high voltage supply, and the capital investment is reduced also. Eight transformer stations with a total of 18 transformers and a total capacity of 18,720 kVA are located on various floors throughout the building (Table 5).

Busbar System

The busbar systems for the various electricity supply installations are housed in vertical ducts. The cross sections of the busbars have been computer-calculated to ensure optimum utilization.

Floor Conduit

On the typical office floors, a floor conduit system with junction boxes is cast in the concrete floor slab for the wiring of the tenants' power supply and telephone systems.

Emergency Generator Sets and Supply System

An emergency power supply (Table 6) is provided for emergency lighting, emergency exit signs, elevators, the sprinkler system, fire pumps, and the pressurization system by connection of these to the distribution board. In the case of main power failure, an automatic change-over contactor switch, built

Table 5 Electrical power supply system: transformers

Supply	Quantity	Rated voltage (v)	Rated power output (kVA)/ transformer	Total (kVA)	Remarks
Tenant	2 (16th floor)	11,000/346.200	1500	3000	By HEC
	1 (2nd floor)	11,000/346.200	800	800	By HEC
Landlord	4 (58th, 45th floors)	11,000/380.220	630	2520	By owner
(general	4 (32nd, 8th floors)	"	800	3200	"
services)	3 (11th, 8th floors)	"	1000	3000	"
	4 (8th floor for A/C chillers)	11,000/3300	1500	6200	"
Totals	18 nos.			18720 (kVA)	

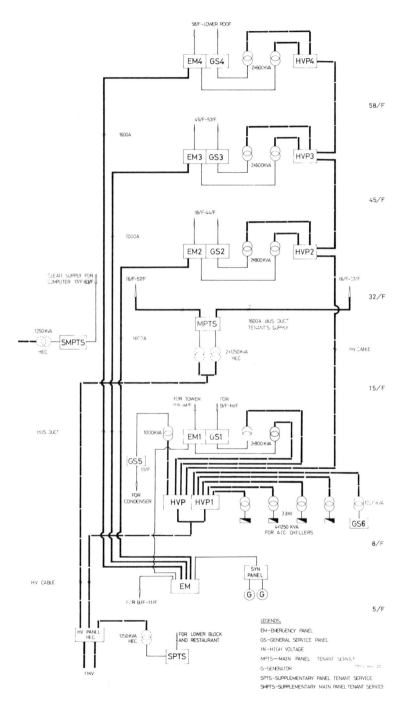

Fig. 12 Schematic diagram for high- and medium-voltage distribution

into the relevant main medium-voltage board of the general supply, will activate the emergency supply system. The distribution is also by busbar system in the vertical ducts.

GENERAL LIGHTING

The typical office floor is lit with an air-light trunking system with a plan that is radially diverted from the central core (Fig. 13) and, hence, harmonizes with the cricular plan shape. As the upper portion is an air supply duct and the middle portion is the air return duct through the lighting fittings, the air-light trunking system is advantageous in terms of the following: longer lift time, good air circulation for a better working environment by returning air of the air-conditioning system through lighting fittings, and uniformity of lighting level and glareless condition because of the specially designed diffuser and layout.

GONDOLA

A gondola is installed on the 58th floor for window cleaning and mosaic wall maintenance. It is a track system on the roof (58th floor) and has a guide-rail system along all columns. It covers two structural bays per run from the 58th floor to the 6th floor [171.5 m (562.5 ft)]. The carrying load is 300 kg (for 3 persons and tools).

Table 6 Emergency generator sets

Qty.	Rated voltage (v)	Rated power output (kVA/set)	Total (kVA)	Remarks
2	380/220	750	1500	By owner

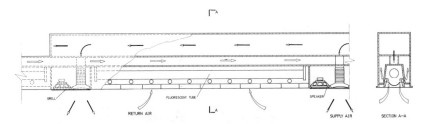

Fig. 13 Sectional view of air-light trunking

The gondola can be controlled from the carriage and cage, including hoisting and lowering; moving the arm inward and outward; and making tranversing left and right movements. It has an interphone system as well.

The gondola's emergency devices include an electro-magnetic brake, a mechanical disc brake, a limit switch to prevent over speed, a manual crank in case of power failure, electric leakage protection, and electric overcurrent protection.

REVOLVING RESTAURANT TURNTABLE

A revolving restaurant is located on the 62nd floor to provide visitors the opportunity to enjoy the spectacular views of the panoramic scene of Hong Kong City (Table 7).

The doughnut-shaped turntable rotates by supports of 96 wheels at the pit of 1.98m (6 ft 6 in) depth; 24 side wheels are also provided at the brackets of the supporting wheels to create an accurate circular and uninterrupted movement. The supporting and sliding roller wheels are of cast steel type, whereas the driving wheels are of synthetic rubber.

Both a short-circuit and an earth-leakage protection device were provided to protect against human and fire hazard. Electricity supply to the bar counter is provided by the installation of a slip-ring at the inner ring. Water tanks and booster pumps underneath the bar counter provide for plumbing and drainage.

The timber flooring consists of 2 layers of 19mm (34 in) thick plywood sandwiched with laminated iron plate and fixed onto 75mm X 75mm (3 in X 3 in) hardwood batten at 600mm (2 ft) center-to-center both ways. The laminate iron plate is installed for protection against fire. Anti-corrosion paint was also applied to the main U-shaped channel framework of the turntable for protection, although corrosion is very rare.

Table 7 Revolving restaurant turntable

Location:	62nd floor
Seating capacity:	447 persons
Outer diameter:	33.3 m (110 ft) (revolving portion)
Inner diameter:	21.6 m (71 ft) "
Area:	2,018 m² (6,484 ft²) "
Speed:	Variable (120 min/rev to 60 min/rev)
Motors/power source:	3 each of continuous 2.2 kw/346 v, 50 Hz, 3 phase
Designed live load:	4.788 kPa (100 psf)

ELEVATORS AND ESCALATORS

There are 29 elevators and 5 escalators (Table 8). The two high-rise, heavy duty semi-outdoor-type escalators between the ground-floor level and the third floor are the most frequently used vertical transportation devices in Hopewell Centre, carrying a maximum of 18,000 persons per hour. The third-floor level is the main lobby for the 18 passenger elevators and 2 lower-restaurant elevators that cater to 80 to 90% of the total passenger traffic in the building (Fig. 14).

Since the floors above floor 58 are served by the two VIP elevators, the 56th floor acts as a sky lobby also, to which the three zone elevators and two external elevators carry penthouse occupants from the 3rd or 17th floor.

The car park elevators bring passengers, after they park their cars in the car park area, down to the 7th floor, where the Chinese restaurant is, or up to 17th floor, where office goers can take any zone elevator to their office or one of the external elevators to the 56th floor, where they can transfer to the VIP elevators that reach the penthouse floors.

Table 8 Elevators and escalators

		Qty	Stops at floors	No. of stops	Speed (m/sec)	Speed (ft/min)	Loading capacity
Zone elevator-1		3	3,17,18–24	(9)	4	800	20 passengers — 1,360 kg (3,000 lbs)
"	" 2	3	3,17,25–31	(9)	5	1,000	"
"	" 3	3	3,17,33–38	(8)	5	1,000	"
"	" 4	3	3,17,39–33	(8)	5	1,000	"
"	" 5	3	3,17,46–51	(8)	6.3	1,260	"
"	" 6	3	3,17,52–57	(8)	7	1,400	"
Service/fire fighters' lift		2	2–58,61	(58)	3.15	630	18 passengers — 1,230 kg (2,700 lbs)
Service lift		1	B–4	(5)	0.75	150	27 passengers — 1,845 kg (4,050 lbs)
Lower restaurant		2	B–7	(9)	1.75	350	22 passengers — 1,500 kg (3,300 lbs)
Car park		2	7,9–12,14, 15,17	(8)	1.75	350	16 passengers — 1,090 kg (2,400 lbs)
VIP (elevator shaft above zone 3 elevators)		2	55–60, 62–64	(9)	1.5	300	16 passengers — 1,130 kg (2,500 lbs)
External lift		2	17, 56	(2)	2.5	500	17 passengers — 1,190 kg (2,618 lbs)
Escalator		4	2 B–GF 2 GF–3				

All exposed parts of the external elevator cars and shaft equipment are either fiber glass, stainless steel, or hot-dipped galvanized steel to protect all parts from rust and deterioration. The car bodies are of molded one-piece fiber glass to guarantee water- and weather-proofing.

Control

Each of the six triplex groups of the zone elevators are equipped with solid-state Aconic Variomatic 2 control equipment, which is a computerized digital data processing system that continuously evaluates every change in the traffic floors and reassesses demand. The system thus directs each car to ensure the most logical and economical moves and shortens the waiting time

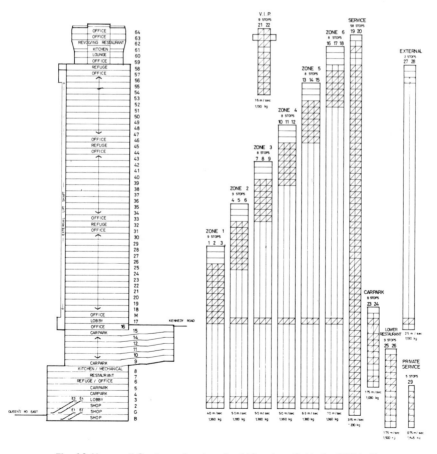

Fig. 14 Hopewell Centre—elevator chart [*Courtesy: Schindler (HK) Ltd.*]

at each stop. Signals may be issued to send a free car to a traffic-concentrated area or to jump floors in the downward direction during heavy collecting periods.

The elevator cars travel at optimum speed, depending on the distance covered, or can home-in to a landing in a direct floor approach by slowing down in a straight line from traveling speed into a landing.

Safety Aspects

Intercommunication systems between all elevator cars, the machine room, and the main supervisory panels on the attendant's counters at the 17th and 4th floors are tied in with the BAS.

Audio and visual alarms for overloading are provided. In case of fire or power failure, emergency supply will be provided and the control will send all elevators, one elevator per zone in sequence, down to home landing at the 3rd or the 17th floor, to be decided on by management depending on situations.

The two services/fire fighters' elevators are equipped with fire fighters' switches for use in case of emergency.

All elevator cars are equipped with CCTV cameras to further enhance the security of the building.

An anemometer is equipped on the top of the building and is connected to the control of the two external elevators. It will order the elevators to automatically return to the sheltered 17th or 56th floor should the wind speed exceed a certain limit.

Project Descriptions

Sunshine 60

Kiyoshi Muto

The Japanese Building Standard Law was revised in 1963 to permit building heights over the limit of 31 m that had hitherto been observed. The earthquake-resistant design of tall buildings was then finally given special approval by the Ministry of Construction. The effect was that the safety of structures should be assured by dynamic analysis for checking earthquake response on strength and deformation.

In 1968, the first high-rise building in Japan was completed—the Kasumi-gaseki Building, which is 147 m tall and 36 stories in height. Since its appearance, many other tall buildings have been emerging in major cities at a fast pace, as shown in Table 1.

GENERAL FEATURES OF IKEBUKURO SUBCENTER DEVELOPMENT

1. Developer: The Japan Urban Development Co., Ltd.
2. Building use and layout: shown in Figs. 1 and 2.
3. Site area: 55,000 m².
4. Building area: 40,000 m².
5. Total floor area: 587,000 m².
6. Structural materials used: concrete—300,000 m³; steel—120,000 tons.

Table 1 Tallest buildings in Japan (exceeding 100 meters) as of May, 1981

No.	Building	City	Year completed	Number of stories	Height (m)	Material	Use
1	Sunshine 60 (Ikebukuro)	Tokyo	1978	60	226	steel	office
2	Shinjuku Center	Tokyo	1979	54	216	steel	office
3	Shinjuku Mitsui	Tokyo	1974	55	211	steel	office
4	Shinjuku Nomura	Tokyo	1978	53	203	steel	office
5	Shinjuku Sumitomo	Tokyo	1974	52	200	steel	office
6	Yasuda Fire Insurance	Tokyo	1976	43	193	steel	office
7	Keio Plaza Hotel	Tokyo	1971	47	170	steel	hotel
8	Minato	Tokyo	U.C.	40	165	steel	office
9	Tokyo World Trade Center	Tokyo	1970	40	152	steel	office
10	Kokusai Den-den (KDD)	Tokyo	1974	32	151	steel	telcom
11	Kasumigaseki	Tokyo	1968	36	147	steel	office
12	Akasaka Prince Hotel	Tokyo	U.C.	39	139	steel	hotel
13	Nankai Namba-eki Hotel	Osaka	1978	38	134	steel	hotel
14	Keio Plaza Hotel-South Annex	Tokyo	1980	35	132	steel	hotel
15	Dai-ichi Kangin	Tokyo	1980	32	132	steel	office
16	Osaka-ekimae Kaizo No. 3	Osaka	1979	34	132	steel	office
17	Hibiya Kokusai	Tokyo	1981	34	132	steel	office
18	Hotel New Ohtani Tower	Tokyo	1974	39	127	steel	hotel
19	Nakanoshima Center	Osaka	1975	30	122	steel	office
20	Toho Life Insurance	Tokyo	1975	31	122	steel	office
21	Ikebukuro Hotel	Tokyo	1980	37	122	steel	hotel
22	Shinjuku NS	Tokyo	U.C.	30	122	steel	office
23	Osaka Kokusai	Osaka	1973	32	121	steel	office
24	Umeda Hankyu	Osaka	1977	32	121	steel	office
25	Osaka Data Communication	Osaka	1974	24	120	steel	telcom
26	Fukoku Life Insurance	Tokyo	1980	30	120	steel	office
27	Osaka Ohbayashi	Osaka	1974	32	120	steel	office
28	Imperial Tower	Tokyo	U.C.	31	119	steel	hotel
29	Hotel Century Hyatt	Tokyo	1980	28	114	steel	hotel
30	Shinjuku Dai-ichi Life Insurance	Tokyo	1980	24	114	steel	office
31	Osaka Maru-biru (Yoshimoto)	Osaka	1976	30	114	steel	hotel

Table 1 Tallest buildings in Japan (exceeding 100 meters) as of May, 1981 (continued)

32	Hotel Pacific Tokyo	Tokyo	1971	30	112	steel	hotel
33	Kobe Port-Island Hotel	Kobe	1981	31	111	steel	hotel
34	OMB (DT)	Osaka	U.C.	32	111	steel	hotel
35	Asahi Tokai	Tokyo	1971	29	110	steel	office
36	Osaka Terminal	Osaka	U.C.	27	110	steel	hotel
37	Osaka Royal Hotel	Osaka	1973	30	107	steel	hotel
38	Kobe Trade Center	Kobe	1969	26	107	steel	office
39	Mita Kokusai	Tokyo	1975	26	106	steel	office
40	Bussan Main	Tokyo	U.C.	26	106	steel	office
41	Yamato Life Insurance	Tokyo	UC.	27	104	steel	office
42	Shin-gofukubashi (G)	Tokyo	1977	21	102	steel	office
43	Yokohama Tenri-kyokan	Yokohama	1973	27	102	steel	office
44	Mitsui Bussan	Tokyo	1976	24	100	steel	office
45	Taiyo Gyogyo	Tokyo	1978	24	100	steel	office
46	Chuo Godo Chosha	Tokyo	U.C.	26	100	steel	office
47	Osaka-ekimae Kaizo No. 4	Osaka	U.C.	25	100	steel	office

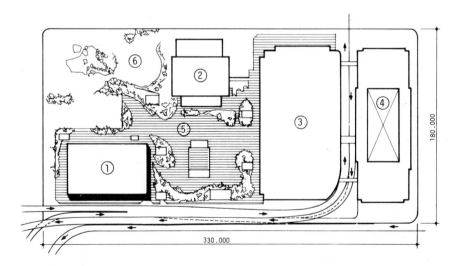

Fig. 1 Layout of buildings in Ikebukuro Subcenter
(1) Office (60 stories)
(2) Hotel (36 stories)
(3) Department stores (11 stories)
(4) Bus terminal and cultural facilities (12 stories)
(5) Pedestrian deck (3 stories)
(6) Park

OUTLINE OF 60-STORY OFFICE BUILDING—
SUNSHINE 60 (FIG. 3)

1. Architect: Mitsubishi Estate Co., Ltd.
2. Structural Consultant: Muto Institute of Structural Mechanics, Inc.
3. General Contractors: a joint venture of Kajima Corporation and others.
4. Total floor area: 204,000 m².
5. Typical floor area: 3,160 m².
6. Number of stories: 60 stories with 3 basements.
7. Total height: 226 m high above the ground.
8. Typical story height: 3.7 m.
9. Number of elevators: 40.

STRUCTURAL DESIGN OF THE OFFICE BUILDING

Structural Features

1. Structural System: Tower part—steel skelton with slitted wall;
   Lower part—reinforced concrete with steel skelton;
   Foundation—reinforced concrete.

Fig. 2 Bird's-eye view of the Ikebukuro Subcenter

Fig. 3 General view of Sunshine 60, a 60-story office building

Figure 4 shows the framing plan of a typical floor and Fig. 5 shows the framing sections.

2. Steel framing: Figs. 6 and 7 show the typical framing details and Figs. 8 and 9 show the steel framing views.

3. Reinforced concrete slitted shear wall: the slitted shear wall has been developed by the Muto Institute as ductile shear wall. By providing slits in the reinforced concrete wall, it can conform to the large defo mation of the steel frame. Figure 10 shows the layout of slits, and Fig. 11 indicates the test result of the hysteresis loop of a slitted wall. Figure 12 shows the installed slitted wall in the steel framing.

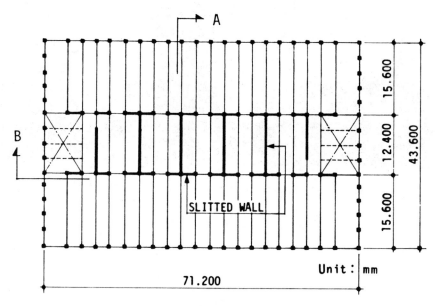

Fig. 4 Framing plan of typical floor

Structural Design and Analysis

In Japan, the special approval of the construction minister should be given for the design and construction of high-rise buildings if the structural safety is assured by dynamic analysis, as follows:

1. Design Procedure: see Fig. 13.

2. Stress analysis by FAPP program: see Fig. 14.

3. Dynamic analysis (for transverse framing):
   (a) Free vibration—Fig. 15 shows the vibration modes, and the vibration periods are first–5.9 sec, second–1.9 sec, third–1.1 sec.
   (b) Earthquake response: Figs. 16 and 17 show the maximum response values.

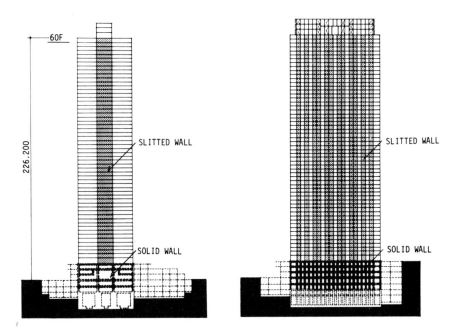

Fig. 5 Framing sections in the two elevations

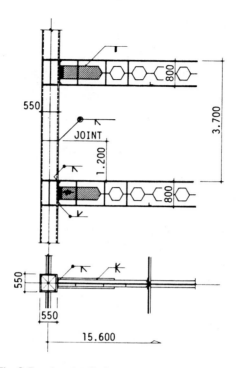

Fig. 6 Framing detail of transverse typical framing

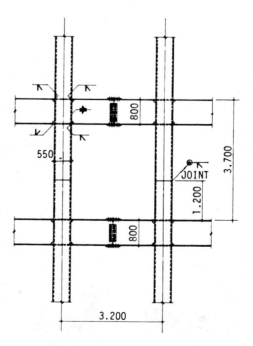

Fig. 7 Framing detail of longitudinal typical framing

Fig. 9 Outside view

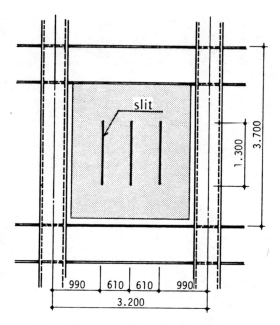

Fig. 10 Layout of slitted wall

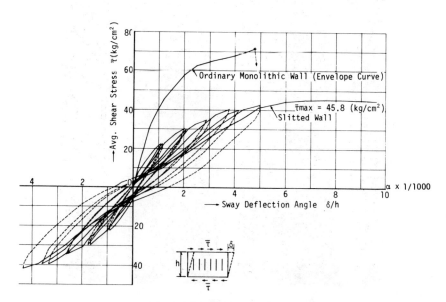

Fig. 11 Hysteresis loop of slitted wall

Fig. 12 Slitted wall in steel framing

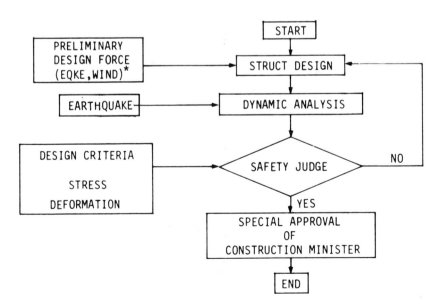

Fig. 13 Flow diagram for dynamic design procedure

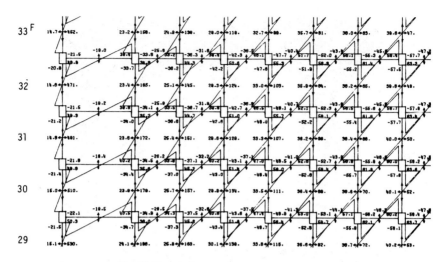

Fig. 14 Stress diagram for longitudinal framing

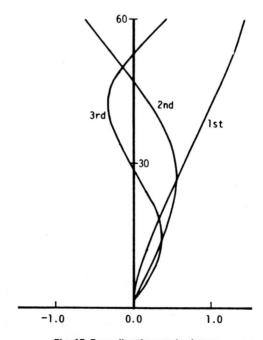

Fig. 15 Free vibration mode shapes

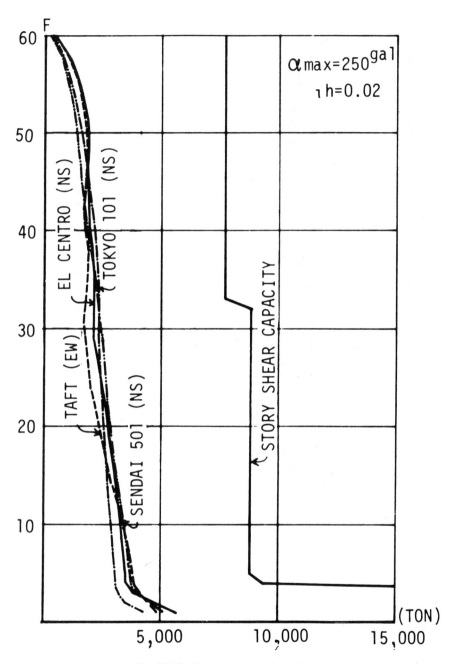

Fig. 16 Maximum response story shear

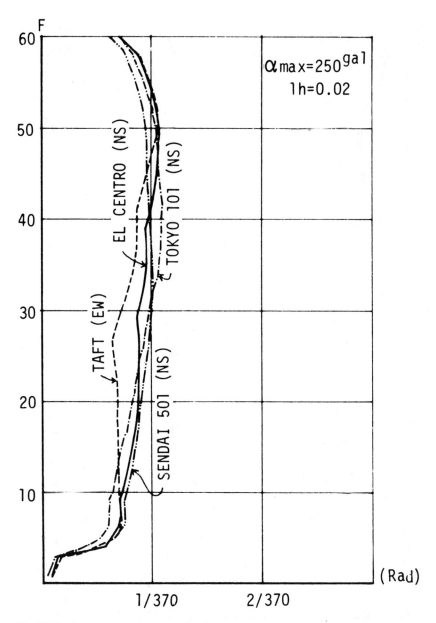

Fig. 17 Maximum response story deflection angle (story deflection/story height)

Shinjuku Sumitomo

Kobe Trade Center

Tokyo World Trade Center

Appendix

High-Rise Building Data Base

Since the inception of the Council, various surveys have been made concerning the location, number of stories, height, material, and the use of tall buildings around the world. The first report on these surveys was published in the Council's Proceedings of the First International Conference. *Tall Building Systems and Concepts* (Volume SC) brought that information up to date with a detailed survey in 1980.

This present document represents only the changes revealed to the Council since the publication of Volume SC.

The survey was originally based mainly on information collected from individuals in the major cities of the world. The criterion for the selection of a city was generally its population, and at the same time the availability of a Council member or other contact who might have provided the needed information. In addition to information collected by questionnaires, data were also obtained from a few selected references.

This appendix updates Tables 1 and 4 from Volume SC. In certain instances the data are incomplete. This is due to the fact that information came from a number of sources. Also, some of the sources reported only the height or number of stories. The remainder of the information had to be obtained separately. Because the data came from so many sources, complete accuracy cannot be guaranteed. Buildings change names from time to time, and this information is sometimes slow in reaching the Council headquarters. In this sense the survey keeps its nature as a "living document."

Additions and corrections to the information presented herein are welcomed, and should be brought to the attention of headquarters staff at Lehigh University.

Table 1: **World's Tallest Buildings.** This is a list of the world's 100 tallest buildings. In common with the other similar tables in this appendix, the information presented includes the country and city in which each building is located, the year of completion, the number of stories, the height (in meters and feet), the structural material, and the use of each building. This table originally appeared in Volume SC, *Tall Building Systems and Concepts.*

Table 1 The one-hundred tallest buildings in the world

Building	City	Year completed	Number of stories	Height meters	feet	Material	Use
Sears Tower	Chicago	1974	110	443	1454	steel	office
World Trade Center South	New York	1973	110	412	1350	steel	office
World Trade Center North	New York	1972	110	412	1350	steel	office
Empire State	New York	1931	102	381	1250	steel	office
Standard Oil (Indiana)	Chicago	1973	80	346	1136	steel	office
John Hancock	Chicago	1968	100	344	1127	steel	multiple
Chrysler	New York	1930	77	319	1046	steel	office
Texas Commerce Plaza	Houston	1981	75	305	1002	mixed	office
Allied Bank Plaza	Houston	1983	71	296	970	steel	office
American International	New York	1931	66	290	950	steel	office
Columbia Center	Seattle	1983	76	287	940	mixed	office
First Bank Tower	Toronto	1975	72	285	935	steel	office
40 Wall Tower	New York	1966	71	283	927	steel	office
Dallas Main Center	Dallas	1985	70	281	921	mixed	office
Citicorp Center	New York	1977	59	280	919	steel	multiple
Transco Tower II	Houston	1983	64	275	901	steel	office
Water Tower Place	Chicago	1976	74	262	859	concrete	multiple
United California Bank	Los Angeles	1974	62	261	858	steel	office
Transamerica	San Francisco	1972	48	260	853	steel	office
RCA Rockefeller Center	New York	1933	70	259	850	steel	office
First National Bank	Chicago	1968	60	259	850	steel	office
U.S. Steel	Pittsburgh	1970	64	256	841	steel	office
One Chase Manhattan Plaza	New York	1961	60	248	813	steel	office
Pan American	New York	1963	59	246	808	steel	office
Woolworth	New York	1913	57	242	792	steel	office
1 Palac Kultury i Nauki	Warsaw	1955	42	241	790	steel/concrete	office
John Hancock Tower	Boston	1973	60	241	790	steel	office
M.L.C. Centre	Sydney	1976	70	240	786	concrete	office

Table 1 The one-hundred tallest buildings in the world (continued)

Building	City	Year completed	Number of stories	Height meters	feet	Material	Use
Commerce Court West	Toronto	1974	57	239	784	steel	office
Republic Bank Center	Houston	1983	56	238	780	steel	office
Bank of America	San Francisco	1969	52	237	778	steel	office
3 First National Plaza	Chicago	1981	58	236	775	mixed	office
IDS Center	Minneapolis	1972	57	235	772	mixed	office
Singapore Treasury Building	Singapore	1986	52	235	770	mixed	office
One Penn Plaza	New York	1972	57	234	766	steel	office
Equitable Tower West	New York	1985	51	230	755	steel	office
Maine Montparnasse	Paris	1973	64	229	751	mixed	office
Prudential Center	Boston	1964	52	229	750	steel	office
Exxon	New York	1971	54	229	750	steel	office
First International Plaza	Houston	1981	55	228	748	mixed	office
1 Liberty Plaza (U.S. Steel)	New York	1972	54	227	743	steel	office
Sunshine 60	Tokyo	1978	60	226	742	steel	office
20 Exchange Place (Citibank)	New York	1931	55	226	741	steel	office
Raffles City Hotel	Singapore	1986	70	226	741	concrete	hotel
Renaissance 1	Detroit	1977	73	225	739	concrete	hotel
World Financial Center	New York	1987	51	225	739	steel	office
Security Pacific National Bank	Los Angeles	1974	57	225	738	steel	office
Toronto Dominion Bank Tower	Toronto	1967	56	224	736	steel	office
Cullen Center	Houston	1984	55	223	732	steel	office
One Astor Plaza	New York	1972	54	222	730	mixed	office
Olympia Centre	Chicago	1981	63	222	728	concrete	multiple
One Mellon Bank Center	Pittsburgh	1983	54	222	727	steel	office
The Gulf Tower	Houston	1982	52	221	726	mixed	office
9 West 57th Street	New York	1974	50	221	725	steel	office
Peachtree Center Plaza	Atlanta	1975	71	220	723	concrete	hotel
Crocker Center	Los Angeles	1983	55	220	723	steel	multiple
Carlton Centre	Johannesburg	1973	50	220	722	concrete	office
Detroit Plaza Hotel	Detroit	1977	73	219	720	concrete	hotel
Republic Plaza	Denver	1983	56	219	718	steel/concrete	office
One Shell Plaza	Houston	1971	50	218	714	concrete	office
First International	Dallas	1973	56	216	710	steel	office
Shinjuku Center	Tokyo	1979	54	216	709	steel/concrete	office
Hopewell Centre	Hong Kong	1980	65	216	709	concrete	multiple

Table 1 The one-hundred tallest buildings in the world (continued)

Building	City	Year completed	Number of stories	Height meters	Height feet	Material	Use
Terminal Tower	Cleveland	1930	52	216	708	steel	office
Union Carbide	New York	1960	52	215	707	steel	office
General Motors	New York	1968	50	214	705	steel	office
Metropolitan Life	New York	1909	50	213	700	steel	office
Atlantic Richfield Plaza A	Los Angeles	1972	52	213	699	steel	office
Atlantic Richfield Plaza B	Los Angeles	1972	52	213	699	steel	office
One Shell Square	New Orleans	1972	51	212	697	steel	office
500 Fifth Avenue	New York	1931	58	212	697	steel	office
Shinjuku Mitsui	Tokyo	1974	55	212	696	steel	office
IBM	Chicago	1973	52	212	695	steel	office
Shinjuku Nomura	Tokyo	1978	53	210	690	steel	office
Four Allen Center	Houston	1983	50	210	690	steel	office
Marine Midland Building	New York	1966	52	210	688	steel	office
55 Water Street	New York	1972	53	209	687	steel	office
Chemical Bank Trust	New York	1964	50	209	687	steel	office
Capital Bank Plaza	Houston	1980	50	209	685	steel	office
One Houston Center	Houston	1978	46	208	681	mixed	office
Chanin	New York	1929	55	207	680	steel	office
Gulf & Western	New York	1970	44	207	679	steel	office
Minneapolis City Center	Minneapolis	1983	51	207	679	steel/concrete	office
Southern Bell	Atlanta	1981	46	206	677	concrete	office
Lincoln Bldg.	New York	1930	55	205	673	steel	office
Georgia Pacific Tower	Atlanta	1982	52	205	671	steel	office
McGraw-Hill	New York	1972	51	204	670	steel	office
1633 Broadway	New York	1972	48	204	670	steel	office
Bank of Oklahoma Tower	Tulsa	1976	50	203	667	steel/concrete	office
Trump Tower	New York	1983	68	202	664	concrete	multiple
Civic Center	Chicago	1965	38	202	662	steel	office
First City Tower	Houston	1981	49	201	660	mixed	office
Overseas-Chinese Banking Corp.	Singapore	1976	52	201	660	concrete	office
One Magnificent Mile	Chicago	1983	57	201	660	concrete	multiple
Shinjuku Sumitomo	Tokyo	1974	52	200	656	steel	office
Parque Central Torre Oficinas	Caracas	1979	56	200	656	concrete	office
1100 Milam	Houston	1974	47	198	651	steel	office
Ukraine Hotel	Moscow	1961	34	198	650	steel/concrete	hotel
American Brands	New York	1967	47	198	648	steel	office
Lake Point Towers	Chicago	1968	70	197	645	concrete	apartment

Table 4: Tallest Buildings in Major Cities. This is a listing of additions to the data base of the tallest buildings in major cities around the world. These data have been supplied to the Council since Volume SC was published. Information on Kenya and the People's Republic of China is new. In the case of Japan, only the additions or corrections are indicated. Buildings shorter than nine stories are excluded.

Table 4 Tallest buildings in major cities

Building	Year completed	Number of stories	Height meters	feet	Material	Use
		Japan				
		Hamamatsu				
Hotel Concord Hamamatsu	1981	18/2	62.5	208	mixed	hotel
		Hiroshima				
Hiroshima Telephone Office	1979	15/1	80.0	267	steel	telephone
		Kanazawa				
Musashigatsuji Building	1973	18/2	68.8	229	steel/mixed	hotel/department store
		Kobe				
Kobe Portpia Hotel	1981	31/2	111.4	371	steel/mixed	hotel
		Maebashi				
Taisei Sogo Bank	1979	15/3	65.9	220	steel	bank
		Matsudo				
Matsudo Building	1974	20/2	75.5	252	steel/mixed	apartment
		Nagoya				
Den-Den Togin Building	1980	18/3	89.3	298	steel	telecom/bank
Unryu Building	1973	23/2	76.8	256	mixed	apartment/office
Meitetsu Bus Terminal	1967	18/2	72.0	240	mixed	terminal/multiple
		Narashino				
Tsudanuma Ekimae Building	1978	21/3	73.9	246	steel/mixed	apartment/office
		Nishinomiya				
Chidorigahama Apartments	1980	25/1	77.3	283	mixed	apartment
		Ogaki				
Ogaki Kyodo Bank	1973	18/2	67.7	226	mixed	bank
		Okayama				
Sumitomo Life Ins. Building	1977	21/1	74.8	249	steel	office
		Osaka				
Osaka Midosuji Building	1982	32/4	110.6	369	steel/mixed	hotel
4 Osakaekimae Building	1981	25/4	100	333	steel	office
Sumitomo Life Ins. Building	1983	20/1	79.0	263	steel	office
Hankyu Terminal Building	1971	21/4	77.8	259	steel/mixed	terminal/office
Asahi Broadcasting Center	1966	22/3	77.0	257	mixed	broadcast
		Sapporo				
Keio Plaza Hotel	1982	23/2	79.1	264	steel	hotel
		Sendai				
Sendai Resort Hotel	1975	17/1	72.4	241	steel/mixed	hotel
Kogin Kowa Building	1979	15/2	56.2	187	steel	office
Sendai Government Office	1972	15/2	55.4	185	steel	office
Big Plaza Sendai	1977	17/0	53.4	178	mixed	apartment
		Shizuoka				
New Akao	1972	18/0	58.4	195	mixed	hotel
		Suita				
Esaka-T Building	1975	20/(1)/2	74.6	249	steel	office
		Takamatsu				
114 Bank	1966	16/2	63.0	210	mixed	bank
		Tokyo				
Minata	UC	40	165	541	steel	office
Akasaka Prince Hotel	1982	39/2	138.9	463	steel	hotel
Keio Plaza Hotel South Building	1980	35/5	132.1	440	steel	hotel

Table 4 Tallest buildings in major cities (continued)

Building	Year completed	Number of stories	Height meters	feet	Material	Use
Tokyo Kaijo-Kasai Ins. Building	1974	32/5	130.6	435	steel	office
Hibiya Kokusai Building	1981	31/5	127.9	426	steel	office
Sunshine Prince Hotel	1980	37/4	121.6	405	steel	hotel
Shinjuku NS Building	1982	30/3	121.5	405	steel/mixed	office
Fukoku Life Ins. Building	1980	30/5	120.0	400	steel	office
Imperial Tower	1982	31/4	118.9	396	steel	hotel
Odakyu Hotel Century	1980	28/4,26/4	114.5	382	steel/mixed	hotel
Shinjuku Daiichi Life Ins.	1980	24	114	375	steel	office
Bussan Main	UC	26	106	347	steel	office
Toyota Tokyo	1982	23/5	105.3	351	steel	office
Yamato Life Ins.	UC	27	104	342	steel	office
New Gofukubashi Building	1977	21(2)/4	102.2	341	steel	office
Teikoku Hotel	1970	26/3	100.9	336	steel/mixed	hotel
Taiyo Fishery Company	1978	24/4	100.0	333	steel	office
Kokusai New Akasaka Building	1980	24/3	99.1	330	steel	office
NHK Broadcasting Center	1973	23/1	94.3	314	steel	office
New Aoyama Building	1978	23/4	94.1	314	steel	office
New Ochanomizu Building	1983	22/3	90.8	303	steel	office
Itochu Commercial Company	1980	22/4	90.2	301	steel/mixed	office
Working Youths Center	1973	21/2	89.0	297	mixed	hotel
New IBM Building	1971	22/2	87.4	291	steel	office
Togeki Building	1975	20/3	85.6	285	steel	office
25 Mori Building	1973	25/2	83.8	276	mixed	office
Seibu Shinjuku Station	1977	25(2)/4	83.5	278	steel	hotel/terminal
Hotel Grand Palace	1972	24/4	81.0	270	steel/mixed	hotel
Tokyodo Chiyoda Building	1977	20/4	81.0	270	steel	office
Daichi-Kangyo Bank	1975	20(3)/4	79.8	226	steel	bank
Shiba Building	1981	21/3	78.9	263	steel	office
Nihon Building	1970	20/5	78.0	260	steel/mixed	office
Denki Building	1975	20(2)/4	77.6	259	mixed	office
Hamarikyu Building	1976	20(1)/2	77.3	258	steel	office
22 Sotoyama Kowa Building	1973	20/2	74.7	249	steel	office
Kokusai Jidosha Building	1973	20/4	74.6	249	mixed	office
Sankei Building	1973	20/3	72.2	241	steel	office
Sun City G Building	1980	25	71.4	238	concrete	apartment
Kajima Const. Co. Building	1971	21/3	68.8	229	steel	office
Sun City D Building	1979	23/0	64.1	214	steel	apartment
Metropolitan Police Office	1972	21/1	61.7	203	mixed	office/apartment
Wakayama						
President Tsubaki	1976	28/1	92.9	310	steel	apartment
City Hall	1976	16/2	53.0	177	mixed	office
Yamagata						
City Hall	1975	16/1	62.4	208	steel	office
Yokohama						
Yokohama Dream Land Hotel	1965	21/2	77.7	259	mixed	hotel
Industrial Worker Center	1972	15/2	55.3	184	steel	office
Yono						
Yono House	1976	21/2	61.5	205	mixed	apartment
Kenya						
Mombasa						
Bima Towers	1982	16	67	220	concrete	office
Ambalal House—South Tower	1981	13	44	145	concrete	office
Ambalal House—North Tower	1974	11	38	123	concrete	office
Mombasa Plaza	1981	11	37	120	concrete	office
Coast Provincial Headquarters	1975	9	31	100	concrete	office
Ambalal House—Car Park	1982	9	26	86	concrete	carpark
Nairobi						
Kenyatta Conference Centre	1974	33	105	345	concrete	office
Provincial Headquarters	1982	27	84	276	concrete	office
Cooperative House	1981	25	83	272	concrete	office
National Bank House	1976	21	82	268	concrete	office
Reinsurance Plaza	1982	20	77	252	concrete	office
Uchumi House	1972	21	71	232	concrete	office
I.C.E.A. Building	1981	19	69	237	concrete	office
International House	1971	17	66	215	concrete	office
Hilton Hotel	1969	20	61	200	concrete	hotel
City Hall Annexe	1980	18	60	197	concrete	office
Electricity House	1974	18	60	102	concrete	office
Roman Catholic Church-Belfry	1962	—	59	194	concrete	bell-tower
Development House—E. Tower	1982	16	57	188	concrete	office
Bruce House	1971	17	55	179	concrete	office
Rehani House	1978	13	50	164	concrete	office

Table 4 Tallest buildings in major cities (continued)

Building	Year completed	Number of stories	Height meters	Height feet	Material	Use
Treasury Building	1980	15	48	157	concrete	office
Union Towers	1977	14	48	156	concrete	office
Hotel 680	1972	14	47	153	concrete	hotel
Bima House	1973	13	45	146	concrete	office
Ministry of Works Building	1968	14	43	140	concrete	office
Office of the President	1967	14	43	140	concrete	office
Harambee House	1962	12	40	130	concrete	office
N.H.C. House	1975	13	40	131	concrete	office
Development House—W. Tower	1972	12	39	128	concrete	office
Kencom House	1977	10	38	126	concrete	office
K.C.S. House	1975	13	38	126	concrete	office
Extelcoms House	1973	10	34	110	concrete	office
I.P.S. Building	1971	10	33	108	concrete	office

Peoples Republic of China

Beijing

Building	Year completed	Number of stories	Height meters	Height feet	Material	Use
Beijing Hotel—East Wing	1974	20	77	252	concrete	hotel
CAAC Office Building	1964	15	61	200	concrete	office
No. 10 Apartments for Foreigners	1973	18	58	190	concrete/ aerocrete	apartment
No. 10 Apartments Dongda Bridge	1979	15	52	170	concrete	apartment
National Minority Hotel	1959	12	48	160	concrete	hotel
Main Building Ching Hua Univ.	1962	10	44	144	concrete	teaching
Beijing Hotel—West Wing	1954	9	41	134	concrete	hotel
Foreign Trade Negotiation Building	1976	9	40	130	concrete/ ceramsite	office
CAAC Apartment Building	1975	12	38	126	concrete	apartment
First Guest House	1960	9	35	114	brick & concrete	hotel
Qian San Men Apartments Group	1977	8-16	23-46	78-150	concrete	apartment

Changchun

Building	Year completed	Number of stories	Height meters	Height feet	Material	Use
Color Television Centre	1981	17	64	210	concrete	office
Friendship Guest House	1980	12	46	150	concrete	hotel

Dalian

Building	Year completed	Number of stories	Height meters	Height feet	Material	Use
Bo Hai Hotel	1976	12	46	150	concrete	hotel

Fuzhou

Building	Year completed	Number of stories	Height meters	Height feet	Material	Use
Broadcasting & Television Centre	1978	18	69	225	concrete	office
Min Jiang Hotel	1979	16	68	222	concrete	hotel

Guangzhou

Building	Year completed	Number of stories	Height meters	Height feet	Material	Use
Baiyun Hotel	1976	33	107	350	concrete	hotel
Guangzhou Hotel	1968	27	88	289	concrete	hotel
People's Building of Guangzhou	1966	18	66	216	concrete	department store
New Building of Dongfang Hotel	1973	12	43	141	concrete	hotel
Aquatic Products Company Building	1976	10	35	114	concrete	office

Guilin

Building	Year completed	Number of stories	Height meters	Height feet	Material	Use
Lijiang Hotel	1975	12	45	148	concrete	hotel

Hefei

Building	Year completed	Number of stories	Height meters	Height feet	Material	Use
Jiao Tong Hotel	1979	10	35	114	concrete	hotel

Kunming

Building	Year completed	Number of stories	Height meters	Height feet	Material	Use
Kunming Hotel	1981	13	52	170	concrete	hotel

Lanzhou

Building	Year completed	Number of stories	Height meters	Height feet	Material	Use
No. 1 Apartment	1980	14	48	157	concrete	apartment
Friendship Hotel	1964	9	32	105	concrete	hotel

Nanchang

Building	Year completed	Number of stories	Height meters	Height feet	Material	Use
Qing Shan Hu Hotel	1981	15	54	177	concrete	hotel
Hongdu Hotel	1981	13	45	148	concrete	hotel

Nanjing

Building	Year completed	Number of stories	Height meters	Height feet	Material	Use
Great Bridge Hotel	1977	10	32	105	concrete	hotel

Nanning

Building	Year completed	Number of stories	Height meters	Height feet	Material	Use
Yongjiang Hotel	1973	12	44	144	concrete	hotel

Table 4 Tallest buildings in major cities (continued)

Building	Year completed	Number of stories	Height meters	feet	Material	Use
Qingdao						
Jing Shan Hotel	1981	21	66	216	concrete	hotel
Huiguan Hotel	1979	12	38	126	concrete	hotel
Qingdao Hotel	1980	11	38	126	concrete	hotel
Shanghai						
International Hotel	1930	22	83	272	steel	hotel
Tilanqiao Hotel	1976	20	68	223	concrete	hotel
Hengshan Hotel	1933	17	62	203	concrete	hotel
Yanan Hotel	1972	12	46	150	concrete	hotel
Liu Jia Zhai Apartment	1976	14	43	140	concrete	apartment
Jingan Temple Apartment	1976	12	37	121	concrete	apartment
Kangle Road No. 1 Apartment	1975	12	37	121	concrete	apartment
Huasheng Road Apartment	1976	12	37	121	concrete	apartment
Shenyang						
Railway Staff Apartment	1976	16	49	161	concrete	apartment
Taiyun						
May Day Hotel	1980	14	47	153	concrete	hotel
Shanxi Broadcasting & Television Centre	1980	12	46	150	concrete	office
Tianjin						
Friendship Hotel	1975	11	47	153	concrete	hotel
Wuhan						
Qing Chuan Hotel	1981	26	90	295	concrete	hotel
Telecommunication Building	1980	12	62	203	concrete	office
Xian						
Xian Hotel	1979	13	44	144	concrete	hotel
Railway Complex Building	1977	9	30	98	concrete	office
Zhengzhou						
Zhongyuan Building	1974	18	62	203	concrete	hotel
Zhengzhou Hotel	1978	17	60	197	concrete	hotel
Railway Station Hotel	1976	16	50	164	concrete	hotel

Nomenclature

The following list of symbols and abbreviations contains those that are included in the preceding manuscripts. In most cases, only symbols and abbreviations not already included in the five volumes of the Monograph on the Planning and Design of Tall Buildings will be included here. Some repetition may be necessary, however, for the sake of reader understanding.

SYMBOLS

A = sectional area
A_F = amplification factor
A_w = area of web
a = distance from top
β, B^w = outside width square hollow section
b = half-width of flange
C_L = reduction coefficient for reduction in column stiffness
D = diameter of circular hollow section
d = depth of member
ϵ = base shear coefficient
f = uniformly distributed lateral load per unit height
H = applied lateral force
H = height
h = story height
K_p = stiffness ratio of strain-hardening region
$\overline{K}$ = mean stiffness of member element of unit force
$\overline{K}_r$ = mean stiffness of unit force

k_p, k_d = stiffness ratios of members in plastic region

l' = shear span

$M_{cr,e}$ = critical value of maximum bending moment causing bifurcation of equilibrium

$M_y (p = o)$ = full plastic moment without axial stress

$M_y (p = p)$ = full plastic moment with axial stress

$\overline{M}_y$ = mean yield moment of member element

M_u = ultimate value of bending moment

P_c = total vertical force to cause lateral buckling

P_c = critical load for torsional buckling of story

$p = P/P_v$ = axial stress ratio

p_c = uniformly distributed vertical load per unit height

Q_y = yield shear capacity of unit frame

r = polar radius of gyration of vertical loading

S_x = section modulus

t, t_f, t_w = thickness of plate elements of section

t_w = thickness of web

τ_p = yield strength (shear)

T = applied torsional load

τ_m = maximum strength index

V = shear force

V = effective volume of joint-panel

V_{nb} = nominal shear-bond strength of slab

X_1, X_2 = dimensions of each column and beam

Z_p, Z_p' = plastic section modulus

λ_y, λ = slenderness ratio

δ = lateral deformation caused by V

η, η_o = ductility ratio of member

Δ = lateral story deflection

ϕ = strength reduction factor

Θ = torsional deformation of story (radians)

μ_δ = frame deflection ductility

σ_y = yield stress

μ = magnification factor

γ = load factor

Δ_p = amplification factor

ABBREVIATIONS

ACI — American Concrete Institute

AISC — American Institute of Steel Construction

AISI — American Iron and Steel Institute

ANSI—American National Standards Institute
ASCE—American Society of Civil Engineers
ASD—Allowable Stress Design
ASHRAE—American Society of Heating, Refrigerating, and Air-
          Conditioning Engineers
ASTM—American Society for Testing and Materials
ATC—Applied Technology Council
CBD—Central Business District
CEB-FIP—Comité Européen du Béton (since 1976 Comité
          Euro-International du Béton), European Concrete Committee/
          Fédération Internationale de la Précontrainte, International
          Federation for Prestressing
CIB—International Council for Building Research
CMEA—Council of Mutual Economic Aid
CSICC—Canadian Steel Industries Construction Council
CWOWE—Canadian Workshop on Wind Engineering
ECCS—European Convention for Constructional Steelwork
EPA—Environmental Protection Agency
FAR—Floor Area Ratio
GWB—Gypsum Wallboard
HUD—U.S. Department of Housing and Urban Development
HVAC—Heating, Ventilating, and Air-Conditioning
ISO—International Standards Organization
LRFD—Load and Resistance Factor Design
NBC—National Building Code of Canada
NBS—National Bureau of Standards
NFPA—National Fire Protection Association
NSF—National Science Foundation
OSHA—Occupational Safety and Health Administration
OTTV—Overall Thermal Transfer Value
PCA—Portland Cement Association
PCI—Prestressed Concrete Institute, U.S.A.
RC—Reinforced Concrete
RSA—Republic of South Africa
SOM—Skidmore, Owings and Merrill
SSRC—Structural Stability Research Council
TBE—European Association of Brick and Tile Manufacturers
UB—Universal Box
UBC—Uniform Building Code
UL—Underwriters' Laboratories
VAV—Variable Air Volume

UNITS

In the table below are given conversion factors for commonly used units. The numerical values have been rounded off to the values shown. The British (Imperial) System of units is the same as the American System except where noted. Le Système International d'Unités (abbreviated "SI") is the name formally given in 1960 to the system of units partly derived from, and replacing, the old metric system.

SI	American	Old Metric
	Length	
1 mm	0.03937 in.	1 mm
1 m	3.28083 ft	1 m
	1.093613 yd	
1 km	0.62137 mile	1 km
	Area	
1 mm^2	0.00155 in.^{2}	1 mm^2
1 m^2	10.76392 ft^2	1 m^2
	1.19599 yd^2	
1 km^2	247.1043 acres	1 km^2
1 hectare	2.471 acres[1]	1 hectare
	Volume	
1 cm^3	0.061023 in.^{3}	1 cc
		1 ml
1 m^3	35.3147 ft^3	1 m^3
	1.30795 yd^3	
	264.172 gal[2] liquid	
	Velocity	
1 m/sec	3.28084 ft/sec	1 m/sec
1 km/hr	0.62137 miles/hr	1 km/hr
	Acceleration	
1 m/sec^2	3.28084 ft/sec^2	1 m/sec^2
	Mass	
1 g	0.035274 oz	1 g
1 kg	2.2046216 lb[3]	1 kg
	Density	
1 kg/m^3	0.062428 lb/ft^3	1 kg/m^3

SI	American	Old Metric
	Force, Weight	
1 N	0.224809 lbf	0.101972 kgf
1 kN	0.1124045 tons[4]	
1 MN	224.809 kips	
1 kN/m	0.06853 kips/ft	
1 kN/m^2	20.9 lbf/ft^2	
	Torque, Bending Moment	
1 N-m	0.73756 lbf-ft	0.101972 kgf-m
1 kN-m	0.73756 kip-ft	101.972 kgf-m
	Pressure, Stress	
1 N/m^2 = 1 Pa	0.000145038 psi	0.101972 kgf/m^2
1 kN/m^2 = 1 kPa	20.8855 psf	
1 MN/m^2 = 1 MPa	0.145038 ksi	
	Viscosity (Dynamic)	
1 N-sec/m^2	0.0208854 lbf-sec/ft^2	0.101972 kgf-sec/m^2
	Viscosity (Kinematic)	
1 m^2/sec	10.7639 ft^2/sec	1 m^2/sec
	Energy, Work	
1 J = 1 N-m	0.737562 lbf-ft	0.00027778 w-hr
1 MJ	0.37251 hp-hr	0.27778 kw-hr
	Power	
1 W = 1 J/sec	0.737562 lbf ft/sec	1 w
1 kW	1.34102 hp	1 kw
	Temperature	
K = 273.15 + °C	°F = (°C × 1.8) + 32	°C = (°F − 32)/1.8
K = 273.15 + 5/9(°F − 32)		
K = 273.15 + 5/9(°R − 491.69)		

(1) Hectare as an alternative for km^2 is restricted to land and water areas.
(2) 1 m^3 = 219.9693 Imperial gallons.
(3) 1 kg = 0.068522 slugs.
(4) 1 American ton = 2000 lb.   1kN = 0.1003612 Imperial ton.   1 Imperial ton = 2240 lb.

Abbreviations for Units

Btu	British Thermal Unit	kW	kilowatt
°C	degree Celsius (centigrade)	lb	pound
cc	cubic centimeters	lbf	pound force
cm	centimeter	lb_m	pound mass
°F	degree Fahrenheit	MJ	megajoule
ft	foot	MPa	megapascal
g	gram	m	meter
gal	gallon	ml	milliliter
hp	horsepower	mm	millimeter
hr	hour	MN	meganewton
Imp	British Imperial	N	newton
in.	inch	oz	ounce
J	joule	Pa	pascal
K	kelvin	psf	pounds per square foot
kg	kilogram	psi	pounds per square inch
kgf	kilogram-force	°R	degree Rankine
kip	1000 pound force	sec	second
km	kilometer	slug	14.594 kg
kN	kilonewton	U_o	heat transfer coefficient
kPa	kilopascal	W	watt
ksi	kips per square inch	yd	yard

References/Bibliography

The citations that follow include both references and a bibliography. The list includes all publications referred to or cited in the articles, and it also includes a bibliography for further reading. The material is arranged alphabetically by author, followed by the year of publication. Since the citation in the text is to author and year, there will be instances in which reference is made to two different articles published in the same year by the same author. In those instances it has been necessary to affix letters to the year to provide proper identification.

Where articles are published in a language other than English, the translation of the title is given first, followed by the title in the original language.

The numbers in parentheses following the citation designate the committee number (e.g. 21A) or the Monograph volume and chapter (e.g. SB-2) for which the citation is appropriate.

Additional bibliographies are available through the Council.

Abercombie, S. 1980
  TWENTY-FIVE YEAR AWARD GOES TO LEVER HOUSE. AIA Journal 69(3):77.
ACI 1973
  RESPONSE OF MULTISTORY CONCRETE STRUCTURES TO LATERAL FORCES. ACI
    SP-36 (21A).
ACI 1977
  BUILDING CODE REQUIREMENTS FOR REINFORCED CONCRETE.ACI, Detroit. (5).
ACI Committee 408 1979
  SUGGESTED DEVELOPMENT, SPLICE, AND STANDARD HOOK PROVISIONS FOR
    DEFORMED BARS IN TENSION. Concrete International, ACI 1(7):44-46. (21D).
ACI 1979
  CONCLUSIONS OF THE HUBERT RUSCH WORKSHOP ON CREEP AND CON-
    CRETE. Concrete International, ACI 2(11):77. (21D).

Ackroyd, M. H. and Gerstle, K. H. 1982
BEHAVIOR OF TYPE 2 STEEL FRAMES. Journal of the Structural Division, ASCE 108. (SB-2,SB-7).

Aderibigbe, A. B. 1979
LAGOS—THE DEVELOPMENT OF AN AFRICAN CITY. Technical Report, Longman Nigeria, Lagos. (29).

Adham, S. A. 1980
INVESTIGATION OF REINFORCED BRICK MASONRY BUILDINGS UNDAMAGED BY THE SAN FERNANDO EARTHQUAKE. In Proceedings of Conference on Research Progress on Masonry Construction, Paper No. 4, Marina del Ray, Calif. (27).

Adham, S. A. and Ewing, R. D. 1978
INTERACTION BETWEEN UNREINFORCED MASONRY STRUCTURES AND THEIR ROOF DIAPHRAGMS DURING EARTHQUAKES. In Proceedings of North American Masonry Conference, Paper No. 57, University of Colorado, Boulder, Col. (27).

Ahm, P. B., Clarke, F. G., Grut, E. L. and Rice, P. 1979
DESIGN AND CONSTRUCTION OF THE GEORGE POMPIDOU NATIONAL CENTER OF ARTS AND CULTURE. Proc. Instn. Civil Engineers 66(Part 1):557-593. (8A).

AISC 1953
SALVAGING FIRE DAMAGED STEEL. Steel Construction Digest 10(3). (8A).

AISC 1978
SPECIFICATIONS FOR THE DESIGN, FABRICATION AND ERECTION OF STEEL BUILDINGS.AISC, Chicago, Il. (5).

AISC 1980
MANUAL OF STEEL CONSTRUCTION 8th edition, American Institute of Steel Construction, Chicago, IL, 1980. (18).

AISI 1968
SPECIFICATION FOR THE DESIGN OF COLD-FORMED STEEL STRUCTURAL MEMBERS. American Iron and Steel Institute.

AISI 1979
FIRE-SAFE STRUCTURAL STEEL. A DESIGN GUIDE. Washington, D. C. Ft800-0379-5M-NB, American Iron and Steel Institute. (8A).

AISI 1980a
DESIGNING FIRE PROTECTION FOR STEEL COLUMNS. Technical Report Third Edition, American Iron and Steel Institute. (8A).

AISI 1980b
SPECIFICATION FOR THE DESIGN OF COLD-FORMED STEEL STRUCTURAL MEMBERS. Technical Report, American Iron and Steel Institute, (13).

Allen, D. E. 1978
MERCHANT-RANKINE APPROACH TO MEMBER STABILITY. Journal of the Structural Division, ASCE, Proc. Paper 14201 104(ST12):1909-1914. (16).

Allen, D. E. 1969
SAFETY FACTORS FOR STRESS REVERSAL. International Association for Bridge and Structural Engineering Publications 29(II):19-27. (5).

Allen, D. E. 1981a
CRITERIA FOR DESIGN SAFETY FACTORS AND QUALITY ASSURANCE EXPENDITURE. In Proceedings of Third International Conference on Structural Safety and Reliability, pages 23-25., Trondheim. (CL).

Allen, D. E. 1981b
LIMIT STATES DESIGN: WHAT DO WE REALLY WANT?. Canadian Journal of Civil Engineering 8(1). (CB,SB).

Allen, D. E. and Lie, T. T. 1977
FIRE RESISTANCE OF REINFORCED CONCRETE COLUMNS AND WALLS. In Proceedings of the Canadian Structural Concrete Conference, Ottawa. (CL).

Allen, D. E., Rainer, J. H. and Pernica, G. 1979
VIBRATION CRITERIA FOR LONG-SPAN CONCRETE FLOORS. ACI Special Publication SP-60, (CB).

Alpsten, G. 1975
RESIDUAL STRESSES, YIELD STRESS AND COLUMN STRENGTH OF HOT-ROLLED AND ROLLER-STRAIGHTENED STEEL SHAPES. In Proceedings of the International Colloquium on Column Strength, Reports of the Working Commissions, Vol. 23, Paris. IABSE, (16).

Aluminum Association 1976
Third Edition: SPECIFICATIONS FOR ALUMINUM STRUCTURES. The Aluminum Association (5).

American Institute of Timber Construction 1974
STANDARD SPECIFICATIONS FOR STRUCTURAL GLUED-LAMINATED TIMER OF DOUGLAS FIR, WESTERN LARCH, SOUTHERN PINE AND CALIFORNIA RED-WOOD. AITC, Englewood, Col., (5).

Ang, A. H. and Cornell, C. A. 1974
RELIABILITY BASES OF STRUCTURAL SAFETY AND DESIGN. Journal of the Structural Division, ASCE Proc. Paper 10777 100(ST9):1755-1769.

Anicic, D., Zamolo, M. and Soric, Z. 1980
EXPERIMENTS ON NON-STRUCTURAL PARTITION WALLS EXPOSED TO SEISMIC FORCES. In Proceedings of Seventh World Conference on Earthquake Engineering, Vol. 6, pages 144-150., Istanbul, Turkey. (17).

ANSI 1981
MINIMUM DESIGN LOADS FOR BUILDING AND OTHER STRUCTURES. Technical Report A58.1, ANSI, New York. (SB-1).

ANSI 1982
BUILDING CODE REQUIREMENTS FOR MINIMUM DESIGN LOADS IN BUILD-INGS AND OTHER STRUCTURES. ANSI, New York, (5).

Arens, E. A. 1980
GEOGRAPHICAL EXTRAPOLATION OF TYPICAL HOURLY WEATHER DATA FOR ENERGY CALCULATIONS IN BUILDINGS. US Government Printing Office, Building Science Series 126, National Bureau of Standards.

Arvidsson, K. 1979
INTERACTION BETWEEN COUPLED SHEAR WALLS AND FRAMES. In Proceedings of Institute for Civil Engineers, Paper 8174, Vol. 67, Part 2, pages 589-596. ICE, London. (21C).

ASHRAE 1975
ENERGY CONSERVATION IN NEW BUILDING DESIGN, STANDARD 90-75 ASHRAE, New York, NY, (2B/2C).

ASHRAE 1980
ENERGY CONSERVATION IN NEW BUILDING DESIGN. ASHRAE Standard (90-75). (40).

ASHRAE 1981a
STANDARD 62-1981, ASHRAE, New York, NY, 1981. (2B/2C).

ASHRAE 1981b
THE ASHRAE HANDBOOK: 1981 FUNDAMENTALS American Society of Heating, Refrigerating, and Air-Conditioning Engineers, Inc., New York, NY, (40).

ASTM 1980
STANDARD METHODS OF FIRE TESTS OF BUILDING CONSTRUCTION AND MA-TERIALS. ANSI/ASTM E119-80. : American Society for Testing and Materials, (8A).

ATC 1978
TENTATIVE PROVISIONS FOR THE DEVELOPMENT OF SEISMIC REGULATIONS FOR BUILDINGS. Applied Technology Council associated with the Structural Engineers Association of California—NBS Special Publication 510, US Government Printing Office, California. (21D).

Atkins, R. E., Peterka, J. A. and Cermak, J. E. 1979
AVERAGED PRESSURE COEFFICIENTS FOR RECTANGULAR BUILDINGS. In Proceedings of Fifth International Conference on Wind Engineering, pages 369-380. Pergamon Press, Fort Collins, Col. (CL-7).

Awni, A. A. and Hendry, A. W. 1979
A SIMPLIFIED METHOD FOR ECCENTRICITY CALCULATIONS. In Proceedings of Vth International Brick & Masonry Conference, Washington, D.C. (27).

Awni, A. A. and Hendry, A. W. 1981
THE STRENGTH OF MASONRY WALLS COMPRESSED BETWEEN FLOOR SLABS. International Journal of Masonry Construction 1(3):110-118. (27).

Awni, A. A. and Hendry, A. W. 1982
ECCENTRICITY MEASUREMENTS ON LOAD BEARING MASONRY STRUCTURES. Proceedings of British Ceramics Society. (27).

AWS 1981
SPECIFICATION FOR WELDING SHEET STEEL IN STRUCTURES. Technical Report D1.3-81, AWS, New York. (13).

Bandyszewski, W. and Sawczuk, A. 1974
METHOD OF ASSESSING DEFLECTIONS IN ELASTIC-PLASTIC BEAMS IN FRAMES. Archiwum Inzynierii Ladowej, Panstwowe Wydawnictwo Naukowe 20(1):63-80. (15).

Basu, A. K. and Nagpal, A. K. 1980
FRAME-WALL SYSTEMS WITH RIGIDLY-JOINTED LINK BEAMS. Journal of Structural Division, ASCE 106(ST5):1175-1192. (CB-5).

Batten, D. F. 1974
ENVIRONMENTAL IMPACT OF BUILDINGS. Building Forum 6:17-23. (PC-7).

Batten, D. F. 1978a
DESIGN STUDIES OF MEDIUM-RISE STEEL BUILDINGS. In Proceedings of Institution of Civil Engineers, Vol. 65, pages 589-600., London. (SB-2,SB-3).

Batten, D. F. 1978b
COMPUTER-AIDED PLASTIC DESIGN OF UNBRACED FRAMEWORKS. Computers and Structures 9:409-415. (SB-3).

Battermann, R. H. and Johnston, B. G. 1967
BEHAVIOUR AND MAXIMUM STRENGTH OF METAL COLUMNS. Journal of the Structural Division, ASCE 93(ST2):205-230. (16).

Beason, W. L. and Minor, J. E. 1978
RESPONSE OF WINDOW GLASS TO WIND LOADS. 3rd U.S. National Conference on Wind Engineering Research, University of Florida, Gainesville. (17).

Beason, W. L. and Minor, J. E. 1981
WINDOW GLASS RESEARCH AT TEXAS TECH. UNIVERSITY. Preprints of the Fourth U.S. National Conference on Wind Engineering Research, University of Washington, Seattle, Washington.

Beaulieu, D. et al 1976
THE EFFECTS OF COLUMN OUT-OF-PLUMBS ON THE STABILITY OF CORE-BRACED BUILDINGS. Canadian Journal of Civil Engineering 3(3):417-427. (SB-9).

Beaulieu, D. and Adams, P. F. 1976
STABILITY OF CORE-BRACED BUILDINGS. In Proceedings of National Structural Engineering Conference, ASCE, Madison, Wis. (SB-9).

Beaulieu, D. and Adams, P. F. 1977
THE DESTABILIZING FORCES CAUSED BY GRAVITY LOADS ACTING ON INITIALLY OUT-OF-PLUMB MEMBERS IN STRUCTURES. Structural Engineering Report 59, Dept. of Civil Engineering, University of Alberta, Edmonton. (SB-9).

Beaulieu, D. and Adams, P. F. 1978a
THE EFFECTS OF WALL OUT-OF-PLUMBS ON THE STABILITY OF CORE-BRACED BUILDINGS. Canadian Journal of Civil Engineering 4(5):471-478. (SB-9).

Beaulieu, D. and Adams, P. F. 1978b
THE RESULTS OF A SURVEY ON STRUCTURAL OUT-OF-PLUMBS. Canadian Journal of Civil Engineering 4(5):462-470. (SB-9).

Beaulieu, D. and Adams, P. F. 1980
SIGNIFICANCE OF STRUCTURAL OUT-OF-PLUMB FORCES AND RECOMMENDATIONS FOR DESIGN. Canadian Journal of Civil Engineering 1(7):105-113. (SB-9).

Beaulieu, D., Kelker, D. and Adams, P. F. 1979
PROBABILITY CONSIDERATIONS IN ASSESSING THE EFFECTS OF STRUCTURAL OUT-OF-PLUMBS. Canadian Journal of Civil Engineering 3(6):610-616. (SB-9).

Becker, J. M.; Llorente, C. and Mueller, P. 1980
SEISMIC RESPONSE OF PRECAST CONCRETE WALLS. John Wiley & Sons, Ltd., pages 545-564. (21E).

Beer, H. and Schulz, G. 1969
THE MAXIMUM STRENGTH OF AXIALLY LOADED COLUMNS WITH IMPERFEC-
TIONS. Verein Deutscher Ingenieure 111(21, 23, 24). (16).

Beer, H. and Schulz, G. 1970
THE THEORETICAL BASIS OF THE NEW COLUMN CURVES OF THE EUROPEAN
CONVENTION FOR CONSTRUCTIONAL STEELWORK. Construction Metallique
(3):37-57. (16).

Behets, J. F. and Law, M. 1980
STUDY OF RESEARCH INTO THE BEHAVIOR OF STRUCTURAL STEEL ELEMENTS
EXPOSED TO FIRE. Ove Arup & Partners, London 7210 Sa/001 and 002, Centre Belgo-
Luxembourgeois d'Information de l'Acier, Brussels. (8A).

Bergquist, D. J. 1977
TESTS ON COLUMNS RESTRAINED BY BEAMS WITH SIMPLE CONNECTIONS.
American Iron and Steel Institute Project No. 189, The University of Texas at Austin,
Texas. (43).

Bertero, V. V., Editor 1978
PROCEEDINGS OF A WORKSHOP ON EARTHQUAKE-RESISTANT REINFORCED
CONCRETE BUILDING CONSTRUCTION. In 3 Volumes, NSF Grant No. 76-01923,
pages 1941. University of Caifornia, Berkeley. (21E).

Bertero, V. V., Popov, E. P. and Krawinkler, H. 1972
BEAM-COLUMN SUBASSEMBLAGES UNDER REPEATED LOADING. Journal of the
Structural Division, ASCE 98(ST5):1137-1159. (15).

Birnstiel, C. and Iffland, J. S. B. 1980
FACTORS INFLUENCING FRAME STABILITY. Journal of the Structural Division, ASCE
Proc. Paper 15196 106(ST2):491-504. (16).

Birnstiel, C. and Iffland, J. S. B. (to be published)
STABILITY DESIGN PROCEDURES. Report Project 21.62, AISC, Chicago, Il. (16).

Biswas, M. and Earwood, R. 1981
CRITERIA, ANALYSIS AND DESIGN OF BRACED AND UNBRACED FRAMES. In Proceedings of SSRC., (16).

Bjorhovde, R. 1972
DETERMINISTIC AND PROBABILISTIC APPROACHES TO THE STRENGTH OF
STEEL COLUMNS. Ph.D. Dissertation, Lehigh University. (16).

Black, D., Pulmano, V. A. and Kabaila, A. P. 1974
STIFFNESS OF FLAT PLATES IN CROSS-WALL STRUCTURES. UNICIV Report R-133,
University of New South Wales, Kennington, Australia. (21C).

Blake, P. 1977
FORM FOLLOWS FIASCO, WHY MODERN ARCHITECTURE HASN'T WORKED.
Little, Brown (31).

Blanchard, B. S. 1979
LIFE CYCLE COSTING—A REVIEW. Terotechnica 1:9-15. (35).

Blessmann, J. and Riera, J. D. 1979
INTERACTION EFFECTS IN NEIGHBOURING TALL BUILDINGS. In Proceedings of
Fifth International Conference on Wind Engineering, pages 381-396. Pergamon Press,
Fort Collins, Col. (CL-7,CL-3).

Blessmann, J. 1979
WIND PRESSURES IN NEIGHBOURING TALL BUILDINGS (IN PORTUGUESE). In
Proceedings of 20th South American Conference on Structural Engineering, Vol. 1, Paper
B5, Universidad Nacional de Cordoba, Cordoba, Argentina. (CL-3).

BOCA 1970
APPROVED FIRE-RESISTANCE RATINGS OF ASSEMBLIES OF COMMON MATERIALS.
2nd Edition, Building Officials Conference of America. (8A/C).

BOCA 1979
UNIFORM BUILDING CODE. International Conference of Building Officials, Whittier,
Calif. (17).

BOCA 1981
THE BOCA BASIC BUILDING CODE/1981 8th edition, Interstate Printers and Publishers,
Inc., Danville, IL, (8A).

Bolotin, V. V. 1959
POSTBUCKLING DEFORMATION OF BEAMS (IN RUSSIAN). Raschot Prostranstvennih Konstrukcij V(5):3-18. (16).
Bond, G. V. L. 1975
WATER COOLED HOLLOW COLUMNS. Technical Report, Constrado, Croydon, England. (8A).
Bouwkamp, J. G. and Meehan, J. F. 1960
DRIFT LIMITATIONS IMPOSED BY GLASS. In Proceedings, Second World Conference on Earthquake Engineering, Vol. III, pages 1763-1777., Tokyo and Kyoto, Japan. (17)
Bowles, R. and Sugarman, B. 1962
THE STRENGTH AND DEFLECTION CHARACTERISTICS OF LARGE RECTANGULAR GLASS PANELS UNDER UNIFORM PRESSURE. Glass Technology 3(5):156-170. (17).
Braham, M., Grimault, J. P., Massonnet, C., Mouty, J. and Rondal, J. 1980
BUCKLING OF THIN-WALLED HOLLOW SECTIONS. CASES OF AXIALLY LOADED RECTANGULAR SECTIONS.. Acier-Stahl-Steel, Bruxelles Belgium 45(1):30-36. (16).
Braham,M., Grimault, J. P. and Rondal, J. 1979
BUCKLING OF THIN-WALLED TUBULAR SECTIONS, SPECIFICALLY OF RECTANGULAR SECTIONS UNDER AXIAL COMPRESSION (FLAMBEMENT DES PROFILS CREUX A PAROIS MINCES. CAS DES PROFILS RECTANGULAIRES CHARGES EXIALEMENT). Final Report, Research 6210.SA/3/301, Commission des Communautes Europeenes. (16).
Brainov, M. 1972
DIFFERENTIAL STRUCTURAL ANALYSIS, OPTIMAL STRUCTURAL COMPOSITION, AUTOMATIC DESIGN SYSTEMS OF BUILDING STRUCTURES. Technical Report, Technika, Sofia. (3).
Brainov, M. 1979
HUMAN SETTLEMENTS - TALL BUILDINGS - ARCHITECTURE, CONSTRUCTION, INDUSTRIALIZATION - STRUCTURAL SYSTEMS. Technical Report, Technika, Sofia. (3).
Brainov, M. 1980a
STRUCTURES - COMPLEX SCIENCE - SYSTEMATIC THEORY - STRUCTURAL CREATIVITY. Technical Report, Bulgarian Academy of Science, Sofia. (3).
Brainov, M. 1980b
AESTHETICS IN STRUCTURAL ENGINEERING. 11th IABSE Congress, Vienna 11: 93-100.(3).
Breen, J. E. 1976
SUMMARY REPORT OF RESEARCH WORKSHOP ON PROGRESSIVE COLLAPSE OF BUILDING STRUCTURES. Technical Report, University of Texas, Austin. (21E).
Brick Institute of America 1969
BUILDING CODE REQUIREMENTS FOR ENGINEERED BRICK MASONRY. BIA, McLean, Va. (5).
British Standards Institute 1972a
CODE OF PRACTICE FOR THE STRUCTURAL USE OF CONCRETE. British Standard Institute CP110, London (1).
British Standards Institute 1972b
WIND LOADS. British Standard (CP3).
Bromilow, F. J. 1982
TEROTECHNOLOGY RESEARCH IN AUSTRALIA - AN OVERVIEW. Civil Engineering Transactions 24(1):34-39. (35).
Brotchie, J. F. 1981
UNIFICATION OF SOCIAL AND PHYSICAL SCIENCE MODELS. In Proceedings of First International Conference on Computing in Civil Engineering, ASCE, pages 184-199., New York. (35).
Brotchie, J. F., Lesse, P. F. and Roy, J. R. 1979
PHYSICS, ECONOMICS AND PLANNING - A NEW GENERATION OF URBAN AND BUILDING MODELS. In Proceedings of International Conference on the Application of Computers in Architecture, Building Design and Urban Planning, pages 505-516., Berlin. (35).

Broude, B. M. 1958
STABILITY OF I-BEAMS WITH INITIAL CURVATURE AND ECCENTRIC LOADS (IN RUSSIAN). Raschot Prostranstvennih Konstrukcij IV:5-36. (16).

Broude, B. M. 1959
A MORE ACCURATE SOLUTION OF PRANDTL-TIMO-SHENKO PROBLEM (IN RUSSIAN). Raschot Prostransvennih Konstrukcij V:51-56. (16).

Brown, R. H. and Wattar, F. N. 1980
AN EVALUATION OF THE MOMENT MAGNIFIER TECHNIQUE FOR DESIGN OF UNREINFORCED MASONRY. In Proceedings of 2nd Canadian Masonry Symposium, pages 229-244., Ottawa, Canada. (27).

Bryl, S. and Sagelsdorff, R. 1971
FIRE RESISTANCE OF CONCRETE PANELS, STEEL SHELTERS AND REINFORCED CONCRETE PANELS(RESISTANCE AU FEU DESLANCHERS EN BETON ET TOLE D'ACIER ET DES PLANCHERS EN BETON ARME). Construction Metallique CTICM, Paris(1):5-11. (8A).

Brzezinski, R. and Konig, J. A. 1973
DEFLECTION ANALYSIS OF ELASTIC PLASTIC FRAMES AT SHAKEDOWN. Journal of Structural Mechanics 2(3):211-228. (15).

Bucheli, P. and Crisinel, M. 1982
COMPOSITE BEAMS FOR BUILDINGS (IN FRENCH AND GERMAN). In Schweizerische Zentrallstelle fur Stahlbau, Vol. A3, Zurich, Switzerland. (SB-9).

Burns, P. D. 1972
UNREINFORCED BRICK MASONRY WALLS UNDER VERTICAL LOADS. Structural Masonry Series 72-1, McGill University, Montreal, Canada. (27).

Butcher, E. G. 1968
FIRE AND CAR-PARK BUILDINGS. Fire Note No. 10, Her Majesty's Stationery Office, London. (8A).

Canadian Standards Association 1973
CODE FOR DESIGN OF CONCRETE STRUCTURES FOR BUILDINGS. CSA Standard A 23.3-1973 Edition, Canadian Standards Association, Rexdale, Ontario.

Canadian Standards Association 1981
GUIDELINES FOR THE DEVELOPMENT OF LIMIT STATES DESIGN. Canadian Standards Association, (CB).

Canadian Steel Industries Construction Council 1974
FIRE-DAMAGE AND REPAIR. Fire Protection Bulletin 3, Canadian Steel Industries Construction Council. (8A).

CEB-FIB 1978
Third Edition. Volume II: FOR CONCRETE STRUCTURES (POUR LES STRUCTURES EN BETON). Federaton Internationale de la Precontrainte, Paris. (21D).

Centre Scientifique et Technique de Batiment, 1981
CONSTRUIRE AVEC LE VENT (DESIGNING WITH THE WIND), Nantes, France.

Centre Technique Industriel de la Construction Metallique 1976
METHOD OF ANALYTICAL PREDICTION OF THE FIRE BEHAVIOR OF STEEL STRUCTURES (METHODE DE PREVISION PAR LE CALCUL DU COMPORTEMENT AU FEU DES STRUCTURES EN ACIER). Construction Metallique (4):55-93. (8A).

Centre Technique Industriel de la Construction Metallique 1977
METHODOLOGY OF CHARACTERISTICS OF PRODUCTS OF PROTECTION (MEHODOLOGIE DE CARACTERISATION DES PRODUITS DE PROTECTION). Technical Report, Paris. (8A).

Cermak, J. E., ed. 1980
WIND ENGINEERING. In Proceedings of the Fifth International Conference, 2 Volumes, Pergamon, Fort Collins, Col.

Chan, H. C. and Cheung, Y. K. 1979
ANALYSIS OF SHEAR WALLS USING HIGHER ORDER FINITE ELEMENTS. Building and Environment 14(3):217-224. (21C).

Chan, P. C. K., Heidebrecht, A. C. and Tso, W. K. 1975
APPROXIMATE ANALYSIS OF MULTI-STOREY MULTI-BAY FRAMES. Journal of Structural Division, ASCE 101(ST5):1021-1035. (CB-5,CB-2).

Chen, W. F. 1977a
THEORY OF BEAM-COLUMNS—THE STATE-OF-THE-ART REVIEW. In Proceedings of the Stability of Structures under Static and Dynamic Loads, pages 631-648. ASCE, New York (SB-4).

Chen, W. F. 1977b
STUDIES OF AXIALLY LOADED FABRICATED TUBULAR COLUMNS. In Second International Colloquium on Stability of Steel Structures, pages 61-70. ECCS-IABSE, Liege. (SB-4).

Chen, W. F. 1977c
DESIGN OF BOX COLUMNS UNDER BIAXIAL BENDING. In Preliminary Report, Second International Colloquium on Stability of Steel Structures, pages 355-361. ECCS-IABSE, Liege. (SB-4).

Chen, W. F. 1979
INFLUENCE OF END RESTRAINT ON COLUMN STABILITY. In Preprint 3608, ASCE Convention and Exposition. ASCE, Atlanta, Georgia. (16).

Chen, W. F. 1979
CONSTITUTIVE EQUATIONS FOR CONCRETE. In IABSE Colloquium on Plasticity in Reinforced Concrete, IABSE Publication, (CB-6).

Chen, W. F. 1980a
NONLINEAR ANALYSIS OF CONCRETE CYLINDERS UNDER HYDROSTATIC LOADING. Pergamon Press, U.K., (CB-7).

Chen, W. F. 1980b
END RESTRAINT AND COLUMN STABILITY. Journal of the Structural Division, ASCE 106(ST11):2279-2295. (SB-4).

Chen, W. F. 1981
RECENT ADVANCES ON ANALYSIS AND DESIGN OF STEEL BEAM-COLUMNS IN USA. Structural Engineering Report CE-STR-81-13, School of Civil Engineering, Purdue University, West Lafayette, IN. (SB-4).

Chen, W. F. 1982
PLASTICITY IN REINFORCED CONCRETE. McGraw-Hill, New York. (CB-6).

Chen, W. F. and Atsuta, T. 1976
IN-PLANE BEHAVIOR AND DESIGN. Volume 1: Theory of Beam-Columns. McGraw-Hill Publishing Co., Inc., New York, NY. (43).

Chen, W. F. and Atsuta, T. 1977
SPACE BEHAVIOR AND DESIGN. Volume 2: Theory of Beam-Columns. McGraw-Hill Publishing Co., Inc., New York, NY. (43).

Chen, W. F. and Chang, M. F. 1981
LIMIT ANALYSIS IN SOIL MECHANICS AND ITS APPLICATIONS TO LATERAL EARTH PRESSURE PROBLEMS. Solid Mechanics Archives 6(3). (SC-7).

Chen, W. F. and Cheong-Siat-Moy, F. 1980
LIMIT STATES DESIGN OF STEEL BEAM-COLUMNS—A STATE-OF-THE-ART REVIEW. Solid Mechanics Archives 5(1):29-74. (43,SB-4).

Chen, W. F. and Patel, K. V. 1981
STATIC BEHAVIOR OF BEAM-TO-COLUMN MOMENT CONNECTIONS. Journal of the Structural Division, ASCE 107(ST9):1815-1838. (SB-7).

Chen, W. F. and Ross, D. A. 1977a
THE AXIAL STRENGTH AND BEHAVIOR OF CYLINDRICAL COLUMNS. Journal of Petroleum Technology, AIME :239-242. (SB-4).

Chen, W. F. and Ross, D. A. 1977b
TESTS OF FABRICATED TUBULAR COLUMNS. Journal of the Structural Division, ASCE 102(ST3):619-634. (SB-4).

Chen, W. F. and Saleeb, A. F. 1982
CONSTITUTIVE EQUATIONS FOR ENGINEERING MATERIALS. Wiley-Interscience, New York, (SC-7).

Chen, W. F. and Suzuki, H. 1980
CONSTITUTIVE MODELS FOR CONCRETE. Pergamon Press, U.K., pages 23-32. (CB-6).

Chen, W. F., Suzuki, H. and Chang, T. Y. 1980
END EFFECTS OF PRESSURE-RESISTANT CONCRETE SHELLS. Journal of the Structural Division, ASCE 106(ST4):751-771. (CB-6).

Chen, W. F. and Ting, E. C., ed. 1980a
FRACTURE IN CONCRETE. ASCE Special Publications, New York, (CB-9).
Chen, W. F. and Ting, E. C. 1980b
CONSTITUTIVE MODELS FOR CONCRETE STRUCTURES. Journal of the Structural
Division, ASCE 106(EM1):1-19. (CB-6).
Cheng, F. Y. 1977
COMPARATIVE STUDIES OF BUCKLING CAPACITY OF THREE-DIMENSIONAL
BUILDING SYSTEMS. In Proceedings of an International Colloquium on Stability of
Structures Under Static and Dynamic Loads, Washington, D.C., pages 179-193. ASCE,
New York, NY. (16).
Cheng, F. Y. and Botkin, M. E. 1972
SECOND-ORDER ELASTO-PLASTIC ANALYSIS OF TALL BUILDINGS WITH DAMPED
DYNAMIC EXCITATIONS. In Proceedings of Specialty Conference for Finite Elements
Method in Civil Engineering held at Montreal, Canada, pages 549-563. Engineering
Institute of Canada, Montreal, Canada. (16).
Cheng, F. Y. and Botkin, M. E. 1974
P-DELTA EFFECT ON OPTIMUM DESIGN OF DYNAMIC TALL BUILDINGS. In Pro-
ceedings of the Regional Conference on Tall Buildings, pages 621-631. Asian Institute of
Technology, Bangkok, Thailand. (16).
Cheng, F. Y. and Oster, K. B. 1974
ULTIMATE INSTABILITY OF EARTHQUAKE STRUCTURES. Meeting Preprint 2357,
ASCE Annual and National Environmental Engineering Convention, Kansas City, Mo,
October 21-25, p. 1-20. (16).
Cheng, F. Y. and Oster, K. B. 1976
EFFECT OF COUPLING EARTHQUAKE MOTIONS ON INELASTIC STRUCTURAL
MODELS. In Proceedings of the International Symposium on Earthquake Structural
Engineering, pages 107-125. University of Missouri-Rolla, St. Louis, Missouri. (16).
Cheong-Siat-Moy, F., Downs, T. 1980
NEW INTERACTION EQUATIONS FOR STEEL BEAM-COLUMNS. Journal of the Struc-
tural Division, ASCE 106(ST5):1047-1061. (16).
Cheung, Y. K. and Swaddiwudhipong, S. 1978
ANALYSIS OF FRAME SHEAR WALL STRUCTURES USING FINITE STRIP ELE-
MENTS. In Proceedings of ICE, Vol. 65, Part 2, pages 517-535., (CB-5).
Choate, P. and Susan, W. 1981
AMERICA IN RUINS: BEYOND THE PUBLIC WORKS PORK BARREL. Technical
Report, Council of State Planning Agencies, Washington, D.C. (38).
Choay, F. 1981
LE CORBUSIER.George Braziller, Inc., New York. (31).
Chuvikin, G. M. 1958
EXPERIMENTAL INVESTIGATION OF LATERAL-TORSIONAL BUCKLING OF I-
BEAMS IN THE INELASTIC RANGE (IN RUSSIAN). Raschot Prostranstvennih
Konstrukcij IV:37-56. (16).
Chwalla, E. 1934
THEORY OF COMPRESSED STEEL MEMBERS. Der Stahlbau, p. 193,207. (16).
Ciesielski, R., Flaga, A. and Kawecki, J. 1974
ANALYSIS OF DYNAMIC RIGIDITY OF TALL BUILDING STRUCTURES IN THE
ASPECT OF VIBRATIONS PERCEPTIBILITY BY THE INHABITANTS (IN POLISH).
In Proceedings of XX Conference KIL PAN, Vol. 1, pages 47-59., Krynica. (CL-6).
Ciesielski, R. and Kawecki, J. 1971
DYNAMIC MODELS OF MULTISTORY BUILDINGS IN COMPARISON WITH MEA-
SUREMENT RESULTS (IN POLISH). In Proceedings of XVII Conference KIL PAN,
Vol. 1, pages 25-36., Krynica. (CB-1).
Ciesielski, R. and Kawecki, J. 1980
EXPERIMENTAL METHOD FOR EVALUATION OF STIFFNESS OF MULTISTORY
BUILDING. In Proceedings of 5th Symposium, Construction of Multistory Building
Under Extreme Conditions, CIB, pages 289-305., Madrid. (SB-5,CB-9).
Ciesielski, R., Kawecki, J., Maciag, E. and Pieronek, M. 1980
METHODS OF DETERMINATION OF FREE VIBRATIONS OF TOWER-TYPE STRUC-
TURES. In Bracketing of Eigenfrequencies of Continuous Structures, pages 81-104. Pub-
lishing House of the Hungarian Academy of Sciences, Budapest. (CB-1).

CIRIA 1977
RATIONALIZATION OF SAFETY AND SERVICEABILITY FACTORS IN STRUC-
TURAL CODES. Report No. 63, London, UK. (5).
CIRIA 1980
WIND ENGINEERING IN THE EIGHTIES, PROCEEDINGS OF THE CIRIA CON-
FERENCE, London, England.
CIRIA 1981
WIND ENGINEERING IN THE 1980's, London, England, November 12-13, 1980 (7).
City of Chicago 1981
NORTH LOOP GUIDELINES FOR CONSERVATION AND REDEVELOPMENT. Tech-
nical Report, City of Chicago. (32).
Civil Engineering ASCE 1980
INCLUDE STRUCTURAL FUSE IN DESIGN. Civil Engineering, ASCE 50(8):14. (22).
Clough, R. W., Mayes, R. L. and Gulkan, P. 1980
SHAKING TABLE STUDY OF SINGLE-STORY MASONRY HOUSES. In Proceedings of
Conference on Research & Progress on Masonry Construction, Paper No. 1, Brick
Institute of America, Marina del Ray, Calif. (27).
Comision de Normas para Estructuras de Edificaciones 1980
STEEL BUILDING STRUCTURES. DESIGN, FABRICATION AND ERECTION (ES-
TRUCTURAS DE ACERO PARA EDIFICACIONES. PROYECTO, FABRICACION Y
CONSTRUCCION) Comision Venezolana de Normas Industriales, Caracas, Venezuela,
1980. (PC).
Comite Europeen du Beton. 1976
FIRST ORDER RELIABILITY CONCEPTS FOR DESIGN CODES. Bulletin D'Information
No. 112, Comite European du Beton, Munich. (5).
Comite European du Beton 1978
COMMON UNIFIED RULES FOR DIFFERENT TYPES OF CONSTRUCTION AND
MATERIAL. Bulletin D'Information 124E, CEB, Paris. (5).
Communaute Europeenne du Charbon et de l'Acier 1974
RESEARCH ON THE BEHAVIOR OF STEEL STRUCTURES IN FIRE (RECHERCHE
SUR LA TENUE AU FEU DES CONSTRUCTION METALLIQUES). Technical Report
EUR 5180, Communaute Europeenne du Charbon et de l'Acier. (8A).
Contaldo, M., Faellan, C. and Mazzolani, F. M. 1979
THE NUMERICAL SIMULATION FOR THE PREDICTION OF THE LOAD CARRYING
CAPACITY OF MASONRY STRUCTURES. In Proceedings of Vth International Brick
& Masonry Conference, Washington, D. C. (27).
Corbit, C. M.,Jr. 1950
STRUCTURAL STEEL AFTER A FIRE. District Engineers Conference, American Institute
of Steel Construction. (8A).
Cornell, C. A. 1969
A PROBABILITY-BASED STRUCTURAL CODE. Journal of the American Concrete In-
stitute, Proc. 66(12):974-985. (5).
Corotis, R. B. and Doshi, V. A. 1977
PROBABILITY MODELS FOR LIVE LOAD SURVEY RESULTS. Journal of the Structural
Division, ASCE 103(ST6):1257-1274. (5).
Coull, A. 1975
TORSION OF STRUCTURAL CORES ON DEFORMABLE FOUNDATIONS. Building
Science 10:57-64. (CB-5).
Coull, A. and Abu El Magd, S. A. 1980
ANALYSIS OF WIDE-FLANGED SHEAR WALL STRUCTURES. Publication SP-63.:
American Concrete Institute, pages 575-607. (21D).
Coull, A. and Abuel-Magd, S. A. 1980
ANALYSIS OF WIDE FLANGED SHEAR WALL STRUCTURES. SP-63.: ACI Special
Publication, Detroit, (CB-5).
Coull, A. and Adams, N. W. 1980
VARIABLE STIFFNESS ELASTIC BASE MECHANISM FOR MODEL SHEAR WALL
STRUCTURES. Journal of Strain Analysis for Engineering Design 15(3):145-149. (CB-7).
Coull, A. and Ahmed, A. K. 1978
DEFLECTIONS OF FRAMED-TUBE STRUCTURES. Journal of Structural Division,
ASCE 104(ST5):857-862. (CB-5,SB-2).

Coull, A. and Bose, B. 1975
SIMPLIFIED ANALYSIS OF FRAME-TUBE STRUCTURES. Journal of Structural Division, ASCE 101(ST11):2223-2240. (CB-5,SB-2).

Coull, A. and Bose, B. 1976
TORSION OF FRAMED TUBE STRUCTURES. Journal of Structural Division, ASCE 102(ST12):2366-2370. (CB-5,SB-2).

Coull, A., Bose, B. and Ahmed, A. K. 1982
SIMPLIFIED ANALYSIS OF BUNDLED-TUBE STRUCTURES. Journal of Structural Division, ASCE 108(ST5). (21C).

Coull, A. and Low, C. K. 1979
ANALYSIS OF STIFFENED NON-PLANAR COUPLED SHEAR WALLS. In Proceedings of ICE, Vol. 67, Part 2, Paper 8255, pages 971-986., (CB-5).

Coull, A. and Mukherjee, P. R. 1978
NATURAL VIBRATIONS OF SHEAR WALL BUILDINGS ON FLEXIBLE SUPPORTS. International Journal of Earthquake Engineering and Structural Dynamics 6:295-315. (CB-9).

Coull, A. and Stafford-Smith, B. 1966
TALL BUILDINGS. In Proceedings of a Symposium on Tall Buildings with particular reference to shear wall structures. Department of Civil Engineering, University of Southampton, Southampton, England. (21A).

Coull, A. and Tawfik, S. Y. 1981a
ANALYSIS OF CORE STRUCTURES SUBJECTED TO TORSION. Building and Environment 16(3):221-228. (21C).

Coull, A. and Tawfik, S. Y. 1981b
ELASTO-PLASTIC ANALYSIS OF CORE STRUCTURES SUBJECTED TO TORSION. In Proceedings for Institute for Civil Engineers, Vol. 71, Part 2, pages 789-804., (21C).

Coull, A. and Wong, Y. C. 1980
EFFECTIVE SLAB STIFFNESS IN FLAT PLATE STRUCTURES. In Proceedings of ICE, Vol. 69, Part 2, Paper 8355, pages 721-735., (CB-5).

Coull, A. and Wong, Y. C. 1981
BENDING STIFFNESS OF FLOOR SLABS IN CROSS-WALL STRUCTURES. In Proceedings for Institute for Civil Engineers, Paper 8384, Vol. 71, Part 2, pages 17-35. Institute for Civil Engineers, (21C).

Coull, A. and Wong, Y. C. 1981
BENDING STIFFNESS OF FLOOR SLABS IN CROSS-WALL STRUCTURES. In Proceedings of ICE, Vol. 71, Part 2, Paper 8384, pages 17-35., (CB-5).

Council on Tall Buildings, Headquarters Staff, Ed. 1982
COUNCIL MEETING RECORD—MAY 9, 1981 . Fritz Laboratory Report 369.276, (Proceedings of Annual Council Meeting held in New York) Lehigh University, Bethlehem, Pa.

Council on Tall Buildings, Group CB 1978
Monograph on Planning and Design of Tall Buildings. Volume CB: STRUCTURAL DESIGN OF TALL CONCRETE AND MASONRY BUILDINGS.ASCE, New York (21C).

Craig, J. I. and Goodno, B. J. 1979
RESPONSE STUDIES OF GLASS CLADDING PANELS. In Proceedings of International Symposium on Behavior of Building Systems and Building Components, pages 137-158. Vanderbilt University, Nashville, Tenn. (17).

Craig, J. I. and Goodno, B. J. 1981
RESPONSE MEASUREMENTS FOR GLASS CLADDING PANELS. Journal of the Structural Division, ASCE 107(ST11):2199-2214. (17).

Craig, J. I., Goodno, B. J. and Deo, R. B. 1978
WINDOW AND CURTAIN PERFORMANCE IN HIGHRISE BUILDINGS. National Science Foundation Final Report No. GITAER-78-100/SCEGIT-78-170, Georgia Institute of Technology, Atlanta. (17).

Craig, J. I., Palfery, J. G. and Martin, C. S. 1975
WIND PRESSURE SIMULATION AND RESPONSE MEASUREMENTS FOR WINDOWS. 2nd United States National Conference on Wind Engineering Research, Colorado State University. (17).

Crawford, J. R. and Sharpe, R. 1979
COMPUTER GRAPHICS FOR A PLANNING MODEL. In Proceedings of Conference on Computer Graphics and Spatial Analysis, pages 19-24. Institution of Engineers, Adelaide, Australia. (35).

Cruz, M. F. and Lopez, O. A. 1980
NUMBER OF MODES FOR THE SEISMIC ANALYSIS OF BUILDINGS (NUMERO DE MODOS PARA EL ANALISIS SISMICO DE EDIFICIOS). Boletin IMME 67, Universidad Central de Venezuela, Caracas. (CL2,CB5).

CSA 1973
CODE FOR DESIGN OF CONCRETE STRUCTURES FOR BUILDINGS CSA Standard A23.3-1973 edition, Canadian Standards Association, Rexdale, Ontario, 1973.

CWOWE 1981
DESIGN AGAINST WIND, Third Canadian Workshop on Wind Engineering, Vancouver, B. C., May 7-8, 1981. (7)

Dahlstrom, E. 1957
CHILDREN IN HIGH-RISES IN A 3-STORY RESIDENTIAL COMPLEX IN VALLINGBY, STOCKHOLM (BARNFAMILJER I HOGHUS OCH TREVANINGS LAGHUS INVALLINGBY)., Stockholm. (37).

Dalban, C. 1977
REMARKS ON THE ECCS RECOMMENDATIONS AND ON THE DRAFT OF THE CMEA SPECIFICATIONS. In Final Report, Colloquium on Stability of Steel Structures, pages 13-24. Hungarian Academy of Sciences, Budapest. (16).

Dalgliesh, W. A. 1978
MEASUREMENTS OF WIND INDUCED DISPLACEMENTS OF A 57-STORY BUILDING IN TORONTO CANADA. In Proceedings of 3rd Colloquium on Industrial Aerodynamics, Part 2, pages 67-78. Building Aerodynamics, Aachen, Germany. (CL-3).

Dalgliesh, W. A. 1980
ASSESSMENT OF WIND LOADS FOR GLAZING DESIGN. In Proceedings of IAHR/IUTAM Symposium, University of Karlsruhe, Germany, pages 696-708., Springer-Verlag.

Dalgliesh, W. 1982
COMPARISON OF MODEL AND FULL-SCALE TESTS OF THE COMMERCE COURT BUILDING IN TORONTO. In Proceedings of International Workshop on Wind Tunnel Modeling Criteria and Techniques in Civil Engineering Applications, pages 575-589. National Bureau of Standards, U.S. Department of Commerce, Gaithersburg, MD.

Dalgliesh, W. A., Templin, J. T. and Cooper, K. R. 1979
COMPARISONS OF WIND TUNNEL AND FULLSCALE BUILDING SURFACE PRESSURES WITH EMPHASIS ON PEAKS. In Proceedings of Fifth International Conference on Wind Engineering, pages 553-566. Pergamon Press, Fort Collins, Col. (CL-7).

Danay, A., Gellert, M. and Gluck, J. 1974
THE AXIAL STRAIN EFFECTS ON LOAD DISTRIBUTION IN NONSYMMETRIC TIER BUILDINGS. Building Science 9:29-38. (21C).

Darwin, D. and Pecknold, D. A. 1976
ANALYSIS OF RC SHEAR PANELS UNDER CYCLIC LOADING. Journal of the Structural Division, ASCE, Proc. Paper 11896 102(ST2):355-369. (24).

Davenport, A. G. and Tschanz, T. 1981
THE RESPONSE OF TALL BUILDINGS TO WIND: EFFECTS OF WIND DETECTION AND THE DIRECT MEASUREMENT OF DYNAMIC FORCE. In Proceedings of the Fourth U.S. National Conference on Wind Engineering Research, pages 205-223. University of Washington, Seattle, Washington.

Davies, S. R. and El Traify, E. A. 1982
BIAXIAL BENDING OF REINFORCED BRICK MASONRY COLUMNS. Proceedings of British Ceramics Society. (27).

Dayaratnam, P. 1981
DURABILITY OF REINFORCED BRICKWORK. In International Seminar/Workshop on Planning, Design Construction of Load Bearing Brick Buildings for Developing Countries, Delhi, India, pages 283-293. University of Edinburgh, Delhi, India. (27).

Degenkolb, H. 1977
EARTHQUAKE FORCES ON TALL STRUCTURES. Booklet 2717A, Bethlehem Steel, Bethlehem, PA. (S41C).

Deo, R. B. and Craig, J. I. 1978a
FULL SCALE MEASUREMENTS OF CLADDING PRESSURE. 3rd U.S. National Conference on Wind Engineering Research, University of Florida, Gainesville. (17).

Deo, R. B. and Craig, J. I. 1978b
WIND LOAD CASUALITY FOR DYNAMIC RESPONSE OF WINDOWS. 3rd U.S. National Conference on Wind Engineering Research, University of Florida, Gainesville. (17).

Derecho, A. T., Ghosh, S. K., Iqbal, M., Freskakis, G. N. and Fintel, M. 1978
STRUCTURAL WALLS IN EARTHQUAKE-RESISTANT BUILDINGS—ANALYTICAL INVESTIGATION: DYNAMIC ANALYSIS OF ISOLATED STRUCTURAL WALLS—PARAMETRIC STUDIES. Report to the National Science Foundation ENV74-14766, Portland Cement Association, Skokie, Il. (22).

Derecho, A. T., Fugelso, L. E. and Fintel, M. 1977
STRUCTURAL WALLS IN EARTHQUAKE RESISTANT BUILDINGS, DYNAMIC ANALYSIS OF ISOLATED STRUCTURAL WALLS—INPUT MOTIONS. Report to the National Science Foundation ENV74-14766, Portland Cement Association, Skokie, Il. (22).

Desai, C. S. and Christian, J. T. 1977
NUMERICAL METHODS IN GEOTECHNICAL ENGINEERING. Mc-Graw-Hill Book Co., New York. (11).

DeVekey, R. 1981
DURABILITY OF REINFORCED MASONRY. In Symposium on Reinforced & Prestressed Masonry, pages 53-59. Institution of Structural Engineers, London, England. (27).

Dietrich, L., Miastkowski, J. and Szezpinski, W. 1970
ULTIMATE STRENGTH OF STRUCTURAL COMPONENTS (ELEMENTS). Panstwowe Wydawnictwo Naukowe, Warsaw. (15).

Dill, F. H. 1960
STRUCTURAL STEEL AFTER A FIRE. In National Engineering Conference, pages 78-80. American Institute of Steel Construction, (8A).

Drysdale, R. G. 1976
DESIGN OF MASONRY WALLS AND COLUMNS FOR COMBINED AXIAL LOAD AND BENDING MOMENT. In Proceedings of 1st Canadian Masonry Symposium, pages 394-408. University of Calgary, Calgary, Canada. (27).

Dubas, P. 1977
ULTIMATE STRENGTH OF LATERALLY BRACED TRUSSES. Final Report, Int. Colloquium on Stability of Steel Structures, Liege (16).

Dufau, P. 1974
TRAVELS? TRIPS? (LES TOURS). Travaux :10-11. (37).

Duszek, M. 1973
STABILITY OF RIGID PLASTIC STRUCTURES AT THE YIELD POINT LOAD. Eten de l Academic Polonaise des Sciences CL.IV(23):79-87. (15).

Duszek, M. 1974
STABILITY OF RIGID-PLASTIC FRAMES AT THE YIELD POINT LOAD. In Proceedings of Regional Conference on Planning and Design of Tall Buildings, Vol. 2, pages 97-112., Warsaw, Poland. (15).

Dwight, J. B. and Young, B. W. 1971
COMPARISON OF EUROPEAN AND BRITISH COLUMN CURVES. Report to Committee 8, Stability of ECCS, ECCS. (16).

Dye, R. C. F. 1980
COMPARISON OF FULL-SCALE AND WIND-TUNNEL MODEL MEASUREMENTS OF GROUND WINDS AROUND A TOWER BUILDING. Journal of Wind Engineering and Industrial Aerodynamics (6):311-326. (CL-7).

Eastman, C. 1981
RECENT DEVELOPMENTS IN REPRESENTATION IN THE SCIENCE OF DESIGN. In Proceedings of Eighteenth Design Automation Conference, pages 13-21., Nashville, Tenn. (35).

Eatherley, M. J. 1977
THE DESIGN AND CONSTRUCTION OF BUSH LANE HOUSE. The Structural Engineer 55(2):75-85. (8A).

ECCS 1974
FIRE SAFETY IN CONSTRUCTIONAL STEELWORK. Technical Report CECM-III-74-2E, European Convention for Constructional Steelwork, Committee TC3. (8A).

ECCS 1975
STABILITY RECOMMENDATIONS FOR DESIGN. Technical Report, European Convention for Constructional Steelwork, Committee 8. (16).
ECCS 1975 and 1978
EUROPEAN RECOMMENDATIONS FOR STEEL CONSTRUCTION. (16).
ECCS 1976
MANUAL ON THE STABILITY OF STEEL STRUCTURES European Convention for Constructional Steelwork, Second International Colloquium on Stability, Tokyo, 1976. (16E).
ECCS-EG-76-1E 1976
RECOMMENDATIONS FOR STEEL CONSTRUCTIONS. European Convention for Constructional Steelwork, pages 204-271. (16).
ECCS 1980
EUROPEAN RECOMMENDATIONS FOR THE CALCULATION OF THE FIRE RESISTANCE OF LOAD-BEARING STEEL ELEMENTS AND STRUCTURAL ASSEMBLIES EXPOSED TO THE STANDARD FIRE. Technical Report First Edition, ECCS, Committee TC3. (8A).
ECCS (to be published)
EUROPEAN RECOMMENDATIONS FOR THE FIRE SAFETY OF STEEL STRUCTURES. PART 1. CALCULATION OF THE FIRE RESISTANCE OF LOAD BEARING ELEMENTS AND STRUCTURAL ASSEMBLIES EXPOSED TO THE STANDARD FIRE. Technical Report, European Convention for Constructional Steelwork. (8A).
Elias, Z. M. and Georgiadis, C. 1979
FLAT SLAB ANALYSIS USNG EQUIVALENT BEAMS. ACI Journal 76(10):1063-1078. (CB-5).
Ellingwood, B. 1978
RELIABILITY BASIS OF LOAD AND RESISTANCE FACTORS FOR REINFORCED CONCRETE DESIGN. Building Science Series 110, National Bureau of Standards, Washington, D.C. (5).
Ellingwood, B. 1982
ASSESSMENT OF CURRENT DESIGN PRACTICE. Journal of the Structural Division, ASCE. (5).
Emery, A. F., Heerwagen, D. R., Johnson, B. R., Kippenhan, C. J. and Lakin, J. E. 1982
A STUDY METHOD FOR EVALUATING FENESTRATION ASSEMBLIES CONSIDERING THE CONTROL OF SOLAR HEAT GAIN AND THE PROVISION OF DAYLIGHTING. In Seventh National Passive Solar Conference, Knoxville, Tenn. (40B).
Emery, A. F., Kippenhan, C. J., Heerwagen, D. R. and Varey, G. B. 1982
THE SIMULATION OF BUILDING HEAT TRANSFER FOR PASSIVE SOLAR SYSTEMS. Energy and Buildings (40).
Emery, A. F., Kippenhan, C. J. and Johnson, B. R. 1979
THE UWENSOL USER'S MANUAL. Inst. Environmental Studies 4.1, University of Washington. (40).
Emery, A. F., Kippenhan, C. J. and Johnson, B. R. 1981
THE USE OF COST-EFFECTIVENESS AND COMFORT BASES.... In Proceedings for the 6th National Pass. Sol. Conference, pages 256-260., (40).
Engineering Sciences Data Unit 1972
CHARACTERISTICS OF WIND SPEED IN THE LOWER LAYERS OF THE ATMOSPHERE NEAR THE GROUND. Data Item 72026.
ENR 1981
PUMPED CONCRETE CLIMBS 75 FLIGHTS. Engineering News Record 206(10):28-29. (3).
Evans, R. A. and Lee, B. E. 1981
THE ASSESSMENT OF DYNAMIC WIND LOADS ON A TALL BUILDING: A COMPARISON OF MODEL AND FULL-SCALE RESULTS. In Preprints of the Fourth U.S. National Conference on Wind Engineering Research, University of Washington, Seattle, Washington.
Everett, T. W. and Lawson, T. V. 1978
PRESENTATION AND DISCUSSION OF RESULTS AS PERFORMED AT UNIVERSITY OF BRISTOL, U.K. Journal of Industrial Aerodynamics (3):215-225. (CL-7).

Federal Capital Development Authority, The 1980
THE FEDERAL CAPITAL DEVELOPMENT AUTHORITY NEW FEDERAL CAPITAL— ABUJA, MASTER PLAN PHASE 1 REPORT., Nigeria. (29).

Federal Construction Council 1974
EXPANSION JOINTS IN BUILDINGS. Technical Report 65, National Academy of Sciences—
National Research Council, Washington, D.C. (S41).

Federal Ministry of Economic Development, The 1970
SECOND NATIONAL DEVELOPMENT PLAN.Longman Nigeria, Federal Republic of Nigeria, Lagos. (29).

Federal Ministry of Economic Development Lagos, The 1975
THIRD NATIONAL DEVELOPMENT PLAN (1975-1980).Longman Nigeria, Federal Republic of Nigeria, Lagos. (29).

Federal Ministry of Planning Lagos, The 1981
FEDERAL REPUBLIC OF NIGERIA—OUTLINE OF THE FOURTH NATIONAL DEVELOPMENT PLAN (1981-1985). Longman Nigeria, Federal Republic of Nigeria, Lagos. (29).

Ferry Borges, J. and Castanheta, M. 1971
STRUCTURAL SAFETY, 2ND EDITION. Course 101, Laboratorio Nacional de Engenharia Civil, Lisbon, Portugal. (5).

Fintel, M. and Ghosh, S. K. 1980
SEISMIC RESISTANCE OF A 16-STORY COUPLED WALL STRUCTURE: A CASE STUDY USING INELASTIC DYNAMIC ANALYSIS. Engineering Bulletin EB082.01D, Portland Cement Association, Skokie, Il. (22).

Fintel, M. and Ghosh, S. K. 1981
THE STRUCTURAL FUSE: AN INELASTIC APPROACH TO SEISMIC DESIGN OF BUILDINGS. Civil Engineering, ASCE 51(1):48-51. (22).

Fintel, M. and Ghosh, S. K. 1982
EXPLICIT INELASTIC DYNAMIC DESIGN PROCEDURE FOR ASEISMIC STRUCTURES. ACI Journal, Proceedings, American Concrete Institute 79(2):110-118. (22).

Finzi, L. 1977
BUILT-UP MEMBERS, GENERAL REPORT, CONCLUSIONS. In Final Report, Second Int. Colloquium on Stability of Steel Structures, pages 67-70, 79. ECCS/IABSE/SSRC/CRC Japan, Liege. (16).

Ford, J. S., Chang, D. C. and Breen, J. E. 1981
DESIGN INDICATIONS FROM TESTS OF UNBRACED MULTIPANEL FRAMES. Concrete International, ACI 3(3):37-47. (21D).

Foster, D. 1981
ASPECTS OF DURABILITY OF CLAY MASONRY. In Symposium on Reinforced & Prestressed Masonry, pages 60-66. Institution of Structural Engineers, London. (27).

Fransson, B. 1977
A GENERALIZED FINITE STRIP METHOD FOR PLATE AND WALL STRUCTURES. Publication No. 77:1, Department of Structural Mechanics, Chalmers University of Technology, Gateberg, Sweden. (21C).

Freeman, S. A., Czarnecki, R. M. and Honda, K. K. 1980
SIGNIFICANCE OF STIFFNESS ASSUMPTIONS ON LATERAL FORCE CRITERIA. Publication SP-63, American Concrete Institute. (24,21D).

Freudenthal, A. M., Garrelts, J. and Shinozuka, M. 1966
THE ANALYSIS OF STRUCTURAL SAFETY. Journal of the Structural Division, ASCE, Proc. Paper 4682 92(ST1):267-325. (5).

Frey, F. 1969
EFFECT OF COLD-STRAIGHTENING ON THE STRENGTH OF WIDE-FLANGE SHAPES. IABSE Publications, Zurich 29-II. (16).

Fruin, J. J. 1970
PEDESTRIAN PLANNING AND DESIGN Library of Congress, Catalogue No. 70-159312, Metropolitan Association of Urban Design and Environmental Planning, Inc., New York, NY, 1970. (2A).

Fukuchi, Y. 1969
FLANGE BUCKLING AND ULTIMATE LOAD OF BEAMS UNDER MOMENT GRADIENT (IN JAPANESE). Translation of the A. I. J. (166). (16).

Fukumoto, Y., Kajita, N. and Aoki, T. 1976
EVALUATION OF COLUMN CURVES BASED ON PROBABILISTIC CONCEPT. In Preliminary Report, Second Int. Colloquium on Stability, Tokyo, pages 1-37. ECCS/IABSE/SSRC/CRC, (16).

Fukumoto, Y. and Kubo, M. 1977
A SURVEY OF TEST ON LATERAL BUCKLING STRENGTH OF BEAMS. In Preliminary Report, Second International Colloquium, Stability of Steel Structures, pages 233-240. ECCS and IABSE, Liege. (16).

Fuller, G. R. 1978a
PROGRESSIVE COLLAPSE PROVISIONS FOR MULTI-STORY BUILDINGS. In Proceedings of Third International Symposium of CIB S-41 and Joint Committee on Tall Buildings, pages 42-63. Center Research and Design Institute for Dwellings, Moscow, USSR. (21E).

Fuller, G. R. 1978b
SEISMIC RESISTANCE VS. PROGRESSIVE COLLAPSE OF PRECAST CONCRETE PANEL BUILDINGS. In Proceedings of Workshop on Earthquake-Resistant Reinforced Concrete Building Construction, Vol. 3, pages 1852 . University of California, Berkeley, California. (21E).

Furlong, R.W. 1976
AISC COLUMN DESIGN LOGIC MAKES SENSE FOR COMPOSITE COLUMNS, TOO. Engineering Journal, AISC 13(1):1-7. (S41).

Gage-Babcock and Associates, Inc. 1973
AUTOMOBILE BURN-OUT TEST IN AN OPEN-AIR PARKING STRUCTURE. Report No. 7328, Gage-Babcock and Associates, Westchester, Il. (8A).

Galambos, T. V. 1963
INELASTIC LATERAL BUCKLING OF BEAMS. Journal of the Structural Division, ASCE Proc. Paper 3683 39(ST5):217-242. (16).

Galambos, T. V. 1977
LATERALLY UNSUPPORTED BEAMS. In Introductory Report, II International Colloquium on Stability, pages 365-373. ECCS, Liege. (16).

Galambos, T. V. and Ravindra, M. K. 1978
LOAD AND RESISTANCE FACTOR DESIGN. Journal of the Structural Division, ASCE, Proc. Paper 14008 (ST9):1335-1336. (5).

Gallegos, H. and Casabonne, C. 1980
TENSILE STRENGTH OF SAND-LIME AND CLAY BRICK MASONRY (RESISTENCIA A LA TRACCION DE ALABANILERIA DE ARCILLA Y SILICO-CALCAREA). El Ingeniero Civil (8):22-41. (CB-13).

Gandemer, J. 1978
AERODYNAMIC STUDIES OF BUILT-UP AREAS MADE BY C.S.T.B. AT NANTES, FRANCE. Journal of Industrial Aerodynamics (3):227-240. (CL-7).

Gates, W. E. 1978
THE ART OF MODELING BUILDINGS FOR DYNAMIC ANALYSIS. In Proceedings of a Workshop on Earthquake-Resistant Reinforced Concrete Building Construction, pages 857 886. University of California, Berkeley. (21D).

Geilinger, W. and Bryl, S. 1962
FIRE SAFETY OF STEEL STRUCTURES (FEUERSICHERHEIT DER STAHLKON-STRUKITIONEN). Heft 22, Vol. 4, Schweizer Stahlbauverband. (8A).

Georgiou, P. N. and Vickery, B. J. 1979
WIND LOADS ON BUILDING FRAMES. In Proceedings of Fifth International Conference on Wind Engineering, pages 421-434. Pergamon Press, Fort Collins, Col. (CL-7).

Georgiou, P. N., Davenport, A. G. and Vickery, B. J. 1983
DESIGN WIND LOADS IN REGIONS DOMINATED BY TROPICAL CYCLONES. In Proceedings of Sixth International Conference on Wind Engineering, Gold Coast, Australia.

Gergely, P. 1982
THE ROLE OF COVER AND BAR SPACING IN REINFORCED CONCRETE. SP-72: American Concrete Institute, Detroit, (24).

Gero, J. S. and Radford, A. 1981
THE DESIGN IN COMPUTER AIDED DESIGN. In Proceedings of First International Conference on Computing in Civil Engineering, ASCE, pages 876-890., New York, NY. (35).

Gesund, H. 1980
DESIGN FOR PUNCHING STRENGTH OF SLABS AT INTERIOR COLUMNS. Pergamon Press, Oxford, pages 173-184. (21D,22).

Gesund, H. 1981
LIMIT DESIGN OF SLABS FOR CONCENTRATED LOADS. Journal of the Structural Division, Proc. ASCE 107(ST9):1839-1856. (CB-11,CB-6).

Gesund, H. and Goli, H. B. 1979
LIMIT ANALYSIS OF FLAT SLAB BUILDINGS FOR LATERAL LOADS. Journal of the Structural Division, ASCE 105(ST11):2187-2202. (CB-11,CB-6).

Gesund, H. and Goli, H. B. 1980
LOCAL FLEXURAL STRENGTH OF SLABS AT INTERIOR COLUMNS. Journal of the Structural Division, Proc. ASCE 106(ST5):1063-1078. (CB-11,CB-6).

Ghosh, S. K. and Fintel, M. 1979
MODELLING OF FRAME-SHEAR WALL STRUCTURES FOR STATIC AND DYNAMIC ANALYSIS. In Proceedings, Symposium on Behavior of Building Systems and Building Components. Vanderbilt University, Nashville, Tenn. (22).

Gjelsvik, A. 1973
INTERACTION BETWEEN FRAMES AND PRECAST PANEL WALLS. Journal of the Structural Division, ASCE 100(ST2):405-426. (17).

Giddings, T. W. 1978
FIRE RESISTANT CONSTRUCTION IN SHS—TODAY AND TOMORROW. Building Specification 11:65-72. (8A).

Girgis, A. and Stafford Smith, B. 1979
THE TORSION ANALYSIS OF TALL BUILDING CORES PARTIALLY CLOSED BY BEAMS. Behaviour of Building Systems and Building Components, Vanderbilt University, Nashville, Tenn. (21C).

Glogau, O. A. 1977
DAMAGE CONTROL IN NEW ZEALAND PUBLIC BUILDINGS THROUGH SEPA-RATION OF NON-STRUCTURAL COMPONENTS. In Proceedings of Sixth World Conference on Earthquake Engineering, Vol. 5, pages 43-48., Sarita Prakashan, Meerut, India. (17).

Gluck, J. 1973
ELASTO-PLASTIC ANALYSIS OF COUPLED SHEAR WALLS. Jnl. Struct. Div., ASCE 99(ST8):1743-1760. (21C).

Gluck, J., Reinhorn, A. and Rutenberg, A. 1979
DYNAMIC TORSIONAL COUPLING IN TALL BUILDING STRUCTURES. In Proceedings of Institute of Civil Engineers, Part 2, Vol. 67, pages 411-424., (CL-2,CB-9).

Godfrey, R. S. 1981
BUILDING CONSTRUCTION COST DATA.R. S. Means Co., Inc., Kingston, Mass. (40).

Goeben, H. E. 1977
CONTRIBUTION TO THE STABILITY OF CRANE BEAMS (IN GERMAN). In Pro-ceedings of the Regional Colloquium on Stability of Steel Structures, pages 193-208., Budapest. (16).

Goldberg, A. and Sharpe, R. 1977
PROVISIONS FOR SEISMIC DESIGN OF NONSTRUCTURAL BUILDING COMPO-NENTS AND SYSTEMS. In Proceedings of Sixth World Conference on Earthquake Engineering, Vol. 12, pages 1-6., Sarita Prakashan, Meerut, India. (17).

Goldberger, P. 1981
A NEW AMERICAN SKYSCRAPER. New York Times Magazine :68-73. (31).

Goli, H. B. and Gesund, H. 1979
LINEARITY IN LIMIT DESIGN OF ORTHOTROPIC SLABS. Journal of the Structural Division, Proc. ASCE 105(ST10):1901-1915. (CB-11,CB-6).

Goli, H. B. and Gesund, H. 1980
YIELD LINE ANALYSIS OF ORTHOTROPICALLY REINFORCED EXTERIOR PANELS OF FLAT SLAB FLOORS. Pergamon Press, Oxford, pages 149-159. (CB-11,CB-6).

Goodno, B. J. 1978
RESPONSE OF GLASS CLADDING IN HIGHRISE BUILDINGS. 3rd U.S. National Conference on Wind Engineering Research, University of Florida, Gainesville. (17).

Goodno. B. J. 1979
GLASS CURTAIN WALL ELEMENTS: PROPERTIES AND BEHAVIOR. Journal of the Structural Division, ASCE Proc. Paper 14656 105(ST6):1121-1136. (17).

Goodno, B. J. and Gere, J. M. 1976
ANALYSIS OF SHEAR CORES USING SUPERELEMENTS. Journal of Structural Division, ASCE 102(ST1):267-283. (CB-5).

Goodno, B. J. and Palsson, H. 1981
TORSIONAL RESPONSE OF PARTIALLY-CLAD STRUCTURES. In Proceedings of Conference on Earthquakes and Earthquake Engineering: The Eastern U.S., Vol. 2, pages 859-877. Ann Arbor Science Publishers-Ann Arbor, Mich. 48106, Knoxville, Tenn. (17).

Goodno, B. J. and Will, K. M. 1978
DYNAMIC ANALYIS OF A HIGHRISE BUILDING INCLUDING CLADDING—STRUCTURE INTERACTION EFFECTS. In Proceedings of ASCE Specialty Conference on Computing in Civil Engineering, pages 623-638. ASCE, Atlanta, Georgia. (17).

Goodno, B. J. and Will, K. M. 1978
DYNAMIC ANALYSIS OF A HIGHRISE BUILDING INCLUDING CLADDING—STRUCTURE INTERACTION EFFECTS. In Proceedings of ASCE Specialty Conference on Computing in Civil Engineering, pages 623-638. ASCE, Atlanta, Georgia. (17).

Goodno, B. J., Will, K. M. and Craig, J. I. 1979
ANALYSIS OF CLADDING ON TALL BUILDINGS. ASCE National Convention and Exposition, Session on Developments in Methods of Structural Analysis, Atlanta, GA. (17).

Goodno, B. J., Will, K. M. and Palsson, H. 1980
EFFECT OF CLADDING ON BUILDING RESPONSE TO MODERATE GROUND MOTION. In Proceedings of Seventh World Conference on Earthquake Engineering, Vol. 7, pages 449-456., Istanbul, Turkey. (17).

Goschy, B. 1978
SOIL-FOUNDATION-STRUCTURE INTERACTION. Jnl. Struct. Div., ASCE 104(ST5): 749-761. (21C).

Government of Iran 1970
MINIMUM DESIGN LOADS IN BUILDINGS AND OTHER STRUCTURES. Ministry of Economics, ISIRI-519. (S41).

Government of Iran 1979
GEOLOGIC SURVEY SEISMOTECTONIC MAP OF IRAN. Report No. 39 Ministry of Industry and Mines. (S41).

Gregorian, Z. B., 1977
STRUCTURAL BEHAVIOR OF HOTEL GAMERON. During the Bandar Abbas Earthquake of 1977. (S41).

Griffin, O. M. 1979
UNIVERSAL SIMILARITY IN THE WAKES OF STATIONARY AND VIBRATING BLUFF STRUCTURES. In Proceedings of Fifth International Conference on Wind Engineering, pages 607-618. Pergamon Press, Fort Collins, Col. (CL-7).

Grossman, D. A. 1979
THE FUTURE OF NEW YORK CITY'S CAPITAL PLANT.The Urban Institute, Washington, D.C. (38).

Gulkan, P., Mayes, R. L., Clough, R. W. and Hendrickson, R. 1978
AN EXPERIMENTAL INVESTIGATION ON THE SEISMIC BEHAVIOR OF SINGLE-STORY MASONRY HOUSES. In Proceedings of North American Masonry Conference, Paper No. 54, pages 20. University of Colorado, Boulder, Col. (27).

Ha, K. H., Fazio, P. and Moselhi, O. 1978
ORTHOTROPIC MEMBRANE FOR TALL BUILDING ANALYSIS. Journal of Structural Division, ASCE 104(ST9):1495-1505. (CB-5,SB-2).

Haaijer, G., Carskaddan, P. S. and Grubb, M. A. 1981
ECCENTRIC LOAD TEST OF ANGLE COLUMN SIMULATED WITH MSC/NASTRAN FINITE ELEMENT PROGRAM. In Proceedings of SSRC, pages 61-63., (16).

Halasz, O. and Ivanyi, M. 1979
TESTS WITH SIMPLE ELASTIC-PLASTIC FRAMES. Periodica Polytechnica, Budapest 23(3-4):151-183. (16).

Halldane, J. F., Kadlec, J. F., Meckler, G. and Silverio, H. 1977
RECOMMENDATIONS FOR ENERGY CONSERVATION ACTIONS: SOCIAL SECURITY ADMINISTRATION, WOODLAWN COMPLEX. Technical Report PB271426/AS, National Technical Information Service, Springfield, Va. (40).

Halpin, D. and Woodhead, R. 1976
DESIGN OF PROCESS AND CONSTRUCTION OPERATIONS.Wiley & Sons (PC-14).

Halpin, D. and Woodhead, R. 1980
CONSTRUCTION MANAGEMENT.Wiley & Sons (PC-14).

Hamid, A. A. and Drysdale, R. G. 1980
STRENGTH OF CONCRETE MASONRY UNDER BIAXIAL STRESSES. In Proceedings of Conference on Progress on Masonry Construction, Paper No. 14, pages 14-1–14-5., Marina del Ray, Calif. (27).

Haris, A. A. K. 1978
APPROXIMATE STIFFNESS ANALYSIS OF HIGH-RISE BUILDINGS. Jnl. Struct. Div., ASCE 104(ST4):681-696. (21C).

Harman, D. J. and Walker, W. H. 1975
ANALYSIS OF TALL BUILDINGS USING MEMBER GROUPS. Journal of Structural Division, ASCE 101(ST3):567-583. (CB-5).

Hatzinikolas, M., Longworth, J. and Warwaruk, J. 1978
CONCRETE MASONRY WALLS. Structural Engineering Report No. 70, University of Alberta. (27).

Hatzinikolas, M., Longworth, J. and Warwaruk, J. 1980
THE ANALYSIS OF ECCENTRICALLY LOADED MASONRY WALLS BY THE MOMENT MAGNIFIER METHOD. In Proceedings of 2nd Canadian Masonry Symposium, pages 245-258., Ottawa, Canada. (27).

Hawranek, R. 1977
RELIABILITY CALIBRATION FOR STEEL COLUMNS. In Final Report, Second Int. Colloquium on Stability of Steel Structures, pages 53-56. ECCS/IABSE/SSRC/CRC Japan, Liege. (16).

Hawranek,R. 1978
OPTIMIZATION OF STRENGTH COMPUTATIONS PARTICULARLY FOR THE ULTIMATE STRENGTH OF COLD-FORMED COLUMNS (OPTIMIERUNG VON SICHERHEITSNACHWEISEN MIT BESONDEREM BEZUG AUF DEN TRAGSICHERHEITSNACHWEIS VON STUTZEN AUS FORMSTAHL). Berichte zur Zuverlassigkeitstheirie der Bauwerke, Heft 34, Techn. Universitat Munchen. (16).

Hayfield, F. 1979
BASIC FACTORS FOR A SUCCESSFUL PROJECT. In Proceedings of 6th Internet Congress, pages . VDI Verlag, Dusseldorf, Germany. (PC-11).

Heerwagen, D. R., Emery, F. A., Kippenhan, J. C. and Varey, B. G. 1980
DEVELOPING OFFICE DESIGN AND OPERATION STRATEGIES USING UWENSOL AND THE COMFORT ROUTINE. ASHRAE Transactions 86(1). (40).

Hegemeir, G. A., Nunn, R. O. and Arya, S. K. 1978
BEHAVIOR OF CONCRETE MASONRY UNDER BIAXIAL STRESSES. In Proceedings of North American Masonry Conference, Paper No. 1, pages 28. University of Colorado, Boulder, Col. (27).

Hendry, A. W. 1981
THE SHEAR STRENGTH OF REINFORCED BRICKWORK. In Proceedings of Symposium on Reinforced and Prestressed Masonry, pages 29-37. Institution of Structural Engineers, London. (27).

Herlyn, U. 1970
LIVING IN HIGH-RISES (WOHNEN IM HOCHHAUS).Kramer Verlag, Stuttgart. (37).

Herrenkohl, R. C. 1976
SOCIAL EFFECTS OF THE ENVIRONMENT. (Habitat Forum) 1-160 in Planning and Design of Tall Buildings, Joint Committee on Tall Buildings, Bethlehem, PA. (37).

Holmes, J. D. 1979
MEAN AND FLUCTUATING INTERNAL PRESSURES INDUCED BY WIND. In Proceedings of Fifth International Conference on Wind Engineering, pages 435-450. Pergamon Press, Fort Collins, Col. (CL-7).

Horne, M. R. 1963
ELASTIC-PLASTIC FAILURE LOADS OF PLANE FRAMES. Proceeding Roy. Soc., A., London, England 274(1358):343-364. (16).

Hsieh, S. S., Ting, E. C. and Chen, W. F. 1982
A PLASTIC-FRACTURE MODEL FOR CONCRETE. International Journal of Solids and Structures 18(3):181-197. (CB-9).

Hunyadi, F. 1958
LATERAL-TORSIONAL BUCKLING OF STEEL BEAMS WITH CONSTANT AND VARIABLE CROSS-SECTIONS (IN HUNGARIAN). EKME Tudomanyos Kozlemenyek 4(1):11-38. (16).

Huxtable, A. L. 1981
IS MODERN ARCHITECTURE DEAD?. The New York Review of Books 28:17-20. (31).

IABSE-ECCS-SSRC-CRC Japan 1981
STABILITY OF METAL STRUCTURES, A WORLD VIEW. In Proceedings of 2nd International Colloquium on Stability (in preparation), pages 90-126,154-196. IABSE-ECCS-SSRC-CRC, (16).

IAEE 1974
PROCEEDINGS OF FIFTH WORLD CONFERENCE ON EARTHQUAKE ENGINEERING, Rome, Italy. (CL-2).

IAEE 1977
PROCEEDINGS OF SIXTH WORLD CONFERENCE ON EARTHQUAKE ENGINEERING, New Delhi. (CL-2).

IAEE 1980
EARTHQUAKE RESISTANT REGULATIONS – A WORD LIST. (CL-2).

IAEE 1981
PROCEEDINGS OF SEVENTH WORLD CONFERENCE ON EARTHQUAKE ENGINEERING, Istanbul. (CL-2).

ICBO 1979
UNIFORM BUILDING CODE. International Conference of Building Officials, Whittier, California. (21D).

ICBO 1982
UNIFORM BUILDING CODE. International Conference of Building Officials, Whittier, Calif. (15).

Iffland, J. S. B. 1981
STABILITY OF TALL STRUCTURES. Paper presented at the AISC National Engineering Conference, AISC. (16).

Ikenouchi, M. 1979
EXPERIMENTAL AND NUMERICAL STUDIES ON THE AERODYNAMIC INSTABILITY OF TOWER-LIKE STRUCTURES. In Proceedings of Fifth International Conference on Wind Engineering, Vol. 2, pages 747-756. Pergamon Press, Fort Collins, Col. (CL 7).

Inowe, T., Kato, B. and Akiyama, H. 1972
CYCLIC BEHAVIOR OF H-SECTION MEMBERS SUBJECT TO COMBINED BENDING AND AXIAL COMPRESSION (IN JAPANESE). In Proceedings of Symposium of Kanto-Branch of A. I. J., Annual Report, pages 165-168., (16).

Institution of Civil Engineers 1980
DESIGN PARAMETERS IN GEOTECHNICAL ENGINEERING. In Proceedings of 7th European Conference on Soil Mechanics and Foundation Engineering, Institution of Civil Engineers, London, England. (11).

ISO 1975
FIRE RESISTANCE TESTS-ELEMENTS OF BUILDING CONSTRUCTION. Technical Report IS 834, International Standards Organization, 1975-11-01. (8A).

Isyumov, N. 1978
STUDIES OF THE PEDESTRIAN LEVEL WIND ENVIRONMENT AT THE BOUNDARY LAYER WIND TUNNEL LABORATORY OF THE UNIVERSITY OF WESTERN ONTARIO. Journal of Industrial Aerodynamics (3):187-200. (CL-7).

Ivanyi, M. 1974
EXPERIMENTS ON PLASTIC BUCKLING OF STEEL BEAMS. Periodica Polytechnica 18(3):139-167. (16).

Ivanyi, M. 1981
INTERACTION BETWEEN STRENGTH AND STABILITY PHENOMENA (IN HUNGARIAN). PhD thesis, Presented for the degree of Doctor of Sciences, Budapest. (16).

Iyengar, H. S. 1977
STATE-OF-THE-ART REPORT ON COMPOSITE OR MIXED STEEL-CONCRETE CON-
STRUCTION FOR BUILDINGS. American Society of Civil Engineering, New York,
New York. (S41).

Jacobs, A. B. 1980
THEY'RE CLOSING THE DOORS TO DOWNTOWN. Urban Design International. (31).
Jeary, A. P. and Ellis, B. R. 1979
THE RESPONSE OF A 190 METRE TALL BUILDING AND THE RAMIFICATIONS
FOR THE PREDICTION OF BEHAVIOR CAUSED BY WIND LOADING. In Proceed-
ings of Fifth International Conference on Wind Engineering, Vol. 2, pages 1357-1370.
Pergamon Press, Fort Collins, Col. (CL-7).
Jeary, A. P., Lee, B. E. and Sparks, P. R. 1979
THE DETERMINATION OF MODAL WIND LOADS FROM FULL SCALE BUILDING
RESPONSE MEASUREMENTS. In Proceedings of Fifth International Conference on
Wind Engineering, pages 577-592. Pergamon Press, Fort Collins, Col. (CL-7).
Jencks, C. 1980
SKYSCRPAPERS—SKYCITIES.Academy Editions, London. (31).
Jezek, K. 1937
STABILITY OF COMPRESSED STEEL MEMBERS. Verlag von J. Springer, Wien. (16).
Jirsa, J. O., Lutz, L. A. and Gergely, P. 1979
RATIONALE FOR SUGGESTED DEVELOPMENT, SPLICE, AND STANDARD HOOK
PROVISIONS FOR DEFORMED BARS IN TENSION. Concrete International, ACI 1(7):
47-61. (21D).
Johnson, R. P. 1980
LIMIT STATE DESIGN OF COMPOSITE STRUCTURES FOR BUILDINGS. In Proceed-
ings of U.S.A.-Japan Seminar on Composite Structures and Mixed Structural Systems,
pages 52-61., Gihodo Shuppan, Tokyo, Japan. (SB-9).
Johnson, R. P. and Allison, R. W. 1981
SHRINKAGE AND TENSION STIFFENING IN NEGATIVE MOMENT REGIONS OF
COMPOSITE BEAMS. The Structural Engineer 59B(3):10-16. (SB-9).
Johnson, R. P. and Allison, R. W. (to be published)
CRACKING IN CONCRETE TENSION FLANGES OF COMPOSITE T-BEAMS. The
Structural Engineer. (SB-9).
Johnson, R. P. and Law, C. L. C. 1981
SEMI-RIGID JOINTS FOR COMPOSITE FRAMES. In Proceedings of Conference on Joints
in Structural Steelwork, pages 3.3-3.19. Pentech Press, (SB-9).
Johnson, R. P. and Oehlers, D. J. 1981
ANALYSIS AND DESIGN FOR LONGITUDINAL SHEAR IN COMPOSITE T-BEAMS.
In Proceedings of Institution of Civil Engineers, pages 989-1021., London. (SB-9).
Johnson, R. P. and Oehlers, D. J. 1982
DESIGN FOR LONGITUDINAL SHEAR IN COMPOSITE L-BEAMS. In Proceedings of
Institution of Civil Engineers, Part II, pages 147-170., London. (SB-9).
Johnson, R. P. and Smith, D. G. E. 1980
A SIMPLE DESIGN METHOD FOR COMPOSITE COLUMNS. The Structural Engineer
58A(3):85-93. (SB-9).
Johnston, B. G., ed. 1976
Third Edition: GUIDE TO STABILITY DESIGN CRITERIA FOR METAL STRUCTURES.
SSRC, John Wiley Sons, New York. (16).
Johnston, D. C. and Dwight, J. B. 1976
STUDY OF STRUTS IN WELDED STEEL TRUSSES. Technical Report CUED/C-Struct/
TR.58, Department of Engineering, Cambridge University. (16).
Johnston, B. G., ed. 1976b
GUIDE TO DESIGN CRITERIA FOR METAL COMPRESSION MEMBERS 3rd edition,
SSRC, John Wiley & Sons, Inc., New York, 1976b. (16).
Joint Committee on Composite Structures 1981
COMPOSITE STRUCTURES. In European Convention for Constructional Steelwork, pages
183. IABSE-ECCS-CEB-FIP, Construction Press, London and New York. (SB-9).

Jones & Laughlin Steel Co. 1906
    SAFE LOAD TABLES: 8-INCH & 6-INCH Z-BAR COLUMNS. Technical Report, Jones &
    Laughlin Steel Co. (8A/C).
Jones, S. W., Kirby, P. A. and Nethercot, D. A. 1979
    THE ANALYSIS OF FRAMES WITH SEMI-RIGID CONNECTIONS—A STATE-OF-THE-
    ART REPORT. Technical Report, Department of Civil and Structural Engineering, Uni-
    versity of Sheffield, U.K. (43).
Jones, S. W., Kirby, P. A. and Nethercot, D. A. 1980a
    INFLUENCE OF SEMI-RIGID JOINTS OF STEEL COLUMN BEHAVIOR. In ASCE Con-
    vention and Exposition, Preprint 80-179, Portland, Oregon. (43).
Jones, S. W., Kirby, P. A. and Nethercot, D. A. 1980b
    EFFECT OF SEMI-RIGID CONNECTIONS ON STEEL COLUMN STRENGTH. Journal of
    Constructional Steel Research, Department of Civil Engineering, University of Sheffield,
    UK, 1979 1(1):38-46. (43).
Jones, S. W., Kirby, P. A. and Nethercot, D. A. 1982
    COLUMNS WITH SEMI-RIGID JOINTS. Journal of the Structural Division, ASCE
    108(ST2):361-372. (43).

Kaar, P. H., Hanson, N. W. and Capell, H. T. 1977
    STRESS-STRAIN CHARACTERISTICS OF HIGH-STRENGTH CONCRETE. In Douglas
    McHenry International Symposium on Concrete and Concrete Structures, ACI, Portland
    Cement Association, Detroit, Mich. (21D).
Kabaila, A. P. and Edwardes, R. J. 1979
    HYBRID ELEMENT APPLIED TO SHEAR WALL ANALYSIS. Jnl. Struct. Div., ASCE
    105(ST12):2753-2759. (21C).
Kamei, I. and Maruta, E. 1978
    STUDY OF WIND ENVIRONMENTAL PROBLEMS CAUSED AROUND BUILDINGS IN
    JAPAN. Journal of Industrial Aerodynamics (4):307-331. (CL-7).
Kanaan, A. E. and Powell, G. H. 1975
    A GENERAL PURPOSE COMPUTER PROGRAM FOR INELASTIC DYNAMIC RE-
    SPONSE OF PLANE STRUCTURES (DRAIN-2D) WITH USER'S GUIDE AND SUP-
    PLEMENT. Report No. EERC 73-6, 73-22, University of California, Berkeley. (22).
Kanchi, M. B. and Dar, G. Q. 1973
    TORSION OF RECTANGULAR SHEAR CORES OF TALL BUILDINGS. Paper No. 135,
    Vol. 10, Part 3 3, Bull. Indian Soc. of Earthquake Technology. (21C).
Karaboga, E. 1974
    STRENGTH OF HORIZONTAL JOINTS IN LARGE PANEL STRUCTURES. PhD thesis,
    Imperial College of Science and Technology, London. (21E).
Karaboga, E. 1980
    INTERNAL HORIZONTAL JOINTS OF LARGE PANEL CONSTRUCTIONS. Thesis,
    Karadeniz Technical University, Turkey. (21E).
Kareen, A., Cermak, J. E. and Peterka, J. A. 1979
    CROSSWIND RESPONSE OF HIGH-RISE BUILDINGS. In Proceedings of Fifth Inter-
    national Conference on Wind Engineering, pages 659-672. Pergamon Press, Fort Collins,
    Col. (CL-7).
Karman, T. 1910
    REPORTS ON THE RESEARCH IN THE AREA OF ENGINEERING (MITTEILUNGEN
    UBER FORSCHUNGS ARBEITEN AUF DEN GEBIET DES INGENIEUNWESEUS)
    VDI, Vol. 81. (16).
Kato, B. and Akiyawa, H. 1976
    ADVANCED DESIGN FORMULA FOR LATERAL BUCKLING OF H-SECTIONS. In Pre-
    liminary Report, Second International Colloquium on Stability, pages 95-112. ECCS,
    Tokyo. (16).
Kato, B. 1978
    SAFETY ASSESSMENT OF STEEL BUILDING STRUCTURES AGAINST MOST SEVERE
    EARTHQUAKE (IN JAPANESE). Technical Report, Japan Disaster Prevention Center. (16).
Kato, B. (editor) 1978
    SEISMIC DESIGN OF MULTI-STORY STEEL BUILDINGS (IN JAPANESE).Gihodo
    Press, Tokyo (16).

Kato, B. and Akiyama, H. 1973
THEORETICAL PREDICTION OF THE LOAD-DEFLECTION RELATIONSHIP OF STEEL MEMBERS AND FRAMES. Preliminary Publication, Lisbon, IABSE Symposium. (16).

Kato, B. and Akiyama, H. 1978
DAMAGE DISTRIBUTION LAW OF SHEAR TYPE MULTISTORY STRUCTURES UNDER EARTHQUAKE (IN JAPANESE). Translation of A. I. J. (270). (16).

Kato, B. and Akiyama, H. 1981
SEISMIC DESIGN OF STEEL BUILDINGS. Proceedings of 1981 International Convention and Exhibition, ASCE. (16).

Kato, B., Akiyama, H., Inove, T., Kuwamura, H. and Kitazawa, S. 1976
POST BUCKLING BEHAVIOR OF H-SECTION BEAMS. In Proceedings of the Symposium of Kanto Branch of A. I. J., Annual Report, pages 125-128., (16).

Kato, B., Akiyama, H. and Kitazawa, S. 1978
DEFORMATION CHRACTERISTICS OF BOX-SHAPED MEMBERS SUBJECT TO BUCKLING (IN JAPANESE). Translation of A. I. J. (268). (16).

Kato, B., Akiyama, H. and Obi, Y. 1973
STRENGTH AND DEFORMATION OF H-SECTION MEMBERS (IN JAPANESE). In Proceedings of the Symposium of Kanto Branch of A. I. J., pages 185-188., (16).

Kato, B., Akiyama, H. and Obi, Y. 1977
DEFORMATION CHARACTERISTICS OF H-SHAPED MEMBERS SUBJECT TO BUCKLING (IN JAPANESE). Translation of A. I. J. (257). (16).

Kato, B., Akiyama, H. and Suzuki, H. 1973
LOCAL BUCKLING STRENGTH OF CIRCULAR HOLLOW SECTION MEMBERS (IN JAPANESE). Translation in Japanese of the A. I. J. 204, A. I. J. (16).

Kawai, H., Katsura, J. and Ishizaki, H. 1979
CHARACTERISTICS OF PRESSURE FLUCTUATIONS ON THE WINDWARD WALL OF A TALL BUILDING. In Proceedings of Fifth International Conference, pages 519-528. Pergamon Press, Fort Collins, Col. (CL-7).

Kawecki, J. 1981
APPLICATION OF EXPERIMENTAL INVESTIGATIONS IN MODELLING TOWER STRUCTURES (IN POLISH). In Proceedings of 20th Symposium Modelling in Mechanics, Vol. 1, pages 231-241. The Polish Society of Theoretical and Applied Mechanics, Gliwice-Wisla. (CB-1).

Kessler, K. A. and Schomer 1980
PILE DRIVER NOISE CONTROL. In Inter-Noise 80. International Institute of Noise Control Engineering and Institute of Noise Control Engineering, Miami, Florida. (11).

Khachaturian, N. and Horowitz, B. 1977
PROPERTIES OF OPTIMAL STRUCTURES. In Proceedings of the Symposium on Application of Computer Methods in Engineering, pages 533-542. University of Southern California, Los Angeles, Calif. (14).

Khan, F. R. 1967
OPTIMUM DESIGN OF GLASS IN BUILDINGS. Building Research 4(3):45-48. (17).

Khan, M. A. H. and Stafford Smith, B. 1976
A SIMPLE METHOD OF ANALYSIS FOR DEFLECTIONS AND STRESSES IN WALL-FRAME STRUCTURES. Building and Environment 11:69-78. (CB-5).

Konig, J. A. 1971
A METHOD OF SHAKEDOWN ANALYSIS OF FRAMES AND ARCHES. International Journal of Solids and Structures 7:327-344. (15).

Konig, J. A. 1972
SHAKEDOWN DEFLECTIONS. A FINITE ELEMENT APPROACH. In Proceedings of the Theoretical Applied Mechanics Conference, Vol. 3, pages 65-69. Bulgarian Academy of Science, Sofia. (15).

Koolhaas, R. 1978
DELIRIOUS NEW YORK. Oxford University Press, New York, NY, (31).

Krajcinovic, D. 1981
THE EFFECT OF THE MATERIAL DAMAGE ON THE BUCKLING OF STRUCTURES. In Proceedings, SSRC, pages 31. (16).

Krawinkler, H., Bertero, V. V. and Popov, E. P. 1971
INELASTIC BEHAVIOR OF STEEL BEAM TO COLUMN SUBASSEMBLAGES. EERC
Report No. 17-7, University of California, Berkeley. (15).
Kristek, V. 1979
FOLDED PLATE APPROACH TO ANALYSIS OF SHEAR WALL SYSTEMS AND FRAME
STRUCTURES. In Proceedings for Institute of Civil Engineers, Paper 8289, Vol. 67,
Part 2, pages 1065-1075. Institute of Civil Engineers, (21C).
Kropp, J. and Hildorf, H. K. 1979
EVALUATION OF CORROSION RESISTANCE OF REINFORCEMENT EMBEDDED IN
MASONRY JOINTS. In Proceedings of Vth International Brick & Masonry Conference,
pages 51-54. Brick Institute of America, Washington, D.C. (27).
Kruppa, J. 1977
FIRE RESISTANCE OF STRUCTURES AT NON-UNIFORM TEMPERATURES (RESIS-
TANCE AU FEU DES STRUCTURES METALLIQUE EN TEMPERATURE NON
HOMOGENE). PhD thesis, l'Institut Natonal des Sciences Appliquess de Rennes. (8A).
Kruppa, J. 1980
BEHAVIOR OF EXTERNAL STEEL COLUMNS IN FIRE. Acier-Stahl-Steel 45(2):66-74. (8A).
Kusuda, T. 1981
A COMPARISON OF ENERGY CALCULATION PROCEDURES. ASHRAE Journal
23(8). (40).
Kwiecinski, M. 1979
ULTIMATE LOAD OF REINFORCED CONCRETE SLAB-BEAM SYSTEM. Archiwum
Inzynierii Ladowej, Panstwowe Wydawnictwo Naukowe 25(4):527-538. (15).
Kwiecinski, M. and Wojewodzki, W. 1980
ULTIMATE LOAD DESIGN OF REINFORCED CONCRETE SKEW SLAB-BEAM
SYSTEMS. Archiwum Inzynierii Ladowej, Panstwowe Wydawnictwo Naukowe
26(3):443-459. (15).
Kwok, K. C. S. and Melbourne, W. H. 1979
CROSS-WIND RESPONSE OF STRUCTURES DUE TO DISPLACEMENT DEPENDENT
LOCK-IN EXCITATION. In Proceedings of Fifth International Conference on Wind
Engineering, pages 699-708. Pergamon Press, Fort Collins, Col. (CL-7).

Lagos Executive Development Board 1980
ANNUAL REPORT (1980). Technical Report, Lagos Executive Development Board. (29).
Lam, L. C. H., Lam, R. P. and Mackey, S. 1979
FULL-SCALE MEASUREMENT OF WIND PRESSURE FLUCTUATIONS ON A BLUFF
BUILDING. In Proceedings of Fifth International Conference on Wind Engineering,
pages 567-576. Pergamon Press, Fort Collins, Col. (CL-7).
Lamar, S. 1978
STATIC ANALYSIS OF STRUCTURES WITH THIN WALLS SUBJECTED TO HORI-
ZONTAL FORCES (ANALISIS ESTATICO DE ESTRUCTURAS DE EDIFICIOS DE
MUROS DE PARED DELGADA BAJO FUERZAS HORIZONTALES). Boletin IMME
61-62, Universidad Central de Venezuela, Caracas. (CB-5).
Larrabee, R. D. and Cornell, C. A. 1979
A COMBINATION PROCEDURE FOR A WIDE CLASS OF LOADING PROCESSES.
In Probabilistic Mechanics and Structural Reliability, Specialty Conference, ASCE, Tucson,
Arizona. (5).
Law, M. 1973
PREDICTION OF FIRE RESISTANCE. In 1971 Joint Fire Research Organization Symposium
on Fireresistance requirements for buildings—a new approach held at London, England.
HMSO, London, London. (8A).
Law, M. 1978
FIRE SAFETY OF EXTERNAL BUILDING ELEMENTS—THE DESIGN APPROACH.
Engineering Journal, AISC, 2nd Quarter 15:59-74. (8A).
Law, M. and O'Brien, T. 1975
EXPOSED STEELWORK. Building with Steel 19, Constrado. (8A).
Law, M. and O'Brien, T. (to be published)
FIRE SAFETY OF BARE EXTERNAL STRUCTURAL STEEL. Technical Report, Con-
strado. (8A).

Lawson, T. V. 1976
THE DESIGN OF CLADDING. Building and Environment 11(1):37-38.

Lawson, T. V. 1978a
THE WIND CONTENT OF THE BUILT ENVIRONMENT. Journal of Industrial Aerodynamics (3):93-105. (CL-7).

Lawson, T. V. 1978b
WIND TUNNEL INVESTIGATIONS. Journal of Industrial Aerodynamics (3):177-186. (CL-7).

Lecoq-Vallon, A. 1974
SOME ASPECTS OF CONDITIONS OF LIVING IN TALL BUILDINGS (ASPECTS DES CONDITIONS DE VIE DES HABITANTS DANS LES IMMEDUBLES DE GRANDE HAUTEUR). Annales de l'Institut Technique du Batiment et des Travux Publics :12-16. (37).

LeCorbusier, C. E. 1936
WHAT IS AMERICA'S PROBLEM?. American Architect and Architecture 148:116-122. (28).

Lee, B. E. and Hussain, M. 1979
THE GROUND LEVEL WIND ENVIRONMENT AROUND THE SHEFFIELD UNIVERSITY ARTS TOWER. Journal of Industrial Aerodynamics (4):333-341. (CL-7).

LeMessurier, W. J. 1977
A PRACTICAL METHOD OF SECOND-ORDER ANALYSIS, PART 2 — RIGID FRAMES. Engineering Journal, AISC, 2nd Quarter 14(2):49-67. (16).

Liauw, T. C. 1978
TORSION OF MULTI-STOREY SPATIAL CORE WALLS. In Proceedings of ICE, Vol. 65, Part 2, pages 601-609., (CB-5).

Liauw, T. C. and Leung, K. W. 1975
TORSION ANALYSIS OF CORE WALL STRUCTURES BY THE TRANSFER MATRIX METHOD. Structural Engineer 54(4):187-193. (21C).

Lie, T. T. 1965
INSULATION MATERIALS AND BUILDING STRUCTURES UNDER FIRE ACTION (BEKLEDINGSMATERIALEN EN BOUWCONSTRUCTIES BIJ BRAND). Heron 2, Heron, Delft. (8A).

Lie, T. T. 1979
SAFETY FACTORS FOR FIRE LOADS. Canadian Journal of Civil Engineering 6(4):617-628. (8A).

Lie, T. T. and Stanzak, W. W. 1973
FIRE RESISTANCE OF PROTECTED STEEL COLUMNS. Engineering Journal, Third Quarter 10:82-94. (8A/C).

Liebman, J. S., Chanaratna, V. and Khachaturian, N. 1977
DISCRETE OPTIMIZATION IN STRUCTURAL DESIGN. In Proceedings of the Symposium on Application of Computer Methods in Engineering, pages 553-562. University of Southern California, Los Angeles, Calif. (14).

Liebman, J. S., Khachaturian, N. and Chanaratna, V. 1981
DISCRETE STRUCTURAL OPTIMIZATION. Journal of Structural Division, ASCE 107(ST11):2177-2197. (14).

Lind, N. and Nowak, A. 1978
RISK ANALYSIS PROCEDURE II. Technical Report, Department of Civil Engineering, Univesity of Waterloo, Ontario. (5).

Lindner, J., Bos, A. M., Djalaly, H., Fischer, M. and Nethercot, D. A. 1977
LATERALLY SUPPORTED AND UNSUPPORTED BEAMS. In Introductory Report, Second International Colloquium on Stability, pages 127-143. ECCS, Liege. (16).

Litzner, H. U. and Crisinel, M. 1981
EFFECT OF RESIDUAL STRESSES ON THE CARRYING CAPACITY OF COMPOSITE COLUMNS (IN FRENCH). In Proceedings of IABSE P-39/81, pages 13-30. , (SB-9).

Long, A. F. and Kirk, D. W. 1980
LATERAL LOAD STIFFNESS OF SLAB-COLUMN STRUCTURES. American Concrete Institute, Detroit, Michigan, pages 197-220. (21D).

Loos, W. 1953
CONTRIBUTION TO THE COMBINED BUCKLING PHENOMENA OF I-BEAMS. PhD thesis, Presented to the Technical University, Dresden for the degree of Dr. Ing. (16).

Lopez, O. A. and Acuna, R. P. 1980
ESTIMATING SHEARS IN BUILDINGS SUBJECTED TO EARTHQUAKE MOTIONS (ESTIMACION DE CORTANTES EN EDIFICIOS SOMETIDOS A MOVIMIENTOS SISMICOS). Boletin IMME 66, Universidad Central de Venezuela, Caracas. (CL-2,CB-5).

Lu, L. W., Haist, R. M., Lin, T. C. and Beedle, L. S. 1980
RECOMMENDATIONS OF THE AISC TALL BUILDING STUDY COMMITTEE. Fritz Laboratory Report 440.6, Lehigh University, Bethlehem, Pa. (13).

Lugez, M. 1979
WITH REGARD TO THE BUCKLING FUNCTION OF MASONRY WALLS (A PROPOS DE LA FONCTION DE FLAMBEMENT DES MURS EN MACONNERIE). In Proceedings of Vth International Brick & Masonry Conference, pages 195-198. Brick Institute of America, Washington, D.C. (27).

Lukey, A. F. and Adams, P. F. 1969
ROTATION CAPACITY OF BEAMS UNDER MOMENT GRADIENT. Journal of the Structural Division 95(ST.6):1173-1188. (16).

MacGregor, J. G. 1972
STABILITY OF REINFORCED CONCRETE BUILDING FRAMES. In Proceedings of ASCE-IABSE International Conference on Planning and Design of Tall Buildings, Vol. III-23, pages 517-536. Lehigh University, Bethlehem, Pennsylvania. (16).

MacGregor, J. G. 1976
SAFETY AND LIMIT STATES DESIGN FOR REINFORCED CONCRETE. Canadian Journal of Civil Engineering 3(4):484-513. (5).

MacGregor, J. G. 1979
OUT-OF-PLUMB COLUMNS IN CONCRETE STRUCTURES. Concrete International, ACI 1(6):26-31. (24).

Mackey, S. 1971
EXTREME WIND STUDIES IN HONG KONG. In Proceedings of Third International Conference on Wind Effects on Buildings and Structures, pages 3-13. Saikon Co. Ltd., Tokyo.

Macleod, I. A. 1977
STRUCTURAL ANALYSIS OF WALL SYSTEMS. Structural Engineer 55(11):487-495. (CB-5).

Macleod, I. A. and Hosny, H. M. 1977
FRAME ANALYSIS OF SHEAR-WALL CORES. Journal of Structural Division, ASCE 103(ST10):2037-2047. (CB-5).

Maeda, Y. 1978
FATIGUE CRACKS OF DEEP THIN-WALLED PLATE GIRDERS. Bridge Engineering Vol. 1 Transportation Research Record 664, National Academy of Sciences. (SB-6).

Maeda, Y. 1981
APPLICATION OF STEEL-CONCRETE COMPOSITE CONSTRUCTIONS. In Proceedings of IABSE, P-40/81, IABSE, (S-41).

Maeda, Y. and Hayashi, M. 1980a
GEOMETRICAL NON-LINEAR BEHAVIOR OF RIB ARCHES. In Proceedings of Japan Society of Civil Engineers, No. 299, pages 35-47., (SB-2).

Maeda, Y. and Hayashi, M. 1980b
AN INFLUENCE LINE ANALYSIS OF ARCHES. In Proceedings of Japan Society of Civil Engineers, No. 298, pages 49-58., (SB-2).

Maeda, Y. and Hayashi, M. 1980c
GEOMETRICAL NONLINEARITY OF STIFFENING ARCH. In Proceedings of Japan Society of Civil Engineers, No. 304, pages 69-79., (SB-2).

Maeda, Y., Hayashi, M. and Maeda, K. 1976
NON-LINEAR VIBRATION ANALYSIS OF PLANE FRAMED STRUCTURES BY FINITE ELEMENT METHOD. University of Tokyo Press, Tokyo, Japan, pages 37-47. (SB-2).

Maeda, Y., Hayashi, M. and Maeda, K. 1978
NON-LINEAR ANALYSIS OF CABLE-STIFFENED STRUCTURES. University of Tokyo Press, Tokyo, Japan, pages 201-212. (SB-2).

Maeda, Y., Hayashi, M. and Mori, K. 1981
FINITE DISPLACEMENT ANALYSIS OF THIN PLATES BY FINITE STRIP METHOD. In Proceedings of Japan Society of Civil Engineers, No. 316, pages 23-36., (SB-4).

Maeda, Y. and Ishizaki, S. 1979
STRUCTURAL BEHAVIOR OF SLABS AT SKEWED COMPOSITE GIRDERS. Technical Reports 1489, Osaka University, Osaka, Japan. (SB-9).

Maeda, Y. and Kajikawa, Y. 1977
EFFECTS OF COLD-FORMING ON MECHANICAL PROPERTIES AND WELDABILITY OF SHEAR CONNECTOR STUDS. Technical Reports 1391, Osaka University, Osaka, Japan. (SB-1).

Maeda, Y. and Kajikawa, Y. 1980a
EXTENDED STUDY ON FATIGUE OF STEEL PLATE IN TENSION WITH A STUD IN SHEAR. In Proceedings of USA-Japan Seminar on Composite Structures and Mixed Structural Systems, held January 1978, pages 115-119. GIHODO, Tokyo, Japan. (SB-6).

Maeda, Y. and Kajikawa, Y. 1980b
PROGRESS REPORT OF STUDY ON ULTIMATE STRENGTH OF HYBRID COMPOSITE GIRDERS. In Proceedings of USA-Japan Seminar on Composite Structures and Mixed Structural Systems, held in 1978, pages 98-101. GIHODO, Tokyo, Japan. (SB-9).

Maeda, Y. and Kajikawa, Y. 1980c
PROGRESS REPORT OF STUDY ON ULTIMATE STRENGTH OF PARTIAL-COMPOSITE CONTINUOUS BEAMS. In Proceeding of USA-Japan Seminar on Composite Structures and Mixed Structural Systems, held in 1978, pages 93-97. GIHODO, Tokyo, Japan. (SB-9).

Maeda, Y., Kajikawa, Y. and Kida, H. 1982
STATIC AND FATIGUE BEHAVIORS OF CONTINUOUS COMPOSITE BEAMS WITH PREFLEX BEAMS. Technical Reports 1649, Osaka University, Osaka, Japan. (SB-9).

Maeda, Y. and Matsui, S. 1977
STRESS AND DEFLECTION ANALYSIS OF EXPANDED OPEN-WEB STEEL BEAMS. Technical Reports 1362, Osaka University, Osaka, Japan. (SB-1).

Maeda, Y., Matsui, S. and Kushida, K. 1982
FATIGUE STRENGTH OF CONCRETE-FILLED GRILLAGE DECKS. In Proceedings of IABSE Colloquium on Fatigue of Steel and Concrete Structures, pages 609-616., Lausanne, Switzerland. (SB-6).

Maeda, Y. and Okumura, T. 1981
PROGRESS OF PREFLEXED BEAM STRUCTURES. GIHODO, Tokyo, Japan. (SB-9).

Maeda, Y. and Okura, I. 1982a
STUDY ON FINITE OUT-OF-PLANE DEFORMATION OF RECTANGULAR PLATES SUBJECTED TO COMPRESSION AND IN-PLANE BENDING. In Proceedings of Japan Society of Civil Engineers, No. 320, pages 15-23., (SB-4).

Maeda, Y. and Okura, I. 1982b
INFLUENCE OF INITIAL DEFLECTION OF PLATE GIRDER WEB ON FATIGUE CRACK INITIATION. In Proceedings of Japan Society of Civil Engineers, No. 319, pages 1-11., (SB-6).

Maeda, Y., Okura, I. and Yoshii, M. 1982
FINITE OUT-OF-PLANE BEHAVIOR OF RECTANGULAR PLATES IN SHEAR. Technical Reports 1647, Osaka University, Osaka, Japan. (SB-4).

Manheim, D. N. and Popov, E. P. (to be published)
ANALYSIS OF PLASTIC SHEAR HINGES IN STEEL FRAMES. Journal of the Structural Division . (15).

Mann, W. 1979
MECHANICAL TREATMENT OF BUCKLING BEHAVIOR OF SLENDER BRICK PARTITIONS (MECHNISCHE BEHANDLUNG DES KNICKVERHALTENS VON SCHLANKEN GEMAURTEN WANDEN). In Proceedings of Vth International Brick & Masonry Conference, pages 173-175. Brick Institute of America, Washington, D.C. (27).

Mann, W. 1982
FAILURE OF SHEAR-STRESSED MASONRY—AN ENLARGED THEORY, TESTS AND APPLICATION TO SHEAR WALLS. Proceeding of British Ceramic Society, London. (27).

Marin, J. 1974
STRENGTH AND DUCTILITY OF C-SHAPED STRUCTURAL WALLS (RESISTENCIA Y DUCTILIDAD DE MUROS EN FORMA DE CE). Boletin IMME 47, Universidad Central de Venezuela, Caracas. (CB-6,CB-11).

Marin, J. 1977
BEHAVIOR OF REINFORCED CONCRETE IN COMBINED AXIAL LOAD AND BEND-
ING (COMPORTAMIENTO DEL CONCRETO ARMADO EN FLEXOCOMPRESION).
Folleto de Estructuras 6, Universidad Central de Venezuela, Caracas. (CB-6,CB-8,CB-11).

Marin, J. 1978
CHARTS, FORMULAS AND CRITERIA FOR COMPUTING COLUMNS IN RC BUILD-
INGS. SUMMARY OF A RESEARCH (ABACOS, FORMULAS Y CRITERIOS PARA EL
CALCULO DE COLUMNAS EN EDIFICIOS DE CONCRETO ARMADO. RESUMEN
DE UNA INVESTIGACION UCV-BANAP). Boletin IMME 61-62, Universidad Central
de Venezuela, Caracas. (CB-6,CB-11).

Marin, J. 1979
DESIGN AIDS FOR L-SHAPED REINFORCED CONCRETE COLUMNS. Journal American Concrete Institute 76-49(11):1197-1216. (CB-6,CB-11).

Marin, J. 1980a
COMPUTING UNDIMENSIONAL NORMAL STRESS RESULTANTS. Journal Structural
Division, ASCE 106(ST1):233-245. (CB-5,CB-6,CB-11,SB-9).

Marin, J. 1980b
COMPUTATION OF REINFORCED CONCRETE COLUMNS WITH NON-RECTANG-
ULAR CROSS SECTION STATE OF THE ART (ESTADO DEL CALCULO DE LAS
COLUMNAS DE CONCRETO REFORZADO NO RECTANGULARES). Boletin IMME
66, Universidad Central de Venezuela, Caracas. (CB-6,CB-11).

Marin, J. and Martin, I. 1979
DESIGNING COLUMNS WITH NON-RECTANGULAR CROSS SECTIONS. In ASCE
Annual Convention, pages 21. , Atlanta, Ga. (CB-6,CB-11).

Marin, J., Velasquez, J. M. and Guell, A. 1979
A VOCABULARY FOR STEEL STRUCTURES (UN VOCABULARIO PARA LAS
ESTRUCTURAS DE ACERO). Boletin IMME 65, Universidad Central de Venezuela,
Caracas. (S-10,SB).

Marincek, M. 1965
ULTIMATE STRENGTH OF METALLIC COLUMNS. Stahlbau und Baustatik, Springer
Verlag :74-99. (16).

Marryatt, H. 1981
SPRINKLER TRADE-OFFS AND THE AUSTRALIAN EXPERIENCE. Fire Journal, National Fire Protection Association 75(3):59-62. (8A/C).

Marshall, H. E. and Ruegg, R. T. 1980
SIMPLIFIED ENERGY DESIGN ECONOMICS. Technical Report 544, US Government
Printing Office, Springfield, Va. (40).

Massonnet, C. 1976
EUROPEAN RECOMMENDATIONS (F.C.C.S.) FOR THE PLASTIC DESIGN OF STEEL
FRAMES. Acier-Stahl Steel (4):146-153. (16).

Massonnet, C., and Maquoi, R. 1978
RECENT PROGRESS IN THE FIELD OF STRUCTURAL STABILITY OF STEEL STRUC-
TURES. IABSE Surveys S-5 78:1-40. (16).

Mattison, E. N. and Beresford, F. D. 1978
STUDIES OF THE PRODUCTION AND PROPERTIES OF HIGH STRENGTH CON-
CRETE. Division of Building Research, Report 7, Commonwealth Scientific & Industrial
Research Organization, Australia. (21D).

Mayes, R. L., Clough, R. W., Hidalgo, P. A. and McNiven, H. D. 1978
SEISMIC RESEARCH ON MULTI-STORY MASONRY BUILDINGS; UNIVERSITY OF
CALIFORNIA, BERKELEY, 1972 TO 1977. In Proceedings of North American Masonry
Conference, Paper No. 53, pages 19. University of Colorado, Boulder, Col. (27).

McCue, G. M. 1975
BUILDING ENCLOSURE AND FINISH SYSTEMS: THEIR INTERACTION WITH THE
PRIMARY STRUCTURE DURING SEISMIC ACTION. In Proceedings of U.S. National
Conference on Earthquake Engineering, pages 235-244. , Ann Arbor, Mich. (17).

McDonald, J. R. 1980
TORNADO AND STRAIGHT WIND HAZARD PROBABILITY FOR TEN NUCLEAR
POWER REACTOR SITES: A SUMMARY., Institute for Disaster Research, Texas Tech
University.

McNiven, H. D. 1980
SEISMIC BEHAVIOUR OF MASONRY PIERS. In Proceedings of Conference on Research
in Progress on Masonry Construction, Paper No. 3, pages 3-1–3-15., Marina del Ray,
Calif. (27).

McSweeney, M. F. 1978
NEW HQ FOR CENTRAL BANK. Irish Engineers 31(2):3, 5, 7-8. (8A).

Meadaris, K. 1978
AN INVESTIGATION OF THE DYNAMIC RESPONSE OF THE PARK LANE TOWERS
TO EARTHQUAKE LOADINGS. In Proceedings of North American Masonry Con-
ference, Paper No. 51, pages. University of Colorado, Boulder, Col. (27).

Mee, A. L., Jordaan, I. J. and Ward, M. A. 1975
WALL-BEAM FRAMES UNDER STATIC LATERAL LOAD. Journal of Structural Division,
ASCE 101(ST2):377-395. (CB-5).

Meinheit, D. F. and Jirsa, J. O. 1977
THE SHEAR STRENGTH OF REINFORCED CONCRETE, BEAM-COLUMN JOINTS.
CESRL Report 77-1, University of Texas at Austin. (21D).

Melbourne, W. H. 1978a
WIND ENVIRONMENT STUDIES IN AUSTRALIA. Journal of Industrial Aerodynamics
(3):201-214. (CL-7).

Melbourne, W. H. 1978b
CRITERIA FOR ENVIRONMENTAL WIND CONDITIONS. Journal of Industrial Aerodynamics (3):241-249. (CL-7).

Melbourne, W. H. 1979
TURBULENCE EFFECTS ON MAXIMUM SURFACE PRESSURES—A MECHANISM
AND POSSIBILITY OF REDUCTION. In Proceedings of Fifth International Conference
on Wind Engineering, pages 541-552. Pergamon Press, Fort Collins, Col. (CL-7).

Melbourne, W. H. 1980
COMPARISON OF MEASUREMENTS ON THE CAARC STANDARD TALL BUILDING
MODEL IN SIMULATED MODEL WIND FLOWS. Journal of Wind Engineering and
Industrial Aerodynamics (6):73-88. (CL-7).

Michelson, W. 1977
ENVIRONMENTAL CHOICE, HUMAN BEHAVIOR, AND RESIDENTIAL SATISFAC-
TION. Oxford University Press, New York. (37).

Minami, K. and Nishimura, Y. 1980
HYSTERETIC CHARACTERISTICS OF BEAM-TO-COLUMN CONNECTIONS IN
STEEL REINFORCED CONCRETE STRUCTURES. In Proceedings of 6th World Con-
ference on Earthquake Engineering, pages 305-309., Istanbul, Turkey. (SB-9).

Minami, K. and Wakabayashi, M. 1977
SEISMIC RESISTANCE OF REINFORCED CONCRETE BEAM-TO-COLUMN ASSEM-
BLAGES WITH EMPHASIS ON SHEAR FAILURE OF COLUMN. In Proceedings of
6th World Conference on Earthquake Engineering, pages 3101-3106., New Delhi, India. (CB-6).

Minami, K. and Wakabayashi, M. 1980a
SEISMIC RESISTANCE OF DIAGONALLY REINFORCED CONCRETE COLUMNS. In
Proceedings of 6th World Conference on Earthquake Engineering, Vol. 6, pages 215-222.,
Istanbul, Turkey. (CB-6).

Minami, K. and Wakabayashi, M. 1980b
EARTHQUAKE RESISTANT PROPERTIES OF DIAGONALLY REINFORCED CON-
CRETE COLUMNS. Transactions Vol. 2, Transactions of the Japan Concrete Institute. (CB-6).

Minami, K. and Wakabayashi, M. 1980c
RATIONAL ANALYSIS OF SHEAR IN REINFORCED CONCRETE COLUMNS. Transactions Vol. 2, Japan Concrete Institute. (CB-6).

Minami, K. and Wakabayashi, M. 1981
RATIONAL ANALYSIS OF SHEAR IN REINFORCED CONCRETE COLUMNS. In IABSE
Colloquium Delft, Final Report, pages 603-614., (CB-6).

Minor, J. E., and Beason, W. L. 1975
WINDOW GLASS FAILURES IN WINDSTORMS. ASCE National Structural Engineering
Convention, New Orleans, LA. (17).

Mirza, S. A. and MacGregor, J. G. 1976
A STATISTICAL STUDY OF VARIABLES AFFECTING THE STRENGTH OF REIN-
FORCED NORMAL WEIGHT CONCRETE MEMBERS. Structural Engineering Report
No. 58, Department of Civil Engineering, University of Alberta, Edmonton, Alberta,
Canada. (5).

Mitchell, W. J. 1979
SYNTHESIS WITH STYLE. In Proceedings of International Conference on the Application
of Computers in Architecture, Building Design and Urban Planning, pages 119-134.,
Berlin.

Miyata, T. and Miyazaki, M. 1979
TURBULENCE EFFECTS ON AERODYNAMIC RESPONSE OF RECTANGULAR BLUFF
CYLINDERS. In Proceedings of Fifth International Conference on Wind Engineering,
pages 631-642. Pergamon Press, Fort Collins, Col. (CL-7).

Moncarz, P. D. and Gerstle, K. H. 1981
STEEL FRAMES WITH NONLINEAR CONNECTIONS. Journal of the Structural Division,
ASCE 107(ST8):1427-1441. (SB-2,SB-7).

Morreau, P. and Baldock, N. 1978
ROYAL EXCHANGE THEATRE, MANCHESTER. The Structural Engineer 56A(7):
189-197. (8A).

Mortelmans, F. 1980
SWAY BUCKLING OF MULTISTORY FRAMES. IABSE Proceedings: 34-80. (16).

Mortelmans, F., DeRoeck, G. P. M. and Van Gemert, D. A. 1981
APPROXIMATE METHOD FOR LATERAL LOAD ANALYSIS OF HIGH-RISE BUILD-
INGS. Journal of Structural Division, ASCE 107(ST8):1589-1610. (CB-5,SB-2).

Mroz, Z. 1971
ON THE THEORY OF STEADY PLASTIC CYCLES IN STRUCTURES. Structural
Mechanics in Reactor Technology 6(L5/6):489-501. (15).

Mukherjee, P. R. and Coull, A. 1975
VIBRATIONS OF COUPLED SHEAR WALLS ON FRAMED SUPPORTS. In Proceedings
of ICE, Vol. 59, Part 2, Paper 7824, pages 469-485., (CB-9).

Mukherjee, P. R. and Coull, A. 1977
FREE VIBRATIONS OF OPEN-SECTION SHEAR WALLS. International Journal of Earthquake Engineering and Structural Dynamics 5:81-101. (CB-9).

Mukherjee, P. K., Loughborough, M. T. and Malhotra, V. M. 1981
DEVELOPMENT OF HIGH STRENGTH CONCRETE INCORPORATING A LARGE
PERCENTAGE OF FLY ASH AND SUPERPLASTICIZERS. Mineral Sciences Laboratories
Division Report MPR/MSL 81-124, Mineral Sciences Laboratories. (21D).

Murakami, S. and Deguichi, K. 1981
NEW CRITERIA FOR WIND EFFECTS ON PEDESTRIANS. Journal of Wind Engineering
and Industrial Aerodynamics (7):289-309. (CL-7).

Murakami, S., Uehara, K. and Komine, H. 1979
AMPLIFICATION OF WIND SPEED AT GROUND LEVEL DUE TO CONSTRUCTION
OF HIGH-RISE BUILDING IN URBAN AREA. Journal of Industrial Aerodynamics
(4):343-370. (CL-7).

Murphy, J. 1980
THINKING TALL. Progressive Architecture :45FF. (3).

Murzewski, J. 1970
STRUCTURAL SAFETY (POLISH EDITION)., Warsaw, Poland, (CL-7).

Murzewski, J. 1974
STRUCTURAL SAFETY (GERMAN EDITION)., Berlin, (CL-7).

Murzewski, J. 1975
STOCHASTIC MODELS OF STRUCTURAL LOADS. Wissenschaftliche Zeitschrift der
Hochschule fur Architektur und Bauwesen Weimar H.2(22.J):192-194. (CL-7).

Murzewski, J. 1979
CHARACTERISTIC AND DESIGN VALUES FOR THE LIMIT STATES ANALYSES. Bulletin
de l'Academie Polonaise des Sciences, 27(10-11):437-443. (SB-8).

Murzewski, J. 1981
RELIABILITY CONSIDERATION OF BEAM SYSTEMS, DEVELOPMENTS IN CIVIL
ENGINEERING. In Structural Safety and Reliability, pages 371-381. Elsevier Sci. Publ.
Co., The Norwegian Institute of Technology, Trondheim, Norway. (CL-7).

Muskivitch, J. C. 1979
REPORT 2—BEHAVIOR OF PRECAST CONCRETE LARGE PANEL BUILDINGS
UNDER SIMULATED PROGRESSIVE COLLAPSE CONDITIONS. Contract No. H-2589,
U.S. Department of Housing and Urban Development, Drexel University. (21E).

Nachbar, W. and Furgerson, R. 1978
STABILITY UNDER SEISMIC LOADING OF BUILDINGS WITH FULLY CRACKED
WALL-FLOOR JOINTS. In Proceedings of the North American Masonry Conference,
pages 57-1 to 57-16. University of Colorado, Boulder, Co.

Nair, R. S. 1975a
LINEAR STRUCTURAL ANALYSIS OF MULTISTORY BUILDINGS. Jnl. Struct. Div.,
ASCE 101(ST3):551-565. (21C).

Nair, R. S. 1975b
OVERALL ELASTIC STABILITY OF MULTISTORY BUILDINGS. Journal of the Structural Division 101(ST12).(16).

Nair, R. S. 1981
EVALUATION OF OVERALL STABILITY EFFECTS IN TALL BUILDINGS. In Proceedings of SSRC, pages 78-87., (16).

Naka, T., Nakao, M. and Osano, H. 1981
CONTRIBUTION OF THE RESTORING FORCE CHARACTERISTICS OF STEEL
BEAM-TO-COLUMN CONNECTIONS TO THE ASEISMIC BEHAVIOR OF FRAME
(IN JAPANESE). In 27th Symposium of Structural Engineering, pages 163-170. Japan
Society for Promotion of Science, (16).

Nakamura, T., Yoshida, N., Iwai, S. and Takai, H. 1980
SHAKING TABLE TEST OF STEEL FRAMES. In Proceedings of 6th World Conference
on Earthquake Engineering, pages 165-172., Istanbul, Turkey. (SB-3).

National Board of Fire Underwriters 1917-1919
FIRE TESTS OF BUILDING COLUMNS. Jointly conducted at Underwriters' Laboratories,
Associated Factory Mutual Fire Insurance Company. (8A).

National Board of Fire Underwriters 1964
FIRE RESISTANCE RATINGS. Technical Report, National Board of Fire Underwriters. (8A).

National Concrete Masonry Association 1968
SPECIFICATIONS FOR THE DESIGN AND CONSTRUCTION OF LOAD BEARING
CONCRETE MASONRY.NCMA, Herndon, Va. (5).

National Research Council 1975a
NATIONAL BUILDING CODE OF CANADA, NRC NO. 13982 Associated Committee on the
National Building Code, National Research Council, Ottawa, Canada.

National Research Council 1975b
COMMENTARIES ON PART IV—NATIONAL BUILDING CODE OF CANADA, NRC
NO. 13989 Associate Committee on the National Building Code, National Research
Council, Ottawa, Canada.

National Research Council of Canada 1977
NATIONAL BUILDING CODE OF CANADA.NRCC, Ottawa, Canada. (5).

National Research Council of Canada, 1981
DESIGN AGAINST THE WIND: THE 1980 NATIONAL BUILDING CODE OF CANADA,
CWOWE III Third Canadian Workshop on Wind Engineering, Ottawa, Canada.

Nayar, K. K. and Coull, A. 1976
ELASTO-PLASTIC ANALYSIS OF COUPLED SHEAR WALLS. Journal of Structural Division, ASCE 102(ST9):1845-1860. (CB-6).

NBS 1931
RECOMMENDED MINIMUM REQUIREMENTS FOR FIRE RESISTANCE IN BUILDINGS. Building and Housing 14, U. S. Department of Commerce, National Bureau
of Standards. (8A/C).

NBS 1942
BUILDING MATERIALS AND STRUCTURES. Technical Report BMS92, U. S. Department of Commerce, National Bureau of Standards. (8A).

NBS 1973
TECHNICAL OPTIONS FOR ENERGY CONSERVATION IN BUILDINGS. National Conference of States on Building Codes and Standards and National Bureau of Standards Joint Energizing Workshop on Energy Conservation in Buildings, Technical Note No. 789, US Department of Commerce. (40).
NBS 1980
PROBABILITY BASED LOAD CRITERION. Special Publication No. SP577, U. S. Department of Commerce, National Bureau of Standards. (5).
NBS/NCSBSC 1973
TECHNICAL OPTIONS FOR ENERGY CONSERVATION IN BUILDINGS. NBS Technical Note 789, National Bureau of Standards/National Conference of States on Building Codes and Standards, Proceedings of Conference held in Washington, D.C. (40).
Nixon, D., Beaulieu, D. and Adams, P. F. 1975
SIMPLIFIED SECOND ORDER FRAME ANALYSIS. Canadian Journal of Civil Engineering, Proc. No. 2 (2):602-605. (16,21C).

Oesterle, R. G., Fiorato, A. E. and Corley, W. G. 1980
REINFORCEMENT DETAILS FOR EARTHQUAKE-RESISTANT STRUCTURAL WALLS. Concrete International, ACI 2(12):55-66. (21D).
Oesterle, R. G., Fiorato, A. E., Aristizabal and Corley, W. G. 1980
HYSTERETIC RESPONSE OF REINFORCED CONCRETE STRUCTURAL WALLS. ACI, Detroit, Michigan, pages 243-273. (21D).
Oliva, M. G. 1980
SHAKING TABLE TESTING OF A REINFORCED CONCRETE FRAME WITH BIAXIAL RESPONSE. Report UCB/EERC-80/28, Earthquake Engineering Research Center, University of California, Berkeley. (21D).
Olmer, J. 1980
METHOD OF VIBRATION MEASUREMENT OF TALL STRUCTURES. Journal of Wind Engineering and Industrial Aerodynamics (6):39-48. (CL-7).
Oppenheim, I. 1973
DYNAMIC BEHAVIOR OF TALL BUILDINGS WITH CLADDING. In Proceedings of Fifth World Conference on Earthquake Engineering, pages 2769-2773. Edigraf, Rome, Italy, (17).
Oppenheim, I. 1978
HIGH RISE BUILDING VIBRATION PROPERTIES: AN UNEXPECTED BEHAVIOUR MECHANISM. In Proceedings of North American Masonry Conference, pages 56-1/15. University of Colorado.
Osman, Y. A. and Hendry, A. W. 1982
AN INVESTIGATION INTO THE BEHAVIOUR OF REINFORCED GROUTED CAVITY BRICK BEAMS UNDER BENDING AND SHEAR. Proceedings of British Ceramics Society. (27).
Ove Arup & Partners 1977
DESIGN GUIDE FOR FIRE SAFETY OF BARE EXTERIOR STRUCTURAL STEEL. TECHNICAL REPORTS. Technical Report, Constrado. (8A).

Page, A. W., Samarasinghe, W. and Hendry, A. W. 1982
THE IN-PLANE FAILURE OF MASONRY—AN OVERVIEW. Proceedings of British Ceramics Society (30). (27).
Parrish, R. L., Beck, H. L. and Gerard, J. C. 1981
HIGH RISE FIRE!: A REALIZATION OF THE POTENTIAL FOR DISASTER. The International Fire Chief 47(1):11-16. (38).
Parrott, L. J. 1969
THE PRODUCTION AND PROPERTIES OF HIGH-STRENGTH CONCRETE: 443-448. (21D).
PCI 1977
PCI MANUAL FOR STRUCTURAL DESIGN OF ARCHITECTURAL PRECAST CONCRETE. PCI Publication No. MNL-121-77, Prestressed Concrete Institute, Chicago, Ill. (17).
Pedereschi, R. F. and Sinha, B. P. 1982
DEVELOPMENT AND INVESTIGATION OF THE ULTIMATE LOAD BEHAVIOUR OF POST-TENSIONED BRICKWORK BEAMS. Structural Engineering, London 60B(3). (27).

Pei, I. M. 1981
REFLECTIONS ON THE RESSURRECTION OF URBAN DESIGN. Technology Review 83:18-23. (5).

Pekau, O. A. and Gocevski, V. 1981
ELASTO-PLASTIC ANALYSIS OF COUPLED SHEAR WALLS. Engineering Structures 3:87-95. (CB-6).

Perenchio, W. F. and Klieger, P. 1978
SOME PHYSICAL PROPERTIES OF HIGH-STRENGTH CONCRETE. RDO56.01T, Portland Cement Association. (21D,25).

Perera, M. D. 1978
A WIND-TUNNEL STUDY OF THE INTERACTION BETWEEN ALONG-WIND AND CROSS-WIND VIBRATIONS OF TALL, SLENDER STRUCTURES. Journal of Industrial Aerodynamics (3):315-341. (CL-7).

Person, W. J. 1978
BULLETIN OF THE SEISMOLOGICAL SOCIETY OF AMERICA. Seismological Note 68(6):1781. (S41).

Petersson, H. 1972
BENDING STIFFNESS OF SLABS IN SHEAR WALL STRUCTURES. Draft Report, Div. of Structural Design, Chalmers University of Technology, Goteborg, Sweden. (21C).

Pettersson, O. 1976
THE CONNECTION BETWEEN A REAL FIRE EXPOSURE AND THE HEATING CONDITIONS ACCORDING TO STANDARD FIRE RESISTANCE TESTS, WITH SPECIAL APPLICATION TO STEEL STRUCTURES. 4 . (8A).

Pettersson, O., Magnusson, S. E. and Thor, J. 1976
FIRE ENGINEERING DESIGN OF STEEL STRUCTURES. Publication 50, Swedish Intitute of Steel Construction, Stockholm. (8A).

Pettersson, O and Witteveen, J. 1978
ON THE FIRE RESISTANCE OF STRUCTURAL STEEL ELEMENTS DERIVED FROM STANDARD TESTS OR BY CALCULATION. Fire Safety Journal, Elsevier Sequoia S.A., Lausanne (2):73-87. (8A).

Pettersson, O. and Witteveen, J. 1979/80
ON THE FIRE RESISTANCE OF STRUCTURAL STEEL ELEMENTS, DERIVED FROM STANDARD FIRE TESTS OR BY CALCULATION. Fire Safety Journal, Elsevier Sequoia S.A., Lausanne Elsevier Sequoia S. A., Lausanne(2):73-87. (8A).

Phillips, E. L. 1973
WASHINGTON CLIMATE FOR KING, KITSAP, MASON, AND PIERCE COUNTIES. U. S. Department of Commerce, Seattle, Wash. (40).

Pirner, M. 1977
SOME RESULTS OF MODEL MEASUREMENTS ON TALL BUILDINGS. Journal of Industrial Aerodynamics (2):243-254. (CL-7).

Popov, E. P. 1980a
AN UPDATE ON ECCENTRIC SEISMIC BRACING. Engineering Journal 17(3):70-71. (15).

Popov, E. P. 1980b
SEISMIC BEHAVIOR OF STRUCTURAL SUBASSEMBLAGES. Journal of the Structural Division, ASCE 106(ST7):1451-1474. (15).

Popov, E. P. and Bertero, V. V. 1980
SEISMIC ANALYSIS OF SOME STEEL BUILDING FRAMES. Journal of the Engineering Mechanics Division 106(EM1):75-92. (15).

Popov, E. P. and Hjilmstad 1981
WEB BUCKLING UNDER CYCLIC LOADING. In Proceedings of SSRC held in Chicago, IL, pages 57-59. SSRC, Chicago, IL. (15).

Popov, E. P. and Manheim, D. N. 1981
ECCENTRIC BRACING OF STEEL FRAMES IN SEISMIC DESIGN. In Proceedings of 6th International Conference on Structural Mechanics in Reactor Technology, International Association for Structural Mechanics in Reactor Technology, Paris, France. (15).

Porter, M. L., and Ekberg, Jr., C. E. 1976
DESIGN RECOMMENDATIONS FOR STEEL DECK FLOOR SLABS. Journal of Structural Division, ASCE 102(ST11):2255-2268. (S41).

Porter, M. L., Ekberg, Jr., C. E. Greimann, L. G. and Ellebey, H. A. 1976
SHEAR-BOND ANALYSIS OF STEEL-DECK REINFORCED SLABS. Journal of Structural Division, ASCE 102(ST12):2255-2268. (S41).

Potapkin, A. A. 1977
UP-TO-DATE METHODS IN STABILITY ANALYSIS OF STEEL BRIDGE STRUCTURES (IN RUSSIAN). In Final Report of Regional Colloquium on Stability of Steel Structures, pages 25-56. Hungarian Academy of Sciences-Technical University of Budapest, Budapest. (16).

Powell, B. and Hodgkinson, H. R. 1976
THE DETERMINATION OF STRESS/STRAIN RELATIONSHIP OF BRICKWORK. In Proceedings of 4th International Brick & Masonry Conference, Paper 2.a.5, pages 2a 5.1-5., Brugge. (27).

Priestly, M. J. N., Park, R. and Pontagaroa, R. T. 1981
DUCTILITY OF SPIRALLY-CONFINED CONCRETE COLUMNS. Journal of the Structural Division, ASCE 107(ST1):181-202. (21D).

Progressive Architecture 1980
THINKING TALL: INTRODUCTION. Progressive Architecture 61(12):45. (3).

Public Works Department 1976
CODE OF PRACTICE ON WIND EFFECTS. Technical Report, Public Works Department, Hong Kong.

Rackwitz, R. and Fiessler, B. 1976
NOTE ON DISCRETE SAFETY CHECKING WHEN USING NON-NORMAL STOCHASTIC MODELS FOR BASIC VARIABLES. Loads Project Working Session, MIT, Cambridge. (5).

Rackwitz,R. and Fiessler, B. 1977
AN ALGORITHM FOR THE CALCULATION OF STRUCTURAL RELIABILITY UNDER COMBINED LOADING. Heft 17, Technische Universitat Munchen. (5).

Rathbone, A. J. 1981
THE SHEAR BEHAVIOUR OF REINFORCED CONCRETE BLOCKWORK BEAMS. In Proceedings of Symposium on Reinforced and Prestressed Masonry, pages 17-28. International Structural Engineers, London. (27).

Razzaq, Z. and Naim, M. M. 1980
ELASTIC INSTABILITY OF UNBRACED SPACE FRAMES. Journal of the Structural Division, ASCE, Proc. paper 15535 106(ST7):1389-1400. (16).

Reinhold, T. A., ed. 1982
WIND TUNNEL MODELING FOR CIVIL ENGINEERING APPLICATIONS, Proceedings of the International Workshop on Wind Tunnel Modeling Criteria and Technics in Civil Engineering Applications, Gaithersburg, Maryland, April, Cambridge University Press. (7A)

Reinhold, T. A. and Sparks, P. R. 1979
THE INFLUENCE OF WIND DIRECTION ON THE RESPONSE OF A SQUARE-SECTION TALL BUILDING. In Proceedings of Fifth International Conference on Wind Engineering, pages 685-698. Pergamon Press, Fort Collins, Col. (CL-7).

Reinhorn, A., Rutenberg, A. and Gluck, J. 1977
DYNAMIC TORSIONAL COUPLING IN ASYMMETRIC BUILDING STRUCTURES. Building & Environment 12:251-260. (CL-2,CB-9).

Reis, A. J. and Roorda, I. 1977
THE INTERACTION BETWEEN LATERAL-TORSIONAL AND LOCAL PLATE BUCKLING IN THIN-WALLED BEAMS. In Preliminary Report, Second International Colloquium on Stability of Steel Structures, pages 415-425. ECCS and IABSE, Liege. (16).

Rentschler, G. P., Chen, W. F. and Driscoll, G. C. 1980
TESTS OF BEAM-TO-COLUMN WEB MOMENT CONNECTIONS. Journal of the Structural Division, ASCE 106(ST5):1005-1022. (SB-7).

Rentschler, G. P., Chen, W. F. and Driscoll, G. C. 1982
BEAM-TO-COLUMN WEB CONNECTION DETAILS. Journal of the Structural Division, ASCE 108(ST2):393-409. (SB-7).

Rhodes-Harrison, G. W. 1975
TALL BUILDINGS: THE STATE OF THE ART IN SOUTH AFRICA PAPER 7. In Proceedings of Thirty-Fifth Regional Conference, pages. Hortors Printers, Johannesburg, South Africa. (29).

Riera, J. and Blessmann, J. 1979
ALONG WIND STRUCTURAL DYNAMIC RESPONSE (IN SPANISH). In Proceedings of 20th South American Conference on Structural Engineering, Vol. 11, Paper B8, Universidad Nacional de Cordoba, Cordoba, Argentina. (CL-3).

Roberts, J. J. 1980
FURTHER WORK ON THE BEHAVIOUR OF REINFORCED CONCRETE BLOCKWORK SUBJECT TO LATERAL LOADING. Technical Report 531, Cement & Concrete Association, London. (27).

Robertson, L. E. 1974
WIND ENGINEERING OF TALL BUILDINGS. In Proceedings of the Symposium on Tall Buildings, pages 259-290. Vanderbilt University, Nashville, Tenn. (17).

Robertson, L. E. and Chen, P. W. 1967
GLASS DESIGN AND CODE IMPLICATIONS FOR EXTREMELY TALL BUILDINGS. Building Research 4(3):6-11. (17).

Rohner, E., Knoepfel, H. and Burger, R 1980
THE MANAGEMENT OF THE ZURICH FRUIT AND VEGETABLE MARKET PROJECT. In Proceedings of 11th IABSE Congress Vienna, IABSE, Zurich. (PC-11).

Rondal, J. and Maquoi, R. 1979
SINGLE EQUATION FOR SSRC COLUMN-STRENGTH CURVES. Journal of the Structural Division, ASCE, Proc. Paper 14201 105(ST1):245-250. (16).

Rosman, R. 1976
STATICS AND STABILITY OF PARTIALLY RESTRAINED COLUMN SYSTEMS (IN GERMAN). Beton-und Stahlbetonbau 71(9):215-220. (CB-8).

Rosman, R. 1977a
DESIGN OF OPEN FRAMES (IN GERMAN). Deutsche Bauzeitschrift (2):211-215. (CB-3).

Rosman, R. 1977b
MECHANICS OF WALLBEAM FRAMES (IN GERMAN). Bautechnik 55(5):154-166. (CB-5).

Rosman, R. 1980a
ECCENTRICITY OF EARTHQUAKE LOADS IN REGULAR MULTISTORY BUILDINGS. In Proceedings of 5th Symposium on Construction of Multistory Buildings Under Extreme Conditions, Madrid. (CL-2).

Rosman, R. 1980b
DYNAMIC CHARACTERISTICS OF NONSYMMETRIC BUILDING STRUCTURES. In Proceedings of Seventh World Conference on Earthquake Engineering, Istanbul. (CL-2).

Rosman, R. 1981a
BUCKLING AND VIBRATION OF SPATIAL BUILDING STRUCTURES. Engineering Structures 3(4):194-202. (CL-2,CB-8).

Rosman, R. 1981b
CLASSIFICATION OF FLOOR STRUCTURES. In Proceedings of International Congress on Housing, the Impact of Economy and Technology, pages 142-150. Pergamon Press, Vienna. (SC-1,SB-9).

Ross, D. A. and Chen, W. F. 1976
DESIGN CRITERIA FOR STEEL I-COLUMNS UNDER AXIAL LOAD AND BIAXIAL BENDING. Canadian Journal of Civil Engineering 3(3):466-473. (SB-4).

Ross, D. A., Chen, W. F. and Tall, L. 1980
FABRICATED TUBULAR STEEL COLUMNS. Journal of the Structural Division 106(ST1):265-282. (SB-4).

Roy, H. E. H. and Marin, J. 1977
INTRODUCTION TO TALL BUILDING STRUCTURES (INTRODUCCION A LA ESTRUCTURACION DE EDIFICIOS ALTOS). Folleto de Estructuras 13, Universidad Central de Venezuela, Caracas. (PC-1,PC-5,PC-13,CB-3,CB-4,CB-5,SC-1,SC-8,CL-1,CL-2).

Ruchelman, Leonard I. 1977
THE WORLD TRADE CENTER: POLITICS AND POLICIES OF SKYSCRAPER DEVELOPMENT. Syracuse University Press, Syracuse, New York. (38).

Ruscheweyh, H. 1979
DYNAMIC RESPONSE OF HIGH RISE BUILDINGS UNDER WIND ACTION WITH INTERFERENCE EFFECTS FROM SURROUNDING BUILDINGS OF SIMILAR SIZE. In Proceedings of Fifth International Conference on Wind Engineering, pages 725-734. Pergamon Press, Fort Collins, Col. (CL-7).

Russell, H. G. and Corley, W. G. 1976
TIME DEPENDENT DEFORMATIONS OF VERTICAL MEMBERS IN ULTRA-HIGH CONCRETE BUILDINGS. Technical Report, Portland Cement Association, Skokie, Ill. (25).

Rutenberg, A. 1975a
ANALYSIS OF SPIRAL STAIRS SUPPORTED ON A CENTRAL COLUMN. Building Science 10:37-42. (CB-11,CB-12).

Rutenberg, A. 1975b
APPROXIMATE NATURAL FREQUENCIES FOR COUPLED SHEAR WALLS. International Journal Earthquake Engineering and Structural Dynamics 4:95-100. (CL-2,CB-9).

Rutenberg, A. 1979a
A CONSIDERATION OF THE TORSIONAL RESPONSE OF BUILDING FRAMES. Bulletin of New Zealand National Society for Earthquake Engineering 12(1):11-21. (CL-2).

Rutenberg, A. 1979b
EARTHQUAKE ANALYSIS OF BELTED HIGH-RISE BUILDING STRUCTURES. Engineering Structures 1(4):190-196. (CL-2,CB-9).

Rutenberg, A. 1979c
PLANE FRAME ANALYSIS OF LATERALLY LOADED ASYMMETRIC BUILDINGS—AN UNCOUPLED SOLUTION. Computers & Structures 10:553-555. (CB-5).

Rutenberg, A. 1980
LATERALLY LOADED FLEXIBLE DIAPHRAGM BUILDINGS: PLANAR ANALOGY. Journal of the Structural Division, ASCE 106(ST9):1969-1973. (CB-5).

Rutenberg, A. 1981a
A DIRECT P-DELTA ANALYSIS USING STANDARD PLANE FRAME PROGRAMS. Computers & Structures 14:97-102. (SB-4,CB-8).

Rutenberg, A. 1981b
SIMPLIFIED P-DELTA ANALYSES FOR ASYMMETRIC STRUCTURES. Publication No. 279, Faculty of Civil Engineering, Technion, Heifa, Israel. (21C).

Rutenberg, A. 1982
SIMPLIFIED P-DELTA ANALYSES FOR ASYMMETRIC STRUCTURES. Journal of the Structural Division, ASCE 107. (SB-4,CB-8).

Rutenberg, A., Gluck, J. and Reinhorn, A. 1978
ON THE DYNAMIC PROPERTIES OF ASYMMETRIC WALL FRAME STRUCTURES. International Journal of Earthquake Engineering and Structural Dynamics 6:317-320. (CL-2,CB-9).

Rutenberg, A. and Heidebrecht, A. C. 1975
APPROXIMATIONS FOR NATURAL FREQUENCIES OF INTERCONNECTED WALLS AND FRAMES. Canadian Journal of Civil Engineering 2:116-119. (CL-2,CB-9).

Rutenberg, A., Hsu, T. I. and Tso, W. K. 1978
RESPONSE SPECTRUM TECHNIQUES FOR ASYMMETRIC BUILDINGS. International Journal of Earthquake Engineering and Structural Dynamics 6:427-435. (CL-2).

Rutenberg, A. and Pekau, O. A. 1981
DYNAMIC TORSIONAL EFFECTS IN BUILDINGS: A BIBLIOGRAPHY. Report, Dept. of Civil Engineering, Concordia University, Montreal. (PC).

Rutenberg, A. and Tso, W. K. 1975a
TORSION OF PERFORATED CORE STRUCTURES. In Proceedings of 5th Canadian Congress of Applied Mechanics, pages 111-112. , Fredericton, Canada. (CB-5,CB-9).

Rutenberg, A. and Tso, W. K. 1975b
TORSIONAL ANALYSIS OF PERFORATED CORE STRUCTURES. Journal of the Structural Division, ASCE 101(ST3):539-550. (CB-5,CB-9).

Rutenberg, A. and Tso, W. K. 1975c
CONTRIBUTION TO EARTHQUAKE ANALYSIS OF COUPLED SHEAR WALLS. In Proceedings of 5th European Conference on Earthquake Engineering, Vol. 1, Paper No. 78, Istanbul. (CL-2).

Rutenberg, A., Tso, W. K. and Heidebrecht, A. C. 1977
DYNAMIC PROPERTIES OF ASYMMETRIC WALL-FRAME STRUCTURES. International Journal of Earthquake Engineering and Structural Dynamics 5:41-51. (CL-2,CB-9).

Sack, R. L. and Perry, D. C. 1981
SEISMIC BEHAVIOR OF PRECAST CURTAIN WALLS IN HIGH-RISE BUILDINGS. Final Project Report to the National Science Foundation, NSF Grant PFR77-20884, University of Idaho. (17).

Sales News 1977
THE STANDARD OIL BUILDING: A REPORT FROM THE CONSULTING ENGINEER. Sales News. (40).

Samarasinghe, W. and Hendry, A. W. 1982
STRENGTH OF BRICKWORK UNDER BIAXIAL STRESS. In Proceedings of British Ceramics Society. , (27).

Samarasinghe, W., Page, A. W. and Hendry, A. W. 1981
BEHAVIOUR OF BRICK MASONRY SHEAR WALLS. Structural Engineering, London 59B(3):42-48. (27).

Sanada, S., Iwasa, Y. and Yoshida, M. 1980
FULL-SCALE MEASUREMENT OF ENVIRONMENTAL WIND IN THE SHINJUKU NEW METROPOLITAN CENTER. Journal of Wind Engineering and Industrial Aerodynamics (6):291-309. (CL-7).

Sarrazin, M. and Ropert, M. 1979
ISOLATION AND ABSORPTION OF SEISMIC ACTIONS IN BUILDINGS (AISLACION Y ABSORCION DE SOLICITACIONES SISMICAS EN EDIFICIOS). Boletin IMME 65, Universidad Central de Venezuela, Caracas. (SC-1,SC-7,SC-8,CL-2).

Saunders, J. W. and Melbourne, W. H. 1979
BUFFETING EFFECTS OF UPSTREAM BUILDINGS. In Proceedings of Fifth International Conference on Wind Engineering, pages 593-606. Pergamon Press, Fort Collins, Col. (CL-7).

Sawczuk, A. 1972
ENGINEERING METHOD OF ELASTIC-PLASTIC ANALYSIS. Mechanika Teoretyczna i Stosowana 10(2):489-501. (15).

Sawczuk, A., Janas, M. and Konig, J. A. 1972
PLASTIC ANALYSIS OF STRUCTURES.Pan Ossolineum (15).

Sawko, F. and Rahman, M. A. 1980
NUMERICAL SOLUTION OF ECCENTRICALLY LOADED STRUTS IN NO-TENSION MATERIAL. Pieridge Press, pages 751-762. (27).

Scheer, J. and Bohm, M. 1978
EVALUATION OF ULTIMATE LOAD TESTS OF BOX STEEL COLUMNS MADE OF THINWALLED UNSTIFFENED PLATES (AUSWERTUNG VON TRAGLASTVERSUCHEN AN GEDRUCKTEN KASTENSTUTZER MIT DUNNWANDIGEN, UNANSGESTEIFTEN PLATTEN AUS STAHL. In Proceedings P13/78 of IABSE, pages 1-16. (16).

Schriftenreihe des Bundesminisres fur Raumordnung, Bauwesen and Stadtebau 1978
FIRE SAFETY THEORY (BRANDVERSUCHE LEHRTE). Technical Report 37, Bauwesen and Stadtebau, Bonne. (8A).

Schultz, D. M. 1979
DESIGN METHODOLOGY, DESIGN AND CONSTRUCTION OF LARGE PANEL CONCRETE STRUCTURES. Technical Report 6, Portland Cement Association, Skokie, Il. (21E).

Schulz, G. 1977
THE ROLE OF MULTIPLE COLUMN CURVES IN THE ECCS DESIGN CONCEPT. In Proceedings of the Regional Colloquium on Stability of Steel Structures, pages 75-83. Hungarian Academy of Sciences - Technical University of Budapest, Budapest. (16).

Schuster, R. M. 1976
COMPOSITE STEEL-DECK FLOOR SYSTEMS. Journal of Structural Division, ASCE 102(ST5):899-917. (S41).

Schuster, R. M. 1980
MECHANICAL INTERLOCKING OF COMPOSITE SLABS. In Proceedings of Fifth International Specialty Conference on Cold-Formed Steel Structures, pages 387-407. University of Missouri-Rolla, Rolla, Missouri. (S41).

Schuyler, M. 1913
TOWERS OF MANHATTAN AND NOTES ON THE WOOLWORTH BUILDING. Architectural Record 33:98-122. (28).

Schwaighofer, J. and Collins, M.P. 1977
EXPERIMENTAL STUDY OF THE BEHAVIOR OF REINFORCED CONCRETE COUPL-
ING SLABS. ACI Journal 74(3):123-127. (21C).

Schwaighofer, J. and Ho, W. N. 1980
ELASTO-PLASTIC ANALYSIS OF A CORE SUBJECTED TO TORSION. Reinforced Concrete Structures Subjected to Wind and Earthquake Forces, Publication No. SP-63, ACI. (21C).

Seigel, L. G. 1967
WATER-FILLED TUBULAR STEEL COLUMNS—FIRE PROTECTION WITHOUT
COATING. Civil Engineering, ASCE 37(9):65-67. (8A).

Selna, L. G. 1978
MODELING OF REINFORCED CONCRETE BUILDINGS. In Proceedings of a Workshop
on Earthquake Resistant Reinforced Concrete Building Construction, pages 887-937. University of California, Berkeley, California. (21D).

Selna, L. G., Martin, I., Park, R. and Wyllie, L. 1980
STRONG AND TOUGH CONCRETE COLUMNS FOR SEISMIC FORCES. Journal of
the Structural Division, ASCE Proc. 106(ST8):1717-1734. (21D).

Sfintesco, D. 1970
EXPERIMENTAL BASIS OF THE EUROPEAN COLUMN CURVES. Construction Metallique (3). (16).

Shah, S. P., ed 1979
HIGH STRENGTH CONCRETE. In Proceedings of a Workshop held at the University
of Illinois, Chicago, Ill. (21D).

Sharpe, R. L. 1972
SEISMIC DESIGN OF NONSTRUCTURAL ELEMENTS. In Proceedings of the Interna-
tional Conference on Planning and Design of Tall Buildings, Vol. Ia-12, pages 1143-1148.
ASCE-IABSE Joint Committee, Bethlehem, PA. (17).

Shibata, A. 1980
PREDICTION OF THE PROBABILITY OF EARTHQUAKE DAMAGE TO REINFORCED
CONCRETE BUILDING GROUPS IN A CITY. In Proceedings of Seventh World Con-
ference on Earthquake Engineering, Vol. 4, pages 395-402. , Istanbul, Turkey. (6).

Shibuya, J., Kimura, H. and Shiga, T. 1980
EFFECTS OF LOCAL SITE CONDITIONS ON DAMAGE TO BUILDINGS DURING AN
EARTHQUAKE. In Proceedings of Seventh World Conference on Earthquake Engineering,
Vol. 2, pages 199-206. , Istanbul, Turkey. (6).

Shiga, T., Shibata, A., Shibuya, J. and Takahashi, J. 1980
PERFORMANCE OF THE BUILDING OF ENGINEERING. In Proc., Seventh World
Conf. on Earthquake Engineering, Vol. 7, pages 357-364. Tohoku University, Istanbul,
Turkey. (6).

Sidarous, J. F. Y. and Vanderbilt, M. D. 1979
AN ANALYTICAL METHODOLOGY FOR PREDICTING DYNAMIC BUILDING RE-
SPONSE TO WIND. In Proceedings of Fifth International Conference on Wind Engineering,
pages 709-724. Pergamon Press, Fort Collins, Col. (CL-7).

Simiu, E. and Filliben, J. 1975
STATISTICAL ANALYSIS OF EXTREME WINDS. Note No. 868, National Bureau of
Standards, Washington, D.C. (5).

Singh, G. and Schwaighofer, J. 1976
A BIBLIOGRAPHY ON SHEAR WALLS. Publication No. 76-02, Department of Civil
Engineering, University of Toronto, Canada. (21C).

Singleton 1929
FIREPROOFING STRUCTURAL STEEL. Technical Report, American Institute of Steel
Construction, Inc. (8A).

Sinha, B. P. 1981
AN ULTIMATE LOAD ANALYSIS OF REINFORCED BRICKWORK FLEXURAL MEM-
BERS. International Journal of Masonry Construction 4:151-155. (27).

Skidmore, Owings & Merrill 1973
CHICAGO 21. Technical Report, Chicago Central Area Committee, Chicago. (PC-9).

Sochor, R. 1977
BEARING CAPACITY OF ROOF PURLINS. In Proceedings of the Regional Colloquium
on Stability of Steel Structures, pages 185-192. Hungarian Academy of Sciences—Technical
University of Budapest, Budapest. (16).

Sockel, H. and Taucher, R. 1981
THE INFLUENCE OF A PARAPET ON LOCAL PRESSURE FLUCTUATIONS. Journal of Wind Engineering and Industrial Aerodynamics (8):31-38. (CL-7).

Solari, G. and Stura, D. 1979
DYNAMIC ALONGWIND RESPONSE OF A STRUCTURAL SYSTEM INCLUDING SOIL FLEXIBILITY. In Proceedings of Fifth International Conference on Wind Engineering, Vol. 2, pages 735-746. Pergamon Press, Fort Collins, Col. (CL-7).

Sozen, M. A. and Marin, J. 1977
INTRODUCTION TO THE BEHAVIOR OF REINFORCED CONCRETE BUILDINGS (INTRODUCCION AL COMPORTAMIENTO DE EDIFICIOS DE CONCRETO ARMADO). Folleto de Estructuras 14, Universidad Central de Venezuela, Caracas. (CL-2, CB-6,CB-11).

Speyer, I. J. 1976
CONSIDERATIONS FOR DESIGN OF PRECAST CONCRETE BEARING WALL BUILDINGS TO WITHSTAND ABNORMAL LOADS. Prestressed Concrete Institute Journal 21(2):18-51. (21E).

SSRC 1981
GENERAL PRINCIPLES FOR THE STABILITY DESIGN OF METAL STRUCTURES. Technical Memorandum No. 5, SSRC, Civil Engineering, ASCE, Vol. 51, No. 2. (16, SB-1).

SSRC-ECCS-CRC-CMEA 1981
STABILITY OF METAL STRUCTURES, A WORLD VIEW. Engineering Journal 18(3, 4):90-126, 154-196. (16).

SSRC-ECCS-CRC-CMEA 1982
STABILITY OF METAL STRUCTURES, A WORLD VIEW. Engineering Journal 19(1):154-196. (16).

SSRC Task Group 20 1979
A SPECIFICATION FOR THE DESIGN OF STEEL CONCRETE COMPOSITE COLUMNS. Engineering Journal, AISC, 4th Quarter 4(16):101-115. (S41).

Stafford Smith, B. and Abate, A. 1981
ANALYSIS OF NON-PLANAR SHEAR WALL ASSEMBLIES BY ANALOGOUS FRAME. In Proceedings of Institute of Civil Engineers, Paper 8448, Vol. 71, Part 2, pages 395-406. Institute of Civil Engineers, London. (21C).

Stafford Smith, B., Kuster, M. and Hoenderkamp, J. C. D. 1980
A GENERALIZED APPROACH TO THE DEFLECTION ANALYSIS OF BRACED FRAME, RIGID FRAME AND COUPLED WALL STRUCTURES. Canadian Journal of Civil Engineering 8:230-240. (21C).

Stafford Smith, B. and Salim, I. 1981
PARAMETER STUDY OF OUTRIGGER-BRACED TALL BUILDINGS. Journal of the Structural Division, ASCE 107(ST10):2001-2014. (21C).

Standard Research Institute 1972
PATTERNS OF ENERGY CONSUMPTION IN THE UNITED STATES. Technical Report, Standard Research Institute.

Standig, K. F., Rentschler, G. P. and Chen, W. F. 1976
TESTS OF BOLTED BEAM-TO-COLUMN FLANGE MOMENT CONNECTIONS. Bulletin 218, Welding Research Council. (SB-7).

Stanzak, W. W. and Lie, T. T. 1973
FIRE RESISTANCE OF UNPROTECTED STEEL COLUMNS. Journal of the Structural Division, ASCE 99(ST5):837-852. (8A).

Steel Structures Research Committee 1931, 1934, 1936
RECOMMENDATIONS FOR DESIGN. First, second, and final reports, Dept. of Scientific and Industrial Research, His Majesty's Stationary Office. (43).

Stiny, G. 1979
A GENERATIVE APPROACH TO COMPOSITION AND STYLE IN ARCHITECTURE. In Proceedings of International Conference on the Application of Computers in Architecture, Building Design and Urban Planning, pages 435-446. , AMK, Berlin. (35).

Strating, J. and Vos, H. J. 1975
COMPUTER SIMULATION OF THE ECCS BUCKLING CURVE USING A MONTE-CARLO METHOD. In Proceedings of International Colloquium on Column Strength, Reports of the Working Commissions, Paris, pages 331-358. IABSE (16).

Sugimoto, H. and Chen, W. F. 1981
EFFECT OF SMALL END RESTRAINT ON STRENGTH OF H-COLUMNS. Structural Engineering Report No. CE-STR-81-1, Purdue University, West Lafayette. (43).

Sugimoto, H. and Chen, W. F. 1982
SMALL END RESTRAINT EFFECTS ON STRENGTH OF H-COLUMNS. Journal of the Structural Division, ASCE 108(ST3):661-681. (SB-4).

Suzuki, H., Kato, B. and Akiyama, H. 1974
FLANGE BUCKLING STRENGTH OF H-SECTION STUB-COLUMNS (IN JAPANESE). In Proceedings of the Symposium of Kanto Branch of A. I. J., pages 125-128. A. I. J., (16).

Svojsik de Beek, M. 1980
SEISMIC BEHAVIOR OF MACUTO-SHERATON BUILDING DURING THE CARACAS 1967 EARTHQUAKE (COMPORTAMIENTO SISMICO DEL MACUTO SHERATON DURANTE EL TERREMOTO DE CARACAS DE 1967). Boletin IMME 66, Universidad Central de Venezuela, Caracas. (CL-2,CB-3,CB-6).

Szczepinski, W. 1968
DESIGN OF MACHINE PARTS ACCORDING TO THE LIMIT ANALYSIS. Panstwowe Wydawnictwo Naukowe, Warsaw, Poland. (15).

Takeda, T., Sozen, M. A. and Nielsen, N. N. 1970
REINFORCED CONCRETE RESPONSE TO SIMULATED EARTHQUAKE. Journal of the Structural Division, ASCE 96(ST12):2557-2573. (22).

Talaboc, C. P. 1980
ELASTIC-PLASTIC ANALYSIS AND DESIGN OF MULTISTORY STEEL FRAMES BY SUBASSEMBLY METHOD. Thesis Proposal, Department of Civil and Environmental Engineering, University of Wisconsin-Madison, Madison, Wisc. (16).

Taranath, B. S. 1975
OPTIMUM BELT TRUSS LOCATIONS FOR HIGH-RISE STRUCTURES. Structural Engineer 53(8):345-347. (CB-5,SB-2).

Taranath, B. S. 1976
THE EFFECT OF WARPING ON INTER-CONNECTED SHEAR WALL-FLAT PLATE STRUCTURES. In Proceedings of ICE, Vol. 61, Part 2, pages 711-724. , (CB-5).

Tarnai, T. 1978a
LATERAL BUCKLING OF ELASTIC BEAMS WITH INITIAL STRESSES AND INITIAL DEFORMATIONS. Acta Technica Academiae Scientiarum Hungaricae 87:187-192. (16).

Tarnai, T. 1978b
LATERAL BUCKLING ANALYSIS OF BEAMS BY THE THEORY OF QUADDRATIC OPERATOR PENCILS. Acta Technica Academiae Scientiarum Hungaricae 87:293-254. (16).

Templin, J. T. and Cooper, K. R. 1981
DESIGN AND PERFORMANCE OF A MULTI-DEGREE-OF-FREEDOM AEROELASTIC BUILDING MODEL. Journal of Wind Engineering and Industrial Aerodynamics (8)·157-175. (CL-7).

Thompson, J. M. T. and Hunt, G. W. 1973
A GENERAL THEORY OF ELASTIC STABILITY. John Wiley and Sons Inc., New York. (16).

Thor, J. and Sedin, G. 1977
SOME RESULTS OF INDUSTRIAL FIRES IN SWEDEN. Publication No. 56, Swedish Institute of Steel Construction. (8A).

Toma, S. and Chen, W. F. 1979
ANALYSIS OF FABRICATED TUBULAR COLUMNS. Journal of the Structural Division, ASCE 105(ST11):2343-2366. (SB-4).

Tomasetti, R. L. 1981
DEVELOPMENT OF THE STRESSED SKIN TUBE-DRAVO BUILDING. Presented at the National Engineering Conference, Dallas, TX, May. (14).

Topping, P. 1978
THE CLIENT'S QUESTION—A CASE HISTORY OF THE USE OF A WIND TUNNEL INVESTIGATION AROUND THE PROPOSED DEVELOPMENT OF WHITBREAD & COMPANY SITE AT CHISWELL STREET. Journal of Industrial Aerodynamics (3):107-115. (CL-7).

Trewartha, G. T. and Horn, L. H. 1980
(Fifth Edition): AN INTRODUCTION TO CLIMATE.McGraw-Hill Book Company, New York, NY. (40).

Troup, E. W. J. 1970
THE HIGH-CHALLENGE FIREBALL - A TRADEMARK OF THE SEVENTIES. Fire Technology, The Society of Fire Protection Engineers 6(3):211-223. (8A/C).

Troup, E. W. J. 1974
NEW DEVELOPMENTS IN CEILING-LEVEL PROTECTION FOR THE HIGH-CHALLENGE FIRE. Unpublished Technical Report 22435, Factory Mutual Research Corporation. (8A).

Troup, E. W. J. 1975
FIRE ENDURANCE FOR STEEL FRAME NURSING HOMES. Modern Steel Construction, AISC XV(4):10-13. (8A).

Tso, W. I. and Mahmoud, A. A. 1977
EFFECTIVE WIDTH OF COUPLING SLABS IN SHEAR WALL BUILDINGS. Journal of Structural Division, ASCE 103(ST3):573-586. (CB-5).

Tso, W. K., and Rutenberg, A. 1977
SEISMIC SPECTRAL RESPONSE OF COUPLED SHEAR WALLS. Journal of the Structural Division, ASCE 103(ST1):181-196. (CL-2).

Tso, W. K., Rutenberg, A. and Heidebrecht, A. C. 1975
CYCLIC LOADING OF EXTERNALLY REINFORCED MASONRY WALLS CONFINED BY FRAMES. Canadian Journal of Civil Engineering 2:489-493. (CB-13).

Tuma, I. 1977
LATERAL BUCKLING OF STEEL GIRDERS. In Proceedings of the Regional Colloquium on Stability of Steel Structures, pages 169-176. Hungarian Academy of Sciences—Technical University of Budapest, Budapest. (16).

Turkstra, C. J. 1972
Solid Mechanics Study No. 2: THEORY OF STRUCTURAL DESIGN DECISIONS. University of Waterloo, Ontario, Canada. (5).

Turkstra, C. and Ojinaga, J. 1976
THE MOMENT MAGNIFIER METHOD APPLIED IN BRICK WALLS. In Proceedings of 4th International Brick & Masonry Conference, Paper No. 4.b.3, pages 4.b.3.1-4. , Brugge. (27).

Uhlmann, W. 1977
SOME PROBLEMS CONCERNING DESIGN RECOMMENDATIONS FOR CENTRALLY COMPRESSED BUILT-UP MEMBERS. In Preliminary Report, Second Int. Colloquium on Stability of Steel Structures, pages 121-130. ECCS/IABSE/SSRC/CRC Japan, Liege. (16).

UL 1980
FIRE RESISTANCE DIRECTORY. January, Underwriters Laboratories, Inc. (8A).

Unemori, A. L., Roesset, J. M. and Becker, J. M. 1980
EFFECT OF INPLANE FLOOR SLAB FLEXIBILITY ON THE RESPONSE OF CROSS-WALL BUILDING SYSTEMS. SP-63. : ACI, Detroit, Michigan, pages 113-134. (21D).

United States Department of Energy 1979
STANDARD BUILDING OPERATING CONDITIONS. Technical Support Document for Notice of Proposed Rulemaking on Energy Performance Standards for New Buildings (DOE/CS-0118). (40).

United States Department of Energy 1980
DOE-2 REFERENCE MANUAL VERSION 2.1 PART I Available from National Technical Information Services, Washington, D.C., 1980. (40).

Universidad Central de Venezuela Caracas 1978
BIBLIOGRAPHY ON EARTHQUAKE ENGINEERING (BIBLIOGRAFIA SOBRE INGENIERIA SISMO RESISTENTE). Boletin IMME 61-62, Universidad Central de Venezuela, Caracas. (PC).

Universidad Central de Venezuela Caracas 1979
BIBLIOGRAPHY ON EARTHQUAKE ENGINEERING (BIBLIOGRAFIA SOBRE INGENIERIA SISMO RESISTENTE). Boletin IMME 64, Universidad Central de Venezuela, Caracas. (PC).

Universidad Central de Venezuela Caracas 1980
BIBLIOGRAPHY ON EARTHQUAKE ENGINEERING (BIBLIOGRAFIA SOBRE INGENIERIA SISMO RESISTENTE). Boletin IMME 63, Universidad Central de Venezuela, Caracas. (PC).

University of Washington, 1981
PREPRINTS AND PROCEEDINGS OF THE FOURTH U.S. NATIONAL CONFERENCE
ON WIND ENGINEERING RESEARCH, Seattle, Washington.
Uzumeri, S. M. and Sheikh, S. A. 1978
STRENGTH AND DUCTILITY OF REINFORCED CONCRETE COLUMNS WITH
RECTAGULAR TIES. In Proceedings of a Workshop on Earthquake Resistant Reinforced
Concrete Building Construction, pages 611-623. University of California, Berkeley,
California.

Vandepitte, D. 1981
DESIGN OF STRUCTURES (WETENSCHAPPELIJKE UITGEVERIJ). E Story Scienta,
Brussels III. (16).
Vanderbilt, M. P. 1979
EQUIVALENT FRAME ANALYSIS FOR LATERAL LOADS. Journal of Structural Division,
ASCE 105(ST10):1981-1998. (CB-5).
Veletsos, A. S. and Newmark, N. M. 1960
EFFECT OF INELASTIC BEHAVIOR ON THE RESPONSE OF SIMPLE SYSTEMS TO
EARTHQUAKE MOTIONS. In Proceedings, Second World Conference on Earthquake
Engineering, Vol. 2, pages 895-912. , Tokyo, Japan. (22).
Ville de Goyet, V. 1979
CONTRIBUTIONS TO THE ULTIMATE STRENGTH ANALYSIS OF TRUSSES. PhD
thesis, University Liege. (16).
Vlasov, V. Z. 1940
THIN-WALLED ELASTIC BARS (IN RUSSIAN).Stroizdat Wakomstroja, Moskow-Leningrad.
(16).
Wakabayashi, M. 1977a
A NEW DESIGN METHOD OF LONG COMPOSITE BEAM-COLUMNS. In International
Colloquium on Stability of Structures under Static and Dynamic Loads, pages 742-756. ,
Washington, D.C. (SB-9).
Wakabayashi, M. 1977b
BEHAVIOR OF SYSTEMS. In Proceedings of 6th World Conference on Earthquake En-
gineering, pages 65-75. , New Delhi, India. (CB-6).
Wakabayashi, M. 1977c
SEISMIC DESIGN OF MIXED STEEL CONCRETE STRUCTURES IN JAPAN. In Inter-
national Colloquium on Stability of Structures under Static and Dynamic Loads, pages 40-58.
Washington, D.C. (SB-9).
Wakabayashi, M., Matsui, C. and Mitani, I. 1977
CYCLIC BEHAVIOR OF A RESTRAINED STEEL BRACE UNDER AXIAL LOADING.
In Proceedings of 6th World Conference on Earthquake Engineering, Vol. 3, pages
3181-3187. , New Delhi, India. (SB-3).
Wakabayashi, M. and Nakamura, T. 1976
A STUDY ON THE SUPERPOSITION METHOD TO ESTIMATE THE ULTIMATE
STRENGTH OF STEEL REINFORCED CONCRETE COLUMN SUBJECTED TO AXIAL
THRUST AND BENDING MOMENT SIMULTANEOUSLY. Bulletin of the Disaster
Prevention Research Institute Vol. 26, Kyoto University, Uji. (SB-9).
Wakabayashi, M., Nakamura, T., Shibata, M., Yoshida, N. and Masuda, H. 1977
HYSTERETIC BEHAVIOR OF STEEL BRACES SUBJECTED TO HORIZONTAL LOAD
DUE TO EARTHQUAKE. In Proceedings of 6th World Conference on Earthquake En-
gineering, Vol. 3, pages 3188-3194. , New Delhi, India. (SB-3).
Wakabayashi, M., Nakamura, T. and Yoshida, N. 1977
EXPERIMENTAL STUDIES ON THE ELASTIC-PLASTIC BEHAVIOR OF BRACED
FRAMES UNDER REPEATED HORIZONTAL LOADING, PART 1, EXPERIMENTS
OF BRACES WITH AN H-SHAPED CROSS SECTION IN A FRAME. Bulletin of the
Disaster Prevention Research Institute Vol. 29, Kyoto University, Uji. (SB-3).
Wakabayashi, M., Nakamura, T. and Yoshida, N. 1980a
EXPERIMENTAL STUDIES ON THE ELASTIC-PLASTIC BEHAVIOR OF BRACED
FRAMES UNDER REPEATED HORIZONTAL LOADING, PART 2, EXPERIMENTS
OF BRACES COMPOSED OF STEEL CIRCULAR TUBES, ANGLE-SHAPES, FLAT
BARS OR ROUND BARS. Bulletin of the Disaster Prevention Research Institute Vol. 29,
Kyoto University, Uji. (SB-3).

Wakabayashi, M., Nakamura, T. and Yoshida, N. 1980b
EXPERIMENTAL STUDIES ON THE ELASTIC-PLASTIC BEHAVIOR OF BRACED FRAMES UNDER REPEATED HORIZONTAL LOADING, PART 3, EXPERIMENTS OF ONE STOREY-ONE BAY BRACED FRAMES. Bulletin of the Disaster Prevention Research Institute Vol. 29, Kyoto University, Uji. (SB-3).

Wakabayashi, M., Nakamura, T., Yoshida, N. and Iwai, S. 1978
EFFECT OF STRAIN RATE ON STRESS-STRAIN RELATIONSHIPS OF CONCRETE AND STEEL. In Proceedings of 5th Japan Earthquake Engineering Symposium, pages 1313-1320. , Tokyo. (CB-6).

Wakabayashi, M., Nakamura, T., Yoshida, N., Iwai, S. and Takai, H. 1978
EXPERIMENTAL STUDY ON THE ELASTIC-PLASTIC RESPONSE OF STEEL FRAMES UNDER DYNAMIC EXCITATION BY MEANS OF A SHAKING TABLE. In Proceedings of 5th Japan Earthquake Engineering Symposium, pages 165-172. , Tokyo. (SB-3).

Wakabayashi, M., Nakamura, T., Yoshida, N., Iwai, S. and Watanabe, Y. 1980
DYNAMIC LOADING EFFECTS OF CONCRETE AND STEEL MATERIALS AND BEAMS. In Proceedings of 6th World Conference on Earthquake Engineering, Vol. 6, pages 271-278. , Istanbul, Turkey. (CB-6).

Wang, S. T. and Wright, R. S. 1977
TORSIONAL-FLEXURAL BUCKLING OF LOCALLY BUCKLED BEAMS AND COLUMNS. In Proceedings of the International Colloquium on Stability of Structures under Static and Dynamic Loads, pages 587-608. SSRC, Washington. (16).

Wardenier, J. 1982
HOLLOW SECTION JOINTS, FIRST EDITION.Delft University Press, Mynbouwplein 11 2628 RT Delft. (SB).

Weaver, W., Lee, D. G. and Derbalian, G. 1981
FINITE ELEMENT FOR SHEAR WALLS IN MULTI-STORY FRAMES. Journal of Structural Division, ASCE 107(ST7):1365-1369. (CB-5).

Webster, R. and Miner, L. 1982
EXPERT SYSTEMS, PROGRAMMING PROBLEM SOLVING. Technology 2(1):62-73. (35).

Weidlinger, P. 1973
SHEAR FIELD PANEL BRACING. Journal of the Structural Division, ASCE 99(ST7): 1615-1631. (17,21A).

Weltman 1980
NOISE AND VIBRATION FROM PILING OPERATIONS. Publication PG9 0-86017-137-X, Construction Industry Research and Information Associate, London. (11).

Wen, Y. K. 1977
STATISTICAL COMBINATION OF EXTREME LOADS. Journal of the Structural Division, ASCE, Proc. Paper 12930 103(ST6):1079-1095. (5).

Whyte, W. H. 1981
HOW TO MAKE MIDTOWN LIVABLE. New York 14(10):24-30. (38).

Will, K. M., Goodno, B. J. and Saurer, G. 1979
DYNAMIC ANALYSIS OF BUILDINGS WITH PRECAST CLADDING. In Proceedings of ASCE Seventh Conference on Electronic Computation, pages 251-264. , St. Louis, Missouri. (17).

Williamson, R. C. 1978
SOCIALIZATION IN THE HIGHRISE: A CROSS-NATIONAL COMPARISON. Ekistics Spring Issue 12(1):122-130. (37).

Williamson, R. C. 1981
ADJUSTMENT TO THE HIGHRISE: VARIABLES IN A GERMAN SAMPLE. Environment and Behavior 13(3):289-310. (37).

Winnicki, L., Kleiber, M. and Kwiecinski, M. 1977
NUMERICAL LIMIT ANALYSIS OF PERFORATED PLATES. International Journal of Numerical Methods in Engineering 11(3):553-561. (15).

Winter, G. and Nelson, A. H. 1979
DESIGN OF CONCRETE STRUCTURES, 9th ed., McGraw-Hill, New York.

Witteveen, J. 1965
FIRE SAFETY OF STEEL STRUCTURES (BRANDVEILIGHEID STAALCONSTRUC-TIES). Technical Report, Stichting Centrum Bouwen in Staal, Rotterdam. (8A).

Witteveen, J. and Twilt, L. 1975
  BEHAVIOR OF STEEL COLUMNS UNDER FIRE ACTION. In Proceedings of International Colloquium on Column Strength, Reports of the Working Commissions, Vol. 23, pages 162-170. IABSE, Paris. (8A).
Witteveen, J., Twilt, L. and Bijlaard, F. S. K. 1977
  THE STABILITY OF BRACED AND UNBRACED FRAMES AT ELEVATED TEMPERATURES. In Preliminary Report of the Second International Colloquium on the Stability of Steel Structures, pages 647-655. , Liege. (8A).
Wolsiefer, J. 1982
  ULTRA HIGH STRENGTH FIELD PLACEABLE CONCRETE IN THE RANGE 10,000 TO 18,000 PSI. In 1982 Annual Convention of the American Concrete Institute, Atlanta, GA. (21D).
Wong, Y. C. 1980
  INTERACTION BETWEEN FLOOR SLABS AND SHEAR WALLS IN TALL BUILDINGS. PhD thesis, University of Strathclyde, Glasglow. (21C).
Wong, Y. C. and Coull, A. 1980a
  STRUCTURAL BEHAVIOUR OF FLOOR SLABS IN SHEAR WALL BUILDINGS. Pergamon Press, London, pages 301-312. (CB-5).
Wong, Y. C. and Coull, A. 1980b
  INTERACTION BETWEEN FLOOR SLABS AND SHEAR WALLS IN TALL BUILDINGS. In Reinforced Concrete Structures Subjected to Wind and Earthquake Forces, pages 543-573. American Concrete Institute, Detroit, Michigan. (21C).
World Computer Graphics Association 1982
  PROCEEDINGS OF INTERNATINAL CONFERENCE ON COMPUTERS/GRAPHICS IN THE BUILDING PROCESS. Washington, D.C.

Yamazaki, J. and Hawkins, N. M. 1980
  FINITE ELEMENT PREDICTIONS OF THE BEHAVIOR OF SLAB-COLUMN CONNECTIONS TRANSFERRING MOMENT. SP-63. : ACI , Detroit, Michigan, pages 49-78. (21D).
Young, B. W. 1971
  AXIALLY LOADED STEEL COLUMNS. CIRIA TN 33, Techn. Report CUED/C-Struct/TR.11, Department of Engineering, Cambridge University. (16E).
Yura, J. A. and Galambos, T. V. 1978
  THE BENDING RESISTANCE OF STEEL BEAMS. Journal of the Structural Division, ASCE Proc. Paper 14015 106(ST9):1355-1370. (16).

Zetlin, L. 1971
  AN APPROACH TO THE INTERNAL STRAINING OF CONCRETE. ACI, Detroit, Michigan, pages 323-347. (25).

Indexes

Building Index

The following index enables the reader to identify the page number on which a particular building is mentioned. Numbers in italics that follow cities refer to panoramic photographic views.

773

Name Index

The following list cites the page number on which the indicated names are mentioned. This list includes the authors, as well as other individuals or organizations named in the text.

Names followed by years refer to bibliographic citations that are included in the appendix entitled "References/Bibliography".

Subject Index

horizontal acceleration, 253
horizontal air space, 164
horizontal bracing member, 340
horizontal connection shear capacity, 613
horizontal crack, 545
horizontal deflection, 673
horizontal deflection limitation, 594
horizontal diaphragm, 661
horizontal displacement absorption, 54
horizontal displacement envelope, 586
horizontal displacement time history, 586
horizontal element, 662
horizontal equilibrium equation, 416
horizontal expansion joint, 263
horizontal expansion limit, 63
horizontal force, 212
horizontal framing system, 217
horizontal framing system/floor, 218
horizontal ground motion input, 495
horizontal joint spacing, 263
horizontal joint strength, 617
horizontal load, 213, 435
horizontal load framing system, 217
horizontal load resistance, 214, 219
horizontally organized tall building, 127
horizontal mail delivery, 253
horizontal member discrete action, 577
horizontal member stiffness, 606
horizontal moment, 212
horizontal reinforcement end hook, 608
horizontal resistance, 54
horizontal shear development, 561
horizontal shear force, 439
horizontal shear resistant joint, 612
horizontal steel threading, 677
horizontal stiff arm, 661–662
horizontal stress distribution, 673
horizontal tie, 614
horizontal transportation, 247–255
horizontal transverse reinforcement, 612
horizontal wall, 59
horizontal wall reinforcement, 608
horizontal wind load, 649
horizontal wind shear transfer, 559
horsepower reduction, 138
hose-stream test, 249
hospital, 253, 366
hostel, 366
host fabric grain, 124

hot and cold water, 149
hot ashes, 365
hot-dipped galvanized steel, 693
hotel, 53, 366, 697
hotel and convention center, 75
hotel building, 42, 73–74
hotel design, 54, 70
hotel development, 132–133
hotel enclosure, 214
hotel facility, 126
hotel fire, 54
hotel room, 215
hotel segment, 224
hotel space, 107, 215, 225
hotel suite, 367
hot-gas reclaim system, 245
hot-rolled steel, 284, 382
hot water piping, 683
hot-water storage tank, 156
hot-water system, 245
hot weather, 245
hour-by-hour simulation, 164
hourly fire rating, 348–350
hours of accessibility, 23
housing, 77–78, 108, 222
housing allotment norm, 205
housing area expansion, 42
Housing Authority, 675
housing block, 675
housing complex, 87
housing construction development, 202
housing design, 9, 207–208
housing design renovation, 203
housing development land, 200
housing development location, 200
housing expansion, 199
housing group density, 202
housing maintenance, 203–204
housing obligation, 10
housing project plot plan, 203
housing requirement, 202
housing shortage, 63, 199
housing unit investment, 201
housing use, 127
housing volume, 199
H section dimension, 443
H-section member, 440–442, 444–445
H-section web plate inside depth, 455
H-shaped column, 55